CHANGE
of HEART

ALSO BY JODI PICOULT

Nineteen Minutes
The Tenth Circle
Vanishing Acts
My Sister's Keeper
Second Glance
Perfect Match
Salem Falls
Plain Truth
Keeping Faith
The Pact
Mercy
Picture Perfect
Harvesting the Heart
Songs of the Humpback Whale

CHANGE
of HEART

A NOVEL

Jodi Picoult

**Doubleday Large Print
Home Library Edition**

ATRIA BOOKS

NEW YORK LONDON TORONTO SYDNEY

This Large Print Edition, prepared especially for Doubleday Large Print Home Library, contains the complete, unabridged text of the original Publisher's Edition.

ATRIA BOOKS

A Division of Simon & Schuster, Inc.
1230 Avenue of the Americas
New York, NY 10020

First Atria Books hardcover edition March 2008

ATRIA BOOKS and colophon are trademarks of Simon & Schuster, Inc.

Manufactured in the United States of America

ISBN-13: 978-0-7394-9361-8

**This Large Print Book carries the
Seal of Approval of N.A.V.H.**

With love, and too much admiration to fit on these pages

To my grandfather, Hal Friend, who has always been brave enough to question what we believe . . .

And to my grandmother, Bess Friend, who has never stopped believing in me.

ACKNOWLEDGMENTS

Writing this book was its own form of miracle; it's very hard to write about religion responsibly, and that means taking the time to find the right people to answer your questions. For their time and their knowledge, I must thank Lori Thompson, Rabbi Lina Zerbarini, Father Peter Duganscik, Jon Saltzman, Katie Desmond, Claire Demarais, and Pastor Ted Brayman. Marjorie Rose and Joan Collison were willing to theorize about religion whenever I brought it up. Elaine Pagels is a brilliant author herself and one of the smartest women I've ever spoken with—I chased her down and begged her for a private tutorial on the Gnostic Gospels, one of her academic specialties, and would hang up the phone after each conversation with my mind buzzing and a thousand more questions to explore—surely something the Gnostics would have heartily endorsed.

Jennifer Sternick is still the attorney I'd want fighting for me, no matter what, Chris Keating provides legal information for me at blistering speed, and Chris Johnson's expertise on the appeals process for death penalty cases was invaluable.

Thanks to the medical team that didn't mind when I asked how to kill someone, instead of how to save them—among other things: Dr. Paul Kispert, Dr. Elizabeth Martin, Dr. David Axelrod, Dr. Vijay Thadani, Dr. Jeffrey Parsonnet, Dr. Mary Kay Wolfson, Barb Danson, James Belanger. Jacquelyn Mitchard isn't a doc, but a wonderful writer who gave me the nuts and bolts of LD kids. And a special thank-you to Dr. Jenna Hirsch, who was so generous with her knowledge of cardiac surgery.

Thanks to Sindy Buzzell, and Kurt Feuer, for their individual expertise. Getting to death row was a significant challenge. My New Hampshire law enforcement contacts included Police Chief Nick Giaccone, Captain Frank Moran, Kim Lacasse, Unit Manager Tim Moquin, Lieutenant Chris Shaw, and Jeff Lyons, PIO of the New Hampshire State Prison. For finessing my trip to the Arizona State Prison Florence, thanks to Sergeant Janice Mallaburn, Deputy Warden Steve Gal, CO II Dwight Gaines, and Judy Frigo (former warden). Thanks also to Rachel Gross and Dale Baich. However, this book would not be what it was without the prisoners who opened up to me both in person and via mail: Robert Purtell, a former death row inmate; Samuel Randolph, currently on death row in Pennsylvania; and Robert Towery, currently on death row in Arizona.

Thanks to my dream team at Atria: Carolyn Reidy, Judith Curr, David Brown, Danielle Lynn, Mellony Torres, Kathleen Schmidt, Sarah Branham, Laura Stern, Gary Urda, Lisa Keim, Christine Duplessis, and everyone else who has worked so hard on my behalf. Thanks to Camille McDuffie—who was so determined to make people stop asking "Jodi Who?" and who exceeded my expectations beyond my wildest dreams. To my favorite first reader, Jane Picoult, who I was fortunate enough to get as a mom. To Laura

Gross, without whom I'd be completely adrift. To Emily Bestler, who is just so damn good at making me look brilliant.

And of course, thanks to Kyle, Jake, Sammy—who keep me asking the questions that might make the world a better place—and Tim, who makes it possible for me to do that. It just doesn't get better than all of you, all of this.

Alice laughed. "There's no use trying," she said. "One can't believe impossible things."

"I dare say you haven't had as much practice," said the Queen. "When I was your age I did it for half an hour a day. Why sometimes I've believed as many as six impossible things before breakfast."

—Lewis Carroll, *Through the Looking-Glass*

CHANGE
of HEART

PROLOGUE: 1996

June
||||||||||||||||||||||||||||||||||||||||||||||||||||||||||||||||||||||||||||||||||||||||||||||||||||||||||

In the beginning, I believed in second chances. How else could I account for the fact that years ago, right after the accident—when the smoke cleared and the car had stopped tumbling end over end to rest upside down in a ditch—I was still alive; I could hear Elizabeth, my little girl, crying? The police officer who had pulled me out of the car rode with me to the hospital to have my broken leg set, with Elizabeth—completely unhurt, a miracle—sitting on his lap the whole time. He'd held my hand when I was taken to identify my husband Jack's body. He came to the funeral. He showed up at my door to personally inform me when the drunk driver who ran us off the road was arrested.

The policeman's name was Kurt Nealon. Long after the trial and the conviction, he kept coming around just to make sure that Elizabeth and I were all right. He brought toys for her birthday and Christmas. He fixed the clogged drain in the upstairs bathroom. He came over after he was off duty to mow the savannah that had once been our lawn.

I had married Jack because he was the love of my life; I had planned to be with him forever. But that was before the definition of forever was changed by a man with a blood alcohol level of .22. I was surprised that Kurt seemed to understand that you might never love someone as hard as you had the first time you'd fallen; I was even more surprised to learn that maybe you *could*.

Five years later, when Kurt and I found out we were going to have a baby, I almost regretted it—the same way you stand beneath a perfect blue sky on the most glorious day of the summer and admit to yourself that all moments from here on in couldn't possibly measure up. Elizabeth had been two when Jack died; Kurt was the only father she'd ever known. They had a connection so special it sometimes made me feel I should turn away, that I was intruding. If Elizabeth was the princess, then Kurt was her knight.

The imminent arrival of this little sister (how strange is it that none of us ever imagined the new baby could be anything but a girl?) energized Kurt and Elizabeth to fever pitch. Elizabeth drew elaborate sketches of what the baby's room should look like. Kurt hired a contractor to build the addition. But then the builder's mother had a stroke and he had to move unexpectedly to Florida; none of the other crews had time to fit our job into their schedules before the baby's birth. We had a hole in our wall and rain leaking through the attic ceiling; mildew grew on the soles of our shoes.

When I was seven months pregnant, I came downstairs to find Elizabeth playing in a pile of leaves that had blown past the plastic sheeting into the living room. I was deciding between crying and raking my carpet when the doorbell rang.

He was holding a canvas roll that contained his tools, something that never left his possession, like another man might tote around his wallet. His hair brushed his shoulders and was knotted. His clothes were filthy and he smelled of snow—although it wasn't the right season. Shay Bourne arrived, unexpected, like a flyer from a summer carnival that blusters in on a winter wind, making you wonder just where it's been hiding all this time.

He had trouble speaking—the words tangled, and he had to stop and unravel them before he could say what he needed to say. "I want to . . ." he began, and then started over: "Do you, is there, because . . ." The effort made a fine sweat break out on his forehead. "Is there anything I can do?" he finally managed, as Elizabeth came running toward the front door.

You can leave, I thought. I started to close the door, instinctively protecting my daughter. "I don't think so . . ."

Elizabeth slipped her hand into mine and blinked up at him. "There's a lot that needs to be fixed," she said.

He got down to his knees then and spoke to my daughter easily—words that had been full of angles and edges for him a minute before now flowed like a waterfall. "I can help," he replied.

Kurt was always saying people are never who you think they are, that it was necessary to get a complete background check on a person before you made any promises. I'd tell him he was being too suspicious, too much the cop. After all, I had let Kurt himself into my life simply because he had kind eyes and a good heart, and even *he* couldn't argue with the results.

"What's your name?" I asked.

"Shay. Shay Bourne."

"You're hired, Mr. Bourne," I said, the beginning of the end.

SEVEN MONTHS LATER

Michael

||||||||||||||||||||||||||||||||||||||||||||||||||||||||||||||||||||||||||||||||||||||||||||||||||||||

Shay Bourne was nothing like I expected.

I had prepared myself for a hulking brute of a man, one with hammy fists and no neck and eyes narrowed into slits. This was, after all, the crime of the century—a double murder that had captured the attention of people from Nashua to Dixville Notch; a crime that seemed all the worse because of its victims: a little girl, and a police officer who happened to be her stepfather. It was the kind of crime that made you wonder if you were safe in your own house, if the people you trusted could turn on you at any moment—and maybe because of this, New Hampshire prosecutors sought the death penalty for the first time in fifty-eight years.

Given the media blitz, there was talk of whether twelve jurors who hadn't formed a reaction to this crime could even be found, but they managed to locate us. They unearthed me in a study carrel at UNH, where I was writing a senior honors thesis in mathematics. I hadn't had a decent meal in a month, much less read a newspaper—and so I was the perfect candidate for Shay Bourne's capital murder case.

The first time we filed out of our holding pen—a small room in the superior courthouse that would begin to feel as familiar as my apartment—I thought maybe some bailiff had let us into the wrong courtroom. This defendant was small and delicately proportioned—the kind of guy who grew up being the punch line to high school jokes. He wore a tweed jacket that swallowed him whole, and the knot of his necktie squared away from him at the perpendicular, as if it were being magnetically repelled. His cuffed hands curled in his lap like small animals; his hair was shaved nearly to the skull. He stared down at his lap, even when the judge spoke his name and it hissed through the room like steam from a radiator.

The judge and the lawyers were taking care of housekeeping details when the fly came in. I noticed this for two reasons: in March, you don't see many flies in New Hampshire, and I wondered how you went about swatting one away from you when you were handcuffed and chained at the waist. Shay Bourne stared at the insect when it paused on the legal pad in front of him, and then in a jangle of metal, he raised his bound hands and crashed them down on the table to kill it.

Or so I thought, until he turned his palms upward, his fingers opened one petal at a time, and the insect went zipping off to bother someone else.

In that instant, he glanced at me, and I realized two things:

1. He was terrified.
2. He was approximately the same age that I was.

This double murderer, this *monster,* looked like the water polo team captain who had sat next to me in an economics seminar last semester. He resembled the deliveryman from the pizza place that had a thin crust, the kind I liked. He even reminded me of the boy I'd seen walking in the snow on my way to court, the one I'd rolled down my window for and asked if he wanted a ride. In other words, he didn't look the way I figured a killer would look, if I ever ran across one. He could have been any other kid in his twenties. He could have been me.

Except for the fact that he was ten feet away, chained at the wrists and ankles. And it was my job to decide whether or not he deserved to live.

A month later, I could tell you that serving on a jury is nothing like you see on TV. There was a lot of being paraded back and forth between the courtroom and the jury room; there was bad food from a local deli for lunch; there were lawyers who liked to hear themselves talk, and trust me, the DAs were never as hot as the girl on *Law & Order: SVU*. Even after four weeks, coming into this courtroom felt like landing in a foreign country without a guidebook . . . and yet, I couldn't plead ignorant just because I was a tourist. I was expected to speak the language fluently.

Part one of the trial was finished: we had convicted Bourne. The prosecution presented a mountain of evidence proving Kurt Nealon had been shot in the line of duty, attempting to arrest Shay Bourne after he'd found him with his stepdaughter, her underwear in Bourne's pocket. June Nealon had come home from her OB appointment to find her husband and daughter dead. The feeble argument offered up by the defense—that Kurt had misunderstood a verbally paralyzed Bourne; that the gun had gone off by accident—didn't hold a candle to the overwhelming evidence presented by the prosecution. Even worse, Bourne never took the stand on his own behalf—which could have been because of his poor language skills . . . or because he was not only guilty as sin but such a wild card that his own attorneys didn't trust him.

We were now nearly finished with part two of the trial—the sentencing phase—or in other words, the part that separated this trial from every other criminal murder trial for the past half century in New Hampshire. Now that we knew Bourne had committed the crime, did he deserve the death penalty?

This part was a little like a *Reader's Digest* condensed version of the first one. The prosecution gave a recap of evidence presented during the criminal trial; and then the defense got a chance to garner sympathy for a murderer. We learned that Bourne had been bounced around the foster care system. That when he was sixteen, he set a fire in his foster home and spent two years in a juvenile detention facility. He had untreated bipolar disorder, central auditory processing disorder, an inability to deal with sensory overload, and difficulties with reading, writing, and language skills.

We heard all this from witnesses, though. Once again, Shay Bourne never took the stand to beg us for mercy.

Now, during closing arguments, I watched the prosecutor smooth down his striped tie and walk forward. One big difference between a regular trial and the sentencing phase of a capital punishment trial is who gets the last word in edgewise. I didn't know this myself, but Maureen—a really sweet older juror I was crushing on, in a wish-you-were-my-grandma kind of way—didn't miss a single *Law & Order* episode, and had practically earned her JD via Barcalounger as a result. In most trials, when it was time for closing arguments, the prosecution spoke last . . . so that whatever they said was still buzzing in your head when you went back to the jury room to deliberate. In a capital punishment sentencing phase, though, the prosecution went *first*, and then the defense got that final chance to change your mind.

Because, after all, it really *was* a matter of life or death.

He stopped in front of the jury box. "It's been fifty-eight years in the history of the state of New Hampshire since a member of my office has had to ask a jury to make a decision as difficult and as serious as the one you twelve citizens are going to have to make. This is not a decision that any of us takes lightly, but it is a decision that the facts in this case merit, and it is a decision that must be made in order to do justice to the memories of Kurt Nealon and Elizabeth Nealon, whose lives were taken in such a tragic and despicable manner."

He took a huge, eleven-by-fourteen photo of Elizabeth Nealon and held it up right in front of me. Elizabeth had been one of those little girls who seem to be made out of something lighter than flesh, with their filly legs and their moonlight hair; the ones you think would float off the jungle gym if not for the weight of their sneakers. But this photo had been taken after she was shot. Blood splattered her face and matted her hair; her eyes were still wide open. Her dress, hiked up when she had fallen, showed that she was naked from the waist down. "Elizabeth Nealon will never learn how to do long division, or how to ride a horse, or do a back handspring. She'll never go to sleepaway camp or her junior prom or high school graduation. She'll never try on her first pair of high heels or experience her first kiss. She'll never bring a boy home to meet her mother; she'll never be walked down a wedding aisle by her stepfather; she'll never get to know her sister, Claire. She will miss all of these moments, and a thousand more—not because of a tragedy like a car accident or childhood leukemia—but because Shay Bourne made the decision that she didn't deserve any of these things."

He then took another photo out from behind Elizabeth's and held it up. Kurt Nealon had been shot in the stomach. His blue uniform shirt was purpled with his blood, and Elizabeth's. During the trial we'd heard that when the paramedics reached him, he wouldn't let go of Elizabeth, even as he was bleeding out. "Shay Bourne didn't stop at ending Elizabeth's life. He took Kurt Nealon's life, as well. And he didn't just take away Claire's father and June's husband—he took away Officer Kurt Nealon of the Lynley Police. He took away the coach of the Grafton County championship Little League team. He took away the founder of Bike Safety Day at Lynley Elementary School. Shay Bourne took away a public servant who, at the time of his death, was not just protecting his daughter . . . but protecting a citizen, and a community. A community that includes each and every one of you."

The prosecutor placed the photos facedown on the table. "There's a reason that New Hampshire hasn't used the death penalty for fifty-eight years, ladies and gentlemen. That's because, in spite of the many cases that come through our doors, we hadn't seen one that merited that sentence. However, by the same token, there's a reason why the good people of this state have reserved the option to use the death penalty . . . instead of overturning the capital punishment statute, as so many other states have done. And that reason is sitting in this courtroom today."

My gaze followed the prosecutor's, coming to rest on Shay Bourne. "If any case in the past fifty-eight years has ever cried out for the ultimate punishment to be imposed," the attorney said, "this is it."

College is a bubble. You enter it for four years and forget there is a real world outside of your paper deadlines and midterm exams and beer-pong championships. You don't read the newspaper—you read textbooks. You don't watch the news—you watch Letterman. But even so, bits and snatches of the universe manage to leak in: a mother who locked her children in a car and let it roll into a lake to drown them; an estranged husband who shot his wife in front of their kids; a serial rapist who kept a teenager tied up in a basement for a month before he slit her throat. The murders of Kurt and Elizabeth Nealon were horrible, sure—but were the others any *less* horrible?

Shay Bourne's attorney stood up. "You've found my client guilty of two counts of capital murder, and he's not contesting that. We accept your verdict; we respect your verdict. At this point in time, however, the state is asking you to wrap up this case—one that involves the death of two people—by taking the life of a third person."

I felt a bead of sweat run down the valley between my shoulder blades.

"You're not going to make anyone safer by killing Shay Bourne. Even if you decide not to execute him, he's not going anywhere. He'll be serving two life sentences without parole." He put his hand on Bourne's shoulder. "You've heard about Shay Bourne's childhood. Where was he supposed to learn what all the rest of you had a chance to learn from your families? Where was he supposed to learn right from wrong, good from bad? For that matter, where was he even supposed to learn his colors and his numbers? Who was supposed to read him bedtime stories, like Elizabeth Nealon's parents had?"

The attorney walked toward us. "You've heard that Shay Bourne has bipolar disorder, which was going untreated. You heard that he suffers from learning disabilities, so tasks that are simple for us become unbelievably frustrating for him. You've heard how hard it is for him to communicate his thoughts. These all contributed to Shay making poor choices—which you agreed with, beyond a reasonable doubt." He looked at each of us in turn. "Shay Bourne made poor choices," the attorney said. "But don't compound that by making one of your own."

June
|||||||||||||||||||||||||||||||||||||||||||||||||||||||||||||||||||||||||||||||||||||||||||||||||||

It was up to the jury. Again.

It's a strange thing, putting justice in the hands of twelve strangers. I had spent most of the sentencing phase of the trial watching their faces. There were a few mothers; I would catch their eye and smile at them when I could. A few men who looked like maybe they'd been in the military. And the boy, the one who barely looked old enough to shave, much less make the right decision.

I wanted to sit down with each and every one of them. I wanted to show them the note Kurt had written me after our first official date. I wanted them to touch the soft cotton cap that Elizabeth had worn home from the hospital as a newborn. I wanted to play them the answering machine message that still had their voices on it, the one I couldn't bear to erase, even though it felt like I was being cut to ribbons every time I heard it. I wanted to take them on a field trip to see Elizabeth's bedroom, with its Tinker Bell night-light and dress-up clothes; I wanted them to bury their faces in Kurt's pillow, breathe him in. I wanted them to live my life, because that was the only way they'd really know what had been lost.

That night after the closing arguments, I nursed Claire in the middle of the night and then fell asleep with her in my arms. But I dreamed that she was upstairs, distant, and crying. I climbed the stairs to the nursery, the one that still smelled of virgin wood and drying paint, and opened the door. "I'm coming," I said, and I crossed the threshold only to realize that the room had never been built, that I had no baby, that I was falling through the air.

Michael

Only certain people wind up on a jury for a trial like this. Mothers who have kids to take care of, the accountants with deadlines, doctors attending conferences—they all get excused. What's left are retired folks, housewives, disabled folks, and students like me, because none of us have to be any particular place at any particular time.

Ted, our foreman, was an older man who reminded me of my grandfather. Not in the way he looked or even the way he spoke, but because of the gift he had of making us measure up to a task. My grandfather had been like that, too—you wanted to be your best around him, not because he demanded it, but because there was nothing like that grin when you knew you'd impressed him.

My grandfather was the reason I'd been picked for this jury. Even though I had no personal experience with murder, I knew what it was like to lose someone you loved. You didn't get past something like that, you got *through* it—and for that simple reason alone, I understood more about June Nealon than she ever would have guessed. This past winter, four years after my grandfather's death, someone had broken into my dorm and stolen my computer, my bike, and the only picture I had of my grandfather and me together. The thief left behind the sterling silver frame, but when I'd reported the theft to the cops, it was the loss of that photograph that hurt the most.

Ted waited for Maureen to reapply her lipstick, for Jack to go to the bathroom, for everyone to take a moment for themselves before we settled down to the task of acting as a unified body. "Well," he said, flattening his hands on the conference table. "I suppose we should just get down to business."

As it turned out, though, it was a lot easier to say that someone deserved to die for what they did than it was to take the responsibility to make that happen.

"I'm just gonna come right out and say it." Vy sighed. "I really have no idea what the judge told us we need to do."

At the start of the testimony, the judge had given us nearly an hour's worth of verbal instructions. I figured there'd be a handout, too, but I'd figured wrong. "I can explain it," I said. "It's kind of like a Chinese food menu. There's a whole checklist of things that make a crime punishable by death. Basically, we have to find one from column A, and one or more from column B . . . for each of the murders to qualify for the death penalty. If we check off one from column A, but none from column B . . . then the court automatically sentences him to life without parole."

"I don't understand what's in column A or B," Maureen said.

"I never liked Chinese food," Mark added.

I stood up in front of the white board and picked up a dry-erase marker. COLUMN A, I wrote. PURPOSE. "The first thing we have to decide is whether or not Bourne *meant* to kill each victim." I turned to everyone else. "I guess we've pretty much answered that already by convicting him of murder."

COLUMN B. "Here's where it gets trickier. There are a whole bunch of factors on this list."

I began to read from the jumbled notes I'd taken during the judge's instructions:

**Defendant has already been
convicted of murder once before.
Defendant has been convicted of
two or more different offenses for
which he's served imprisonment
for more than a year—a three-
strikes rule.
Defendant has been convicted of
two or more offenses involving
distribution of drugs.
In the middle of the capital murder,
the defendant risked the death of
someone in addition to the victims.
The defendant committed the
offense after planning and
premeditation.
The victim was vulnerable due to
old age, youth, infirmity.
The defendant committed the
offense in a particularly heinous,
cruel, or depraved manner that
involved torture or physical abuse
to the victim.**

**The murder was committed for the
purpose of avoiding lawful arrest.**

Ted stared at the board as I wrote down
what I could remember. "So if we find one
from column A, and one from column B, we
have to sentence him to death?"

"No," I said. "Because there's also a column C."

MITIGATING FACTORS, I wrote. "These are the
reasons the defense gave as excuses."

**Defendant's capacity to appreciate
what he was doing was wrong, or
illegal, was impaired.
Defendant was under unusual and
substantial duress.
Defendant is punishable as an
accomplice in the offense which
was committed by another.
Defendant was young, although not
under the age of 18.
Defendant did not have a significant
prior criminal record.
Defendant committed the offense
under severe mental or emotional
disturbance.**

Another defendant equally culpable will not be punished by death.
Victim consented to the criminal conduct that resulted in death.
Other factors in the defendant's background mitigate against the death sentence.

Underneath the columns, I wrote, in large red letters: $(A + B) - C = $ SENTENCE.

Marilyn threw up her hands. "I stopped helping my son with math homework in sixth grade."

"No, it's easy," I said. "We need to agree that Bourne intended to kill each victim when he picked up that gun. That's column A. Then we need to see whether any other aggravating factor fits from column B. Like, the youth of the victim—that works for Elizabeth, right?"

Around the table, people nodded.

"If we've got A and B, then we take into account the foster care, the mental illness, stuff like that. It's just simple math. If $A + B$ is greater than all the things the defense said, we sentence him to death. If $A + B$ is less than all the things the defense said, then we don't." I circled the equation. "We just need to see how things add up."

Put that way, it hardly had anything to do with us. It was just plugging in variables and seeing what answer we got. Put that way, it was a much easier task to perform.

1:12 P.M.

"Of course Bourne planned it," Jack said. "He got a job with them so that he'd be near the girl. He picked this family on purpose, and had access to the house."

"He'd gone home for the day," Jim said. "Why else would he come back, if he didn't need to be there?"

"The tools," Maureen answered. "He left them behind, and they were his prized possessions. Remember what that shrink said? Bourne stole them out of other people's garages, and didn't understand why that was wrong, since he needed them, and they were pretty much just gathering dust otherwise."

"Maybe he left them behind on purpose," Ted suggested. "If they were really so precious, wouldn't he have taken them with him?"

There was a general assent. "Do we agree that there was substantial planning involved?" Ted asked. "Let's see a show of hands."

Half the room, myself included, raised our hands. Another few people slowly raised theirs, too. Maureen was the last, but the minute she did, I circled that factor on the white board.

"That's two from column B," Ted said.

"Speaking of which . . . where's lunch?" Jack asked. "Don't they usually bring it by now?"

Did he really want to eat? What did you order off a deli menu when you were in the process of deciding whether to end a man's life?

Marilyn sighed. "I think we ought to talk about the fact that this poor girl was found without her underpants on."

"I don't think we can," Maureen said. "Remember when we were deliberating over the verdict, and we asked the judge about Elizabeth being molested? He said then that since it wasn't being charged, we couldn't use it to find him guilty. If we couldn't bring it up then, how can we bring it up *now*?"

"This is different," Vy said. "He's *already* guilty."

"The man was going to rape that little girl,"

Marilyn said. "That counts as cruel and heinous behavior to me."

"You know, there wasn't any evidence that that's what was happening," Mark said.

Marilyn raised an eyebrow. "Hello?! The girl was found without her panties. Seven-year-olds don't go running around without their panties. Plus, Bourne had the underwear in his pocket . . . what else would he be doing with them?"

"Does it even matter? We already agree that Elizabeth was young when she was killed. We don't need any more from column B." Maureen frowned. "I think I'm confused."

Alison, a doctor's wife who hadn't said much during the original deliberations, glanced at her. "When I get confused, I think about that officer who testified, the one who said that he heard the little girl screaming when he was running up the stairs. *Don't shoot*—she was begging. She begged for her life." Alison sighed. "That sort of makes it simple again, doesn't it?"

As we all fell quiet, Ted asked for a show of hands in favor of the execution of Shay Bourne.

"No," I said. "We still have the rest of the equation to figure out." I pointed to column C. "We have to consider what the defense said."

"The only thing I want to consider right now is where is my lunch," Jack said.

The vote was 8–4, and I was in the minority.

3:06 P.M.

I looked around the room. This time, nine people had their hands in the air. Maureen, Vy, and I were the only ones who hadn't voted for execution.

"What is it that's keeping you from making this decision?" Ted asked.

"His age," Vy said. "My son's twenty-four," she said. "And all I can think is that he doesn't always make the best decisions. He's not done growing up yet."

Jack turned toward me. "You're the same age as Bourne. What are you doing with *your* life?"

I felt my face flame. "I, um, probably I'll go to graduate school. I'm not really sure."

"You haven't killed anyone, have you?"

Jack got to his feet. "Let's take a bathroom break," he suggested, and we all jumped at the chance to separate. I tossed the dry-erase marker on the table and walked to the window. Outside, there were courthouse employees eating their lunch on benches. There were clouds caught in the twisted fingers of the trees. And there were television vans with satellites on their roofs, waiting to hear what we'd say.

Jim sat down beside me, reading the Bible that seemed to be an extra appendage. "You religious?"

"I went to parochial school a long time ago." I faced him. "Isn't there something in there about turning the other cheek?"

Jim pursed his lips and read aloud. *"If thy right eye offend thee, pluck it out, and cast it from thee; for it is profitable for thee that one of thy members should perish, and not that thy whole body should be cast into hell.* When one apple's gone bad, you don't let it ruin the whole bunch." He passed the Bible to me. "See for yourself."

I looked at the quote, and then closed the book. I didn't know nearly as much as Jim did about religion, but it seemed to me that no matter what Jesus said in that passage, he might have taken it back after being sentenced to death himself. In fact, it seemed to me that if Jesus were here in this jury room, he'd be having just as hard a time doing what needed to be done as I was.

4:02 P.M.

Ted had me write Yes and No on the board, and then he polled us, one by one, as I wrote our names in each of the columns.

Jim?
Yes.
Alison?
Yes.
Marilyn?
Yes.
Vy?
No.

I hesitated, then wrote my own name beneath Vy's.

"You agreed to vote for death if you had to," Mark said. "They asked each of us before we got picked for the jury if we could do that."

"I know." I *had* agreed to vote for the death penalty if the case merited it. I just hadn't realized it was going to be this difficult to do.

Vy buried her face in her hands. "When my son used to hit his little brother, I didn't smack him and say 'Don't hit.' It felt hypocritical then. And it feels hypocritical now."

"Vy," Marilyn said quietly, "what if it had been *your* seven-year-old who was killed?" She reached onto the table, where we had piled up transcripts and evidence, and took the same picture of Elizabeth Nealon that the prosecutor had presented during his closing argument. She set it down in front of Vy, smoothed its glossy surface.

After a minute, Vy stood up heavily and took the marker out of my hand. She wiped her name off the No column and wrote it beneath Marilyn's, with the ten other jurors who'd voted Yes.

"Michael," Ted said.

I swallowed.

"What do you need to see, to hear? We can help you find it." He reached for the box that held the bullets from ballistics, the bloody clothing, the autopsy reports. He let photos from the crime scene spill through his hands like ribbons. On some of them, there was so much blood, you could barely see the victim lying beneath its sheen. "Michael," Ted said, "do the math."

I faced the white board, because I couldn't stand the heat of their eyes on me. Next to the list of names, mine standing alone, was the original equation I'd set up for us when we first came into this jury room: $(A + B) - C =$ SENTENCE.

What I liked about math was that it was safe. There was always a right answer—even if it was imaginary.

This, though, was an equation where math did not hold up. Because $A + B$—the factors that had led to the deaths of Kurt and Elizabeth Nealon—would always be greater than C. You couldn't bring them back, and there was no sob story in the world big enough to erase that truth.

In the space between yes and no, there's a lifetime. It's the difference between the path you walk and one you leave behind; it's the gap between who you thought you could be and who you really are; it's the legroom for the lies you'll tell yourself in the future.

I erased my name on the board. Then I took the pen and rewrote it, becoming the twelfth and final juror to sentence Shay Bourne to death.

III

"If God did not exist, it would be necessary
to invent him."

—*VOLTAIRE*, FOR AND AGAINST

If God did not exist, it would be necessary to invent him?

—VOLTAIRE

ELEVEN YEARS LATER

Lucius

||||||||||||||||||||||||||||||||||||||||||||||||||||||||||||||||||||||||||||||||||||||||||||||||||||||||||||||||||||||||||||||||||||

I have no idea where they were keeping
Shay Bourne before they brought him to us.
I knew he was an inmate here at the state
prison in Concord—I can still remember
watching the news the day his sentence was
handed down and scrutinizing an outside
world that was starting to fade in my mind:
the rough stone of the prison exterior; the
golden dome of the statehouse; even just
the general shape of a door that wasn't made
of metal and wire mesh. His conviction was
the subject of great discussion on the pod all
those years ago—where do you keep an inmate who's been sentenced to death when

your state hasn't had a death row prisoner for ages?

Rumor had it that in fact, the prison did have a pair of death row cells—not too far from my own humble abode in the Secure Housing Unit on I-tier. Crash Vitale—who had something to say about everything, although no one usually bothered to listen—told us that the old death row cells were stacked with the thin, plastic slabs that pass for mattresses here. I wondered for a while what had happened to all those extra mattresses after Shay arrived. One thing's for sure, no one offered to give them to us.

Moving cells is routine in prison. They don't like you to become too attached to anything. In the fifteen years I've been here, I have been moved eight different times. The cells, of course, all look alike—what's different is who's next to you, which is why Shay's arrival on I-tier was of great interest to all of us.

This, in itself, was a rarity. The six inmates in I-tier were radically different from one another; for one man to spark curiosity in all of us was nothing short of a miracle. Cell 1 housed Joey Kunz, a pedophile who was at the bottom of the pecking order. In Cell 2 was Calloway Reece, a card-carrying member of the Aryan Brotherhood. Cell 3 was me, Lucius DuFresne. Four and five were empty, so we knew the new inmate would be put in one of them—the only question was whether he'd be closer to me, or to the guys in the last three cells: Texas Wridell, Pogie Simmons, and Crash, the self-appointed leader of I-tier.

As Shay Bourne was escorted in by a phalanx of six correctional officers wearing helmets and flak jackets and face shields, we all came forward in our cells. The COs passed by the shower stall, shuffled by Joey and Calloway, and then paused right in front of me, so I could get a good look. Bourne was small and slight, with close-cropped brown hair and eyes like the Caribbean Sea. I knew about the Caribbean, because it was the last vacation I'd taken with Adam. I was glad I didn't have eyes like that. I wouldn't want to look in the mirror every day and be reminded of a place I'd never see again.

Then Shay Bourne turned to me.

Maybe now would be a good time to tell you what I look like. My face was the reason the COs didn't look me in the eye; it was why I sometimes preferred to be hidden inside this cell. The sores were scarlet and purple and scaly. They spread from my forehead to my chin.

Most people winced. Even the polite ones, like the eighty-year-old missionary who brought us pamphlets once a month, always did a double take, as if I looked even worse than he remembered. But Shay just met my gaze and nodded at me, as if I were no different than anyone else.

I heard the door of the cell beside mine slide shut, the clink of chains as Shay stuck his hands through the trap to have his cuffs removed. The COs left the pod, and almost immediately Crash started in. "Hey, Death Row," he yelled.

There was no response from Shay Bourne's cell.

"Hey, when Crash talks, you answer."

"Leave him alone, Crash," I sighed. "Give the poor guy five minutes to figure out what a moron you are."

"Ooh, Death Row, better watch it," Calloway said. "Lucius is kissing up to you, and his last boyfriend's six feet under."

There was the sound of a television being turned on, and then Shay must have plugged in the headphones that we were all required to have, so we didn't have a volume war with one another. I was a little surprised that a death row prisoner would have been able to purchase a television from the canteen, same as us. It would have been a thirteen-inch one, specially made for us wards of the state by Zenith, with a clear plastic shell around its guts and cathodes, so that the COs would be able to tell if you were extracting parts to make weapons.

While Calloway and Crash united (as they often did) to humiliate me, I pulled out my own set of headphones and turned on my television. It was five o'clock, and I didn't like to miss *Oprah*. But when I tried to change the channel, nothing happened. The screen flickered, as if it were resetting to channel 22, but channel 22 looked just like channel 3 and channel 5 and CNN and the Food Network.

"Hey." Crash started to pound on his door. "Yo, CO, the cable's down. We got rights, you know . . ."

Sometimes headphones don't work well enough.

I turned up the volume and watched a local news network's coverage of a fund-raiser for a nearby children's hospital up near Dartmouth College. There were clowns and balloons and even two Red Sox players signing autographs. The camera zeroed in on a girl with fairy-tale blond hair and blue half-moons beneath her eyes, just the kind of child they'd televise to get you to open up your wallet. "Claire Nealon," the reporter's voice-over said, "is waiting for a heart."

Boo-hoo, I thought. Everyone's got problems. I took off my headphones. If I couldn't listen to *Oprah,* I didn't want to listen at all.

Which is why I was able to hear Shay Bourne's very first word on I-tier. "Yes," he said, and just like that, the cable came back on.

You have probably noticed by now that I am a cut above most of the cretins on I-tier, and that's because I don't really belong here. It was a crime of passion—the only discrepancy is that I focused on the *passion* part and the courts focused on the *crime.* But I ask you, what would *you* have done, if the love of your life found a new love of *his* life —someone younger, thinner, better-looking?

The irony, of course, is that no sentence imposed by a court for homicide could trump the one that's ravaged me in prison. My last CD4+ was taken six months ago, and I was down to seventy-five cells per cubic millimeter of blood. Someone without HIV would have a normal T cell count of a thousand cells or more, but the virus becomes part of these white blood cells. When the white blood cells reproduce to fight infection, the virus reproduces, too. As the immune system gets weak, the more likely I am to get sick, or to develop an opportunistic infection like PCP, toxoplasmosis, or CMV. The doctors say I won't die from AIDS—I'll die from pneumonia or TB or a bacterial infection in the brain; but if you ask me, that's just semantics. Dead is dead.

I was an artist by vocation, and now by avocation—although it's been considerably more challenging to get my supplies in a place like this. Where I had once favored Winsor & Newton oils and red sable brushes, linen canvases I stretched myself and coated with gesso, I now used whatever I could get my hands on. I had my nephews draw me pictures on card stock in pencil that I erased so that I could use the paper over again. I hoarded the foods that produced pigment. Tonight I had been working on a portrait of Adam, drawn of course from memory, because that was all I had left. I had mixed some red ink gleaned from a Skittle with a dab of toothpaste in the lid of a juice bottle, and coffee with a bit of water in a second lid, and then I'd combined them to get just the right shade of his skin—a burnished, deep molasses.

I had already outlined his features in black—the broad brow, the strong chin, the hawk's nose. I'd used a shank to shave ebony curls from a picture of a coal mine in a *National Geographic* and added a dab of shampoo to make a chalky paint. With the broken tip of a pencil, I had transferred the color to my makeshift canvas.

God, he was beautiful.

It was after three a.m., but to be honest, I don't sleep much. When I do, I find myself getting up to go to the bathroom—as little as I eat these days, food passes through me at lightning speed. I get sick to my stomach; I get headaches. The thrush in my mouth and throat makes it hard to swallow. Instead, I use my insomnia to fuel my artwork.

Tonight, I'd had the sweats. I was soaked through by the time I woke up, and after I stripped off my sheets and my scrubs, I didn't want to lie down on the mattress again. Instead, I had pulled out my painting and started re-creating Adam. But I got sidetracked by the other portraits I'd finished of him, hanging on my cell wall: Adam standing in the same pose he'd first struck when he was modeling for the college art class I taught; Adam's face when he opened his eyes in the morning. Adam, looking over his shoulder, the way he'd been when I shot him.

"I need to do it," Shay Bourne said. "It's the only way."

He had been utterly silent since this afternoon's arrival on I-tier; I wondered who he was having a conversation with at this hour of the night. But the pod was empty. Maybe he was having a nightmare. "Bourne?" I whispered. "Are you okay?"

"Who's . . . there?"

The words were hard for him—not quite a stutter; more like each syllable was a stone he had to bring forth. "I'm Lucius. Lucius DuFresne," I said. "You talking to someone?"

He hesitated. "I *think* I'm talking to you."

"Can't sleep?"

"I can sleep," Shay said. "I just don't want to."

"You're luckier than I am, then," I replied.

It was a joke, but he didn't take it that way. "You're no luckier than me, and I'm no unluckier than you," he said.

Well, in a way, he was right. I may not have been handed down the same sentence as

Shay Bourne, but like him, I would die within the walls of this prison—sooner rather than later.

"Lucius," he said. "What are *you* doing?"

"I'm painting."

There was a beat of silence. "Your cell?"

"No. A portrait."

"Why?"

"Because I'm an artist."

"Once, in school, an art teacher said I had classic lips," Shay said. "I still don't know what that means."

"It's a reference to the ancient Greeks and Romans," I explained. "And the art that we see represented on—"

"Lucius? Did you see on TV today . . . the Red Sox . . ."

Everyone on I-tier had a team they followed, myself included. We each kept meticulous score of their league standings, and we debated the fairness of umpire and ref calls as if they were law and we were Supreme Court judges. Sometimes, like us, our teams had their hopes dashed; other times we got to share their World Series. But it was still preseason; there hadn't been any televised games today.

"Schilling was sitting at a table," Shay

added, still struggling to find the right words. "And there was a little girl—"

"You mean the fund-raiser? The one up at the hospital?"

"That little girl," Shay said. "I'm going to give her my heart."

Before I could respond, there was a loud crash and the thud of flesh smacking against the concrete floor. "Shay?" I called. "Shay?!"

I pressed my face up against the Plexiglas. I couldn't see Shay at all, but I heard something rhythmic smacking his cell door. "Hey!" I yelled at the top of my lungs. "Hey, we need help down here!"

The others started to wake up, cursing me out for disturbing their rest, and then falling silent with fascination. Two officers stormed into I-tier, still Velcroing their flak jackets. One of them, CO Kappaletti, was the kind of man who'd taken this job so that he'd always have someone to put down. The other, CO Smythe, had never been anything but professional toward me. Kappaletti stopped in front of my cell. "DuFresne, if you're crying wolf—"

But Smythe was already kneeling in front of Shay's cell. "I think Bourne's having a seizure." He reached for his radio and the electronic door slid open so that other officers could enter.

"Is he breathing?" one said.

"Turn him over, on the count of three . . ."

The EMTs arrived and wheeled Shay past my cell on a gurney—a stretcher with restraints across the shoulders, belly, and legs that was used to transport inmates like Crash who were too much trouble even cuffed at the waist and ankles; or inmates who were too sick to walk to the infirmary. I always assumed I'd leave I-tier on one of those gurneys. But now I realized that it looked a lot like the table Shay would one day be strapped onto for his lethal injection.

The EMTs had pushed an oxygen mask over Shay's mouth that frosted with each breath he took. His eyes had rolled up in their sockets, white and blind. "Do whatever it takes to bring him back," CO Smythe instructed; and that was how I learned that the state will save a dying man just so that they can kill him later.

Michael

There was a great deal that I loved about the Church.

Like the feeling I got when two hundred voices rose to the rafters during Sunday Mass in prayer. Or the way my hand still shook when I offered the host to a parishioner. I loved the double take on the face of a troubled teenager when he drooled over the 1969 Triumph Trophy motorcycle I'd restored—and then found out I was a priest; that being cool and being Catholic were not mutually exclusive.

Even though I was clearly the junior priest at St. Catherine's, we were one of only four parishes to serve all of Concord, New Hampshire. There never seemed to be enough hours in the day. Father Walter and I would alternate officiating at Mass or hearing confession; sometimes we'd be asked to drop in and teach a class at the parochial school one town over. There were always parishioners to visit who were ill or troubled or lonely; there were always rosaries to be said. But I looked forward to even the humblest act—sweeping the vestibule, or rinsing the vessels from the Eucharist in the sacrarium so that no drop of Precious Blood wound up in the Concord sewers.

I didn't have an office at St. Catherine's. Father Walter did, but then he'd been at the parish so long that he seemed as much a part of it as the rosewood pews and the velveteen drapes at the altar. Although he kept telling me he'd get around to clearing out a spot for me in one of the old storage rooms, he tended to nap after lunch, and who was I to wake up a man in his seventies and tell him to get a move on? After a while, I gave up asking and instead set a small desk up inside a broom closet. Today, I was supposed to be writing a homily—if I could get it down to seven minutes, I knew the older members of the congregation wouldn't fall asleep—but instead, my mind kept straying to one of our youngest members. Hannah Smythe was the first baby I baptized at St. Catherine's. Now, just one year later, the infant had been hospitalized repeatedly. Without warning, her throat would simply close, and her frantic parents would rush her to the ER for intubation, where the vicious cycle would start all over again. I offered up a quick prayer to God to lead the doctors to cure Hannah. I was just finishing up with the sign of the cross when a small, silver-haired lady approached my desk. "Father Michael?"

"Mary Lou," I said. "How are you doing?"

"Could I maybe talk to you for a few minutes?"

Mary Lou Huckens could talk not only for a few minutes; she was likely to go on for nearly an hour. Father Walter and I had an unwritten policy to rescue each other from her effusive praise after Mass. "What can I do for you?"

"Actually, I feel a little silly about this," she admitted. "I just wanted to know if you'd bless my bust."

I smiled at her. Parishioners often asked us to offer a prayer over a devotional item. "Sure. Have you got it with you?"

She gave me an odd look. "Well, of course I do."

"Great. Let's see it."

She crossed her hands over her chest. "I hardly think *that's* necessary!"

I felt heat flood my cheeks as I realized what she actually wanted me to bless. "I-I'm sorry . . ." I stammered. "I didn't mean . . ."

Her eyes filled with tears. "They're doing a lumpectomy tomorrow, Father, and I'm terrified."

I stood up and put my arm around her, walked her a few yards to the closest pew, offered her Kleenex. "I'm sorry," she said. "I don't know who else to talk to. If I tell my husband I'm scared, he'll get scared, too."

"You know who to talk to," I said gently. "And you know He's always listening." I touched the crown of her head. "Omnipotent and eternal God, the everlasting Salvation of those who believe, hear us on behalf of Thy servant Mary Lou, for whom we beg the aid of Thy pitying mercy, that with her bodily health restored, she may give thanks to Thee in Thy church. Through Christ our Lord, amen."

"Amen," Mary Lou whispered.

That's the other thing I love about the Church: you never know what to expect.

Lucius

When Shay Bourne returned to I-tier after three days in the hospital infirmary, he was a man with a mission. Every morning, when the officers came to poll us to see who wanted a shower or time in the yard, Shay would ask to speak to Warden Coyne. "Fill out a request," he was told, over and over, but it just didn't seem to sink in. When it was his turn in the little caged kennel that was our exercise yard, he'd stand in the far corner, looking toward the opposite side of the prison, where the administrative offices were housed, and he'd yell his request at the top of his lungs. When he was brought his dinner, he'd ask if the warden had agreed to talk to him.

"You know why he was moved to I-tier?" Calloway said one day when Shay was bellowing in the shower for an audience with the warden. "Because he made everyone else on his last tier go deaf."

"He's a retard," Crash answered. "Can't help how he acts. Kinda like our own diaper sniper. Right, Joey?"

"He's not mentally challenged," I said. "He's probably got double the IQ that you do, Crash."

"Shut the fuck up, fruiter," Calloway said. "Shut up, all of you!" The urgency in his voice silenced us. Calloway knelt at the door of his cell, fishing with a braided string pulled out of his blanket and tied at one end to a rolled magazine. He cast into the center of the catwalk—risky behavior, since the COs would be back any minute. At first we couldn't figure out what he was doing—when we fished, it was with one another, tangling our lines to pass along anything from a paperback book to a Hershey's bar—but then we noticed the small, bright oval on the floor. God only knew why a bird would make a nest in a hellhole like this, but one had a few

months back, after flying in through the exercise yard. One egg had fallen out and
cracked; the baby robin lay on its side, unfinished, its thin, wrinkled chest working like
a piston.

Calloway reeled the egg in, inch by inch.
"It ain't gonna live," Crash said. "Its mama
won't want it now."

"Well, *I* do," Calloway said.

"Put it somewhere warm," I suggested.
"Wrap it up in a towel or something."

"Use your T-shirt," Joey added.

"I don't take advice from a cho-mo," Calloway said, but then, a moment later: "You
think a T-shirt will work?"

While Shay yelled for the warden, we all
listened to Calloway's play-by-play: The robin
was wrapped in a shirt. The robin was tucked
inside his left tennis shoe. The robin was
pinking up. The robin had opened its left eye
for a half second.

We all had forgotten what it was like to
care about something so much that you
might not be able to stand losing it. The first
year I was in here, I used to pretend that the
full moon was my pet, that it came once a
month just to me. And this past summer,
Crash had taken to spreading jam on the

louvers of his vent to cultivate a colony of bees, but that was less about husbandry than his misguided belief that he could train them to swarm Joey in his sleep.

"Cowboys comin' to lock 'em up," Crash said, fair warning that the COs were getting ready to enter the pod again. A moment later the doors buzzed open; they stood in front of the shower cell waiting for Shay to stick his hands through the trap to be cuffed for the twenty-foot journey back to his own cell.

"They don't know what it could be," CO Smythe said. "They've ruled out pulmonary problems and asthma. They're saying maybe an allergy—but there's nothing in her room anymore, Rick, it's bare as a cell."

Sometimes the COs talked to one another in front of us. They never spoke to inmates directly about their lives, and that actually was fine. We didn't want to know that the guy strip-searching us had a son who scored the winning goal in his soccer game last Thursday. Better to take the humanity out of it.

"They said," Smythe continued, "that her heart can't keep taking this kind of stress. And neither can I. You know what it's like to see your baby with all these bags and wires coming out of her?"

The second CO, Whitaker, was a Catholic who liked to include, on my dinner tray, hand-written scripture verses that denounced homosexuality. "Father Walter led a prayer for Hannah on Sunday. He said he'd be happy to visit you at the hospital."

"There's nothing a priest can say that I want to hear," Smythe muttered. "What kind of God would do this to a baby?"

Shay's hands slipped through the trap of the shower cell to be cuffed, and then the door was opened. "Did the warden say he'd meet with me?"

"Yeah," Smythe said, leading Shay toward his cell. "He wants you to come for high friggin' tea."

"I just need five minutes with him—"

"You're not the only one with problems," Smythe snapped. "Fill out a request."

"I *can't,*" Shay replied.

I cleared my throat. "Officer? Could I have a request form, too, please?"

He finished locking Shay up, then took one out of his pocket and stuffed it into the trap of my cell.

Just as the officers exited the tier, there was a small, feeble chirp.

"Shay?" I asked. "Why not just fill out the request slip?"

"I can't get my words to come out right."

"I'm sure the warden doesn't care about grammar."

"No, it's when I write. When I start, the letters all get tangled."

"Then tell me, and I'll write the note."

There was a silence. "You'd do that for me?"

"Will you two cut the soap opera?" Crash said. "You're making me sick."

"Tell the warden," Shay dictated, "that I want to donate my heart, after he kills me. I want to give it to a girl who needs it more than I do."

I leaned the ticket up against the wall of the cell and wrote in pencil, signed Shay's name. I tied the note to the end of my own fishing line and swung it beneath the narrow opening of his cell door. "Give this to the officer who makes rounds tomorrow morning."

"You know, Bourne," Crash mused, "I don't know what to make of you. I mean, on the one hand, you're a child-killing piece of shit.

You might as well be fungus growing on Joey, for what you done to that little girl. But on the other hand, you took down a cop, and I for one am truly grateful there's one less pig in the world. So how am I supposed to feel? Do I hate you, or do I give you my respect?"

"Neither," Shay said. "Both."

"You know what I think? Baby killing beats anything good you might have done." Crash stood up at the front of his cell and began to bang a metal coffee mug against the Plexiglas. "Throw him out. Throw him out. *Throw him out!*"

Joey—unused to being even one notch above low-man-on-the-totem-pole—was the first to join in the singing. Then Texas and Pogie started in, because they did whatever Crash told them to do.

Throw him out.
Throw him out.

Whitaker's voice bled through the loudspeaker. "You got a problem, Vitale?"

"I don't got a problem. This punk-ass child killer here's the one with the problem. I tell you what, Officer. You let me out for five minutes, and I'll save the good taxpayers of New Hampshire the trouble of getting rid of him—"

"Crash," Shay said softly. "Cool off."

I was distracted by a whistling noise coming from my tiny sink. I had no sooner stood up to investigate than the water burst out of the spigot. This was remarkable on two counts—normally, the water pressure was no greater than a trickle, even in the showers. And the water that was splashing over the sides of the metal bowl was a deep, rich red.

"Fuck!" Crash yelled. "I just got soaked!"

"Man, that looks like blood," Pogie said, horrified. "I'm not washing up in that."

"It's in the toilets, too," Texas added.

We all knew our pipes were connected. The bad news about this was that you literally could not get away from the shit brought down by the others around you. On the bright side, you could actually flush a note down the length of the pod; it would briefly appear in the next cell's bowl before heading through the sewage system. I turned and looked into my toilet. The water was as dark as rubies.

"Holy crap," Crash said. "It ain't blood. It's *wine*." He started to crow like a madman. "Taste it, ladies. Drinks are on the house."

I waited. I did not drink the tap water in here. As it was, I had a feeling that my AIDS medications, which came on a punch card, might be some government experiment done on expendable inmates . . . I wasn't about to imbibe from a water treatment system run by the same administration. But then I heard Joey start laughing, and Calloway slurping from the faucet, and Texas and Pogie singing drinking songs. In fact, the entire mood of the tier changed so radically that CO Whitaker's voice boomed over the intercom, confused by the visions on the monitors. "What's going on in there?" he asked. "Is there a water main leak?"

"You could say that," Crash replied. "Or you could say we got us a powerful thirst."

"Come on in, CO," Pogie added. "We'll buy the next round."

Everyone seemed to find this hilarious, but then, they'd all downed nearly a half gallon of whatever this fluid was by now. I dipped my finger into the dark stream that was still running strong from my sink. It could have been iron or manganese, but it was true—this water smelled like sugar, and dried sticky. I bent my head to the tap and drank tentatively from the flow.

Adam and I had been closet sommeliers, taking trips to the California vineyards. To that end, for my birthday that last year, Adam had gotten me a 2001 Dominus Estate cabernet sauvignon. We were going to drink it on New Year's Eve. Weeks later, when I came in and found them, twisted together like jungle vines, that bottle was there, too—tipped off the nightstand and staining the bedroom carpet, like blood that had already been spilled.

If you've been in prison as long as I have, you've experienced a good many innovative highs. I've drunk hooch distilled from fruit juice and bread and Jolly Rancher candies; I've huffed spray deodorant; I've smoked dried banana peels rolled up in a page of the Bible. But this was like none of those. This was honest-to-God wine.

I laughed. But before long I began to sob, tears running down my face for what I had lost, for what was now literally coursing through my fingers. You can only miss something you remember having, and it had been so long since creature comforts had been part of my ordinary life. I filled a plastic mug with wine and drank it down; I did this over and over again until it became easier to forget the fact that all extraordinary things must come to an end—a lesson I could have lectured on, given my history.

By now, the COs realized that there had been some snafu with the plumbing. Two of them came onto the tier, fuming, and paused in front of my cell. "You," Whitaker commanded. "Cuffs."

I went through the rigmarole of having my wrists bound through the open trap so that when Whitaker had my door buzzed open I could be secured by Smythe while he investigated. I watched over my shoulder as Whitaker touched a pinky to the stream of wine and held it up to his tongue. "Lucius," he said, "what is this?"

"At first I thought it was a cabernet, Officer," I said. "But now I'm leaning toward a cheap merlot."

"The water comes from the town reservoir," Smythe said. "Inmates can't mess with that."

"Maybe it's a miracle," Crash sang. "You know all about miracles, don't you, Officer Bible-thumper?"

My cell door was closed and my hands freed. Whitaker stood on the catwalk in front of our cells. "Who did this?" he asked, but nobody was listening. "Who's responsible?"

"Who cares?" Crash replied.

"So help me, if one of you doesn't fess up,

I'll have maintenance turn off your water for the next week," Whitaker threatened.

Crash laughed. "The ACLU needs a poster child, Whit."

As the COs stormed off the tier, we were all laughing. Things that weren't humorous became funny; I didn't even mind listening to Crash. At some point, the wine trickled and dried up, but by then, Pogie had already passed out cold, Texas and Joey were singing "Danny Boy" in harmony, and I was fading fast. In fact, the last thing I remember is Shay asking Calloway what he was going to name his bird, and Calloway's answer: Batman the Robin. And Calloway challenging Shay to a chugging contest, but Shay saying he would sit that one out. That actually, he didn't drink.

For two days after the water on I-tier had turned into wine, a steady stream of plumbers, scientists, and prison administrators visited our cells. Apparently, we were the only unit within the prison where this had happened, and the only reason anyone in power even believed it was because when our cells were tossed, the COs confiscated the shampoo bottles and milk containers and even plastic bags that we had all innovatively used to store some extra wine before it had run dry; and because swabs taken in the pipes revealed a matching substance. Although nobody would officially give us the results of the lab testing, rumor had it that the liquid in question was definitely not tap water.

Our exercise and shower privileges were revoked for a week, as if this had been our fault in the first place, and forty-three hours passed before I was allowed a visit from the prison nurse, Alma, who smelled of lemons and linen; and who had a massive coiled tower of braided hair that, I imagined, required architectural intervention in order for her to sleep. Normally, she came twice a day to bring me a card full of pills as bright and big as dragonflies. She also spread cream on inmates' fungal foot infections, checked teeth that had been rotted out by crystal meth, and did anything else that didn't require a visit to the infirmary. I admit to faking illness several times so that Alma would take my temperature or blood pressure. Sometimes, she was the only person who touched me for weeks.

"So," she said, as she was let into my cell by CO Smythe. "I hear things have been pretty exciting on I-tier. You gonna tell me what happened?"

"Would if I could," I said, and then glanced at the officer accompanying her. "Or maybe I wouldn't."

"I can only think of one person who ever turned water into wine," she said, "and my pastor will tell you it didn't happen in the state prison this Monday."

"Maybe your pastor can suggest that next time, Jesus try a nice full-bodied Syrah."

Alma laughed and stuck a thermometer into my mouth. Over her back, I stared at CO Smythe. His eyes were red, and instead of watching me to make sure I didn't do any-thing stupid, like take Alma hostage, he was staring at the wall behind my head, lost in thought.

The thermometer beeped. "You're still run-ning a fever."

"Tell me something I don't know," I replied. I felt blood pool under my tongue, courtesy of the sores that were part and parcel of this horrific disease.

"You taking those meds?"

I shrugged. "You see me put them in my mouth every day, don't you?"

Alma knew there were as many different

ways for a prisoner to kill himself as there were prisoners. "Don't you check out on me, Jupiter," she said, rubbing something viscous on the red spot on my forehead that had led to this nickname. "Who else would tell me what I miss on *General Hospital*?"

"That's a pretty paltry reason to stick around."

"I've heard worse." Alma turned to CO Smythe. "I'm all set here."

She left, and the control booth slid the door home again, the sound of metallic teeth gnashing shut. "Shay," I called out. "You awake?"

"I am now."

"Might want to cover your ears," I offered.

Before Shay could ask me why, Calloway let out the same explosive run of curses he always did when Alma tried to get within five feet of him. "Get the fuck out, nigger," he yelled. "Swear to God, I'll fuck you up if you put your hand on me—"

CO Smythe pinned him against the side of his cell. "For Christ's sake, Reece," he said. "Do we have to go through this every single day for a goddamn Band-Aid?"

"We do if that black bitch is the one putting it on."

Calloway had been convicted of burning a synagogue to the ground seven years ago. He sustained head injuries and needed massive skin grafts on his arms, but he considered the mission a success because the terrified rabbi had fled town. The grafts still needed checking; he'd had three surgeries alone in the past year.

"You know what," Alma said, "I don't really care if his arms rot off."

She didn't, that much was true. But she *did* care about being called a nigger. Every time Calloway hurled that word at her, she'd stiffen. And after she visited Calloway, she moved a little more slowly down the pod.

I knew exactly how she felt. When you're different, sometimes you don't see the millions of people who accept you for what you are. All you notice is the one person who doesn't.

"I got hep C because of you," Calloway said, although he'd probably gotten it from the blade of the barber's razor, like the other inmates who'd contracted it in prison. "You and your filthy nigger hands."

Calloway was being particularly awful today, even for Calloway. At first I thought he was cranky like the rest of us, because our meager privileges had been taken away. But then it hit me—Calloway couldn't let Alma into his house, because she might find the bird. And if she found the bird, CO Smythe would confiscate it.

"What do you want to do?" Smythe asked Alma.

She sighed. "I'm not going to fight him."

"That's right," Calloway crowed. "You know who's boss. *Rahowa!*"

At his call, short for Racial Holy War, inmates from all over the Secure Housing Unit began to holler. In a state as white as New Hampshire, the Aryan Brotherhood ran the prison population. They controlled drug deals done behind bars; they tattooed one another with shamrocks and lightning bolts and swastikas. To be jumped into the gang, you had to kill someone sanctioned by the Brotherhood—a black man, a Jew, a homosexual, or anyone else whose existence was considered an affront to your own.

The sound became deafening. Alma walked past my cell, Smythe following. As they passed Shay, he called out to the officer, "Look inside."

"I know what's inside Reece," Smythe said. "Two hundred and twenty pounds of crap."

As Alma and the CO left, Calloway was still yelling his head off. "For God's sake," I hissed at Shay. "If they find Calloway's stupid bird they'll toss *all* our cells again! You want to lose the shower for *two* weeks?"

"That's not what I meant," Shay said.

I didn't answer. Instead I lay down on my bunk and stuffed more wadded-up toilet paper into my ears. And still, I could hear Calloway singing his white-pride anthems. Still, I could hear Shay when he told me a second time that he hadn't been talking about the bird.

That night when I woke up with the sweats, my heart drilling through the spongy base of my throat, Shay was talking to himself again. "They pull up the sheet," he said.

"Shay?"

I took a piece of metal I'd sawed off from the lip of the counter in the cell—it had taken months, carved with a string of elastic from my underwear and a dab of toothpaste with baking soda, my own diamond band saw. Ingeniously, the triangular result doubled as both a mirror and a shank. I slipped my hand beneath my door, angling the mirror so I could see into Shay's cell.

He was lying on his bunk with his eyes closed and his arms crossed over his heart. His breathing had gone so shallow that his chest barely rose and fell. I could have sworn I smelled the worms in freshly turned soil. I heard the ping of stones as they struck a grave digger's shovel.

Shay was practicing.

I had done that myself. Maybe not quite in the same way, but I'd pictured my funeral. Who would come. Who would be well dressed, and who would be wearing something outrageously hideous. Who would cry. Who wouldn't.

God bless those COs; they'd moved Shay Bourne right next door to someone else serving a death sentence.

Two weeks after Shay arrived on I-tier, six officers came to his cell early one morning and told him to strip. "Bend over," I heard Whitaker say. "Spread 'em. Lift 'em. Cough."

"Where are we going?"

"Infirmary. Routine checkup."

I knew the drill: they would shake out his clothes to make sure there was no contraband hidden, then tell him to get dressed again. They'd march him out of I-tier and into the great beyond of the Secure Housing Unit.

An hour later, I woke up to the sound of Shay's cell door being opened again as he returned to his cell. "I'll pray for your soul," CO Whitaker said soberly before leaving the tier.

"So," I said, my voice too light and false to fool even myself. "Are you the picture of health?"

"They didn't take me to the infirmary. We went to the warden's office."

I sat on my bunk, looking up at the vent through which Shay's voice carried. "He finally agreed to meet with—"

"You know why they lie?" Shay interrupted. "Because they're afraid you'll go ballistic if they tell you the truth."

"About what?"

"It's all mind control. And we have no choice but to be obedient because what if this is the one time that really—"

"Shay," I said, "did you talk to the warden or not?"

"*He* talked to *me*. He told me my last appeal was denied by the Supreme Court," Shay said. "My execution date is May twenty-third."

I knew that before he was moved to this tier, Shay had been on death row for eleven years; it wasn't like he hadn't seen this coming. And yet, that date was only two and a half months away.

"I guess they don't want to come in and say hey, we're taking you to get your death warrant read out loud. I mean, it's easier to just pretend you're going to the infirmary, so that I wouldn't freak out. I bet they talked about how they'd come and get me. I bet they had a *meeting*."

I wondered what I would prefer, if it were my death that was being announced like a future train departing from a platform. Would I want the truth from an officer? Or would I consider it a kindness to be spared knowing the inevitable, even for those four minutes of transit?

I knew what the answer was for me.

I wondered why, considering that I'd only known Shay Bourne for two weeks, there was a lump in my throat at the thought of his execution. "I'm really sorry."

"Yeah," he said. "Yeah."

"Po-lice," Joey called out, and a moment later, CO Smythe walked in, followed by CO Whitaker. He helped Whitaker transport Crash to the shower cell—the investigation into our bacchanal tap water had yielded nothing conclusive, apparently, except some mold in the pipes, and we were now allowed personal hygiene hours again. But afterward, instead of leaving I-tier, Smythe doubled back down the catwalk to stand in front of Shay's cell.

"Listen," Smythe said. "Last week, you said something to me."

"Did I?"

"You told me to look inside." He hesitated. "My daughter's been sick. Really sick. Yesterday, the doctors told my wife and me to say good-bye. It made me want to explode. So I grabbed this stuffed bear in her crib, one we'd brought from home to make going to the hospital easier for her—and I ripped it wide open. It was filled with peanut shells, and we never thought to look there." Smythe shook his head. "My baby's not dying; she was never even sick. She's just allergic," he said. "How did you know?"

"I didn't—"

"It doesn't matter." Smythe dug in his pocket for a small square of tinfoil, unwrapping it to reveal a thick brownie. "I brought this in from home. My wife, she makes them. She wanted you to have it."

"John, you can't give him contraband," Whitaker said, glancing over his shoulder at the control booth.

"It's not contraband. It's just me . . . sharing a little bit of my lunch."

My mouth started to water. Brownies were not on our canteen forms. The closest we came was chocolate cake, offered once a year as part of a Christmas package that also included a stocking full of candy and two oranges.

Smythe passed the brownie through the trap in the cell door. He met Shay's gaze and nodded, then left the tier with CO Whitaker.

"Hey, Death Row," Calloway said, "I'll give you three cigarettes for half of that."

"I'll trade you a whole pack of coffee," Joey countered.

"He ain't going to waste it on you," Calloway said. "I'll give you coffee and *four* cigarettes."

Texas and Pogie joined in. They would trade Shay a CD player. A *Playboy* magazine. A roll of tape.

"A teener," Calloway announced. "Final offer."

The Brotherhood made a killing on running the methamphetamine trade at the New

Hampshire state prison; for Calloway to solicit his own personal stash, he must have truly wanted that chocolate.

As far as I knew, Shay hadn't even had a cup of coffee since coming to I-tier. I had no idea if he smoked or got high. "No," Shay said. "No to all of you."

A few minutes passed.

"For God's sake, I can still smell it," Calloway said.

Let me tell you, I am not exaggerating when I say that we were forced to inhale that scent—that glorious scent—for hours. At three in the morning, when I woke up as per my usual insomnia, the scent of chocolate was so strong that the brownie might as well have been sitting in my cell instead of Shay's. "Why don't you just eat the damn thing," I murmured.

"Because," Shay replied, as wide awake as I, "then there wouldn't be anything to look forward to."

Maggie

There were many reasons I loved Oliver, but first and foremost was that my mother couldn't stand him. *He's a mess*, she said every time she came to visit. *He's destructive. Maggie,* she said, *if you got rid of him, you could find Someone.*

Someone was a doctor, like the anesthesiologist from Dartmouth-Hitchcock they'd set me up with once, who asked me if I thought laws against downloading child porn were an infringement on civil rights. Or the son of the cantor, who actually had been in a monogamous gay relationship for five years but hadn't told his parents yet. *Some-*

one was the younger partner in the accounting firm that did my father's taxes, who asked me on our first and only date if I'd always been a *big* girl.

On the other hand, Oliver knew just what I needed, and when I needed it. Which is why, the minute I stepped on the scale that morning, he hopped out from underneath the bed, where he was diligently severing the cord of my alarm clock with his teeth, and settled himself squarely on top of my feet so that I couldn't see the digital readout.

"Nicely done," I said, stepping off, trying not to notice the numbers that flashed red before they disappeared. Surely the reason there was a seven in there was because Oliver had been on the scale, too. Besides, if I were going to be writing a formal complaint about any of this, I'd have said that (a) size fourteen isn't really all that big, (b) a size fourteen here was a size sixteen in London, so in a way I was thinner than I'd be if I had been born British, and (c) weight didn't really matter, as long as you were healthy.

All right, so maybe I didn't exercise all that much either. But I would, one day, or so I told my mother the fitness queen, as soon as all the people on whose behalf I worked tirelessly were absolutely, unequivocally rescued. I told her (and anyone else who'd listen) that the whole reason the ACLU existed was to help people take a stand. Unfortunately, the only stands my mother recognized were pigeon pose, warrior two, and all the other staples of yoga.

I pulled on my jeans, the ones that I admittedly didn't wash very often because the dryer shrank them just enough that I had to suffer half a day before the denim stretched to the point of comfort again. I picked a sweater that didn't show my bra roll and then turned to Oliver. "What do you think?"

He lowered his left ear, which translated to, "Why do you even care, since you're taking it all off to put on a spa robe?"

As usual, he was right. It's a little hard to hide your flaws when you're wearing, well, nothing.

He followed me into the kitchen, where I poured us both bowls of rabbit food (his literal, mine Special K). Then he hopped off to the litter box beside his cage, where he'd spend the day sleeping.

I'd named my rabbit after Oliver Wendell Holmes Jr., the famous Supreme Court Justice known as the Great Dissenter. He once said, "Even a dog knows the difference between being kicked and being tripped over." So did rabbits. And my clients, for that matter.

"Don't do anything I wouldn't do," I warned Oliver. "That includes chewing the legs of the kitchen stools."

I grabbed my keys and headed out to my Prius. I had used nearly all my savings last year on the hybrid—to be honest, I didn't understand why car manufacturers charged a premium if you were a buyer with a modicum of social conscience. It didn't have all-wheel drive, which was a real pain in the neck during a New Hampshire winter, but I figured that saving the ozone layer was worth sliding off the road occasionally.

My parents had moved to Lynley—a town twenty-six miles east of Concord—seven years ago when my father took over as rabbi at Temple Beth Or. The catch was that there *was* no Temple Beth Or: his reform congregation held Friday night services in the cafeteria of the middle school, because the original temple had burned to the ground. The expectation had been to raise funds for a new temple, but my father had overestimated the size of his rural New Hampshire congregation, and although he assured me that they were closing in on buying land somewhere, I didn't see it happening any-time soon. By now, anyway, his congregation had grown used to readings from the Torah that were routinely punctuated by the cheers of the crowd at the basketball game in the gymnasium down the hall.

The biggest single annual contributor to my father's temple fund was the ChutZpah, a wellness retreat for the mind, body, and soul in the heart of Lynley that was run by my mother. Although her clientele was nonde-nominational, she'd garnered a word-of-mouth reputation among temple sisterhoods, and patrons came from as far away as New York and Connecticut and even Maryland to relax and rejuvenate. My mother used salt from the Dead Sea for her scrubs. Her spa cuisine was kosher. She'd been written up in *Boston* magazine, the *New York Times,* and *Luxury SpaFinder.*

The first Saturday of every month, I drove to the spa for a free massage or facial or pedicure. The catch was that afterward, I had to suffer through lunch with my mother. We had it down to a routine. By the time we were served our passion fruit iced tea, we'd al-ready covered "Why Don't You Call." The salad course was "I'm Going to Be Dead Before You Make Me a Grandmother." The entrée—fittingly—involved my weight. Needless to say, we never got around to dessert.

The ChutZpah was white. Not just white, but scary, I'm-afraid-to-breathe white: white carpets, white tiles, white robes, white slippers. I have no idea how my mother kept the place so clean, given that when I was growing up, the house was always comfortably cluttered.

My father says there's a God, although for me the jury is still out on that one. Which isn't to say that I didn't appreciate a miracle as much as the next person—such as when I went up to the front desk and the receptionist told me my mother was going to have to miss our lunch because of a last-minute meeting with a wholesale orchid salesman. "But she said you should still have your treatment," the receptionist said. "DeeDee's going to be your aesthetician, and you've got locker number two twenty."

I took the robe and slippers she handed me. Locker 220 was in a bank with fifty others, and several toned middle-aged women were stripping out of their yoga clothes. I breezed into another section of lockers, one that was blissfully empty, and changed into my robe. If someone complained because I was using locker 664 instead, I didn't think my mother would disown me. I punched in my key code——2358, for ACLU—took a bracing breath, and tried not to glance in the mirror as I walked by.

There wasn't very much that I liked about the outside of me. I had curves, but to me, they were in all the wrong places. My hair was an explosion of dark curls, which could have been sexy if I didn't have to work so hard to keep them frizz-free. I'd read that stylists on the *Oprah* show would straighten the hair of guests with hair like mine, because curls added ten pounds to the camera— which meant that even my *hair* made objects like me look bigger than they appeared. My eyes were okay—they were mud-colored on an average day and green if I felt like embellishing—but most of all, they showed the part of me I *was* proud of: my intelligence. I might never be a cover girl, but I was a girl who could cover it all.

The problem was, you never heard anyone say, "Wow, check out the brain on that babe."

My father had always made me feel special, but I couldn't even look at my mother without wondering why I hadn't inherited her tiny waist and sleek hair. As a kid I had only wanted to be just like her; as an adult, I'd stopped trying.

Sighing, I entered the whirlpool area: a white oasis surrounded by white wicker benches where primarily white women waited for their white-coated therapists to call their name.

DeeDee appeared in her immaculate jacket, smiling. "You must be Maggie," she said. "You look just like your mother described you."

I wasn't about to take *that* bait. "Nice to meet you." I never quite figured out the protocol for this part of the experience—you said hello and then disrobed immediately so that a total stranger could lay their hands on you . . . and you *paid* for this privilege. Was it just me, or was there a great deal that spa treatments had in common with prostitution?

"You looking forward to your Song of Solomon Wrap?"

"I'd rather be getting a root canal."

DeeDee grinned. "Your mom told me you'd say something like that, too."

If you haven't had a body wrap, it's a sin-gular experience. You're lying on a cushy table covered by a giant piece of Saran Wrap and you're naked. Totally, completely naked. Sure, the aesthetician tosses a washcloth the size of a gauze square over your privates when she's scrubbing you down, and she's got a poker face that never belies whether she's calculating your body mass index under her palms—but still, you're painfully aware of your physique, if only because someone's ex-periencing it firsthand with you.

I forced myself to close my eyes and re-member that being washed beneath a Vichy shower by someone else was supposed to make me feel like a queen and not a hospi-talized invalid.

"So, DeeDee," I said. "How long have you been doing this?"

She unrolled a towel and held it like a screen as I rolled onto my back. "I've been working at spas for six years, but I just got hired on here."

"You must be good," I said. "My mother doesn't sweat amateurs."

She shrugged. "I like meeting new people."

I like meeting new people, too, but when they're fully clothed.

"What do you do for work?" DeeDee asked.

"My mother didn't tell you?"

"No . . . she just said—" Suddenly she broke off, silent.

"She said *what*."

"She, um, told me to treat you to an extra helping of seaweed scrub."

"You mean she told you I'd need twice as much."

"She didn't—"

"Did she use the word *zaftig*?" I asked. When DeeDee didn't answer—wisely—I blinked up at the hazy light in the ceiling, listened to Yanni's canned piano for a few beats, and then sighed. "I'm an ACLU lawyer."

"For real?" DeeDee's hands stilled on my feet. "Do you ever take on cases, like, for free?"

"That's *all* I do."

"Then you must know about the guy on death row . . . Shay Bourne? I've been writing to him for ten years, ever since I was in eighth grade and I started as part of an assignment for my social studies class. His last appeal just got rejected by the Supreme Court."

"I know," I said. "I've filed briefs on his behalf."

DeeDee's eyes widened. "So you're his lawyer?"

"Well . . . no." I hadn't even been living in New Hampshire when Bourne was convicted, but it was the job of the ACLU to file amicus briefs for death row prisoners. *Amicus* was Latin for *friend of the court*; when you had a position on a particular case but weren't directly a party involved in it, the court would let you legally spell out your feelings if it might be beneficial to the decision-making process. My amicus briefs illustrated how hideous the death penalty was; defined it as cruel and unusual punishment, as unconstitutional. I'm quite sure the judge looked at my hard work and promptly tossed it aside.

"Can't you do something else to help him?" DeeDee asked.

The truth was, if Bourne's last appeal had been rejected by the Supreme Court, there wasn't much *any* lawyer could do to save him now.

"Tell you what," I promised. "I'll look into it."

DeeDee smiled and covered me with heated blankets until I was trussed tight as a burrito. Then she sat down behind me and wove her fingers into my hair. As she massaged my scalp, my eyes drifted shut.

"They say it's painless," DeeDee murmured. "Lethal injection."

They: the establishment, the lawmakers,
the ones assuaging their guilt over their own
actions with rhetoric. "That's because no one
ever comes back to tell them otherwise," I
said. I thought of Shay Bourne being given
the news of his own impending death. I thought
of lying on a table like this one, being put to
sleep.

Suddenly I couldn't breathe. The blankets
were too hot, the cream on my skin too thick.
I wanted out of the layers and began to fight
my way free.

"Whoa," DeeDee said. "Hang on, let me
help you." She pulled and peeled and handed
me a towel. "Your mother didn't tell me you
were claustrophobic."

I sat up, drawing great gasps of air into my
lungs. *Of course she didn't,* I thought. *Because she's the one who's suffocating me.*

Lucius

It was late afternoon, almost time for the shift change, and I-tier was relatively quiet. Me, I'd been sick all day, hazing in and out of sleep brought on by fever. Calloway, who usually played chess with me, was playing with Shay instead. "Bishop takes a6," Calloway called out. He was a racist bigot, but Calloway was also the best chess player I'd ever met.

During the day, Batman the Robin resided in his breast pocket, a small lump no bigger than a pack of Starburst candies. Sometimes it crawled onto his shoulder and pecked at the scars on his scalp. At other times, he kept Batman in a paperback copy of *The Stand* that had been doctored as a hiding place—starting on chapter six, a square had been cut out of the pages of the thick book with a pilfered razor blade, creating a little hollow that Calloway lined with tissues to make a bed. The robin ate mashed potatoes; Calloway traded precious masking tape and twine and even a homemade handcuff key for extra portions.

"Hey," Calloway said. "We haven't made a wager on this game."

Crash laughed. "Even Bourne ain't dumb enough to bet you when he's losing."

"What have you got that I want?" Calloway mused.

"Intelligence?" I suggested. "Common sense?"

"Keep out of this, homo." Calloway thought for a moment. "The brownie. I want the damn brownie."

By now, the brownie was two days old. I doubted that Calloway would even be able to swallow it. What he'd enjoy, mostly, was the act of taking it away from Shay.

"Okay," Shay said. "Knight to g6."

I sat up on my bunk. "Okay? Shay, he's beating the pants off you."

"How come you're too sick to play, Du-Fresne, but you don't mind sticking your two cents into every conversation?" Calloway said. "This is between me and Bourne."

"What if *I* win?" Shay asked. "What do I get?"

Calloway laughed. "It won't happen."

"The bird."

"I'm not giving you Batman—"

"Then I'm not giving you the brownie." There was a beat of silence.

"Fine," Calloway said. "You win, you get the bird. But you're not going to win, because my bishop takes d3. Consider yourself officially screwed."

"Queen to h7," Shay replied. "Checkmate."

"What?" Calloway cried. I scrutinized the mental chessboard I'd been tracking—Shay's queen had come out of nowhere, screened by his knight. There was nowhere left for Calloway to go.

At that moment the door to I-tier opened, admitting a pair of officers in flak jackets and helmets. They marched to Calloway's cell and brought him onto the catwalk, securing his handcuffs to a metal railing along the far wall.

There was nothing worse than having your

cell searched. In here, all we had were our belongings, and having them pored over was a gross invasion of privacy. Not to mention the fact that when it happened, you had an excellent chance of losing your best stash, be that drugs or hooch or chocolate or art supplies or the stinger rigged from paper clips to heat up your instant coffee.

They came in with flashlights and long-handled mirrors and worked systematically. They'd check the seams of the walls, the vents, the plumbing. They'd roll deodorant sticks all the way out to make sure nothing was hidden underneath. They'd shake containers of powder to hear what might be inside. They'd sniff shampoo bottles, open envelopes, and take out the letters inside. They'd rip off your bedsheets and run their hands over the mattresses, looking for tears or ripped seams.

Meanwhile, you were forced to watch.

I could not see what was going on in Calloway's cell, but I had a pretty good idea based on his reactions. He rolled his eyes as his blanket was checked for unraveled threads; his jaw tensed when a postage stamp was peeled off an envelope, revealing the black tar heroin underneath. But

when his bookshelf was inspected, Calloway flinched. I looked for the small bulge in
his breast pocket that would have been the
bird and realized that Batman the Robin was
somewhere inside that cell.

One of the officers held up the copy of *The
Stand*. The pages were riffled, the spine
snapped, the book tossed against the cell
wall. "What's this?" an officer asked, focusing not on the bird that had been whipped
across the cell but on the baby-blue tissues
that fluttered down over his boots.

"Nothing," Calloway said, but the officer
wasn't about to take his word for it. He picked
through the tissues, and when he didn't find
anything, he confiscated the book with its
carved hidey-hole.

Whitaker said something about a write-up,
but Calloway wasn't listening. I could not
remember ever seeing him quite so unraveled. As soon as he was released back into
his cell, he ran to the rear corner where the
bird had been flung.

The sound that Calloway Reece made was
primordial; but then maybe that was always
the case when a grown man with no heart
started to cry.

There was a crash, and a sickening

crunch. A whirlwind of destruction as Calloway fought back against what couldn't be fixed. Finally spent, Calloway sank down to the floor of his cell, cradling the dead bird. "Motherfucker. Mother*fucker*."

"Reece," Shay interrupted, "I want my prize."

My head snapped around. Surely Shay wasn't stupid enough to antagonize Calloway.

"What?" Calloway breathed. "What did you say?"

"My prize. I won the chess game."

"Not *now*," I hissed.

"Yes, now," Shay said. "A deal's a deal."

In here, you were only as good as your word, and Calloway—with his Aryan Brotherhood sensibilities—would have known that better than anyone else. "You better make sure you're always behind those bars," Calloway vowed, "because the next time I get the chance, I'm going to mess you up so bad your own mama wouldn't know you." But even as he threatened Shay, Calloway gently wrapped the dead bird in a tissue and attached the small, slight bundle to the end of his fishing line.

When the robin reached me, I drew it under

the three-inch gap beneath the door of my cell. It still looked half cooked, its closed eye translucent blue. One wing was bent at a severe backward angle; its neck lolled sideways.

Shay sent out his own line of string, with a weight made of a regulation comb on one end. I saw his hands gently slide the robin, wrapped in tissue, into his cell. The lights on the catwalk flickered.

I've often imagined what happened next. With an artist's eye, I like to picture Shay sitting on his bunk, cupping his palms around the tiny bird. I imagine the touch of someone who loves you so much, he cannot bear to watch you sleep; and so you wake up with his hand on your heart. In the long run, though, it hardly matters how Shay did it. What matters is the result: that we all heard the piccolo trill of that robin; that Shay pushed the risen bird beneath his cell door onto the catwalk, where it hopped, like broken punctuation, toward Calloway's outstretched hand.

June

If you're a mother, you can look into the face of your grown child and see, instead, the one that peeked up at you from the folds of a baby blanket. You can watch your eleven-year-old daughter painting her nails with glitter polish and remember how she used to reach for you when she wanted to cross the street. You can hear the doctor say that the real danger is adolescence, because you don't know how the heart will respond to growth spurts—and you can pretend that's ages away.

"Best two out of three," Claire said, and from the folds of her hospital johnny she raised her fist again.

I lifted my hand, too. *Rock, paper, scissors, shoot.*

"Paper." Claire grinned. "I win."

"You totally do not," I said. "Hello? Scissors?"

"What I forgot to tell you is that it's raining, and the scissors got rusty, and so you slip the paper underneath them and carry them away."

I laughed. Claire shifted slightly, careful not to dislodge all the tubes and the wires. "Who'll feed Dudley?" she asked.

Dudley was our dog—a thirteen-year-old springer spaniel who, along with me, was one of the only pieces of continuity between Claire and her late sister. Claire may never have met Elizabeth, but they had both grown up draping faux pearls around Dudley's neck, dressing him up like the sibling they never had. "Don't worry about Dudley," I said. "I'll call Mrs. Morrissey if I have to."

Claire nodded and glanced at the clock. "I thought they'd be back already."

"I know, baby."

"What do you think's taking so long?"

There were a hundred answers to that, but the one that floated to the top of my mind was that in some other hospital, two counties away, another mother had to say good-bye to her child so that I would have a chance to keep mine.

The technical name for Claire's illness was pediatric dilated cardiomyopathy. It affected twelve million kids a year, and it meant that her heart cavity was enlarged and stretched, that her heart couldn't pump blood out efficiently. You couldn't fix it or reverse it; if you were lucky you could live with it. If you weren't, you died of congestive heart failure. In kids, 79 percent of the cases came from an unknown origin. There was a camp that attributed its onset to myocarditis and other viral infections during infancy; and another that claimed it was inherited through a parent who was a carrier of the defective gene. I had always assumed the latter was the case with Claire. After all, surely a child who grew out of grief would be born with a heavy heart.

At first, I didn't know she had it. She got tired more easily than other infants, but I was still moving in slow motion myself and did not notice. It wasn't until she was five, hospitalized with a flu she could not shake, that she was diagnosed. Dr. Wu said that Claire had a slight arrhythmia that might improve and might not; he put her on Captopril, Lasix,

Lanoxin. He said that we'd have to wait and see.

On the first day of fifth grade, Claire told me it felt like she had swallowed a hummingbird. I assumed it was nerves about starting classes, but hours later—when she stood up to solve a math problem at the chalkboard—she passed out cold. Progressive arrhythmias made the heart beat like a bag of worms—it wouldn't eject any blood. Those basketball players who seemed so healthy and then dropped dead on the court? That was ventricular fibrillation, and it was happening to Claire. She had surgery to implant an AICD—an automatic implantable cardioverter-defibrillator, or, in simpler terms, a tiny, internal ER resting right on her heart, which would fix future arrhythmias by administering an electric shock. She was put on the list for a transplant.

The transplant game was a tricky one—once you received a heart, the clock started ticking, and it wasn't the happy ending everyone thought it was. You didn't want to wait so long for a transplant that the rest of the bodily systems began to shut down. But even a transplant wasn't a miracle: most recipients could only tolerate a heart for ten or fifteen years before complications ensued, or there was outright rejection. Still, as Dr. Wu said, fifteen years from now, we might be able to buy a heart off a shelf and have it installed at Best Buy . . . the idea was to keep Claire alive long enough to let medical innovation catch up to her.

This morning, the beeper we carried at all times had gone off. *We have a heart*, Dr. Wu had said when I called. *I'll meet you at the hospital.*

For the past six hours, Claire had been poked, pricked, scrubbed, and prepped so that the minute the miracle organ arrived in its little Igloo cooler, she could go straight into surgery. This was the moment I'd waited for, and dreaded, her whole life.

What if . . . I could not even let myself say the words.

Instead, I reached for Claire's hand and threaded our fingers together. *Paper and scissors*, I thought. *We are between a rock and a hard place.* I looked at the fan of her angel hair on the pillow, the faint blue cast of her skin, the fairy-light bones of a girl whose body was still too much for her to handle. Sometimes, when I looked at her, I didn't see her at all; instead, I pretended that she was—

"What do you think she's like?"

I blinked, startled. "Who?"

"The girl. The one who died."

"Claire," I said. "Let's not talk about this."

"Why not? Don't you think we should know all about her if she's going to be a part of me?"

I touched my hand to her head. "We don't even know it's a girl."

"Of course it's a girl," Claire said. "It would be totally gross to have a boy's heart."

"I don't think that's a qualification for a match."

She shuddered. "It *should* be." Claire struggled to push herself upright so that she was sitting higher in the hospital bed. "Do you think I'll be different?"

I leaned down and kissed her. "You," I pronounced, "will wake up and still be the same kid who cannot be bothered to clean her room or walk Dudley or turn out the lights when she goes downstairs."

That's what I said to Claire, anyway. But all I heard were the first four words: *You will wake up.*

A nurse came into the room. "We just got word that the harvest's begun," she said. "We should have more information shortly;

Dr. Wu's on the phone with the team that's on-site."

After she left, Claire and I sat in silence. Suddenly, this was real—the surgeons were going to open up Claire's chest, stop her heart, and sew in a new one. We had both heard numerous doctors explain the risks and the rewards; we knew how infrequently pediatric donors came about. Claire shrank down in the bed, her covers sliding up to her nose. "If I die," Claire said, "do you think I'll get to be a saint?"

"You won't die."

"Yeah, I will. And so will you. I just might do it a little sooner."

I couldn't help it; I felt tears welling up in my eyes. I wiped them on the edge of the hospital sheets. Claire fisted her hand in my hair, the way she used to when she was little. "I bet I'd like it," Claire said. "Being a saint."

Claire had her nose in a book constantly, and recently, her Joan of Arc fascination had bloomed into all things martyred.

"You aren't going to be a saint."

"You don't know that for sure," Claire said.

"You're not Catholic, for one thing. And besides, they all died horrible deaths."

"That's not always true. You can be killed

while you're being good, and that counts. St. Maria Goretti was my age when she fought off a guy who was raping her and was killed and *she* got to be one."

"That's atrocious," I said.

"St. Barbara had her eyeballs cut out. And did you know there's a patron saint of heart patients? John of God?"

"The question is, why do *you* know there's a patron saint of heart patients?"

"Duh," Claire said. "I *read* about it. It's all you let me do." She settled back against the pillows. "I bet a saint can play softball."

"So can a girl with a heart transplant."

But Claire wasn't listening; she knew that hope was just smoke and mirrors; she'd learned by watching me. She looked up at the clock. "I think I'll be a saint," she said, as if it were entirely up to her. "That way no one forgets you when you're gone."

The funeral of a police officer is a breathtaking thing. Officers and firemen and public officials will come from every town in the state and some even farther away. There is a procession of police cruisers that precedes the hearse; they blanket the highway like snow.

It took me a long time to remember Kurt's funeral, because I was working so hard at the time to pretend it wasn't happening. The police chief, Irv, rode with me to the graveside service. There were townspeople lining the streets of Lynley, with handmade signs that read PROTECT AND SERVE, and THE ULTIMATE SACRIFICE. It was summertime, and the asphalt sank beneath the heels of my shoes where I stood. I was surrounded by other policemen who'd worked with Kurt, and hundreds who didn't, a sea of dress blue. My back hurt, and my feet were swollen. I found myself concentrating on a lilac tree that shuddered in the breeze, petals falling like rain.

The police chief had arranged for a twenty-one-gun salute, and as it finished, five fighter jets rose over the distant violet mountains. They sliced the sky in parallel lines, and then, just as they flew overhead, the plane on the far right broke off like a splinter, soaring east.

When the priest stopped speaking—I didn't listen to a word of it; what could he tell me about Kurt that I didn't already know?—Robbie and Vic stepped forward. They were Kurt's closest friends in the department. Like the rest of the Lynley force, they had covered their badges with black fabric. They reached for the flag that draped Kurt's coffin and began to fold it. Their gloved hands moved so fast—I thought of Mickey Mouse, of Donald Duck, with their oversized white fists. Robbie was the one who put the triangle into my arms, something to hold on to, something to take Kurt's place.

Through the radios of the other policemen came the voice of the dispatcher: *All units stand by for a broadcast.*

Final call for Officer Kurt Nealon, number 144.

144, report to 360 West Main for one last assignment.

It was the address of the cemetery.

You will be in the best of hands. You will be deeply missed.

144, 10-7. The radio code for end of shift.

I have been told that afterward, I walked up to Kurt's coffin. It was so highly polished I could see my own reflection, pinched and unfamiliar. It had been specially made, wider than normal, to accommodate Elizabeth, too.

She was, at seven, still afraid of the dark. Kurt would lie down beside her, an elephant perched among pink pillows and satin blankets, until she fell asleep; then he'd creep out of the room and turn off the light. Sometimes, she woke up at midnight shrieking. *You turned it off*, she'd sob into my shoulder, as if I had broken her heart.

The funeral director had let me see them. Kurt's arms were wrapped tight around my daughter; Elizabeth rested her head on his chest. They looked the way they looked on nights when Kurt fell asleep waiting for Elizabeth to do that very thing. They looked the way I wished *I* could: smooth and clear and peaceful, a pond with a stone unthrown. It was supposed to be comforting that they would be together. It was supposed to make up for the fact that I couldn't go with them.

"Take care of her," I whispered to Kurt, my breath blowing a kiss against the gleaming wood. "Take care of my baby."

As if I'd summoned her, Claire moved inside me then: a slow tumble of butterfly limbs, a memory of why I had to stay behind.

There was a time when I prayed to saints. What I liked about them were their humble beginnings: they were human, once, and so you knew that they just *got* it in a way Jesus never would. They understood what it meant to have your hopes dashed or your promises broken or your feelings hurt. St. Therese was my favorite—the one who believed you could be perfectly ordinary, but that great love could somehow transport you. However, this was all a long time ago. Life has a way of pointing out, with great sweeping signs, that you are looking at the wrong things, doesn't it? It was when I started to admit to myself that I'd rather be dead that I was given a child who had to fight to stay alive.

In the past month, Claire's arrhythmias had worsened. Her AICD was going off six times a day. I'd been told that when it fired, it felt like an electric current running through the body. It restarted your heart, but it hurt like hell. Once a month would be devastating; once a day would be debilitating. And then there was Claire's frequency.

There were support groups for adults who had to live with AICDs; there were stories of those who preferred the risk of dying from an arrhythmia to the sure knowledge that they would be shocked by the device sooner or later. Last week, I had found Claire in her room reading the *Guinness Book of World Records*. "Roy Sullivan was struck by lightning seven times over thirty-six years," she'd said. "Finally, he killed himself." She lifted her shirt, staring down at the scar on her chest. "Mom," she begged, "please make them turn it off."

I did not know how long I would be able to convince Claire to stay with me, if this was the way she had to do it.

Claire and I both turned immediately when the hospital door opened. We were expecting the nurse, but it was Dr. Wu. He sat down on the edge of the bed and spoke directly to Claire, as if she were my age instead of eleven. "The heart we had in mind for you had something wrong with it. The team didn't know until they got inside . . . but the right ventricle is dilated. If it isn't functioning now, chances are it will only get worse by the time the heart's transplanted."

"So . . . I can't have it?" Claire asked.

"No. When I give you a new heart, I want it to be the healthiest heart possible," the doctor explained.

My body felt stiff. "I don't—I don't understand."

Dr. Wu turned. "I'm sorry, June. Today's not going to be the day."

"But it could take years to find another

donor," I said. I didn't add the rest of my sentence, because I knew Wu could hear it anyway: *Claire can't last that long.*

"We'll just hope for the best," he said.

After he left, we sat in stunned silence for a few moments. Had *I* done this? Had the fear I'd tried to quash—the one that Claire wouldn't survive this operation—somehow bled into reality?

Claire began to pull the cardiac monitors off her chest. "Well," she said, but I could hear the hitch in her voice as she struggled not to cry. "What a total waste of a Saturday."

"You know," I said, forcing the words to unroll evenly, "you were *named* for a saint."

"For real?"

I nodded. "She founded a group of nuns called the Poor Clares."

She glanced at me. "Why did you pick her?"

Because, on the day you were born, the nurse who handed you to me shook her head and said, "Now there's a sight for sore eyes." And you were. And she is the patron saint of that very thing. And I wanted you protected, from the very first moment I spoke your name.

"I liked the way it sounded," I lied, and I

held up Claire's shirt so that she could shimmy into it.

We would leave this hospital, maybe go get chocolate Fribbles at Friendly's and rent a movie with a happy ending. We'd take Dudley for a walk and feed him. We'd act like this was an ordinary day. And after she went to sleep, I would bury my face in my pillow and let myself feel everything I wasn't letting myself feel right now: shame over knowing that I've had five more years in Claire's company than I did with Elizabeth, guilt over being relieved this transplant did not happen, since it might just as easily kill Claire as save her.

Claire stuffed her feet into her pink Converse high-tops. "Maybe I'll join the Poor Clares."

"You still can't be a saint," I said. And added silently, *Because I will not let you die.*

Lucius

||||||||||||||||||||||||||||||||||||||||||||||||||||||||||||||||||||||||||||||||||||||||||||||||||||||||||||||||||||||||||||||||||||||||

Shortly after Shay brought Batman the Robin back to life, Crash Vitale lit himself on fire.

He'd created a makeshift match the way we all do—by pulling the fluorescent bulb out of its cradle and holding the metal tines just far enough away from the socket to have the electricity arc to meet it. Stick a piece of paper in the gap, and it becomes a torch. Crash had crumpled up pages of a magazine and set them around himself in a circle. By the time Texas started screaming for help, smoke was filling the pod. The COs held the fire hose at full spray as they opened his cell door; we could hear Crash being knocked against the far wall by the stream. Dripping wet, he was strapped onto a gurney to be transported, his hair a matted mess, his eyes wild. "Hey, Green Mile," he yelled as he was wheeled off the tier, "how come you didn't save *me*?"

"Because I *like* the bird," Shay murmured.

I was the first one to laugh, then Texas snickered. Joey, too—but only because Crash wasn't present to shut him up.

"Bourne," Calloway said, the first words any of us had heard from him since the bird had hopped back to his cell. "Thanks."

There was a beat of silence. "It deserved another chance," Shay said.

The pod door buzzed open, and this time CO Smythe walked in with the nurse, doing her evening rounds. Alma came to my cell first, holding out my card of pills. "Smells like someone had a barbecue in here and forgot to invite me," she said. She waited for me to put the pills in my mouth, take a swallow of water. "You sleep well, Lucius."

As she left, I walked to the front of the cell. Rivulets of water ran down the cement catwalk. But instead of leaving the tier, Alma stopped in front of Calloway's cell. "Inmate Reece, are you going to let me take a look at that arm?"

Calloway hunched over, protecting the bird he held in his hand. We all knew he was holding Batman; we all held our collective breath. What if Alma saw the bird? Would she rat him out?

I should have known Calloway would never let that happen—he'd be offensive enough to scare her off before she got too close. But before he could speak, we heard a fluted chirp—not from Calloway's cell but from Shay's. There was an answering call—the robin looking for its own kind. "What the hell's that?" CO Smythe asked, looking around. "Where's it coming from?"

Suddenly, a twitter rose from Joey's cell, and then a higher cheep from Pogie's. To my surprise, I even heard a tweet come from the vicinity of my own bunk. I wheeled around, tracing it to the louvers of the vent. Was there a whole colony of robins in here? Or was it Shay, a ventriloquist in addition to a magician, this time throwing his voice?

Smythe moved down the tier, hands covering his ears as he peered at the skylight and into the shower cell to find the source of the noise. "Smythe?" an officer said over the control booth intercom. "What the hell's going on?"

A place like this wears down everything, and tolerance is no exception. In here, coexistence passes for forgiveness. You do not learn to like something you abhor; you come to live with it. It's why we submit when we are told to strip; it's why we deign to play chess with a child molester; it's why we quit crying ourselves to sleep. You live and let live, and eventually that becomes enough.

Which maybe explains why Calloway's muscled arm snaked through the open trap of his door, his "Anita Bryant" patch shadowing his biceps. Alma blinked, surprised.

"I won't hurt you," she murmured, peering at the new skin growing where it had been grafted, still pink and evolving. She took a pair of latex gloves out of her pocket and snapped them on, making her hands just as lily-white as Calloway's. And wouldn't you know it—the moment Alma touched him, all of that crazy noise fell dead silent.

Michael

||||||||||||||||||||||||||||||||||||||||||||||||||||||||||||||||||||||||||||||||||||||||||||||||||||||||

A priest has to say Mass every day, even if no one shows up, although this was rarely the case. In a city as large as Concord there were usually at least a handful of parishioners, already praying the rosary by the time I came out in my vestments.

I was just at the part of the Mass where miracles occurred. "For this is my body, which will be given up for you," I said aloud, then genuflected and lifted the host.

Next to "How the heck is one God also a Holy Trinity?" the most common question I got asked as a priest by non-Catholics was about transubstantiation: the belief that at consecration, the elements of bread and wine truly became the Body and Blood of Christ. I could see why people were baffled—if this was true, wasn't Holy Communion cannibalistic? And if a change really occurred, why couldn't you see it?

When I went to church as a kid, long before I came back to it, I received Holy Communion like everyone else, but I didn't really give much thought to what I received. It looked, to me, like a cracker and a cup of wine . . . before *and* after the priest consecrated it. I can tell you now that it still looks like a cracker and a cup of wine. The miracle part comes down to philosophy. It isn't the accidents of an object that make it what it is . . . it's the essential parts. We'd still be human even if we didn't have limbs or teeth or hair; but if we suddenly stopped being mammals, that wouldn't be the case. When I consecrated the host and the wine at Mass, the very substance of the elements changed; it was the other properties—the shape, the taste, the size—that remained the same. Just like John the Baptist saw a man and knew, right away, that he was looking at God; just like the wise men came upon a baby and knew He was our Savior . . . every day I held what looked like crackers and wine but actually *was* Jesus.

For this very reason, from this point on in the Mass, my fingers and thumb would be kept pinched together until washed after the Sacrament of the Eucharist. Not even the tiniest particle of the consecrated host could be lost; we went to great pains to make sure of this when disposing of the leftovers from Holy Communion. But just as I was thinking this, the wafer slipped out of my hand.

I felt the way I had when, in third grade, during the Little League play-offs, I'd watched a pop fly come into my corner of left field too fast and too high—knotted with the need to catch it, sick with the knowledge that I wouldn't. Frozen, I watched the host tumble, safely, into the belly of the chalice of wine.

"Five-second rule," I murmured, and I reached into the chalice and snagged it.

The wine had already begun to soak into the wafer. I watched, amazed, as a jaw took shape, an ear, an eyebrow.

Father Walter had visions. He said that the reason he became a priest in the first place was because, as an altar boy, a statue of Jesus had reached for his robe and tugged, telling him to stay the course. More recently, Mary had appeared to him in the rectory kitchen when he was frying trout, and suddenly they began leaping in the pan. *Don't let a single one fall to the floor,* she'd warned, and then disappeared.

There were hundreds of priests who excelled at their calling but never received this sort of divine intercession—and yet, I didn't want to fall among their ranks. Like the teens I worked with, I understood the need for miracles—they kept reality from paralyzing you. So I stared at the wafer, hoping the wine-sketched features would solidify into a portrait of Jesus . . . and instead I found myself looking at something else entirely. The shaggy dark hair that looked more like a grunge-band drummer than a priest, the nose broken while wrestling in junior high, the razor stubble. Engraved onto the surface of the host, with a printmaker's delicacy, was a picture of me.

What is my *head doing on the body of Christ?* I thought as I placed the host on the paten, plum-stained and dissolving already. I lifted the chalice. "This is my blood," I said.

June

When Shay Bourne was working at our house as a carpenter, he gave Elizabeth a birthday present. Made of scrap wood and crafted after hours wherever he went when he left our house, it was a small, hinged chest. He had carved it intricately, so that each face portrayed a different fairy, dressed in the trappings of the seasons. Summer had bright peony wings, and a crown made of the sun. Spring was covered in climbing vines, and a bridal train of flowers swept beneath her. Autumn wore the jewel tones of sugar maples and aspen trees, the cap of an acorn balanced on her head. And Winter skated across a frozen lake, leaving a trail of silver frost in her wake. The cover was a painted picture of the moon, rising through a field of stars with its arms outstretched toward a sun that was just out of reach.

Elizabeth loved that box. The night that Shay gave it to her, she lined it with blankets and slept inside. When Kurt and I told her she couldn't do that again—what if the top fell on her while she was sleeping?—she turned it into a cradle for her dolls, then a toy chest. She named the fairies. Sometimes I heard her talking to them.

After Elizabeth died, I took the box out to the yard, planning to destroy it. There I was, eight months pregnant and grieving, swinging Kurt's axe, and at the last minute, I could not do it. It was what Elizabeth had treasured; how could I stand to lose that, too? I put the box in the attic, where it remained for years.

I could tell you I forgot about the box, but I would be lying. I knew it was there, buried behind our luggage and old toddler clothes and paintings with broken frames. When Claire was about ten, I found her trying to lug the box downstairs. "It's so pretty," she said, winded with the effort. "And no one's using it." I snapped at her and told her to go lie down and rest.

But Claire kept asking about it, and eventually I brought the box to her room, where it sat at the end of her bed, just like it had for Elizabeth. I never told her who'd carved it. And yet sometimes, when Claire was at school, I found myself peeking inside. I wondered if Pandora, too, wished she had scrutinized the contents first—heartache, cleverly disguised as a gift.

Lucius

||||||||||||||||||||||||||||||||||||||||||||||||||||||||||||||||||||||||||||||||||||||||||||||||||||||||||||||||||||||||||||||

It had been said, among those on I-tier, that I had achieved Bassmaster status when it came to fishing. My equipment was a sturdy line made from yarn I'd stored up over the years, tempered by weight—a comb, or a deck of cards, depending on what I was angling for. I was known for my ability to fish from my cell into Crash's, at the far end of the tier; and then down to the shower cell at the other end. I suppose this was why, when Shay cast out his own line, I found myself watching out of curiosity.

It was after *One Life to Live* but before *Oprah*, the time of day when most of the guys napped. I myself was not feeling so well. The sores in my mouth made it difficult to speak; I had to keep using the toilet. The skin around my eyes, stained by Kaposi's sarcoma, had swollen to the point where I could barely see. Then suddenly, Shay's fishing line whizzed into the narrow space beneath my cell door. "Want some?" he asked.

When we fish, it's to get something. We trade magazines; we barter food; we pay for drugs. But Shay didn't want anything, except to give. Wired to the end of his line was a piece of Bazooka bubble gum.

It's contraband. Gum can be used as putty to build all sorts of things, and to tamper with locks. God only knew where Shay had come across this bounty—and, even more astounding, why he wouldn't just hoard it.

I swallowed, and my throat nearly split along a fault line. "No thanks," I rasped.

I sat up on my bunk and peeled the sheet off the plastic mattress. One of the seams had been carefully doctored by me. The thread, laced like a football, could be loosened enough for me to rummage around inside the foam padding. I jammed my forefinger inside, scooping out my stash.

There were the 3TC pills—Epivir—and the

Sustiva. Retrovir. Lomotil for my diarrhea. All the medications that, for weeks, Alma had watched me place on my tongue and apparently swallow—when in fact they were tucked up high in the purse of my cheek.

I had not yet made up my mind whether I would use these to kill myself . . . or if I'd just continue to save them instead of ingest them: a slower but still sure suicide.

It's funny how when you are dying, you still fight for the upper hand. You want to pick the terms; you want to choose the date. You'll tell yourself anything you have to, to pretend that you're still the one in control.

"Joey," Shay said. "Want some?" He cast again, his line arcing over the catwalk.

"For real?" Joey asked. Most of us just pretended Joey wasn't around; it was safer for him. No one went out of their way to acknowledge him, much less offer him something as precious as a piece of gum.

"I want some," Calloway demanded. He must have seen the bounty going by, since his cell was between Shay's and Joey's.

"Me, too," Crash said.

Shay waited for Joey to take the gum, and then pulled his line gently closer, until it was within reach of Calloway. "There's plenty."

"How many pieces you got?" Crash asked.

"Just the one."

Now, you've seen a piece of Bazooka gum. *Maybe* you can split it with a friend. But to divvy up one single piece among seven greedy men?

Shay's fishing line whipped to the left, past my cell en route to Crash's. "Take some and pass it on," Shay said.

"Maybe I want the whole thing."

"Maybe you do."

"Fuck," Crash said. "I'm taking it all."

"If that's what you need," Shay replied.

I stood up, unsteady, and crouched down as Shay's fishing line reached Pogie's cell. "Have some," Shay offered.

"But Crash took the whole piece—"

"Have some."

I could hear paper being unwrapped, the fullness of Pogie speaking around the bounty softening in his mouth. "I ain't had chewing gum since 2001."

By now, I could smell it. The pinkness, the sugar. I began to salivate.

"Oh, man," Texas breathed, and then everyone chewed in silence, except for me.

Shay's fishing line swung between my own feet. "Try it," he urged.

I reached for the packet on the end of the line. Since six other men had already done the same, I expected to see only a fragment remaining, a smidgen of gum, if anything at all—yet, to my surprise, the piece of Bazooka was intact. I ripped the gum in half and put a piece into my mouth. The rest I wrapped up, and then I tugged on Shay's line. I watched it zip away, back to his own cell.

At first I could barely stand it—the sweetness against the sores in my mouth, the sharp edges of the gum before it softened. It brought tears to my eyes to so badly want something that I knew would cause great pain. I held up my hand, ready to spit the gum out, when the most remarkable thing happened: my mouth, my throat, they stopped aching, as if there were an anesthetic in the gum, as if I were no longer an AIDS patient but an ordinary man who'd picked up this treat at the gas station counter after filling his tank in preparation for driving far, far away. My jaw moved, rhythmic. I sat down on the floor of my cell, crying as

I chewed—not because it hurt, but because it didn't.

We were silent for so long that CO Whitaker came in to see what we were up to; and what he found, of course, was not what he had expected. Seven men, imagining childhoods that we all wished we'd had. Seven men, blowing bubbles as bright as the moon.

For the first time in nearly six months, I slept through the night. I woke up rested and relaxed, without any of the stomach knotting that usually consumed me for the first two hours of every day. I walked to the basin, squeezed toothpaste onto the stubby brush they gave us, and glanced up at the wavy sheet of metal that passed for a mirror.

Something was different.

The sores, the Kaposi's sarcoma that had spotted my cheeks and inflamed my eyelids for a year now, were gone. My skin was clear as a river.

I leaned forward for a better look. I opened up my mouth, tugged my lower lip, searching in vain for the blisters and cankers that had kept me from eating.

"Lucius," I heard, a voice spilling from the vent over my head. "Good morning."

I glanced up. "It is, Shay. God, yes, it is."

In the end, I didn't have to call for a medical consult. Officer Whitaker was shocked enough at my improved appearance to call Alma himself. I was taken into the attorney-client cell so that she could draw my blood, and an hour later, she came back to my own cell to tell me what I already knew.

"Your CD4+ is 1250," Alma said. "And your viral load's undetectable."

"That's good, right?"

"It's normal. It's what someone who doesn't have AIDS would look like if we drew his blood." She shook her head. "Looks to me like your drug regimen's kicked in in a big way—"

"Alma," I said, and I glanced behind her at Officer Whitaker before peeling the sheet off my mattress and ripping open my hiding place for pills. I brought them to her, spilled several dozen into her hand. "I haven't been taking my meds for months."

Color rose in her cheeks. "Then this isn't possible."

"It's not probable," I corrected. *"Anything's possible."*

She stuffed the pills into her pocket. "I'm sure there's a medical explanation—"

"It's Shay."

"Inmate Bourne?"

"He *did* this," I said, well aware of how insane it sounded, and yet desperate to make her understand. "I saw him bring a dead bird back to life. And take one piece of gum and turn it into enough for all of us. He made wine come out of our faucets the first night he was here . . ."

"Okey-dokey. Officer Whitaker, let me see if we can get a psych consult for—"

"I'm not crazy, Alma; I'm—well, I'm healed." I reached for her hand. "Haven't you ever seen something with your own eyes that you never imagined possible?"

She darted a glance at Calloway Reece, who had submitted to her ministrations now for seven days straight. "He did that, too," I whispered. "I know it."

Alma walked out of my cell and stood in front of Shay's. He was listening to his television, wearing headphones. "Bourne," Whitaker barked. "Cuffs."

After his wrists were secured, the door to

his cell was opened. Alma stood in the gap with her arms crossed. "What do you know about Inmate DuFresne's condition?"

Shay didn't respond.

"Inmate Bourne?"

"He can't sleep much," Shay said quietly. "It hurts him to eat."

"He's got AIDS. But suddenly, this morning, that's all changed," Alma said. "And for some reason, Inmate DuFresne thinks you had something to do with it."

"I didn't do anything."

Alma turned to the CO. "Did *you* see any of this?"

"Traces of alcohol were found in the plumbing on I-tier," Whitaker admitted. "And believe me, it was combed for a leak, but nothing conclusive was found. And yeah, I saw them all chewing gum. But Bourne's cell's been tossed religiously—and we've never found any contraband."

"I didn't do anything," Shay repeated. "It was them." Suddenly, he stepped toward Alma, animated. "Are you here for my heart?"

"What?"

"My heart. I want to donate it, after I die." I heard him rummaging around in his box of possessions. "Here," he said, giving Alma a piece of paper. "This is the girl who needs it. Lucius wrote her name down for me."

"I don't know anything about that . . ."

"But you can find out, right? You can talk to the right people?"

Alma hesitated, and then her voice went soft, the flannel-bound way she used to speak to me when the pain was so great that I could not see past it. "I can talk," she said.

It is an odd thing to be watching television and know that in reality, it is happening right outside your door. Crowds had flooded the parking lot of the prison. Camping out on the stairs of the parole office entrance were folks in wheelchairs, elderly women with walkers, mothers clutching sick infants to their chests. There were gay couples, mostly one man supporting another frail, ill partner; and crackpots holding up signs with scriptural references about the end of the world. Lining the street that led past the cemetery and downtown were the news vans—local affiliates, and even a crew from FOX in Boston.

Right now, a reporter from ABC 22 was interviewing a young mother whose son had been born with severe neurological damage.

She stood beside the boy, in his motorized wheelchair, one hand resting on his forehead. "What would I like?" she said, repeating the reporter's question. "I'd like to know that he knows me." She smiled faintly. "That's not too greedy, is it?"

The reporter faced the camera. "Bob, so far there's been no confirmation or denial from the administration that any miraculous behavior has in fact taken place within the Concord state prison. We have been told, however, by an unnamed source, that these occurrences stemmed from the desire of New Hampshire's sole death row inmate, Shay Bourne, to donate his organs post-execution."

I yanked my headphones down to my neck. "Shay," I called out. "Are you listening to this?"

"We got us our own celebrity," Crash said.

The brouhaha began to upset Shay. "I'm who I've always been," he said, his voice escalating. "I'm who I'll always be."

Just then two officers arrived, escorting someone we rarely saw: Warden Coyne. A burly man with a flattop on which you could have served dinner, he stood beside the cell while Officer Whitaker told Shay to strip. His scrubs were shaken out, and then he was allowed to dress again before he was shackled to the wall across from our cells.

The officers started to toss Shay's house—upending the meal he hadn't finished, yanking his headphones out of the television, overturning his small box of property. They ripped his mattress, balled up his sheets. They ran their hands along the edges of his sink, his toilet, his bunk.

"You got any idea, Bourne, what's going on outside?" the warden said, but Shay just stood with his head tucked into his shoulder, like Calloway's robin did when he slept. "You care to tell me what you're trying to prove?"

At Shay's pronounced silence, the warden began to walk the length of our tier. "What about you?" he called out to the rest of us. "And I will inform you that those who cooperate with me will not be punished. I can't promise anything for the rest of you."

Nobody spoke.

Warden Coyne turned to Shay. "Where did you get the gum?"

"There was only one piece," Joey Kunz blurted, the snitch. "But it was enough for all of us."

"You some kind of magician, son?" the

warden said, his face inches away from Shay's. "Or did you hypnotize them into believing they were getting something they weren't? I know about mind control, Bourne."

"I didn't do anything," Shay murmured.

Officer Whitaker stepped closer. "Warden Coyne, there's nothing in his cell. Not even in his mattress. His blanket's intact—if he's been fishing with it, then he managed to weave the strings back together when he was done."

I stared at Shay. Of course he'd fished with his blanket; I'd seen the line he'd made with my own eyes. I'd untied the bubble gum from the braided blue strand.

"I'm watching you, Bourne," the warden hissed. "I know what you're up to. You know damn well your heart isn't going to be worth anything once it's pumped full of potassium chloride in a death chamber. You're doing this because you've got no appeals left, but even if you get Barbara freaking Walters to do an interview with you, the sympathy vote's not going to change your execution date."

The warden stalked off I-tier. Officer Whitaker released Shay's handcuffs from the bar where he was tethered and led him back to his cell. "Listen, Bourne. I'm Catholic."

"Good for you," Shay replied.

"I thought Catholics were against the death penalty," Crash said.

"Yeah, don't do him any favors," Texas added.

Whitaker glanced down the tier, where the warden stood outside the soundproof glass, talking to another officer. "The thing is . . . if you want . . . I could ask one of the priests from St. Catherine's to visit." He paused. "Maybe he can help with the whole heart thing."

Shay stared at him. "Why would you do that for me?"

The officer fished inside the neck of his shirt, pulling out a length of chain and the crucifix that was attached to the end of it. He brought it to his lips, then let it fall beneath his uniform again. "He that believeth on me," Whitaker murmured, "believeth not on me, but on him that sent me."

I did not know the New Testament, but I recognized a biblical passage when I heard one—and it didn't take a rocket scientist to realize that he was suggesting Shay's antics, or whatever you wanted to call them, were heaven-sent. I realized then that even though Shay was a pris-

oner, he had a certain power over Whitaker. He had a certain power over *all* of us.
Shay Bourne had done what no brute force
or power play or gang threat had been
able to do all the years I'd been on I-tier:
he'd brought us together.

Next door, Shay was slowly putting his cell
to rights. The news program was wrapping
up with another bird's-eye view of the state
prison. From the helicopter footage, you could
see how many people had gathered, how
many more were heading this way.

I sat down on my bunk. It wasn't possible,
was it?

My own words to Alma came back to me:
It's not probable. Anything's possible.

I pulled my art supplies out of my hiding
spot in the mattress, riffling through my
sketches for the one I'd done of Shay being
wheeled off the tier after his seizure. I'd
drawn him on the gurney, arms spread and
tied down, legs banded together, eyes
raised to the ceiling. I turned the paper
ninety degrees. This way, it didn't look like
Shay was lying down. It looked like he was
being crucified.

People were always "finding" Jesus in jail.
What if he was already here?

|||||||||||||||||||||||||||||||||||||||||||||||||||||||||||||||||||||||||||||||||||||||||||

"I don't want to achieve immortality through
my work;
I want to achieve immortality through not
dying."

—*WOODY ALLEN, QUOTED IN* WOODY ALLEN
AND HIS COMEDY, *BY ERIC LAX*

Maggie

||||||||||||||||||||||||||||||||||||||||||||||||||||||||||||||||||||||||||||||||||||||||||||||||||||||||||||||||||||||||||||||

There were many things I was grateful for, including the fact that I was no longer in high school. Let's just say it wasn't a walk in the park for a girl who didn't fit into the smorgasbord of clothing at the Gap, and who tried to become invisible so she wouldn't be noticed for her size. Today, I was in a different school and it was ten years later, but I was still suffering from a flashback anxiety attack. It didn't matter that I was wearing my Jones New York I'm-going-to-court suit; it didn't matter that I was old enough to be mistaken for a teacher instead of a student—I still expected a football jock to turn the corner, at any moment, and make a fat joke.

Topher Renfrew, the boy who was sitting beside me in the lobby of the high school, was dressed in black jeans and a frayed T-shirt with an anarchy symbol, a guitar pick strung around his neck on a leather lanyard. Cut him, and he'd bleed antiestablishment. His iPod earphones hung down the front of his shirt like a doctor's stethoscope; and as he read the decision handed down by the court just an hour before, his lips mouthed the words. "So, what does all this bullshit mean?" he asked.

"That you won," I explained. "If you don't want to say the Pledge of Allegiance, you don't have to."

"What about Karshank?"

His homeroom teacher, a Korean War veteran, had sent Topher to detention every time he refused to say the Pledge. It had led to a letter-writing campaign by my office (well, me) and then we'd gone to court to protect his civil liberties.

Topher handed me back the decision. "Sweet," he said. "Any chance you can get pot legalized?"

"Uh, not my area of expertise. Sorry." I

shook Topher's hand, congratulated him, and headed out of the school.

It was a day for celebration—I unrolled the windows of the Prius, even though it was cold outside, and turned up Aretha on the CD player. Mostly, my cases got shot down by the courts; I spent more time fighting than I did getting a response. As one of three ACLU attorneys in New Hampshire, I was a champion of the First Amendment—freedom of speech, freedom of religion, freedom to organize. In other words, I looked really great on paper, but in reality, it meant I had become an expert letter writer. I wrote on behalf of the teenagers who wanted to wear their Hooters shirts to school, or the gay kid who wanted to bring his boyfriend to the prom; I wrote to take the cops to task for enforcing DWB—driving while black—when statistics showed they corralled more minorities than whites for routine traffic stops. I spent countless hours at community meetings, negotiating with local agencies, the AG's office, the police departments, the schools. I was the splinter they couldn't get rid of, the thorn in their side, their conscience.

I took out my cell phone and dialed my mother's number at the spa. "Guess what," I said when she picked up. "I won."

"Maggie, that's fantastic. I'm so proud of you." There was the slightest beat. "What did you win?"

"My case! The one I was telling you about last weekend at dinner?"

"The one against the community college whose mascot is an Indian?"

"Native American. And no," I said. "I lost that one, actually. I was talking about the Pledge case. And"—I pulled out my trump card—"I think I'm going to be on the news tonight. There were cameras all over the courthouse."

I listened to my mother drop the phone, yelling to her staff about her famous daughter. Grinning, I hung up, only to have the cell ring against my palm again. "What were you wearing?" my mother asked.

"My Jones New York suit."

My mother hesitated. "Not the pin-striped one?"

"What's that supposed to mean?"

"I'm just asking."

"Yes, the pin-striped one," I said. "What's wrong with it?"

"Did I *say* there was anything wrong with it?"

"You didn't have to." I swerved to avoid a

slowing car. "I have to go," I said, and I hung up, tears stinging.

It rang again. "Your mother's crying," my father said.

"Well, that makes two of us. Why can't she just be happy for me?"

"She is, honey. She thinks you're too critical."

"*I'm* too critical? Are you kidding?"

"I bet Marcia Clark's mother asked her what she was wearing to the O.J. trial," my father said.

"I bet Marcia Clark's mother doesn't get her daughter exercise videos for Chanukah."

"I bet Marcia Clark's mother doesn't get her *anything* for Chanukah," my father said, laughing. "Her Christmas stocking, though . . . I hear it's full of *The Firm* DVDs."

A smile twitched at the corners of my mouth. In the background, I could hear the rising strains of a crying baby. "Where *are* you?"

"At a bris," my father said. "And I'd better go, because the mohel's giving me dirty looks, and believe me, I don't want to upset him before he does a circumcision. Call me later and tell me every last detail. Your mother's going to TiVo the news for us."

I hung up and tossed my phone into the passenger seat. My father, who had made a living out of studying Jewish law, was always good at seeing the gray areas between the black-and-white letters. My mother, on the other hand, had a remarkable talent for taking a celebratory day and ruining it. I pulled into my driveway and headed into my house, where Oliver met me at the front door. "I need a drink," I told him, and he cocked an ear, because after all it was only 11:45 a.m. I went straight to the refrigerator—in spite of what my mother likely imagined, the only food inside of it was ketchup, a jar of pimientos, Ollie's carrots, and yogurt with an expiration date from Bill Clinton's administration—and poured myself a glass of Yellow Tail chardonnay. I wanted to be pleasantly buzzed before I turned on the television set, where no doubt my fifteen minutes of fame was now going to be marred by a suit with stripes that made my already plus-size butt look positively planetary.

Oliver and I settled onto the couch just as the theme song for the midday news spilled into my living room. The anchor, a woman with a blond helmet head, smiled into the camera. Behind her was a graphic of an

American flag with a line through it, and the caption NO PLEDGE? "In today's top story, a winning decision was handed down in the case of the high school student who refused to say the Pledge of Allegiance." The screen filled with a video of the courthouse steps, where you could see my face with a bouquet of microphones thrust under my nose.

Dammit, I *did* look fat in this suit.

"In a stunning victory for individual civil liberties," I began onscreen, and then a bright blue BREAKING NEWS banner obliterated my face. The picture switched to a live feed in front of the state prison, where there were squatters with tents and people holding placards and . . . was that a chorus line of wheelchairs?

The reporter's hair was being whipped into a frenzy by the wind. "I'm Janice Lee, reporting live from the New Hampshire State Prison for Men in Concord, which houses the man other inmates are calling the Death Row Messiah."

I picked up Oliver and sat down, cross-legged, in front of the television. Behind the reporter were dozens of people—I couldn't tell if they were picketing or protesting. Some stuck out from the crowd: the man with the sandwich board that read JOHN 3:16, the mother clutching a limp child, the small knot of nuns praying the rosary.

"This is a follow-up to our initial report," the reporter said, "in which we chronicled the inexplicable events that have occurred since inmate Shay Bourne—New Hampshire's only death row inhabitant—expressed his desire to donate his organs post-execution. Today there might be scientific proof that these incidents aren't magic . . . but something more."

The screen filled with a uniformed officer's face—Correctional Officer Rick Whitaker, according to the caption beneath him. "The first one was the tap water," he said. "One night, when I was on duty, the inmates got intoxicated, and sure enough the pipes tested positive for alcohol residue one day, although the water source tested perfectly normal. Some of the inmates have mentioned a bird being brought back to life, although I didn't witness that myself. But I'd have to say the most dramatic change involved Inmate DuFresne."

The reporter again: "According to sources, inmate Lucius DuFresne—an AIDS patient in the final stages of the disease—has been miraculously cured. On tonight's six o'clock report, we'll talk to physicians at Dartmouth-Hitchcock Medical Center about whether this can be explained medically . . . but for the newly converted followers of this Death Row Messiah," the reporter said, gesturing to the crowds behind her, "anything's possible. This is Janice Lee, reporting from Concord."

Then I saw a familiar face in the crowd behind the reporter—DeeDee, the spa technician who'd given me my body wrap. I remembered telling her that I'd look into Shay Bourne's case.

I picked up the phone and dialed my boss at the office. "Are you watching the news?"

Rufus Urqhart, the head of the ACLU in New Hampshire, had two televisions on his desk that he kept tuned to different channels so that he didn't miss a thing. "Yeah," he said. "I thought you were supposed to be on."

"I got preempted by the Death Row Messiah."

"Can't beat divinity," Rufus said.

"Exactly," I replied. "Rufus, I want to work on his behalf."

"Wake up, sweetheart, you already *are*. At least, you were *supposed* to be filing amicus briefs," Rufus said.

"No—I mean, I want to take him on as a client. Give me a week," I begged.

"Listen, Maggie, this guy's already been through the state court, the first circuit of the federal court, and the Supreme Court. If I remember correctly, they punted last year and denied cert. Bourne's exhausted all his appeals . . . I don't really see how we can reopen the door."

"If he thinks he's the Messiah," I said, "he just gave us a crowbar."

The Religious Land Use and Institutionalized Persons Act of 2000 didn't actually come into play until five years later, when the Supreme Court upheld the decision in the case of *Cutter v. Wilkinson*, where a bunch of Ohio prisoners who were Satanists sued the state for not accommodating their religious needs. As long as a prison guaranteed the right to practice religion—without *forcing* religion on those who didn't want to practice it—the law was constitutional.

"Satanists?" my mother said, putting down her knife and fork. "That's what this guy is?"

I was at their house, having dinner, like I did every Friday night before they went to Shabbat services. My mother would invite me on Monday, and I'd tell her I'd have to wait and see whether anything came up— like a date, or Armageddon, both of which had the same likelihood of occurring in my life. And then, of course, by Friday, I'd find myself passing the roasted potatoes and listening to my father say the kiddush over the wine.

"I have no idea," I told her. "I haven't met with him."

"Do Satanists have messiahs?" my father asked.

"You're missing the point, both of you. Legally, there's a statute that says that even prisoners have a right to practice their religion as long as it doesn't interfere with the running of the prison." I shrugged. "Besides, what if he *is* the Messiah? Aren't we morally obligated to save his life if he's here to save the world?"

My father cut a slice of his brisket. "He's not the Messiah."

"And you know this because . . . ?"

"He isn't a warrior. He hasn't maintained the sovereign state of Israel. He hasn't ushered in world peace. And okay, so maybe he's brought something dead back to life, but if he was the Messiah he would have resurrected everyone. And if that was the case, your grandparents would be here right now asking if there was more gravy."

"There's a difference between a Jewish messiah, Dad, and . . . well . . . the other one."

"What makes you think that there might be more than one?" he asked.

"What makes you think there might not?" I shot back.

My mother threw her napkin down. "I'm getting a Tylenol," she said, and left the table.

My father grinned at me. "You would have made such a good rabbi, Mags."

"Yeah, if only that pesky religion thing didn't keep getting in the way."

I had, of course, been raised Jewish. I would sit through Friday night services and listen to the soaring, rich voice of the cantor; I would watch my father reverently carry the Torah and it would remind me of how he looked in my baby pictures when he held me. But I'd also grow so bored that I'd find myself memorizing the names of who begat whom in Numbers. The more I learned about Jewish law the more I felt that, as a girl, I was bound to be considered unclean or limited or lacking. I had my bat mitzvah, like my parents wanted; and the day after I read from the Torah and celebrated my transition into adulthood, I told my parents I was never going to temple again.

Why? my father had asked when I told him.

Because I don't think God really cares whether or not I'm sitting there every Friday night. Because I don't buy into a religion that's based on what thou shalt not do, instead of what thou ought to be doing for the greater good. Because I don't know what I believe.

I didn't have the heart to tell him the truth: that I was much closer to an atheist than an agnostic, that I doubted there was a God at all. In my line of work, I'd seen too much injustice in the world to buy into the belief that a merciful, all-powerful deity would continue to allow such atrocities to exist; and I downright detested the party line that there was some divine grand plan for humanity's bumbling existence. It was a little like a parent watching her children playing with fire and thinking, *Well, let them burn. That'll teach 'em.*

Once, when I was in high school, I asked

my father about religions that were, with the passage of time, considered to be false. The Greeks and Romans, with all their gods, thought they were making sacrifices and praying at temples in order to receive favor from their deities; but today, pious people would scoff. How do you know, I'd asked my father, that five hundred years from now, some alien master race won't be picking over the artifacts of your Torah and their crucifix and wondering how you could be so naive?

My father, who was the first to take a controversial situation and say "Let's think about that," had been speechless. Because, he'd said finally, a religion doesn't last two thousand years if it's based on a lie.

Here's my take on it: I don't think religions are based on lies, but I don't think they're based on truths, either. I think they come about because of what people need at the time that they need them. Like the World Series player who won't take off his lucky socks, or the mother of the sick child who believes that her baby can sleep only if she's sitting by the crib—believers need, by definition, something to believe *in*.

"So what's your plan?" my father asked, bringing my attention back.

I glanced up. "I'm going to save him."

"Maybe *you're* the Messiah," he mused.

My mother sat down again, popped two pills into her mouth, and swallowed them dry. "What if he's creating this whole to-do so that somebody like you will come out of the woodwork and keep him from being executed?"

Well, I'd already considered that. "It doesn't matter if it's all a big ruse," I said. "As long as I can get the court to buy it, it's still a blow against the death penalty." I imagined myself being interviewed by Stone Phillips. Who, when the cameras cut, would ask me out to dinner.

"Promise me you won't be one of these lawyers who falls for the criminal and marries him in the prison . . ."

"Mom!"

"Well, it happens, Maggie. Felons are very persuasive people."

"And you know this because you've personally spent so much time in prison?"

She held up her hands. "I'm just saying."

"Rachel, I think Maggie's got this under control," my father said. "Why don't we get ready to go?"

My mother started clearing the dishes, and I followed her into the kitchen. We fell into a familiar routine: I'd load the dishwasher and rinse off the big platters; she'd dry. "I can finish," I said, like I did every week. "You don't want to be late for temple."

She shrugged. "They can't start without your father." I passed her a dripping serving bowl, but she set it on the counter and examined my hand instead. "Look at your nails, Maggie."

I pulled away. "I've got more important things to do than make sure my cuticles are trimmed, Ma."

"It's not about the manicure," she said. "It's about taking forty-five minutes where the most important thing in the world is not someone else . . . but *you*."

That was the thing about my mother: just when I thought I was ready to kill her, she'd say something that made me want to cry. I tried to curl my hands into fists, but she threaded our fingers together. "Come to the spa next week. We'll have a nice afternoon, just the two of us."

A dozen comments sprang to the back of my tongue: *Some of us have to work for a living. It won't be a nice afternoon if it's just the two of us. I may be a glutton, but not for punishment.* Instead, I nodded, even though we both knew I had no intention of showing up.

When I was tiny, my mother would have spa days in the kitchen, just for me. She'd concoct hair conditioners out of papaya and banana; she'd rub coconut oil into the skin of my shoulders and arms; she'd lay slices of cucumber on my eyes and sing Sonny & Cher songs to me. Afterward, she would hold a hand mirror up to my face. *Look at my beautiful girl*, she would say, and for the longest time, I believed her.

"Come to temple," my mother said. "Just tonight. It would make your father so happy."

"Maybe next time," I answered.

I walked them out to their car. My father turned the ignition and unrolled his window. "You know," he said. "When I was in college, there was a homeless guy who used to hang out near the subway. He had a pet mouse that used to sit on his shoulder and nibble at the collar of his coat, and he never took that coat off, not even when it was ninety-five degrees out. He knew the entire first chapter of *Moby-Dick* by heart. I always gave him a quarter when I passed by."

A neighbor's car zoomed past—someone from my father's congregation, who honked a hello.

My father smiled. "The word *Messiah* isn't

in the Old Testament . . . just the Hebrew word for *anointed*. He's not a savior; he's a king or a priest with a special purpose. But the Midrash—well, it mentions the *moshiach* a lot, and he looks different every time. Sometimes he's a soldier, sometimes he's a politician, sometimes he's got supernatural powers. And sometimes he's dressed like a vagrant. The reason I gave that bum a quarter," he said, "is because you never know."

Then he put the car in reverse and pulled out of the driveway. I stood there until I couldn't see them anymore, until there was nothing left to do but go home.

MICHAEL

||||||||||||||||||||||||||||||||||||||||||||||||||||||||||||||||||||||||||||||||||||||||||||||||||||||||||||||

Before you can go into a prison, you're stripped of the trappings that make you *you.* Take off your shoes, your belt. Remove your wallet, your watch, your saint's medal. Loose change in your pockets, cell phone, even the crucifix pin on your lapel. Hand over your driver's license to the uniformed officer, and in return, you become one of the faceless people who has entered a place the residents aren't allowed to leave.

"Father?" an officer said. "Are you okay?"

I tried to smile and nod, imagining what he saw: a big tough guy who was shaking at the thought of entering this prison. Sure, I rode a

Triumph Trophy, volunteered to work with gang youth, and broke the stereotype of a priest any chance I got—but inside here was the man whose life I had voted to end.

And yet.

Ever since I had taken my vows and asked God to help me offset what I had done to one man with what I might yet be able to do for others—I knew this would happen one day. I knew I'd wind up face-to-face with Shay Bourne.

Would he recognize me?

Would I recognize *him*?

I walked through the metal detector, holding my breath, as if I had something to hide. And I suppose I did, but my secrets wouldn't set off those alarms. I started to weave my belt into the loops of my trousers again, to tie the laces of my Converse sneakers. My hands were still trembling. "Father Michael?" I glanced up to find another officer waiting for me. "Warden Coyne's expecting you."

"Right." I followed the officer through dull gray hallways. When we passed inmates, the officer pivoted his body so that he stood between us—a shield.

I was delivered to an administrative office that overlooked the interior courtyard of the state prison. A conga line of prisoners was walking from one building to another. Behind them was a double line of fencing, capped with razor wire.

"Father."

The warden was a stocky man with silver hair who offered a handshake and a grimace that was supposed to pass for a smile. "Warden Coyne. Nice to meet you."

He led me into his private office, a surprisingly modern, airy space with no desk—just a long, spare steel table with files and notes spread across it. As soon as he sat down, he unwrapped a piece of gum. "Nicorette," he explained. "My wife's making me quit smoking and to be honest, I'd rather cut off my left arm." He opened a file with a number on its side—Shay Bourne had been stripped of his name in here as well. "I do appreciate you coming. We're a little short on chaplains right now."

The prison had one full-time chaplain, an Episcopal priest who had flown to Australia to be with his dying father. Which meant that if an inmate requested to speak to a clergyman, one of the locals would be called in.

"It's my pleasure," I lied, and mentally marked the rosary I'd say later as penance.

He pushed the file toward me. "Shay Bourne. You know him?"

I hesitated. "Who doesn't?"

"Yeah, the news coverage is a bitch, pardon my French. I could do without all the attention. Bottom line is the inmate wants to donate his organs after execution."

"Catholics support organ donation, as long as the patient is brain-dead and no longer breathing by himself," I said.

Apparently, it was the wrong answer. Coyne lifted up a tissue, frowned, and spit his gum into it. "Yeah, great, I get it. That's the party line. But the reality of the situation is that this guy's at the twenty-third hour. He's a convicted murderer, two times over. You think he's suddenly developed a humanitarian streak . . . or is it more likely that he's trying to gain public sympathy and stop his execution?"

"Maybe he just wants something good to come out of his death . . ."

"Lethal injection is designed to stop the inmate's heart," Coyne said flatly.

I had helped a parishioner earlier this year when she made the decision to donate her son's organs after a motorcycle accident that had left him brain-dead. Brain death, the doctor had explained, was different from cardiac death. Her son was still irrevocably gone— he would not eventually recover, like people in a coma—but thanks to the respirator, his heart was still beating. If cardiac death had occurred, the organs wouldn't be viable for transplant.

I sat back in the chair. "Warden Coyne, I was under the impression that Inmate Bourne had requested a spiritual advisor . . ."

"He did. And we'd like you to advise him against this crazy idea." The warden sighed. "Look, I know what this must sound like to you. But Bourne's going to be executed by the state. That's a fact. Either it can become a sideshow . . . or it can be done with discretion." He stared at me. "Are we clear on what you need to do?"

"Crystal," I said quietly.

I had once before let myself be led by others, because I assumed they knew more than me. Jim, another juror, had used the "eye for an eye" line from Jesus's Sermon on the Mount to convince me that repaying a death with a death was just. But now, I understood that Jesus had actually been saying the opposite—criticizing those who let the punishment compound the crime.

No way was I going to let Warden Coyne tell me how to advise Shay Bourne.

In that instant, I realized that if Bourne didn't recognize me, I wasn't going to tell him I'd met him before. This wasn't about *my* salvation; it was about *his*. And even if I'd been instrumental in ruining his life, now—as a priest—it was my job to redeem him.

"I'd like to meet Mr. Bourne," I said.

The warden nodded. "I figured." He stood up and led me back through the administrative offices. We took a turn and came to a control booth, a set of double-barred doors. The warden raised his hand and the officer inside unlocked the first steel door with a buzz and a sound of metal scraping metal. We stepped into the midchamber, and that same door automatically sealed.

So this was what it felt like to be locked in.

Before I could begin to panic, the interior door buzzed open, and we walked along another corridor. "You ever been in here?" the warden asked.

"No."

"You get used to it."

I looked around at the cinder-block walls, the rusting catwalks. "I doubt that."

We stepped through a fire door marked I-TIER. "This is where we keep the most hard-core inmates," Coyne said. "I can't promise they'll be on their best behavior."

In the center of the room was a control tower. A young officer sat there, watching a television monitor that seemed to have a bird's-eye view of the inside of the pod. It was quiet, or maybe the door that led inside was soundproof.

I walked up to the door and peered inside. There was an empty shower stall closest to me, then eight cells. I could not see the faces of the men and wasn't sure which one was Bourne. "This is Father Michael," the warden said. "He's come to speak with Inmate Bourne." He reached into a bin and handed me a flak jacket and protective goggles, as if I were going to war instead of death row.

"You can't go in unless you've got the right equipment," the warden said.

"Go in?"

"Well, where'd you think you were going to meet Inmate Bourne, Father? Starbucks?"

I had thought there would be some kind of . . . room, I guess. Or the chapel. "I'll be alone with him? In a cell?"

"Hell, no," Warden Coyne said. "You stand

out on the catwalk and talk through the door."

Taking a deep breath, I slipped the jacket on over my clothes and fitted the goggles to my face. Then I winged a quick prayer and nodded.

"Open up," Warden Coyne said to the young officer.

"Yes, sir," the kid said, clearly flustered to be under Coyne's regard. He glanced down at the control panel before him, a myriad display of buttons and lights, and pushed one near his left hand, only to realize at the last minute it was the wrong choice. The doors of all eight cells opened at once.

"Ohmygod," the boy said, his eyes wide as saucers, as the warden shoved me out of the way and began punching a series of levers and buttons on the control panel.

"Get him out of here," the warden yelled, jerking his head in my direction. Over the loudspeaker came his radio call: *Multiple inmates released on I-tier; need officer assistance immediately.*

I stood, riveted, as the inmates spilled out of their respective cells like poison. And then . . . well . . . all hell broke loose.

Lucius

When the doors released in unison, like all the strings tuning up in an orchestra and magically hitting the right note the first time the bow was raised, I didn't run out of the cell like the others. I stopped for a beat, paralyzed by freedom.

I quickly tucked my painting beneath the mattress of the bunk and stashed my ink in a roll of dirty laundry. I could hear Warden Coyne's voice on the loudspeakers, calling over the radio for the SWAT team. This had happened only once before when I was in prison; a new officer screwed up and two cells were opened simultaneously. The inmate who'd been accidentally freed rushed into the other's cell and cracked his skull open against the sink, a gang hit that had been waiting for years to come to pass.

Crash was the first one out of his cell. He ran past mine with his fist curled around a shank, making a beeline for Joey Kunz—a child molester was fair game for anyone. Pogie and Texas followed him like the dogs they were. "Grab him, boys," Crash hollered. "Let's just cut it right off."

Joey's voice escalated as he was cornered. "For God's sake, someone help!"

There was the sound of a fist hitting flesh, of Calloway swearing. By now, he was in Joey's cell, too.

"Lucius?" I heard, a slow ribbon of a voice, as if it had come from underwater, and I remembered that Joey wasn't the only one on the tier who'd hurt a child. If Joey was Crash's first victim, Shay could very well be the second.

There were people outside the prison praying to Shay; there were religious pundits on TV who promised hell and damnation to those who worshipped a false messiah. I didn't know what Shay was or wasn't, but I credited him for my health one hundred percent. And there was something about him that just didn't fit in here, that made you stop and look twice, as if you'd come across an orchid growing in a ghetto.

"Stay where you are," I called out. "Shay, you hear me?"

But he didn't answer. I stood at the threshold of my cell, trembling. I stared at that invisible line between here and now, no and yes, if and when. With one deep breath, I stepped outside.

Shay was not in his cell; he was moving slowly toward Joey's. Through the door of I-tier, I could see the officers suiting up in flak jackets and shields and masks. There was someone else, too—a priest I'd never seen before.

I reached for Shay's arm to stop him. That's all, just that small heat, and it nearly brought me to my knees. Here in prison we did not touch; we were not touched. I could have held on to Shay, at the innocent crook of his elbow, forever.

But Shay turned, and I remembered the first unwritten rule of being in prison: you did not invade someone's space. I let go. "It's okay," Shay said softly, and he took another step toward Joey's cell.

Joey was spread-eagled on the floor, sobbing, his pants pulled down. His head was twisted away, and blood streamed from his nose. Pogie had one of his arms, Texas the other; Calloway sat on his fighting feet. From this angle, they were obscured from the view of the officers who were mobilizing to subdue everyone. "You heard of Save the Children?" Crash said, brandishing his homemade blade. "I'm here to make a donation."

Just then, Shay sneezed.

"God bless," Crash said automatically.

Shay wiped his nose on his sleeve. "Thanks."

The interruption made Crash lose some of his momentum. He glanced out at the army on the other side of the door, screaming commands we couldn't hear. He rocked back on his heels and surveyed Joey, shivering against the cement floor.

"Let him go," Crash said.

"Let him . . . ?" Calloway echoed.

"You heard me. All of you. Go back."

Pogie and Texas listened; they always did what Crash said. Calloway was slower to leave. "We ain't done here," he said to Joey, but then he left.

"What the fuck are you waiting for?" Crash

said to me, and I hurried back to my own cell, forgetting entirely anyone else's welfare except my own.

I do not know what it was that led to Crash's change of plan—if it was knowing that the officers would storm the tier and punish him; if it was Shay's well-timed sneeze; if it was a prayer—*God bless*—on the lips of a sinner like Crash. But by the time the SWAT team entered seconds later, all seven of us were sitting in our cells even though the doors were still wide open, as if we were angels, as if we had nothing to hide.

There's a flower I can see from the exercise yard. Well, I can't really see it—I have to sort of hook my fingers on the ledge of the only window and spider-walk up the cement wall, but I can glimpse it then before I fall back down. It's a dandelion, which you might think is a weed, but it can be put into salads or soups. The root can be ground up and used as a coffee substitute. The juices can get rid of warts or be used as an insect repellent. I learned all this from a *Mother Earth News* magazine piece that I keep wrapped around my treasures—my shank, my Q-tips, the tiny Visine bottles where I keep the ink I manufacture. I read the article every time I take my supplies out for inventory, which is daily. I keep my cache behind a loosened cinder block beneath my cot, refilling the mortar with Metamucil and toothpaste, mixed, so that the officers don't get suspicious when they toss the cell.

I never gave it much thought before I came in here, but I wish I knew more about horticulture. I wish I'd taken the time to learn what makes things grow. Hell, if I had, maybe I could have started a watermelon plant from a seedling. Maybe I'd have vines hanging all over the place by now.

Adam had the green thumb in our household. I used to find him outside at the crack of dawn, rooting around in the dirt between our daylilies and sedums. *The weeds shall inherit the earth,* he had said.

Meek, I'd corrected. *The meek shall inherit it.*

No way, Adam had said, and laughed. *The weeds will blow right by them.*

He used to say that if you picked a dandelion, two would grow back in its place. I guess they are the botanical equivalent of the men in this prison. Take one of us off the street, and more will sprout up in his wake.

With Crash back in solitary, and Joey in the infirmary, I-tier was oddly quiet. In the wake of Joey's beating, our privileges had been suspended, so all showers and exercise yard visits were canceled for the day. Shay was pacing. Earlier, he'd been complaining that his teeth were vibrating with the air-conditioning unit; sometimes sounds got to be too much for him—usually when he was agitated. "Lucius," he said. "Did you see that priest today?"

"Yeah."

"Do you think he came for me?"

I didn't want to give him false hope. "I don't know, Shay. Maybe someone was dying on another tier and needed last rites."

"The dead aren't alive, and the living don't die."

I laughed. "Thanks for that, Yoda."

"Who's Yoda?"

He was talking crazy, the way Crash had a year ago when he'd started to peel the lead paint from the cinder blocks and eat it, hoping it would serve as a hallucinogen. "Well, if there *is* a heaven, I bet it's full of dandelions." (Actually, I think heaven's full of guys who look like Wentworth Miller from *Prison Break*, but for right now, I was only talking landscaping.)

"Heaven's not a *place*."

"I didn't say it had map coordinates . . ."

"If it was in the sky, then birds would get there before you. If it was under the sea, fish would be first."

"Then where is it?" I asked.

"It's inside you," Shay said, "and outside, too."

If he wasn't eating the lead paint, then he'd been making hooch I didn't know about. "If this is heaven, I'll take a rain check."

"You can't wait for it, because it's already here."

"Well, you're the only one of us who got rose-colored glasses when he was booked, I guess."

Shay was silent for a while. "Lucius," he asked finally. "Why did Crash go after Joey instead of me?"

I didn't know. Crash was a convicted murderer; I had no doubt he could and would kill again if given the opportunity. Technically, both Joey and Shay had sinned equally in Crash's code of justice; they had harmed children. Maybe Crash figured Joey would be easier to kill. Maybe Shay had gained a modicum of respect through his miracles. Maybe he'd just gotten lucky.

Maybe even Crash thought there was something special about Shay.

"He's not any different than Joey . . ." Shay said.

"Teensy suggestion? Don't let Crash hear you say that."

". . . and we're not any different than Crash," he finished. "You don't know what would make you do what Crash did, just like you didn't know what would make you kill Adam, until it happened."

I drew in my breath. No one in prison talked about another person's crime, even if you secretly believed they were guilty. But I *had* killed Adam. It was my hand holding the gun; it was his blood on my clothes. It wasn't what had been done that was at issue for me in court; it was why.

"It's okay to not know something," Shay said. "That's what makes us human."

No matter what Mr. Philosopher Next Door thought, there were things I knew for sure: That I had been loved, once, and had loved back. That a person could find hope in the way a weed grew. That the sum of a man's life was not where he wound up but in the details that brought him there.

That we made mistakes.

I closed my eyes, sick of the riddles, and to my surprise all I could see were dandelions—as if they had been painted on the fields of my imagination, a hundred thousand suns. And I remembered something else that makes us human: faith, the only weapon in our arsenal to battle doubt.

June

||||||||||||||||||||||||||||||||||||||||||||||||||||||||||||||||||||||||||||||||||||||||||||||||||||||||||||||||||||||||||||||

They say God won't give you any more than you can handle, but that begs a more important question: why would God let you suffer in the first place?

"No comment," I said into the phone, and I slammed down the receiver loud enough that Claire—on the couch with her iPod on—sat up and took notice. I reached beneath the table and yanked out the cord completely so that I would not have to hear the phone ring.

They had been calling all morning; they had set up camp outside my home. *How does it feel to know that there are protesters outside the prison, hoping to free the man who murdered your child and your husband?*

Do you think Shay Bourne's request to be an organ donor is a way to make up for what he's done?

What I thought was that nothing Shay Bourne could do or say would ever make up for the lives of Elizabeth and Kurt. I knew firsthand how well he could lie and what might come of it—this was nothing more than some publicity stunt to make everyone feel badly for him, because after a decade, who even remembered feeling badly for that police officer, that little girl?

I did.

There are people who say that the death penalty isn't just because it takes so long to execute a man. That it's inhumane to have to wait eleven years or more for punishment. That at least for Elizabeth and Kurt, death came quickly.

Let me tell you what's wrong with that line of reasoning: it assumes that Elizabeth and Kurt were the only victims. It leaves out me; it leaves out Claire. And I can promise you that every day for the last eleven years I've thought of what I lost at the hands of Shay Bourne.

I've been anticipating his death just as long as he has.

I heard voices coming from the living room and realized that Claire had turned on the television. A grainy photograph of Shay Bourne filled the screen. It was the same photo that had been used in the newspapers, although Claire would not have seen those, since I'd thrown them out immediately. Bourne's hair was cut short now, and there were parenthetical lines around his mouth and fanning from the corners of his eyes, but he otherwise did not look any different.

"That's him, isn't it?" Claire asked.

God, Complex? read the caption beneath the photograph.

"Yes." I walked toward the television, intentionally blocking her view, and turned it off.

Claire looked up at me. "I remember him," she said.

I sighed. "Honey, you weren't even born yet."

She unfolded the afghan that sat on the couch and wrapped it around her shoulders, as if she'd suddenly taken a chill. "I remember him," Claire repeated.

MICHAEL

I would have had to be living under a rock to not know what was being said about Shay Bourne, but I was the last person in the world who would ever have believed him to be messianic. As far as I was concerned, there was one Son of God, and I knew who He was. As for Bourne's showmanship—well, I'd seen David Blaine make an elephant disappear on Fifth Avenue in New York City, but that wasn't a miracle, either. Plain and simple: my job here wasn't to feed into Shay Bourne's delusional beliefs . . . only to help him accept Jesus Christ as his Lord and Savior before his execution so that he'd wind up in the Kingdom of Heaven.

And if I could help him donate his heart somewhere along the way, so be it.

Two days after the incident at I-tier had occurred, I parked my Trophy outside the prison. My mind kept tripping over a verse from Matthew where Jesus spoke to his disciples: *I was a stranger, and you took me in; naked, and you clothed me; I was sick, and you visited me; I was in prison, and you came unto me.* The disciples—who were, to be brutally honest, a thick bunch—were confused. They couldn't remember Jesus being lost or naked or sick or imprisoned. And Jesus told them: *Inasmuch as you have done it unto one of the least of my brethren, you have done it unto me.*

Inside, I was handed a flak jacket and goggles again. The door to I-tier opened, and I was led down the hallway to Shay Bourne's cell.

It wasn't all that different from being in the confessional. The same Swiss-cheese holes perforated the metal door of the cell, so I could get a glimpse of Shay. Although we were the same age, he looked like he'd aged a lifetime. Now gray at the temples, he still was slight and wiry. I hesitated, silent, waiting to see if his eyes would go wide with recognition, if he would start banging on the door and demand to get away from the person who'd set the wheels of his execution in motion.

But a funny thing happens when you're in clerical dress: you aren't a man. You're somehow more than one, and also less. I've had secrets whispered in front of me; I've had women hike up their skirts to fix their panty hose. Like a physician, a priest is supposed to be unflappable, an observer, a fly on the wall. Ask ten people who meet me what I look like, and eight of them won't be able to tell you the color of my eyes. They simply don't look past the collar.

Shay walked directly up to the door of the cell and started to grin. "You came," he said.

I swallowed. "Shay, I'm Father Michael."

He flattened his palms against the door of the cell. I remembered a photograph from the crime evidence, those fingers dark with a little girl's blood. I had changed so much in the past eleven years, but what about Shay Bourne? Was he remorseful? Had he matured? Did he wish, like me, that he could erase his mistakes?

"Hey, Father," a voice yelled out—I would

later learn it was Calloway Reece—"you got any of those wafers? I'm near starving."

I ignored him and focused on Shay. "So . . . I understand you're Catholic?"

"A foster mother had me baptized," Shay said. "A thousand years ago." He glanced at me. "They could put you in the conference room, the one they use for lawyers."

"The warden said we'd have to talk here, at your cell."

Shay shrugged. "I don't have anything to hide."

Do you? I heard, although he hadn't said it.

"Anyway, that's where they give us hep C," Shay said.

"Give you hep C?"

"On haircut day. Every other Wednesday. We go to the conference room and they buzz us. Number two blade, even if you want it longer for winter. They don't make it this hot in here in the winter. It's freezing from November on." He turned to me. "How come they can't make it hot in November and freezing now?"

"I don't know."

"It's on the blades."

"Pardon?"

"Blood," Shay said. "On the razor blades. Someone gets nicked, someone else gets hep C."

Following his conversation was like watching a SuperBall bounce. "Did that happen to you?"

"It happened to other people, so sure, it happened to me."

Inasmuch as you have done it unto one of the least of my brethren, you have done it unto me.

My head was swimming; I hoped it was Shay's nonlinear speech, and not a panic attack coming on. I'd been suffering those for eleven years now, ever since the day we'd sentenced Shay. "But for the most part, you're all right?"

After I said it, I wanted to kick myself. You didn't ask a dying man how he was feeling. *Other than that, Mrs. Lincoln*, I thought, *how was the play?*

"I get lonely," Shay answered.

Automatically, I replied, "God's with you."

"Well," Shay said, "he's lousy at checkers."

"Do you believe in God?"

"Why do *you* believe in God?" He leaned forward, suddenly intense. "Did they tell you I want to donate my heart?"

"That's what I came to talk about, Shay."

"Good. No one else wants to help."

"What about your lawyer?"

"I fired him." Shay shrugged. "He lost all the appeals, and then he started talking about going to the governor. The governor's not even from New Hampshire, did you know that? He was born in Mississippi. I always wanted to see that river, take one of those gambling boats down it like some kind of cardsharp. Or maybe that's *shark*. Do they have those in rivers?"

"Your lawyer . . ."

"He wanted the governor to commute my sentence to life, but that's just another death sentence. So I fired him."

I thought about Warden Coyne, how sure he was that this was all just a ploy to get Shay Bourne's execution called off. Could he have been wrong? "Are you saying that you *want* to die, Shay?"

"I *want* to live," he said. "So I *have* to die."

Finally, something I could latch onto. "You *will* live," I said. "In the Kingdom of the Father. No matter what happens here, Shay. And no matter whether or not you can donate your organs."

Suddenly his face went dark. "What do you mean, whether or not?"

"Well, it's complicated . . ."

"I have to give her my heart. I have to."

"Who?"

"Claire Nealon."

My jaw dropped. This specific part of Shay's request had not made it to the broadcast news. "*Nealon?* Is she related to Elizabeth?" Too late I realized that the average person— one who hadn't been on Shay's jury—might not recognize that name and identify it as quickly. But Shay was too agitated to notice.

"She's the sister of the girl who was killed. She has a heart problem; I saw it on TV. What's inside me is going to save me," Shay said. "If I don't bring it forward, it's going to kill me."

We were making the same mistake, Shay and I. We both believed that you could right a former wrong by doing a good deed later on. But giving Claire Nealon his heart wasn't going to bring her sister back to life. And being Shay Bourne's spiritual advisor wasn't going to erase the fact that I was part of the reason he was here.

"You can't get salvation by donating your organs, Shay. The only way to find salvation is to admit your guilt and seek absolution through Jesus."

"What happened then doesn't matter now."

"You don't have to be afraid to take responsibility; God loves us, even when we screw up."

"I couldn't stop it," Shay said. "But this time, I can fix it."

"Leave that to God," I suggested. "Tell Him you're sorry for what you did, and He'll forgive you."

"No matter what?"

"No matter what."

"Then why do you have to say you're sorry first?"

I hesitated, trying to find a better way to explain sin and salvation to Shay. It was a bargain: you made an admission, you got redemption in return. In Shay's economy of salvation, you gave away a piece of yourself—and somehow found yourself whole again.

Were the two ideas really so different?

I shook my head to clear it.

"Lucius is an atheist," Shay said. "Right, Lucius?"

From next door, Lucius mumbled, "Mm-hmm."

"And he didn't die. He was sick, and he got better."

The AIDS patient; I'd heard about him on the news. "Did you have something to do with it?"

"I didn't do anything."

"Lucius, do you believe that, too?"

I leaned back so that I could make eye contact with this other inmate, a slim man with a shock of white hair. "I think Shay had *everything* to do with it," he said.

"Lucius should believe whatever he needs to," Shay said.

"What about the miracles?" Lucius added.

"What miracles?" Shay said.

Two facts struck me: Shay Bourne was not claiming to be the Messiah, or Jesus, or anyone but himself. And through some misguided belief, he truly felt that he wouldn't rest in peace unless he could donate his heart to Claire Nealon.

"Look," Lucius said. "Are you or are you not going to help him?"

Maybe none of us could compensate for what we'd done wrong in the past, but that didn't mean we couldn't make our futures matter more. I closed my eyes and imagined being the last person Shay Bourne spoke with before he was executed by the State of New Hampshire. I imagined picking a section of the Bible that would resonate with him, a balm of prayer during those last few minutes. I could do this for him. I could be who he needed me to be now, because I hadn't been who he needed me to be back then. "Shay," I said, "knowing that your heart is beating in some other person isn't salvation. It's altruism. Salvation is coming home. It's understanding that you don't have to prove yourself to God."

"Oh, for Christ's sake," Lucius snorted. "Don't listen to him, Shay."

I turned to him. "Do you *mind*?" Then I shifted position, so that I blocked Lucius from my sight, focusing on Shay. "God loves you— whether or not you give up your organs, whether or not you've made mistakes in the past. And the day of your execution, he'll be waiting for you. Christ can save you, Shay."

"Christ can't give Claire Nealon a heart." Suddenly Shay's gaze was piercing and lucid. "I don't need to find God. I don't want catechism," he said. "All I want to know is whether, after I'm killed, I can save a little girl."

"No," I said bluntly. "Not if you're given a lethal injection. The drugs are meant specifically to stop your heart, and after that, it's worthless for donation."

The light in his eyes dimmed, and I drew in my breath. "I'm sorry, Shay. I know you were hoping to hear something different, and your intentions are good . . . but you need to channel those good intentions to make peace with God another way. And that *is* something I can make happen."

Just then a young woman burst onto I-tier. She had a cascade of black curls tumbling down her back, and peeking out from her flak jacket was the ugliest striped suit I'd ever seen. "Shay Bourne?" she said. "I know a way you can donate your organs."

Maggie

IIIIIIIIIIIIIIIIIIIIIIIIIIIIIIIIIIIIIIIIIIIIIIIIIIIIIIIIIIIIIIIIIIIIIIIIIIIIIIIIIIIIIIIIIIIIIIIIIIIIIIIIII

Some people may find it tough to break out of prison, but for me, it was equally as hard to get in. Okay, so I wasn't officially Shay Bourne's attorney—but the prison officials didn't know that. I could argue the technicality with Bourne himself, if and when I reached him.

I hadn't counted on how difficult it would be to get through the throng outside the prison. It's one thing to shove your way past a group of college kids smoking pot in a tent, their MAKE PEACE NOT MIRACLES signs littering the muddy ground; it's another thing entirely to explain to a mother and her smooth-scalped, cancer-stricken toddler why you deserved to cut their place in line. In the end, the only way I could edge forward was by explaining to those who'd been waiting (in some cases, for *days*) that I was Shay Bourne's legal advisor and that I would pass along their pleas: from the elderly couple with knotted hands, whose twin diagnoses—breast cancer and lymphatic cancer—came within a week of each other; to the father who carried pictures of the eight children he couldn't support since losing his job; to the daughter pushing her mother's wheelchair, wishing for just one more lucid moment in the fog of Alzheimer's so that she could say she was sorry for a transgression that had happened years earlier. *There is so much pain in this world,* I thought, *how do any of us manage to get up in the morning?*

When I reached the front gate, I announced that I had come to see Shay Bourne, and the officer laughed at me. "You and the rest of the free world."

"I'm his lawyer."

He looked at me for a long moment, and then spoke into his radio. A moment later, a second officer arrived and escorted me past the blockade. As I left, a cheer went up from the crowd.

Stunned, I turned around, waved hesitantly, and then hurried to catch up.

I had never been to the state prison. It was a large, old brick building; its courtyard stretched out behind the razor-wire fencing. I was told to sign in on a clipboard and to take off my jacket before I went through the metal detector.

"Wait here," the officer said, and he left me sitting in a small anteroom. There was an inmate mopping the floor who did not make eye contact with me. He was wearing white tennis shoes that squelched every time he stepped forward. I watched his hands on the mop and wondered if they'd been part of a murder, a rape, a robbery.

There was a reason I didn't become a criminal defense attorney: this setting freaked me out. I had been to the county jail to meet with clients, but those were small-potatoes crimes: picketing outside a rally for a political candidate, flag burning, civil disobedience. None of my clients had ever killed anyone before, much less a child and a police officer. I found myself considering what it would be like to be locked in here forever. What if my dress clothes and day clothes and pajamas were all the same orange scrubs? What if I was told when to shower, when to eat, when to go to bed? Given that my career was about maintaining personal freedoms, it was hard to imagine a world where they'd all been stripped away.

As I watched the inmate mop beneath a bank of seats, I wondered what would be the hardest luxury to leave behind. There were the trivial things: losing chocolate practically qualified as cruel and unusual punishment; I couldn't sacrifice my contact lenses; I'd sooner die than relinquish the Ouidad Climate Control gel that kept my hair from becoming a frizzy rat's nest. But what about the rest—missing the dizzying choice of all the cereals in the grocery store aisle, for example? Not being able to receive a phone call? Granted, it had been so long since I was intimate with a man that I had spiderwebs between my legs, but what would it be like to give up being touched casually, even a handshake?

I bet I'd even miss fighting with my mother.

Suddenly a pair of boots appeared on the

floor before me. "You're out of luck. He's got his spiritual advisor with him," the officer said. "Bourne's pretty popular today."

"That's fine," I bluffed. "The spiritual advisor can join us during our meeting." I saw the slightest flicker of uncertainty on the face of the officer. Not allowing an inmate to see his attorney was a big no-no, and I was planning to capitalize on that.

The officer shrugged and led me down a hallway. He nodded to a man in a control booth, and a door scraped open. We stepped into a small metal midroom, and I sucked in my breath as the steel door slid home. "I'm a little claustrophobic," I said.

The officer smiled. "Too bad."

The inner door buzzed, and we entered the prison. "It's quiet in here," I remarked.

"That's because it's a good day." He handed me a flak jacket and goggles and waited for me to put them on. For one brief moment, I panicked—what if a man's jacket like this didn't zip shut on me? How embarrassing would *that* be? But there were Velcro straps and it wasn't an issue, and as soon as I was outfitted, the door to a long tier opened. "Have fun," the officer said, and that was when I realized I was supposed to go in alone.

Well. I wasn't going to convince Shay Bourne I was brave enough to save his life if I couldn't muster the courage to walk through that door.

There were whoops and catcalls. Leave it to me to find my only appreciative audience in the maximum-security tier of the state prison. "Baby, you here for me?" one guy said, and another pulled down his scrubs so that I could see his boxer shorts, as if I'd been waiting for that kind of peep show all my life. I kept my eyes focused on the priest who was standing outside one of the cells.

I should have introduced myself. I should have explained why I had lied my way into this prison. But I was so flustered that nothing came out the way it should have. "Shay Bourne?" I said. "I know a way that you can donate your organs."

The priest frowned at me. "Who are you?"

"His lawyer."

He turned to Shay. "I thought you said you didn't have a lawyer."

Shay tilted his head. He looked at me as if he were sifting through the grains of my thoughts, separating the wheat from the chaff. "Let her talk," he said.

My streak of bravery widened after that: leaving the priest with Shay, I went back to the officers and demanded a private attorney-client conference room. I explained that legally, they had to provide one and that due to the nature of our conversation, the priest should be allowed into the meeting. Then the priest and I were taken into a small cubicle from one side, while Shay was escorted through a different entrance by two officers. When the door was closed, he backed up to it, slipping his hands through the trap to have his handcuffs removed.

"All right," the priest said. "What's going on?"

I ignored him and faced Shay. "My name is Maggie Bloom. I'm an attorney for the ACLU, and I think I know a way to save you from being executed."

"Thanks," he said, "but that's not what I'm looking for."

I stared at him. "What?"

"I don't need you to save all of me. Only my heart."

"I . . . I don't understand," I said slowly.

"What Shay means," the priest said, "is that he's resigned to his execution. He just wants to be an organ donor, afterward."

"Who are you, exactly?" I asked.

"Father Michael Wright."

"And you're his spiritual advisor?"

"Yes."

"Since when?"

"Since ten minutes before you became his lawyer," the priest said.

I turned back to Shay. "Tell me what you want."

"To give my heart to Claire Nealon."

Who the hell was Claire Nealon? "Does she *want* your heart?"

I looked at Shay, and then I looked at Michael, and I realized that I had just asked the one question no one had considered up till this point.

"I don't know if she wants it," Shay said, "but she needs it."

"Well, has anyone talked to her?" I turned to Father Michael. "Isn't that *your* job?"

"Look," the priest said, "the state has to execute him by lethal injection. And if that happens, organ donation isn't viable."

"Not necessarily," I said slowly.

A lawyer can't care more about the case

than the client does. If I couldn't convince Shay to enter a courtroom hoping for his life to be spared, then it would be foolish for me to take this on. However, if his mission to donate his heart dovetailed with mine—to strike down the death penalty—then why not use the same loophole law to get what we both wanted? I could fight for him to die on his own terms— donate his organs—and in the process, raise enough awareness about the death penalty to make more people take a stand against it.

I glanced up at my new client and smiled.

MICHAEL

The crazy woman who'd barged in on our little pastoral counseling session was now promising Shay Bourne happy endings she could not deliver. "I need to do a little research," she explained. "I'm going to come back to see you in a few days."

Shay, for what it was worth, was staring at her as if she had just handed him the moon. "But you think . . . you think I'll be able to donate my heart to her?"

"Yes," she said. "Maybe."

Yes. Maybe. Mixed signals, that's what she was giving him. As opposed to my message: *God. Jesus. One true course.*

She knocked on the window, in just as big a hurry to get out of the conference room as she'd been to enter it. As an officer buzzed open the door, I grasped her upper arm. "Don't get his hopes up," I whispered.

She raised a brow. "Don't cut them down."

The door closed behind Maggie Bloom, and I watched her walk away through the oblong window in the conference room. In the faint reflection, I could see Shay watching, too. "I like her," he announced.

"Well," I sighed. "Good."

"Did you ever notice how sometimes it's a mirror, and sometimes it's glass?"

It took me a moment to realize that he was talking about the reflection. "It's the way the light hits," I explained.

"There's light inside a man of light," Shay murmured. "It can light up the whole world." He met my gaze. "So, what were you saying is impossible?"

My grandmother had been so fervently Catholic that she was on the committee of women who would come to scrub down the church, sometimes taking me along. I'd sit in the back, setting up a traffic jam of Matchbox cars on the kneeler. I'd watch her rub Murphy Oil Soap into the scarred wooden pews and sweep down the aisle with a broom; and on Sunday when we went to Mass she'd look around—from the entryway to the arched ceilings to the flickering candles—and nod with satisfaction. On the other hand, my grandfather never went to church. Instead, on Sundays, he fished. In the summer, he went out fly-fishing for bass; in the winter, he cut a hole in the ice and waited, drinking from his thermos of coffee, with steam wreathing his head like a halo.

It wasn't until I was twelve that I was allowed to skip a Sunday Mass to tag along with my grandfather. My grandmother sent me off with a bag lunch and an old baseball hat to keep the sun off my face. "Maybe you can talk some sense into him," she said. I had heard enough sermons to understand what happened to those who didn't truly believe, so I climbed into his little aluminum boat and waited until we had stopped underneath the reaching arm of a willow tree along the shoreline. He took out a fly rod and handed it to me, and then started casting with his own ancient bamboo rod.

One two three, one two three. There was

a rhythm to fly-fishing, like a ballroom dance. I waited until we had both unspooled the long tongue of line over the lake, until the flies that my grandfather laboriously tied in his basement had lightly come to rest on the surface. "Grandpa," I asked, "you don't want to go to hell, do you?"

"Aw, Christ," he had answered. "Did your grandmother put you up to this?"

"No," I lied. "I just don't understand why you never go to Mass with us."

"I have my own Mass," he had said. "I don't need some guy in a collar and a dress telling me what I should and shouldn't believe."

Maybe if I'd been older, or smarter, I would have left it alone at that. Instead, I squinted into the sun, up at my grandfather. "But you got married by a priest."

He sighed. "Yeah, and I even went to parochial school, like you."

"What made you stop?"

Before he could answer, I felt that tug on my line that always felt like Christmas, the moment before you opened the biggest box under the tree. I reeled in, fighting the whistle and snap of the fish on the other end, certain that I'd never caught anything quite like this before. Finally, it burst out of the water, as if it were being born again.

"A salmon!" my grandfather crowed. "Ten pounds, easy . . . imagine all the ladders it had to climb to make its way back here from the ocean to spawn." He held the fish aloft, grinning. "I haven't seen one in this lake since the sixties!"

I looked down at the fish, still on my line, thrashing in splendor. It was silver and gold and crimson all at once.

My grandfather held the salmon, stilling it enough to unhook the fly, and set the fish back into the lake. We watched the flag of its tail, the ruddy back as it swam away. "Who says that if you want to find God on a Sunday morning, you ought to be looking in church?" my grandfather murmured.

For a long time after that, I believed my grandfather had it right: God was in the details. But that was before I learned that the requirements of a true believer included Mass every Sunday and holy day of obligation, receiving the Eucharist, reconciliation once a year, giving money to the poor, observing Lent. Or in other words—just because you say you're Catholic, if you don't walk the walk, you're not.

Back when I was at seminary, I imagined I

heard my grandfather's voice: *I thought God was supposed to love you unconditionally. Those sure sound like a lot of conditions to me.*

The truth is, I stopped listening.

By the time I left the prison, the crowd outside had doubled in size. There were the ill, the feeble, the old and the hungry, but there was also a small cadre of nuns from a convent up in Maine, and a choir singing "Holy Holy Holy." I was surprised at how hearsay about a so-called miracle could produce so many converts, so quickly.

"You see?" I heard a woman say, pointing to me. "Even Father Michael's here."

She was a parishioner, and her son had cystic fibrosis. He was here, too, in a wheelchair being pushed by his father.

"Is it true, then?" the man asked. "Can this guy really work miracles?"

"*God* can," I said, heading that question off at the pass. I put my hand on the boy's forehead. "Dear St. John of God, patron saint of those who are ill, I ask for your intercession that the Lord will have mercy on this child and return him to health. I ask this in Jesus's name."

Not Shay Bourne's, I thought.

"Amen," the parents murmured.

"If you'll excuse me," I said, turning away.

The chances of Shay Bourne being Jesus were about as likely as me being God. These people, these falsely faithful, didn't know Shay Bourne—they'd never *met* Shay Bourne. They were imposing the face of our Savior on a man with a tendency to talk to himself; a man whose hands had been covered with the blood of two innocent people. They were confusing showmanship and inexplicable events with divinity. A miracle was a miracle only until it could be proved otherwise.

I started pushing through the mob, moving in the opposite direction, away from the prison gates, a man on a mission. Maggie Bloom wasn't the only one who could do research.

Maggie

||||||||||||||||||||||||||||||||||||||||||||||||||||||||||||||||||||||||||||||||||||||||||||||||||||||||

In retrospect, it would have been much simpler to place a phone call to a medical professional who might lecture me on the ins and outs of organ donation. But it could take a week for a busy doctor to call me back, and my route home from the prison skirted the grounds of the Concord hospital, and I was still buzzing with righteous legal fervor. These are the only grounds I can offer for why I decided to stop in the emergency room. The faster I could speak to an expert, the faster I could start building Shay's case.

However, the triage nurse—a large graying

woman who looked like a battleship—
compressed her mouth into a flat line when I
asked to talk to a doctor. "What's the problem?" she asked.

"I've got a few questions—"

"So does everyone else in that waiting
room, but you'll still have to explain the nature of the illness to me."

"Oh, I'm not sick . . ."

She glanced around me. "Then where's
the patient?"

"At the state prison."

The nurse shook her head. "The patient
has to be present for registration."

I found that hard to believe. Surely someone knocked unconscious in a car accident
wasn't left waiting in the hall until he came
to and could recite his Blue Cross group
number.

"We're busy," the nurse said. "When the
patient arrives, sign in again."

"But I'm a lawyer—"

"Then sue me," the nurse replied.

I walked back to the waiting room and sat
down next to a college-age boy with a bloody
washcloth wrapped around his hand. "I did
that once," I said. "Cutting a bagel."

He turned to me. "I put my hand through a

plate-glass window because my girlfriend was screwing my roommate."

A nurse appeared. "Whit Romano?" she said, and the boy stood up.

"Good luck with that," I called after him, and I speared my fingers through my hair, thinking hard. Leaving a message with the nurse didn't guarantee a doctor would see it anytime in the next millennium—I had to find another way in.

Five minutes later I was standing in front of the battleship again. "The patient's arrived?" she asked.

"Well. Yes. It's me."

She put down her pen. "You're sick now. You weren't sick before."

I shrugged. "I'm thinking appendicitis . . ."

The nurse pursed her lips. "You know you'll be charged a hundred and fifty dollars for an emergency room visit, even a fabricated one."

"You mean insurance doesn't—"

"Nope."

I thought of Shay, of the sound the steel doors made when they scraped shut in prison. "It's my abdomen. Sharp pains."

"Which side?"

"My left . . . ?" The nurse narrowed her eyes. "I meant my *other* left."

"Take a seat," she said.

I settled in the waiting room again and read two issues of *People* nearly as old as I was before being called into an exam room. A nurse—younger, wearing pink scrubs—took my blood pressure and temperature. She wrote down my health history, while I mentally reviewed whether you could be brought up on criminal charges for falsifying your own medical records.

I was lying on the exam table, staring at a Where's Waldo? poster on the ceiling, when the doctor came in.

"Ms. Bloom?" he said.

Okay, I'm just going to come out and say it—he was stunning. He had black hair and eyes the color of the blueberries that grew in my parents' garden—almost purple in a certain light, and translucent the next moment. He could have sliced me wide open with his smile. He was wearing a white coat and a denim collared shirt with a tie that had Barbie dolls all over it.

He probably had a real live one of those at home, too—a 38-22-36 fiancée who had double-majored in law and medicine, or astrophysics and political science.

Our whole relationship was over, and I hadn't even said a word to him.

"You *are* Ms. Bloom?"

How had I not noticed that British accent? "Yes," I said, wishing I was anyone *but.*

"I'm Dr. Gallagher," he said, sitting down on a stool. "Why don't you tell me what's been going on?"

"Well," I began. "Actually, I'm fine."

"For the record, appendicitis rates as pretty ill."

Ill. I loved that. I bet he said things like *flat* and *loo* and *lift,* too.

"Let's just check you out," he said. He stood and hooked his stethoscope into his ears, then settled it under my shirt. I couldn't remember the last time a guy had slipped his hand under my shirt. "Just breathe," he said.

Yeah, right.

"Really," I said. "I'm not sick."

"If you could just lie back . . . ?"

That was enough to bring me crashing down to reality. Not only would he realize, the moment he palpated my stomach, that I didn't have appendicitis . . . he'd also probably be able to tell that I had the two-donut combo at Dunkin' Donuts for breakfast, when everyone knows they take three days—*each*—to digest.

"I don't have appendicitis," I blurted out. "I just told the nurse I did because I wanted to talk to a doctor for a few minutes—"

"All right," he said gently. "I'm just going to call in Dr. Tawasaka. I'm sure she'll talk to you all you like . . ." He stuck his head out the door. "Sue? Page psych . . ."

Oh, excellent, now he thought I had a mental health problem. "I don't need a psychiatrist," I said. "I'm an attorney and I need a medical consultation about a client."

I hesitated, expecting him to call in security, but instead he sat down and folded his arms. "Go on."

"Do you know anything about heart transplants?"

"A bit. But I can tell you right now that if your client requires one, he'll have to register with UNOS and get in line like everyone else . . ."

"He doesn't need a heart. He wants to *donate* one."

I watched his face transform as he realized that my client had to be the death row inmate. There just weren't a lot of prisoners in New Hampshire clamoring to be organ donors these days. "He's going to be executed," Dr. Gallagher said.

"Yes. By lethal injection."

"Then he won't be able to donate his heart. A heart donor has to be brain-dead; lethal injection causes cardiac death. In other words, once your client's heart stops beating during that execution, it's not going to work in someone else."

I knew this; Father Michael had *told* me this, but I hadn't wanted to believe it.

"You know what's interesting?" the doctor said. "I believe it's potassium that's used in lethal injection—the chemical that stops the heart. That's the same chemical we use in cardioplegia solution, which is perfused into the donor heart just prior to sewing it into the patient. It keeps the heart arrested while it's not receiving a normal blood flow, until all the suturing's finished." He looked up at me. "I don't suppose the prison would agree to a surgical cardiectomy—a heart removal—as a method of execution?"

I shook my head. "The execution has to happen within the walls of the prison."

He shrugged. "I cannot believe I'm saying

this, but it's too bad that they don't use a firing squad anymore. A well-placed shot could leave an inmate a perfect organ donor. Even hanging would work, if one could hook up a respirator after brain death was confirmed." He shuddered. "Pardon me. I'm used to saving patients, not theoretically killing them."

"I understand."

"Then again, even if he *could* donate his heart, chances are it would be too large for a child's body. Has anyone addressed that yet?"

I shook my head, feeling even worse about Shay's odds.

The doctor glanced up. "The bad news, I'm afraid, is that your client is out of luck."

"Is there any good news?"

"Of course." Dr. Gallagher grinned. "You don't have appendicitis, Ms. Bloom."

"Here's the thing," I said to Oliver when I had gotten us enough Chinese takeout to feed a family of four (you could keep the leftovers, and Oliver really did like vegetable moo shu, even if my mother said that rabbits didn't eat real food). "It's been sixty-nine years since anyone's been executed in the state of New Hampshire. We're assuming that lethal injection is the only method, but that doesn't mean we're right."

I picked up the carton of lo mein and spooled the noodles into my mouth. "I know it's here somewhere," I muttered as the rabbit hopped across another stack of legal texts scattered on the floor of the living room. I was not in the habit of reading the New Hampshire Criminal Code; going through the sections and subsections was like navigating through molasses. I'd turn back a page, and the spot I'd been reading a moment before would disappear in the run of text.

Death.
Death penalty.
Capital murder.
Injection, lethal.
630:5 (XXIII). When the penalty of death is imposed, the sentence shall be that the defendant is imprisoned in the state prison at Concord until the day appointed for his execution, which shall not be within

one year from the day sentence is passed.

Or in Shay's case, eleven *years*.

The punishment of death shall be inflicted by continuous, intravenous administration of a lethal quantity of an ultra-short-acting barbiturate in combination with a chemical paralytic agent until death is pronounced by a licensed physician according to accepted standards of medical practice.

Everything I knew about the death penalty I had learned at the ACLU. Prior to working there, I hadn't given the death penalty much thought, beyond when someone was executed and the media made a huge story out of it. Now I knew the names of those who were killed. I heard about their last-minute appeals. I knew that, after death, some inmates were found to be innocent.

Lethal injection was supposed to be like putting a dog to sleep—a drowsiness overcame you, and then you just never woke up. No pain, no stress. It was a cocktail of three drugs: Sodium Pentothal, a sedative to put the inmate to sleep; Pavulon, to paralyze the muscular system and stop breathing; and potassium chloride, to stop the heart. The Sodium Pentothal was ultra-short-acting— which meant that you could recover quickly from its effects. It also meant that a subject might have feeling in his nerves, yet be just sedated enough to be unable to communicate or move.

The British medical journal the Lancet published a 2005 study of the toxicology reports of forty-nine executed inmates in four U.S. states; forty-three of the inmates had a level of anesthesia lower than required for surgery, and twenty-one had levels that would indicate awareness. Anesthesiologists say that if a person were conscious at the time potassium chloride is administered, it would feel like boiling oil in the veins. An inmate might feel as if he were being burned alive from the inside, but be unable to move or speak because of the muscle paralysis and minimal sedation caused by the other two drugs. The Supreme Court had even had its doubts: although they still ruled that capital punishment was constitutional, they'd halted executions of two inmates on a narrower issue: whether the excessive pain caused by lethal injection was a civil rights infraction that could be argued in a lower court.

Or—to put it simply—lethal injection might not be as humane as everyone wanted to believe.

630:5 (XIV). The commissioner of corrections or his designee shall determine the substance or substances to be used and the procedures to be used in any execution, provided, however, that if for any reason the commissioner finds it to be impractical to carry out the punishment of death by administration of the required lethal substance or substances, the sentence of death may be carried out by hanging under the provisions of law for the death penalty by hanging in effect on December 31, 1986.

Oliver settled on my lap as I read the words again.

Shay didn't have to be executed by lethal injection, if I could make the commissioner—

or a court—find it impractical. If you coupled that with the RLUIPA—the law that said a prisoner's religious freedoms had to be protected in prison—and if I could prove that part of Shay's belief system for redemption included organ donation, then lethal injection *was* impractical.

In which case, Shay would be hanged.

And—here was the *real* miracle—according to Dr. Gallagher, that meant Shay Bourne *could* donate his heart.

Lucius

The day the priest returned, I was working on pigments. My favorite substance was tea—it made a stain you could vary in intensity from an almost white to a yellowish brown. M&M's were vibrant, but they were the hardest to work with—you had to moisten a Q-tip and rub it over the surface of the M&M, you couldn't just soak off the pigment like I was doing this morning with Skittles.

I set my jar lid on the table and added about fifteen drops of warm water. The green Skittle went in next, and I rolled it around with my finger, watching the food dye coating come off. The trick here was to pull the candy out just as I started to see the white sugar beneath the coating—if the sugar melted into the paint, it wouldn't work as well.

I popped the bleached button of candy into my mouth—I could do that these days, now that the thrush was gone. As I sucked on it, I poured the contents of the lid (green, like the grass I had not walked on with my bare feet in years; like the color of a jungle; like Adam's eyes) into an aspirin bottle for safekeeping. Later, I could vary the pigment with a dab of white toothpaste, diluted with water to make the right hue.

It was a laborious process, but then again . . . I had time.

I was just about to repeat the endeavor with a yellow jawbreaker—the yield of paint was four times as much as a Skittle—when Shay's priest walked up to my cell door in his flak jacket. I had, of course, seen the priest briefly the day he first visited Shay, but only at a distance. Now, with him directly in front of my cell door, I could see that he was younger than I would have expected, with hair that seemed decidedly un-priestlike and eyes as soft as gray flannel. "Shay's getting his hair cut," I said, because it was barber day, and that's where he had been taken about ten minutes before.

"I know, Lucius," the priest said. "That's why I was hoping to talk to you."

Let me tell you, the last thing I wanted to do was chat with a priest. I hadn't asked for one, certainly, and in my previous experience, the clergy only wanted to give a lecture on how being gay was a choice, and how God loved me (but not my pesky habit of falling in love with other men). Just because Shay had come back to his cell convinced that his new team—some lawyer girl and this priest—were going to move mountains for him didn't mean that I shared his enthusiasm. In spite of the fact that he'd been incarcerated for eleven years, Shay was still the most naive inmate I'd ever met. Just last night, for example, he'd had a fight with the correctional officers because it was laundry day and they'd brought new sheets, which Shay refused to put on the bed. He said he could feel the bleach, and instead insisted on sleeping on the floor of the cell.

"I appreciate you seeing me, Lucius," the priest said. "I'm happy to hear you're feeling better these days."

I stared at him, wary.

"How long have you known Shay?"

I shrugged. "Since he was put in the cell next to me a few weeks ago."

"Was he talking about organ donation then?"

"Not at first," I said. "Then he had a seizure and got transferred to the infirmary. When he came back, donating his heart was all he could talk about."

"He had a seizure?" the priest repeated, and I could tell this was news to him. "Has he had any more since then?"

"Why don't you just ask Shay these questions?"

"I wanted to hear what you had to say."

"What you want," I corrected, "is for me to tell you whether or not he's really performing miracles."

The priest nodded slowly. "I guess that's true."

Some had already been leaked to the press; I imagined the rest would be brought to light sooner or later. I told him what I'd seen with my own eyes, and by the time I was finished, Father Michael was frowning slightly. "Does he go around saying he's God?"

"No," I joked. "That would be Crash."

"Lucius," the priest asked, "do *you* believe Shay is God?"

"You need to back up, Father, because I don't believe in God. I quit around the same time one of your esteemed colleagues told me that AIDS was my punishment for sinning." To be honest, I had split religion along the seam of secular and nonsecular; choosing to concentrate on the beauty of a Caravaggio without noticing the Madonna and child; or finding the best lamb recipe for a lavish Easter dinner, without thinking about the Passion. Religion gave hope to people who knew the end wasn't going to be pretty. It was why inmates started praying in prison and why patients started praying when the doctors said *terminal*. Religion was supposed to be a blanket drawn up to your chin to keep you warm, a promise that when it came to the end, you wouldn't die alone—but it could just as easily leave you shivering out in the cold, if *what* you believed became more important than the fact *that* you believed.

I stared at him. "I don't believe in God. But I do believe in Shay."

"Thank you for your time, Lucius," the priest said softly, and he walked down the tier.

He may have been a priest, but he was looking for his miracles in the wrong place.

That day with the gum, for example. I had seen the coverage on the news—it was reported that Shay had somehow taken one tiny rectangle of Bazooka gum and multiplied it. But ask someone who'd been there—like me, or Crash, or Texas—and you'd know there weren't suddenly seven pieces of bubble gum. It was more like this: when the piece was fished underneath our cell doors, instead of taking as much as we could, we made do with less instead.

The gum was magically replicated. But we—the blatantly greedy—balanced the needs of the other seven guys and in that instant found them just as worthy as our own.

Which, if you asked me, was an even greater miracle.

MICHAEL

The Holy Father has an entire office at the Vatican devoted to analyzing alleged miracles and passing judgment on their authenticity. They scrutinize statues and busts, scrape Crisco out of the corners of supposedly bleeding eyes, track scented oil on walls that emit the smell of roses. I was nowhere as experienced as those priests, but then again, there was a crowd of nearly five hundred people outside the state prison calling Shay Bourne a savior—and I wasn't going to let people give up on Jesus that easily.

To that end, I was now ensconced in a lab on the Dartmouth campus, with a graduate student named Ahmed who was trying to explain to me the results of the test he'd run on the soil sample taken from the vicinity of the pipes that ran into I-tier. "The reason the prison couldn't get a conclusive explanation is because they were looking *in* the pipes, not *outside* them," Ahmed said. "So the water tested positive for something that looked like alcohol, but only in certain pipes. And you'll never guess what's growing near those pipes: rye."

"Rye? Like the grain?"

"Yeah," Ahmed said. "Which accounts for the concentration of ergot into the water. It's a fungal disease of rye. I'm not sure what brings it on—I'm not a botanist—but I bet it had something to do with the amount of rain we've had, and there was a hairline crack in the piping they found when they first investigated, which accounts for the transmission in the first place. Ergot was the first kind of chemical warfare. The Assyrians used it in the seventh century B.C. to poison water supplies." He smiled. "I double-majored in chemistry and ancient history."

"It's deadly?"

Ahmed shrugged. "In repeated doses. But at first, it's a hallucinogen that's related to LSD."

"So, the prisoners on I-tier might not have been drunk . . ." I said carefully.

"Right," Ahmed replied. "Just tripping."

I turned over the vial with the soil sample. "You think the water got contaminated?"

"That would be my bet."

But Shay Bourne, in prison, would not have been able to know that there was a fungus growing near the pipes that led into I-tier, would he?

I suddenly remembered something else: the following morning, those same inmates on I-tier had ingested the same water and had not acted out of the ordinary. "So how did it get uncontaminated?"

"Now that," Ahmed said, "I haven't quite figured out."

"There are a number of reasons that an advanced AIDS patient with a particularly low CD4 count and high viral load might suddenly appear to get better," Dr. Perego said. An autoimmune disease specialist at Dartmouth-Hitchcock Medical Center, he also served as the doctor for HIV/AIDS patients at the state prison and knew all about Lucius and his recovery. He didn't have time for a formal talk, but was perfectly willing to chat if I wanted to walk with him from his office to a meeting at the other end of the hospital—as long as I realized that he couldn't violate doctor-patient confidentiality. "If a patient is hoarding meds, for example, and suddenly decides to start taking them, sores will disappear and health will improve. Although we draw blood every three months from AIDS patients, sometimes we'll get a guy who refuses to have his blood drawn—and again, what looks like sudden improvement is actually a slow turn for the better."

"Alma, the nurse at the prison, told me Lucius hasn't had his blood drawn in over six months," I said.

"Which means we can't be quite sure what his recent viral count was." We had reached the conference room. Doctors in white coats milled into the room, taking their seats. "I'm not sure what you wanted to hear," Dr. Perego said, smiling ruefully. "That he's special . . . or that he's not."

"I'm not sure either," I admitted, and I shook his hand. "Thanks for your time."

The doctor slipped into the meeting, and I started back down the hall toward the parking garage. I was waiting at the elevator, grinning down at a baby in a stroller with a patch over her right eye, when I felt a hand on my shoulder. Dr. Perego was standing there. "I'm glad I caught you," he said. "Have you got a moment?"

I watched the baby's mother push the stroller onto the yawning elevator. "Sure."

"This is what I didn't tell you," Dr. Perego said. "And you didn't hear it from me."

I nodded, understanding.

"HIV causes cognitive impairment—a permanent loss of memory and concentration. We can literally see this on an MRI, and DuFresne's brain scan showed irreparable damage when he first entered the state prison. However, another MRI brain scan was done on him yesterday—and it shows a reversal of that atrophy." He looked at me, waiting for this to sink in. "There's no physical evidence of dementia anymore."

"What could cause that?"

Dr. Perego shook his head. "Absolutely nothing," he admitted.

The second time I went to meet with Shay Bourne, he was lying on his bunk, asleep. Not wanting to disturb him, I started to back away, but he spoke to me without opening his eyes. "I'm awake," he said. "Are you?"

"Last time I checked," I answered.

He sat up, swinging his legs over the side of his bunk. "Wow. I dreamed that I was struck by lightning, and all of a sudden I had the power to locate anyone in the world, anytime. So the government cut a deal with me—find bin Laden, and you're free."

"I used to dream that I had a watch, and turning the hands could take you backward in time," I said. "I always wanted to be a pirate, or a Viking."

"Sounds pretty bloodthirsty for a priest."

"Well, I wasn't born with a collar on."

He looked me in the eye. "If I could turn back time, I'd go out fly-fishing with my grandfather."

I glanced up. "I used to do that with my grandfather, too."

I wondered how two boys—like Shay and me—could begin our lives at the same point and somehow take turns that would lead us to be such different men. "My grandfather's been gone a long time, and I still miss him," I admitted.

"I never met mine," Shay said. "But I must have had one, right?"

I looked at him quizzically. What kind of life had he suffered, to have to craft memories from his imagination? "Where did you grow up, Shay?" I asked.

"The light," Shay replied, ignoring my question. "How does a fish know where it is? I mean, things shift around on the floor of the ocean, right? So if you come back and everything's changed, how can it really be the place you were before?"

The door to the tier buzzed, and one of the officers came down the catwalk, carrying a metal stool. "Here you go, Father," he said, settling it in front of Shay's cell door. "Just in case you want to stay awhile."

I recognized him as the man who had sought me out the last time I'd been here, talking to Lucius. His baby daughter had been critically ill; he credited Shay with her recovery. I thanked him, but waited until he'd left to talk to Shay again.

"Did you ever feel like that fish?"

Shay looked at me as if I were the one who couldn't follow a linear conversation. "*What* fish?" he said.

"Like you can't find your way back home?"

I knew where I was heading with this topic—straight to true salvation—but Shay took us off course. "I had a bunch of houses, but only one home."

He'd been in the foster care system; I remembered that much from the trial. "Which place was that?"

"The one where my sister was with me. I haven't seen her since I was sixteen. Since I got sent to prison."

I remembered he'd been sent to a juvenile detention center for arson, but I hadn't remembered anything about a sister.

"Why didn't she come to your trial?" I asked, and realized too late that I had made a grave mistake—that there was no reason for me to know that, unless I had been there.

But Shay didn't notice. "I told her to stay away. I didn't want her to tell anyone what I'd done." He hesitated. "I want to talk to her."

"Your sister?"

"No. She won't listen. The other one. She'll hear me, after I die. Every time her daughter speaks." Shay looked up at me. "You know how you said you'd ask her if she wants the heart? What if I asked her myself?"

Getting June Nealon to come visit Shay in prison would be like moving Mt. Everest to Columbus, Ohio. "I don't know if it will work . . ."

But then again, maybe seeing June face-to-face would make Shay see the difference between personal forgiveness and divine forgiveness. Maybe putting the heart of a killer into the chest of a child would show—literally—how good might blossom from bad. And the beat of Claire's pulse would bring June more peace than any prayer I could offer.

Maybe Shay *did* know more about redemption than I.

He was standing in front of the cinderblock wall now, trailing his fingertips over the cement, as if he could read the history of the men who'd lived there before him.

"I'll try," I said.

There was a part of me that knew I should tell Maggie Bloom that I had been on the jury that convicted Shay Bourne. It was one thing to keep the truth from Shay; it was another to compromise whatever legal case Maggie was weaving together. On the other hand, it was up to me to make sure that Shay found peace with God before his death. The minute I told Maggie about my past involvement with Shay, I knew she'd tell me to get lost, and would find him another spiritual advisor the judge couldn't find fault with. I had prayed long and hard about this, and for now, I was keeping my secret. God wanted me to help Shay, or so I told myself, because it kept me from admitting that *I* wanted to help Shay, too, after failing him the first time.

The ACLU office was above a printing shop and smelled like fresh ink and toner. It was filled with plants in various stages of dying, and filing cabinets took up most of the floor space. A paralegal sat at a reception desk, typing so furiously that I almost expected her computer screen to detonate. "How can I help," she said, not bothering to look up.

"I'm here to see Maggie Bloom."

The paralegal lifted her right hand, still typing with her left, and hooked a thumb overhead and to the left. I wound down the hallway, stepping over boxes of files and stacks of newspapers, and found Maggie sitting at her desk, scribbling on a legal pad. When she saw me, she smiled. "Listen," she said, as if we were old friends. "I have some fantastic news. I think Shay can be hanged." Then she blanched. "I didn't mean fantastic news, really. I meant . . . well, you know what I meant."

"Why would he want to do that?"

"Because then he can donate his heart." Maggie frowned. "But first we need to get the prison to agree to send him for tests, to make sure it's not too big for a kid—"

I drew in my breath. "Look. We need to talk."

"It's not often I get a priest who wants to confess."

She didn't know the half of it. *This is not about you*, I reminded myself, and firmly settled Shay in the front of my mind. "Shay wants to be the one to ask June Nealon if she'll take his heart. Unfortunately, visiting him is not on her top-ten list of things to do. I want to know if there's some kind of court-ordered mediation we can ask for."

Maggie raised a brow. "Do you really think he's the best person to relay this information to her? I don't see how that will help our case . . ."

"Look, I know you're doing your job," I said, "but I'm doing mine, too. And saving Shay's soul may not be important to you, but it's critical to me. Right now, Shay thinks that donating his heart is the only way to save himself—but there's a big difference between mercy and salvation."

Maggie folded her hands on her desk. "Which is?"

"Well, June can forgive Shay. But only God

can redeem him—and it has nothing to do with giving up his heart. Yes, organ donation would be a beautiful, selfless final act on earth—but it's not going to cancel out his debt with the victim's family, and it's not necessary to get him special brownie points with God. Salvation's not a personal responsibility. You don't have to *get* salvation. You're *given* it, by Jesus."

"So," she said. "I guess you don't think he's the Messiah."

"No, I think that's a pretty rash judgment."

"You're preaching to the choir. I was raised Jewish."

My cheeks flamed. "I didn't mean to suggest—"

"But now I'm an atheist."

I opened my mouth, snapped it shut.

"Believe me," Maggie said, "I'm the last person in the world to buy into the belief that Shay Bourne is Jesus incarnate—"

"Well, of *course* not—"

"—but not because a messiah wouldn't inhabit a criminal," she qualified. "I can tell you right now that there are plenty of innocent people on death row in this country."

I wasn't about to tell her that I knew Shay Bourne was guilty. I had studied the evidence;

I had heard the testimony; I had convicted him. "It's not that."

"Then how can you be so sure he's not who everyone thinks he is?" Maggie asked.

"Because," I replied, "God only had one son to give us."

"Right. And—correct me if I'm wrong—he was a thirty-three-year-old carpenter with a death sentence on his head, who was performing miracles left and right. Nah, you're right. That's *nothing* like Shay Bourne."

I thought of what I'd heard from Ahmed and Dr. Perego and the correctional officers. Shay Bourne's so-called miracles were nothing like Jesus's . . . or were they? Water into wine. Feeding many with virtually nothing. Healing the sick. Making the blind—or in Calloway's case, the prejudiced—see.

Like Shay, Jesus didn't take credit for his miracles. Like Shay, Jesus had known he was going to die. And the Bible even said Jesus *was* supposed to be returning. But although the New Testament is very clear about this coming to pass, it is a bit muddier on the details: the when, the why, the how.

"He's not Jesus."

"Okey-dokey."

"He's *not*," I pressed.

Maggie held up her hands. "Got it."

"If he was Jesus . . . if this was the Second Coming . . . well, there'd be rapture and destruction and resurrections and we wouldn't be sitting here having a normal conversation."

Then again, there was nothing in the Bible that said *before* the Second Coming, Jesus wouldn't pop in to see how things were going here on earth.

I suppose in that case, it would make sense to be incognito—to pose as the least likely person anyone would ever assume to be the Messiah.

For the love of God, what was I *thinking*? I shook my head, clearing it. "Let him meet with June Nealon once before you petition for organ donation, that's all I'm asking. I want the same things you do—Shay's voice to be heard, a little girl to be saved, and capital punishment to be put in the hot seat. I just also want to make sure that if and when Shay does donate his heart, he does it for all the right reasons. And that means untangling Shay's spiritual health from the whole legal component of this mess."

"I can't do that," Maggie said. "It's the crux

of my case. Look, it doesn't matter to me whether you think Shay is Jesus or Shay thinks Shay is Jesus or if he's just plain off his rocker. What does matter is that Shay's rights don't get shuffled aside in the grand mechanism of capital punishment—and if I have to use the fact that other people seem to think he's God to do it, I will."

I raised a brow. "You're using Shay to spotlight an issue you find reprehensible, in the hopes that you can change it."

"Well," Maggie said, coloring, "I guess that's true."

"Then how can you criticize me for having an agenda because of what *I* believe in?"

Maggie raised her gaze and sighed. "There's something called restorative justice," she said. "I don't know if the prison will even allow it, much less Shay or the Nealons. But it would let Shay sit down in a room with the family of his victims and ask for forgiveness."

I exhaled the breath I had not even realized I was holding. "Thank you," I said.

Maggie picked up her pen and began to write on the legal pad again. "Don't thank me. Thank June Nealon—if you get her to agree to it."

Motivated, I started out of the ACLU office, then paused. "It's the right thing to do."

Maggie didn't look up. "If June won't meet with him," she said, "I'm still filing the suit."

June

||||||||||||||||||||||||||||||||||||||||||||||||||||||||||||||||||||||||||||||||||||||||||||||||||||||

At first, when the victim's assistance advocate asked me if I'd attend a restorative justice meeting with Shay Bourne, I started to
laugh. "Yeah," I said. "And maybe after that,
I could get dunked in boiling oil or drawn and
quartered."

But she was serious, and I was just as serious when I refused. The last thing in the
world I wanted to do was sit down with that
monster to make him feel better about himself so that he could die at peace.

Kurt didn't. Elizabeth didn't. Why should
he?

I thought that was that, until one morning

when there was a knock on the door. Claire was lying on the couch with Dudley curled over her feet, watching the Game Show Network. Our days were spent waiting for a heart with the shades drawn, both of us pretending there was nowhere we wanted to go, when in reality, neither of us could stand seeing how even the smallest trips exhausted Claire. "I'll get it," she called out, although we both knew she couldn't and wouldn't. I put down the knife I was using to chop celery in the kitchen and wiped my hands on my jeans.

"I bet it's that creepy guy who was selling magazines," Claire said as I passed her.

"I bet it's not." He'd been a corn-fed Utah boy, pitching subscriptions to benefit the Church of Jesus Christ of Latter-Day Saints. I'd been upstairs in the shower; Claire had been talking to him through the screen door— for which I'd read her the riot act. It was that word *Saints* that had intrigued her; she didn't know it was a fancy word for Mormon. I had suggested that he try a town where there hadn't been a double murder committed by a young man who'd come around door to door looking for work, and after he left, I'd called the police.

No, I was sure it wasn't the same guy.

To my surprise, though, a priest was standing on my porch. His motorcycle was parked in my driveway. I opened the door and tried to smile politely. "I think you have the wrong house."

"I'm sure I don't, Ms. Nealon," I replied. "I'm Father Michael, from St. Catherine's. I was hoping I could speak to you for a few minutes."

"I'm sorry . . . do I know you?"

He hesitated. "No," he said. "But I was hoping to change that."

My natural inclination was to slam the door. (Was that a mortal sin? Did it matter, if you didn't even believe in mortal sins?) I could tell you the exact moment I had given up on religion. Kurt and I had been raised Catholic. We'd had Elizabeth baptized, and a priest presided over their burials. After that, I had promised myself I would never set foot in a church again, that there was nothing God could do for me that would make up for what I'd lost. However, this priest was a stranger. For all I knew, though, this was not about saving my soul but about saving Claire's life. What if this priest knew of a heart that UNOS didn't?

"The house is a mess," I said, but I opened

the door so that he could walk inside. He stopped as we passed the living room, where Claire was still watching television. She turned, her thin, pale face rising like a moon over the back of the sofa. "This is my daughter," I said as I turned to him, and faltered— he was looking at Claire as if she were already a ghost.

I was just about to throw him out when Claire said hello and propped her elbows on the back of the sofa. "Do you know anything about saints?"

"Claire!"

She rolled her eyes. "I'm just *asking*, Mom."

"I do," the priest said. "I've always sort of liked St. Ulric. He's the patron saint who keeps moles away."

"Get *out*."

"Have you ever had a mole in here?"

"No."

"Then I guess he's doing his job," he said, and grinned.

Because he'd made Claire smile, I decided to let him in and give him the benefit of the doubt. He followed me into the kitchen, where I knew we could talk without Claire overhearing. "Sorry about the third degree," I said.

"Claire reads a lot. Saints are her latest obsession. Six months ago, it was blacksmithing." I gestured to the table, offering him a seat.

"About Claire," he said. "I know she's sick. That's why I'm here."

Although I'd hoped for this, my own heart still leapfrogged. "Can you help her?"

"Possibly," the priest said. "But I need you to agree to something first."

I would have become a nun; I would have walked over burning coals. "Anything," I vowed.

"I know the prosecutor's office already asked you about restorative justice—"

"Get out of my house," I said abruptly, but Father Michael didn't move.

My face flamed—with anger, and with shame that I had not connected the dots: Shay Bourne wanted to donate his organs; I was actively searching for a heart for Claire. In spite of all the news coverage from the prison, I had never linked them. I wondered whether I had been naive, or whether, even subconsciously, I'd been trying to protect my daughter.

It took all my strength to lift my gaze to the priest's. "What makes you think I would want a part of that man still walking around on this earth, much less inside my child?"

"June—please, just listen to me. I'm Shay's spiritual advisor. I talk to him. And I think you should talk to him, too."

"Why? Because it rubs your conscience the wrong way to give sympathy to a murderer? Because you can't sleep at night?"

"Because I think a good person can do bad things. Because God forgives, and I can't do any less."

Do you know how, when you are on the verge of a breakdown, the world pounds in your ears—a rush of blood, of consequence? Do you know how it feels when the truth cuts your tongue to ribbons, and still you have to speak it? "Nothing he says to me could make any difference."

"You're absolutely right," Father Michael said. "But what *you* say to *him* might."

There was one variable that the priest had left out of this equation: I owed Shay Bourne nothing. It already felt like a second, searing death to watch the broadcasts each night, to hear the voices of supporters camping out near the prison, who brought their sick children and their dying partners along to be healed. *You fools*, I wanted to shout to them.

Don't you know he's conned you, just like he conned me? Don't you know that he killed my love, my little girl? "Name one person John Wayne Gacy killed," I demanded.

"I . . . I don't know," Father Michael said.

"Jeffrey Dahmer?"

He shook his head.

"But you remember *their* names, don't you?"

He got out of his chair and walked toward me slowly. "June, people can change."

My mouth twisted. "Yeah. Like a mild-mannered, homeless carpenter who becomes a psychopath?"

Or a silver-haired fairy of a girl whose chest, in a heartbeat, blooms with a peony of blood. Or a mother who turns into a woman she never imagined being: bitter, empty, broken.

I knew why this priest wanted me to meet with Shay Bourne. I knew what Jesus had said: *Don't pay back in kind, pay back in kindness. If someone does wrong to you, do right by them.*

I'll tell you this: Jesus never buried his own child.

I turned away, because I didn't want to give him the satisfaction of seeing me cry, but he put his arm around me and led me to a chair. He handed me a tissue. And then his voice, a murmur, clotted into individual words.

"Dear St. Felicity, patron saint of those who've suffered the death of a child, I ask for your intercession that the Lord will help this woman find peace . . ."

With more strength than I knew I had, I shoved him away. "Don't you dare," I said, my voice trembling. "Don't you pray for me. Because *if* God's listening now, he's about eleven years too late." I walked toward the refrigerator, where the only decoration was a picture of Kurt and Elizabeth, held up by a magnet Claire had made in kindergarten. I had fingered the photo so often that the edges had rounded; the color had bled onto my hands. "When it happened, everyone said that Kurt and Elizabeth were at peace. That they'd gone *someplace better.* But you know what? They didn't *go* anywhere. They were *taken.* I was *robbed.*"

"Don't blame God for that, June," Father Michael said. "He didn't take your husband and your daughter."

"No," I said flatly. "That was Shay Bourne." I stared up at him coldly. "I'd like you to leave now."

I walked him to the door, because I didn't want him saying another word to Claire—who twisted around on the couch to see what was going on but must have picked up enough nonverbal cues from my stiff spine to know better than to make a peep. At the threshold, Father Michael paused. "It may not be *when* we want, or *how* we want, but eventually God evens the score," he said. "You don't have to be the one to seek revenge."

I stared at him. "It's not revenge," I said. "It's justice."

After the priest left, I was so cold that I could not stop shivering. I put on a sweater and then another, and wrapped a blanket around myself, but there's no way of warming up a body whose insides have turned to stone.

Shay Bourne wanted to donate his heart to Claire so that she'd live.

What kind of mother would I be if I let that happen?

And what kind of mother would I be if I turned him down?

Father Michael said Shay Bourne wanted to balance the scales: give me one daughter's life because he had taken another's. But

Claire wouldn't replace Elizabeth; I should have had them both. And yet, this was the simplest of equations: *You can have one, or you can have neither. What do you choose?*

I was the one who hated Bourne—Claire had never met him. If I did not take the heart, was I making that choice because of what I thought was best for Claire . . . or what I could withstand myself?

I imagined Dr. Wu removing Bourne's heart from an Igloo cooler. There it was, a withered nut, a crystal black as coal. Put one drop of poison into the purest water, and what happens to the rest?

If I didn't take Bourne's heart, Claire would most likely die.

If I did, it would be like saying I could somehow be compensated for the death of my husband and daughter. And I couldn't—not ever.

I believe a good person can do bad things, Father Michael had said. Like make the wrong decision for the right reasons. Sign your daughter's life away, because she can't have a murderer's heart.

Forgive me, Claire, I thought, and suddenly I wasn't cold anymore. I was burning, seared by the tears on my cheeks.

I couldn't trust Shay Bourne's sudden altruistic turnaround; and maybe that meant he had won: I had gone just as bitter and rotten as he was. But that only made me more certain that I had the stamina to tell him, face-to-face, what balancing the scales really meant. It wasn't giving me a heart for Claire; it wasn't offering a future that might ease the weight of the past. It was knowing that Shay Bourne badly wanted something, and that this time, I'd be the one to take *his* dream away.

Maggie

|||||||||||||||||||||||||||||||||||||||||||||||||||||||||||||||||||||||||||||||||||||||||||||||||||||||||||||||

Stunned, I hung up the phone and stared at the receiver again. I was tempted to *69 the call, just to make sure it hadn't been some kind of prank.

Well, maybe miracles *did* happen.

But before I could mull over this change of events, I heard footsteps heading toward my desk. Father Michael turned the corner, looking like he'd just been through Dante's Inferno. "June Nealon wants nothing to do with Shay."

"That's interesting," I said, "since June Nealon just got off the phone with me, agreeing to a restorative justice meeting."

Father Michael blanched. "You've got to call her back. This isn't a good idea."

"*You're* the one who came up with it."

"That was before I spoke to her. If she goes to that meeting, it's not because she wants to hear what Shay has to say. It's because she wants to run him through before the state finishes him off."

"Did you really think that whatever Shay has to say to her is going to be any less painful than what she says to him?"

"I don't know . . . I thought that maybe if they saw each other . . ." He sank down into a chair in front of my desk. "I don't know what I'm doing. I guess there are just some things you can't make amends for."

I sighed. "You're trying. That's the best any of us can do. Look, it's not like I fight death penalty cases all the time—but my boss used to. He worked down in Virginia before he came up north. They're emotional minefields—you get to know the inmate, and you excuse some heinous crime with a lousy childhood or alcoholism or an emotional upheaval or drugs, until you see the victim's family and a whole different level of suffering. And suddenly you start to feel a little ashamed of being in the defendant's camp."

I walked to a small cooler next to a file cabinet and took out a bottle of water for the priest. "Shay's guilty, Father. A court already told us that. June knows it. I know it. Everyone knows that it's wrong to execute an innocent man. The real question is whether it's still wrong to execute someone who's guilty."

"But you're trying to get him hanged," Father Michael said.

"I'm not trying to get him hanged," I corrected. "I want to champion his civil liberties, and at the same time, bring front and center what's wrong with the death penalty in this country. The only way to do both is to find a way for him to die the way *he* wants to. That's the difference between you and me. You're trying to find a way for him to die the way *you* want him to."

"You're the one who said Shay's heart might not be a viable match. And even if it is, June Nealon will never agree to taking it," the priest said.

That was, of course, entirely possible. What Father Michael had conveniently put out of his mind when he dreamed up a meeting between June and Shay was that in order to forgive, you have to remember how you were hurt in the first place. And that in order to forget, you had to accept your role in what had happened.

"If we don't want Shay to lose hope," I said, "then we'd better not lose it either."

MICHAEL

|||||||||||||||||||||||||||||||||||||||||||||||||||||||||||||||||||||||||||||||||||||||||||||||||||||||||||||||||||||||||||||||

Every day when I wasn't running the noon Mass, I went to visit Shay. Sometimes we talked about television shows we'd seen—we were both pretty upset with Meredith on *Grey's Anatomy*, and thought the girls on *The Bachelor* were hot but dumb as bricks. Sometimes we talked about carpentry, how a piece of wood would tell him what it needed to be, how I could say the same of a parishioner in need. Sometimes we talked about his case—the appeals he'd lost, the lawyers he'd had over the years. And sometimes, he was less lucid. He'd run around his cell like a caged animal; he'd rock back and forth; he'd swing from topic to topic as if it was the only way to cross the jungle of his thoughts.

One day, Shay asked me what was being said about him outside.

"You know," I told him. "You watch the news."

"They think I can save them," Shay said.

"Well. Yeah."

"That's pretty fucking selfish, isn't it? Or is it selfish of me if I don't try?"

"I can't answer that for you, Shay," I said.

He sighed. "I'm tired of waiting to die," he said. "Eleven years is a long time."

I pressed my stool up close to the cell door; it was more private that way. It had taken me a week, but I had managed to separate out the way I felt about Shay's case from the way that he felt. I had been stunned to learn that Shay believed he was innocent—although Warden Coyne told me that everyone in prison believed they were innocent, regardless of the conviction. I wondered if his memory of the events, over time, had blurred—me, I could still remember that awful evidence as if it had been presented to me yesterday. When I pushed a bit—encouraged him to tell me more about his wrongful conviction, suggested that Maggie might be able to use the information in court, asked him why he was willing to go along with an execution so passively if he wasn't guilty—he shut down. He'd say, over and over, that what had happened then didn't matter now. I began to understand that proclaiming his innocence had a lot less to do with the reality of his case and more to do with the fragile connection between us. I was becoming his confidant—and he wanted me to think the best of him.

"What do you think is easier?" Shay asked. "Knowing you're going to die on a certain date and time, or knowing it might happen any moment when you least expect it?"

A thought swam through my mind like a minnow: *Did you ask Elizabeth that?* "I'd rather not know," I said. "Live every day like it's your last, and all that. But I think if you *do* know you're going to die, Christ showed the way to do it with grace."

Shay smirked. "Just think. It took you a whole forty-two minutes to bring up good ol' Jesus today."

"Sorry. Professional hazard," I said. "When He says, in Gethsemane, '*O my Father, if it be possible, let this cup pass from me . . .*'

He's wrestling with destiny . . . but ultimately, He accepts God's will."

"Sucks for him," Shay said.

"Well, sure. I bet His legs felt like Jell-O when He was carrying the Cross. He was human, after all. You can be brave, but that doesn't keep your stomach from doing somersaults."

I finished speaking to find Shay staring at me. "Did you ever wonder if you're dead wrong?"

"About what?"

"All of it. What Jesus said. What Jesus meant. I mean, he didn't even write the Bible, did he? In fact, the people who *did* write the Bible weren't even alive when Jesus was." I must have looked absolutely stricken, because Shay hurried to continue. "Not that Jesus wasn't a really cool guy—great teacher, excellent speaker, yadda yadda yadda. But . . . Son of God? Where's the proof?"

"That's what faith is," I said. "Believing without seeing."

"Okay," Shay argued. "But what about the folks who think Allah's the one to put your money on? Or that the right path is the eightfold one? I mean, how can a guy who walked on water even get *baptized*?"

"We know Jesus was baptized be-cause—"

"Because it's in the Bible?" Shay laughed. "Someone wrote the Bible, and it wasn't God. Just like someone wrote the Quran, and the Talmud. And he must have made decisions about what went in and what didn't. It's like when you write a letter, and you put in all the stuff you did during vacation but you leave out the part where your wallet got stolen and you got food poisoning."

"Do you really need to know if Jesus got food poisoning?" I asked.

"You're missing the point. You can't take Matthew 26:39 or Luke 500:43 or whatever and read it as fact."

"See, Shay, that's where you're wrong. I *can* take Matthew 26:39 and know it's the word of God. Or Luke 500:43, if it went up that high."

By now, other inmates on the pod were eavesdropping. Some of them—like Joey Kunz, who was Greek Orthodox, and Po-gie, who was Southern Baptist—liked to listen when I visited Shay and read scrip-ture; a few of them had even asked if I'd stop by and pray with them when I came in to see Shay. "Shut your piehole, Bourne,"

Pogie yelled out. "You're going to hell as soon as they push that needle in your arm."

"I'm not saying I'm right," Shay said, his voice escalating. "I'm just saying that if *you're* right, it still doesn't mean *I'm* wrong."

"Shay," I said, "you have to stop shouting, or they're going to ask me to leave."

He walked toward me, flattening his hands on the other side of the steel mesh door. "What if it didn't matter if you were a Christian or a Jew or a Buddhist or a Wiccan or a . . . a transcendentalist? What if all those roads led to the same place?"

"Religion brings people together," I said.

"Yeah, right. You can track every polarizing issue in this country to religion. Stem cell research, the war in Iraq, the right to die, gay marriage, abortion, evolution, even the death penalty—what's the fault line? That Bible of yours." Shay shrugged. "You really think Jesus would be happy with the way the world's turned out?"

I thought of suicide bombers, of the radicals who stormed into Planned Parenthood clinics. I thought of the news footage of the Middle East. "I think God would be horrified by some of the things that are done in His name," I admitted. "I think there are places His message has been distorted. Which is why I think it's even more important to spread the one He meant to give."

Shay pushed away from the cell door. "You look at a guy like Calloway—"

"Fuck you, Bourne," Reece called out. "I don't want to be part of your speech. I don't even want your filthy-ass mouth speaking my name—"

"—an AB guy, who burned down a temple—"

"You're dead, Bourne," Reece said. "D-E-A-D."

"—or the CO who walks you to the shower and knows he can't look you in the eye, because if his life had gone just a little different, he might be the one wearing the cuffs. Or the politicians who think that they can take someone they don't really want in society anymore and lock him away—"

At this, the other inmates began to cheer. Texas and Pogie picked up their dinner trays and began to bang them against the steel doors of their cells. On the intercom, an officer's voice rang through. "What's going on in there?"

Shay was standing at the front of his

house now, preaching to his congregation, disconnected from linear thought and everything but his moment of grandstanding. "And the ones who are really monsters, the ones they don't ever want walking around near their wives and children again—the ones like *me*—well, those they get to dispose of. Because it's easier than admitting there isn't much difference between them and me."

There were catcalls; there were cheers. Shay backed up as if he were on a stage, bent at the waist, bowed. Then he came back for his encore.

"The joke's on them. One little hypodermic won't be enough. Split a piece of wood, and they'll find me. Lift up a stone, and they'll find me. Look in the mirror, and they'll find me." Shay gazed squarely at me. "If you really want to know what makes someone a killer," he said, "ask yourself what would make *you* do it."

My hands tightened on the Bible I always brought when I came to visit Shay. As it turned out, Shay wasn't railing about nothing. He wasn't disconnected from reality.

That would have been me.

Because, as Shay was suggesting, we

weren't as different as I would have liked to think. We were both murderers.

The only distinction was that the death I'd caused had yet to happen.

Maggie

||||||||||||||||||||||||||||||||||||||||||||||||||||||||||||||||||||||||||||||||||||||||||||||||||||||||||||||||||

That week, when I showed up at the ChutZ-
pah for lunch with my mother, she was too
busy to see me. "Maggie," she said when I
was standing at the threshold of her office
door. "What are you doing here?"

It was the same day, the same time, we
met for our habitual lunch—the same lunch I
never wanted to go to. But today, I was actually looking forward to zoning out while my
cuticles were being cut and shaped. Ever
since Father Michael had barreled into my
office talking about a meeting between Shay
and June Nealon, I'd been doubting myself
and my intentions. By trying to make it pos-

sible for Shay to donate his heart, was I carrying out what was in his best interests, or my own? Sure, it would be a media boon for the anti–death penalty movement if Shay's last act on earth was as selfless as organ donation . . . but wasn't it morally wrong to try to legally hasten a man's execution, even if it was what he'd asked for? After three sleepless nights, all I wanted was to close my eyes, soak my hands in warm water, and think of anything *but* Shay Bourne.

My mother was wearing a cream-colored skirt so tiny it might as well have come from the American Girl doll store, and her hair was twisted up in a chignon. "I have an investor coming in," she said. "Remember?"

What I remembered was her vague mention of adding another wing to the ChutZpah. And that there was some very rich lady from Woodbury, New York, who wanted to talk about financing it.

"You never told me it was going to be today," I said, and I sank down in one of the chairs opposite her desk.

"You're crushing the pillows," my mother said. "And I *did* tell you. I called you at work, and you were typing, like you always do when I call even though you think I can't hear it in

the background. And I told you I had to post-
pone lunch till Thursday, and you yessed me
and said you were really busy, and did I have
to call you at work?"

My face flushed. "I don't type while I'm on
the phone with you."

Okay, I do. But it's my mother. And she
calls for the most ridiculous reasons: Is it
okay if she makes Chanukah dinner on Saturday, December 16, never mind that it's
currently March? Do I remember the name
of the librarian in my elementary school,
because she thinks she ran into her at the
grocery store? In other words, my mother
phones for reasons that are completely
trivial compared to writing up a brief to save
the life of a man who's going to be executed.

"You know, Maggie, I realize that nothing I
do here could possibly be as important as
what *you* do, but it does hurt me to know that
you don't even listen when I talk to you." Her
eyes were tearing up. "I can't believe you
came here to upset me before I have to sit
down with Alicia Goldman-Hirsch."

"I didn't come here to upset you! I came
here because I always come here the second Tuesday of every month! You can't blame

me because of a stupid phone conversation we probably had six months ago!"

"A stupid phone conversation," my mother said quietly. "Well, it's good to know what you really think of our relationship, Maggie."

I held up my hands. "I can't win here," I said. "I hope your meeting goes well." Then I stormed out of her office, past the white secretary's desk with the white computer and the nearly albino receptionist, all the way to my car in the parking lot, where I tried to tell myself that the reason I was crying had nothing to do with the fact that even when I wasn't trying, all I did was let people down.

I found my father in his office—a rental space in a strip mall, since he was a rabbi without a temple—writing his sermon for Shabbat. As soon as I walked in, he smiled, then lifted a finger to beg a moment's time to finish whatever brilliant thought he was scribbling down. I wandered around, trailing my fingers over the spines of books written in Hebrew and Greek, Old Testaments and New Testaments, books on theurgy and theology and philosophy. I palmed an old paperweight I'd made him in nursery school—a rock painted to look like a crab, although now it seemed to more closely resemble an amoeba, and then took down one of my baby photos, tucked in an acrylic frame.

I had fat cheeks, even then.

My father closed his laptop. "To what do I owe this surprise?"

I set the photo back on the mahogany shelf. "Did you ever wonder if the person in the picture is the same one you see when you look in the mirror?"

He laughed. "That's the eternal question, isn't it? Are we born who we are, or do we make ourselves that way?" He stood up and came around his desk, kissed my cheek. "Did you come here to argue philosophy with your old man?"

"No, I came here because . . . I don't know why I came here." That was the truth; my car had sort of pointed itself in the direction of his office, and even when I realized where it was headed I didn't correct my course. Everyone else came to my father when they were troubled or wanted counseling, why shouldn't I? I sank down onto the old leather couch that he'd had for as long as I could remember. "Do you think God forgives murderers?"

My father sat down next to me. "Isn't your client Catholic?"

"I was talking about me."

"Well, gosh, Mags. I hope you got rid of the weapon."

I sighed. "Daddy, I don't know what to do. Shay Bourne doesn't want to become the poster child against capital punishment, he *wants* to die. And yeah, I can tell myself a dozen times that we can both have our cake and eat it, too—Shay gets to die on his own terms; I get the death penalty put under a microscope and maybe even repealed by the Supreme Court—but it doesn't cancel out the fact that at the end of the day, Shay will be dead, and I'll be just as responsible as the state that signed the warrant in the first place. Maybe I should be trying to convince Shay to get his conviction overturned, to fight for his life, instead of his death."

"I don't think he'd want that," my father said. "You're not murdering him, Maggie. You're fulfilling his last wishes—to help him make amends for what he's done wrong."

"Repentance through organ donation?"

"More like *teshuvah*."

I stared at him.

"Oh, right," he smirked. "I forgot about the post–Hebrew School amnesia. For Jews, repentance is about conduct—you realize you've done something wrong, you resolve to change it in the future. But *teshuvah* means *return*. Inside each of us is some spark of God—the real us. It's there whether you're the most pious Jew or the most marginal. Sin, evil, murder—all those things have the ability to cover up our true selves. *Teshuvah* means turning back to the part of God that's gotten concealed. When you repent, usually, you feel sad—because of the regret that led you there. But when you talk about *teshuvah,* about making that connection with God again—well, it makes you happy," my father said. "Happier even than you were before, because your sins separated you from God . . . and distance always makes the heart grow fonder, right?"

He walked toward the baby picture I'd put back on the shelf. "I know Shay's not Jewish, but maybe that's what's at the root of this desire to die, and to give up his heart. *Teshuvah* is all about reaching for something divine— something beyond the limitations of a body." He glanced at me. "That's the answer to your question about the photo, by the way. You're a different person on the outside than you were when this picture was snapped, but not on the inside. Not at the *core*. And not only is that part of you the same as it was when you were six months old . . . it's also the same as me and your mother and Shay Bourne and everyone else in this world. It's the part of us that's connected to God, and at that level, we're all identical."

I shook my head. "Thanks, but that didn't really make me feel any better. I want to save him, Daddy, and he—he doesn't want that at all."

"Restitution is one of the steps a person has to take for *teshuvah,*" my father said. "Shay has apparently taken a very literal interpretation of this—he took a child's life; therefore he owes that mother the life of a child."

"It's not a perfect equation," I said. "He'd have to bring Elizabeth Nealon back for that."

My father nodded. "That's something rabbis have talked about for years since the Holocaust —if the victim is dead, does the family really have the power to forgive the killer? The victims are the ones with whom he has to make amends. And those victims—they're ashes."

I sat up, rubbing my temples. "It's really complicated."

"Then ask yourself what's the right thing to do."

"I can't even answer that much."

"Well," my father said, "then maybe you should ask Shay."

I blinked up at him. It was that simple. I hadn't seen my client since that first meeting in the prison; the work I'd been doing to set up a restorative justice meeting had been on the phone. Maybe what I really needed was to find out why Shay Bourne was so sure he'd come to the right decision, so that I could start explaining it to myself.

I leaned over and gave him a hug. "Thanks, Daddy."

"I didn't do anything."

"Still, you're a better conversationalist than Oliver."

"Don't tell the rabbit that," he said. "He'd scratch me twice as hard as he already does."

I stood up, heading for the door. "I'll call you later. Oh, and by the way," I said, "Mom's mad at me again."

I was sitting under the harsh fluorescent lights of the attorney-client conference room when Shay Bourne was brought in to meet with me. He backed up to the trap so that his handcuffs could be removed, and he sat down across the table. His hands were small, I realized, maybe even smaller than mine.

"How's it going?" he asked.

"Fine. How's it going with you?"

"No, I meant my lawsuit. My heart."

"Well, we're waiting until after you speak to June Nealon tomorrow." I hesitated. "Shay, I need to ask you a question, as your lawyer." I waited until he looked me in the eye. "Do you really believe that the only way to atone for what you've done is to die?"

"I just want to give her my heart—"

"I get that. But in order to do that, you've basically agreed to your own execution."

He smiled faintly. "And here I thought my vote didn't count."

"I think you know what I mean," I said. "Your case is going to shine a beacon on the issue of capital punishment, Shay—but you'll be the sacrificial lamb."

His head snapped up. "Who do you think I am?"

I hesitated, not quite sure what he was asking.

"Do you believe what they all believe?" he

asked. "Or what Lucius believes? Do you think I can make miracles happen?"

"I don't believe anything I haven't seen," I said firmly.

"Most people just want to believe what someone else tells them," Shay said.

He was right. It was why, in my father's office, I'd had a breakdown: because even as a confirmed atheist, I sometimes found it just too frightening to think that there might not be a God who was watching out for our greater good. It was why a country as enlightened as the United States could still have a death penalty statute in place: it was just too frightening to think about what justice—or lack of it—would prevail if we didn't. There was comfort in facts, so much so that we stopped questioning where those facts had come from.

Was I trying to figure out who Shay Bourne was for myself? Probably. I didn't buy the fact that he was the Son of God, but if it was getting him media attention, then I thought he was brilliant for encouraging that line of thought. "If you can get June to forgive you at this meeting, Shay, maybe you don't have to give up your heart. Maybe you'll feel good about connecting with her again, and then we can get her to talk to the governor on your behalf to commute your sentence to life in prison—"

"If you do that," Shay interrupted, "I will kill myself."

My jaw dropped. "Why?"

"Because," he said, "I have to get out of here."

At first I thought that he was talking about the prison, but then I saw he was clutching his own arms, as if the penitentiary he was referring to was his own body. And that, of course, made me think of my father and *teshuvah*. Could I truly be helping him by letting him die on his own terms?

"Let's take it one step at a time," I conceded. "If you can get June Nealon to understand why you want to do this, then I'll work on making a court understand it, too."

But Shay was suddenly lost in his thoughts, wherever they happened to be taking him. "I'll see you tomorrow, Shay," I said, and I went to touch his shoulder to let him know I was leaving. As soon as I stretched out my arm, though, I found myself flat on the floor. Shay stood over me, just as shocked by the blow he'd dealt me as I was.

An officer bolted into the room, driving

Shay down to the floor with a knee in the small of his back so that he could be hand-cuffed. "You all right?" he called out to me.

"I'm fine . . . I just slipped," I lied. I could feel a welt rising on my left cheekbone, one that I was sure the officer would see as well. I swallowed the knot of fear in my throat. "Could you just give us a couple more minutes?"

I did not tell the officer to remove Shay's handcuffs; I wasn't quite that brave. But I struggled to my feet and waited until we were alone in the room again. "I'm sorry," Shay blurted out. "I'm sorry, I didn't mean it, I some-times, when you . . ."

"Shay," I ordered. "Sit down."

"I didn't mean to do it. I didn't see you coming. I thought you were—would—" He broke off, choking on the words. "I'm sorry."

I was the one who'd made the mistake. A man who had been locked up alone for a decade, whose only human contact was hav-ing his handcuffs chained and removed, would be completely unprepared for a small act of kindness. He would have instinctively seen it as a threat to his personal space, which was how I'd wound up sprawled on the floor.

"It won't happen again," I said.

He shook his head fiercely. "No."

"See you tomorrow, Shay."

"Are you mad at me?"

"No."

"You are. I can tell."

"I'm not," I said.

"Then will you do something for me?"

I had been warned about this by other attorneys who worked with inmates: they will bleed you dry. Beg you for stamps, for money, for food. For phone calls, made by you to their family, on their behalf. They are the ultimate con artists; no matter how much sympathy you feel for them, you have to remind yourself that they will take whatever they can get, because they have nothing.

"Next time, will you tell me what it feels like to walk barefoot on grass?" he asked. "I used to know, but I can't remember anymore." He shook his head. "I just want to . . . I want to know what that's like again."

I folded my notebook beneath my arm. "I'll see you tomorrow, Shay," I repeated, and I motioned to the officer who would set me free.

MICHAEL

Shay Bourne was pacing in his cell. Every fifth turn, he pivoted and started circling the other way. "Shay," I said, to calm myself down as much as him, "it's going to be all right."

We were awaiting his transportation down to the room where our restorative justice meeting with June Nealon would take place, and we were both nervous.

"Talk to me," Shay said.

"All right," I said. "What do you want to talk about?"

"What I'm going to say. What *she's* going to say . . . the words won't come out right, I just know it." He looked up at me. "I'm going to fuck this up."

"Just say what you need to, Shay. Words are hard for everyone."

"Well, it's worse when you know the person you're talking to thinks you're full of shit."

"Jesus managed to do it," I pointed out, "and it wasn't like He was attending the Tuesday Toastmasters meeting in Nineveh." I opened my Bible to the book of Isaiah. "The Spirit of the Lord is on me, because he has anointed me to preach good news . . ."

"Could we just this once *not* have a Bible study moment?" Shay groaned.

"It's an example," I said. "Jesus said that when He came back to the synagogue where He'd grown up. Let me tell you, that congregation had a lot of questions—after all, they'd grown up with Him, and knew Him before He started the miracle train—so before they could doubt Him, what did He do? He gave them the words they'd been waiting to hear. He gave them hope." I looked at Shay. "That's what you need to do, with June."

The door to I-tier opened, and six officers in flak jackets and full face shields entered. "Don't talk until the mediator asks you to.

And make sure you tell her why this is so important to you," I urged, last-minute quarterbacking.

Just then the first officer reached the cell door. "Father," he said, "we're going to have to ask you to meet us down there."

I watched them move Shay down the tier. *Speak from your heart*, I thought, watching him go. *So that she knows it's worth taking.*

I had already been told what they would do with him. He'd be handcuffed and cuffed at the ankles. Both of these would be linked to a belly chain, so that he'd shuffle along inside the human box of officers. He would be taken to the cafeteria, which was now set up for offender counseling. Basically, the warden had explained, when they needed to have group sessions with violent offenders, they bolted several individual metal boxes to the floor—and prisoners were put into these miniature cells along with a counselor, who would sit on a chair in the cafeteria with them. "It's group therapy," Warden Coyne had proudly explained, "but they're still incarcerated."

Maggie had lobbied for a face-to-face visit. Failing that, she wanted to know if we could meet on opposite sides of a glass visiting booth. But there were too many of us, when you added in the moderator and June, or so the administration said (never mind I'd seen families of ten cram into one of those little noncontact booths for a visit with an inmate). Although I—like Maggie—thought that we were starting at a grave disadvantage if one of the participants was restrained and bolted to the floor like Hannibal Lecter, this was the best we were going to get.

The mediator was a woman named Abigail Herrick, who'd come from the attorney general's victim's assistance office and had been trained to do this kind of thing. She and June were talking quietly on one side of the anteroom. I walked up to June as soon as I entered. "Thank you. This means a lot to Shay."

"Which is the last reason I'd ever do it," June said, and she turned back to Abigail.

I slunk across the room to the seat beside Maggie. She was painting a run in her stocking with pink nail polish. "We are in serious trouble," I said.

"Yeah? How's he doing?"

"He's panicked." I squinted in the dim light as she lifted her head. "How'd you get that shiner?"

"In my spare time I'm the welterweight champion of New Hampshire."

There was a buzzing, and Warden Coyne walked in. "Everything's set."

He led us into the cafeteria by way of the metal detector. Maggie and I had already emptied our pockets and taken off our jackets before June and Abigail even realized what was going on; this is the difference between someone who has intimate experience with a detention facility and those who lead normal lives. An officer, still dressed in full riot gear, opened a door for June, who continued to stare at him in horror as she walked inside.

Shay was sitting in what looked like a telephone booth permanently sealed shut with nuts and bolts and metal. Bars vivisected his face; his eyes searched for mine as soon as I walked into the room. When he saw us, he stood up.

At that moment, June froze.

Abigail took her arm and led her to one of the four chairs that were arranged in a semicircle in front of the booth. Maggie and I filled in the remaining seats. Two officers stood behind us; in the distance I could hear the sizzle of something cooking on a grill.

"Well. Let's get started," Abigail said, and she introduced herself. "Shay, I'm Abigail Herrick. I'm going to be the mediator today. Do you understand what that means?"

He hesitated. He looked like he was going to faint.

"Victim-offender mediation is a process that gives a victim the chance to meet her offender in a safe and structured setting," Abigail explained. "The victim will be able to tell the offender about the crime's physical, emotional, and financial impact. The victim also has the chance to receive answers to any lingering questions about the crime, and to be directly involved in trying to develop a plan for the offender to pay back a debt if possible—emotional or monetary. In return, the offender gets the opportunity to take responsibility for his behavior and actions. Everyone with me so far?"

I started to wonder why this wasn't used for every crime committed. Granted, it was labor-intensive for both the AG's office and the prison, but wasn't it better to come face-to-face with the opposing party, instead of having the legal system be the intermediary?

"Now, the process is strictly voluntary. That

means if June wants to leave at any time, she should feel free to do so. But," Abigail added, "I also want to point out that this meeting was initiated by Shay, which is a very good first step."

She glanced at me, at Maggie, and then at June, and finally Shay. "Right now, Shay," Abigail said, "you need to listen to June."

June

They say you get over your grief, but you don't really, not ever. It's been eleven years, and it hurts just as much as it did that first day.

Seeing his face—sliced into segments by those metal bars, like he was some kind of Picasso portrait that couldn't be put together again—brought it all back. That face, his *fucking* face, was the last one Kurt and Elizabeth saw.

When it first happened, I used to make bargains with myself. I'd say that I could handle their deaths, as long as—and here I'd fill in the blank. As long as they had been quick and painless. As long as Elizabeth had died in Kurt's arms. I'd be driving, and I'd tell myself that if the light turned green before I reached the intersection, surely these details were true. I did not admit that sometimes I slowed down to stack the odds.

The only reason I was able to drag myself out of bed at all those first few months was because there was someone more needy than I was. As a newborn, Claire didn't have a choice. She had to be fed and diapered and held. She kept me so grounded in the present that I had to let go of my hold on the past. I credit her with saving my life. Maybe that's why I am so determined to reciprocate.

But even having Claire to care for was not foolproof. The smallest things would send me into a downward spiral: while pressing seven birthday candles into her cake, I'd think of Elizabeth, who would have been fourteen. I'd open a box in the garage and breathe in the scent of the miniature cigars Kurt liked to smoke every now and then. I'd open up a pot of Vaseline and see Elizabeth's tiny fingerprint, preserved on the surface. I would pull a book off a shelf and a shopping list would flutter out of it, in Kurt's handwriting: *thumbtacks, milk, rock salt.*

What I would like to tell Shay Bourne about the impact this crime had on my family is that it erased my family, period. What I would like to do is bring him back to the moment Claire, four, perched on the stairs to stare at a picture of Elizabeth and asked where the girl who looked like her lived. I would like him to know what it feels like to have to run your hand up the terrain of your own body, and underneath your nightshirt, only to realize that you cannot surprise yourself with your own touch.

I would like to show him the spot in the room he built, Claire's old nursery, where there is a bloodstain on the floorboards that I cannot scrub clean. I'd like to tell him that even though I carpeted the room years ago and turned it into a guest bedroom, I still do not walk across it, but instead tiptoe around the perimeter when I have to go inside.

I would like to show him the bills that came from the hospital every time Claire was sent there, which quickly consumed the money we received from the insurance company after Kurt died. I'd like him to come with me to the bank, the day I broke down in front of the teller and told her that I wanted to liquidate the college fund of Elizabeth Nealon.

I would like to feel that moment when Elizabeth was sitting in my lap and I was reading to her, and she went boneless and soft, asleep in my arms. I would like to hear Kurt call me Red again, for my hair, and tangle his fingers in it as we watch television in the bedroom at night. I would like to pick up the dirty socks that Elizabeth strewed about the house, a tiny tornado, the same reason I once yelled at her. I would love to fight with Kurt over the size of the MasterCard bill.

If they had to die, I would have loved to have known in advance, so that I could take each second spent with them and know to hold on to it, instead of assuming there would be a million more. If they had to die, I would have loved to have been there, to be the last face they saw, instead of his.

I would like to tell Shay Bourne to go to hell, because wherever he winds up after he dies, it had better not be anywhere close to my daughter and my husband.

Michael

|||||||||||||||||||||||||||||||||||||||||||||||||||||||||||||||||||||||||||||||||||||||||||||||||||||||||||||||||||||||||||||||||||||||||||

"Why?" June Nealon asked. Her voice was striped with rust and sorrow, and in her lap, her hands twisted. "Why did you do it?" She lifted her gaze, staring at Shay. "I let you into my home. I gave you a job. I *trusted* you. And you, you took everything I had."

Shay's mouth was working silently. He moved from side to side in his little booth, hitting his forehead sometimes. His eyes fluttered, as if he was trying hard to organize what he had to say. "I can fix it," he said finally.

"You can't fix anything," she said tightly.

"Your other little girl—"

June stiffened. "Don't you talk about her. Don't you even breathe her name. Just tell me. I've waited eleven years to hear it. Tell me why you did this."

He squeezed his eyes shut; sweat had broken out on his brow. He was whispering, a litany meant to convince himself, or maybe June. I leaned forward, but the noise from the kitchen obliterated his words. And then whatever had been sizzling was taken off the grill, and we all heard Shay, loud and clear: "She was better off dead."

June shot to her feet. Her face was so pale that I feared she would fall over, and I rose just in case. Then blood rushed, hot, into her cheeks. "You bastard," she said, and she ran outside.

Maggie tugged on my jacket. "Go," she mouthed.

I followed June past the two officers and through the anteroom. She burst through the double doors and into the parking lot without even bothering to pick up her driver's license at the control booth, trading back her visitor's pass. I was certain she would rather go to the DMV and pay for a replacement than set foot in this prison again.

"June," I yelled. "Please. Wait."

I finally cornered her at her car, an old Ford Taurus with duct tape around the rear bumper. She was sobbing so hard that she couldn't get the key into the lock.

"Let me." I opened the door and held it for her so that she could sit down, but she didn't. "June, I'm sorry—"

"How could he say that? She was a little girl. A beautiful, smart, perfect little girl."

I gathered her into my arms and let her cry on my shoulder. Later, she would regret doing this; later, she would feel that I had manipulated the situation. But for right now, I held her until she could catch her breath.

Redemption had very little to do with the big picture, and far more to do with the particulars. Jesus might forgive Shay, but what good was that if Shay didn't forgive himself? It was that impetus that drove him to give up his heart, just as I was driven to help him do it because it would cancel out my vote to execute him in the first place. We couldn't erase our mistakes, so we did the next best thing and tried to do something that distracted attention from them.

"I wish I could have met your daughter," I said softly.

June pulled away from me. "I wish you could have, too."

"I didn't ask you here to hurt you all over again. Shay truly does want to make amends. He knows the one good thing to come out of his life might be his death." I looked at the Constantine wire running along the top of the prison fence: a crown of thorns for a man who wanted to be a savior. "He's taken away the rest of your family," I said. "If nothing else, let him help you keep Claire."

June ducked into her car. She was crying again as she lurched out of the parking spot. I watched her pause at the exit of the prison, her blinker marking time.

Then, suddenly, her brake lights came on. She sped backward, stopping beside me with only inches to spare. She unrolled the window on the driver's side. "I'll take his heart," June said, her voice thick. "I'll take it, and I'll watch that son of a bitch die, and we *still* won't be even."

Too stunned to find any words, I nodded. I watched June drive off, her taillights winking as red as the eyes of any devil.

Maggie

"Well," I said when I saw Father Michael walking back into the prison, dazed, "that sucked."

At the sound of my voice, he looked up. "She's taking the heart."

My mouth dropped open. "You're kidding."

"No. She's taking it for all the wrong reasons . . . but she's taking it."

I could not believe it. Following the debacle in the restorative justice meeting, I would have more easily accepted that she'd gone out to buy an Uzi to exact her own justice against Shay Bourne. My mind began to kick into high gear: if June Nealon wanted Shay's heart—for whatever reason—then there was a great deal I had to do.

"I'll need you to write an affidavit, saying that you're Shay's spiritual advisor and that his religious beliefs include donating his heart."

He drew in his breath. "Maggie, I can't put my name on a court document about Shay—"

"Sure you can. Just lie," I said, "and go to confession afterward. You're not doing this for you; you're doing it for Shay. And we'll need a cardiologist to examine Shay, to see if his heart's even a match for Claire."

The priest closed his eyes and nodded. "Should I go in and tell him?"

"No," I said, smiling. "Let me."

After a slight detour, I walked through the metal detectors again and was taken to the attorney-client room outside I-tier. A few minutes later, a grumbling officer showed up with Shay. "He keeps getting moved around like this, the state's going to have to hire him a chauffeur."

I rubbed my thumb and forefinger together, the world's smallest violin.

Shay ran his hands through his hair, making it stand on end; the shirt of his prison scrubs was untucked. "I'm sorry," he said immediately.

"I'm not the one who could have used the apology," I replied.

"I know." He squinched his eyes shut, shook his head. "There were eleven years of words in my head, and I couldn't get them out the way I wanted."

"Amazingly, June Nealon is willing to accept your heart for Claire."

A few times in my career, I'd been the messenger of information that would change a client's life: the victim of a hate crime whose store was destroyed, receiving reparation and damages that would allow him to build a bigger, better venue; the gay couple who were given the legal stamp of approval to be listed as parents in the elementary school directory. A smile blossomed across Shay's face, and I remembered, at that moment, that *gospel* is another word for good news.

"It's not a done deal yet," I said. "We don't know, medically, if this is viable. And there are a whole bunch of legal hoops to jump through . . . which is what I need to talk to you about, Shay."

I waited until he sat down across from me at the table, and was calm enough to stop grinning and look me in the eye. I had gotten to this point with clients before: you drew them a map and explained where the exit hatch was, and then you waited to see if they understood you needed them to crawl there on their own. That was legitimate, in law; you were not telling them to alter their truth, just explaining the way the courts worked, and hoping they would choose to massage it themselves. "Listen carefully," I said. "There's a law in this country that says the state has to let you practice your own religion, as long as it doesn't interfere with safety in the prison. There's also a law in New Hampshire that says even though the court has sentenced you to die by lethal injection, which wouldn't allow you to donate your heart . . . in certain circumstances, death row inmates can be hanged instead. And if you're hanged, you'd be able to donate your organs."

It was a lot for him to take in, and I could see him ingesting the words as if they were being fed on a conveyor.

"I might be able to convince the state to hang you," I said, "if I can prove to a judge in federal court that donating your organs is part of your religion. Do you understand what I'm saying?"

He winced. "I didn't like being Catholic."

"You don't have to say you're Catholic."

"Tell that to Father Michael."

"Gladly." I laughed.

"Then what *do* I have to say?"

"There are a lot of people outside this prison, Shay, who have no trouble believing that what you're doing in here has some sort of religious basis. But I need you to believe it, too. If this is going to work, *you* have to tell me donating your organs is the only way to salvation."

He stood up and started to pace. "My way of saving myself may not be someone else's way."

"That's okay," I said. "The court doesn't care about anyone else. They just want to know if *you* think that giving your heart to Claire Nealon is going to redeem you in God's eyes."

When he stopped in front of me and caught my eye, I saw something that surprised me. Because I had been so busy crafting an escape hatch for Shay Bourne, I had forgotten that sometimes the outrageous is actually the truth. "I don't think it," he said. "I *know* it."

"Then we're in business." I slipped my hands into my suit pockets and suddenly remembered what else I had to tell Shay. "It's prickly," I said. "Like walking on a board full of needles. But somehow it doesn't hurt. It smells like Sunday morning, like a mower outside your window when you're trying to pretend the sun's not up yet."

As I spoke, Shay closed his eyes. "I think I remember."

"Well," I said. "Just in case you don't." I withdrew the handfuls of grass I'd torn from outside the prison grounds and sprinkled the tufts onto the floor.

A smile broke over Shay's face. He kicked off his prison-issued tennis shoes and began to move back and forth, barefoot, over the grass. Then he bent down to gather the cuttings and funneled them into the breast pocket of his scrubs, against a heart that was still beating strong. "I'm going to save them," he said.

|||||||||||||||||||||||||||||||||||||||||||||||||||||||||||||||||||||||||||||||||||||||||||

"I know God will not give me anything
I can't handle.
I just wish He didn't trust me so much."

—*MOTHER TERESA*

June

Everything comes with a price.

You can have the man of your dreams, but only for a few years.

You can have the perfect family, but it turns out to be an illusion.

You can keep your daughter alive, but only if she hosts the heart of the person you hate most in this world.

I could not go straight home from the prison. I was shaking so hard that at first, I couldn't even drive; and even afterward, I missed the exit off the highway twice. I had gone to that meeting to tell Shay Bourne we didn't want his heart. So why had I changed my mind? Maybe because I was angry. Maybe because I was so shocked by what Shay Bourne had said. Maybe because if we waited for UNOS to find Claire a heart, it could be too late.

Besides, I told myself, this was all likely a moot point. The chance of Bourne even being a good physical match for Claire was negligible; his heart was probably far too large for a child's body; there could be all sorts of compromising diseases or long-term drug use that would prohibit him from being a donor.

And yet, there was another part of me that kept thinking: *But what if?*

Could I let myself hope? And could I stand it if, once again, that hope was shattered by Shay Bourne?

By the time I felt calm enough to drive home and face Claire, it was late at night. I had arranged for a neighbor to check on her hourly throughout the afternoon and evening, but Claire flatly refused a formal babysitter. She was fast asleep on the couch, the dog curled over her feet. Dudley lifted his head when I walked in, a worthy sentry. *Where were you when Elizabeth was taken?*

I thought, not for the first time, rubbing Dudley between the ears. For days after the murders, I had held the puppy, staring into his eyes and pretending he could give me the answers I so desperately needed.

I turned off the television that was chattering to nobody and sat down beside Claire. If she received Shay Bourne's heart, would I look at my daughter but see him staring back at me?

Could I survive that?

And if I couldn't . . . would Claire survive at all?

I fitted myself around Claire's body, stretching beside her on the couch. In her sleep, she curled against me, a puzzle piece fitting back where it belonged. I kissed my daughter's forehead, unconsciously reading it for fever. This was my life now, and Claire's: a waiting game. Like Shay Bourne sitting in his cell, waiting for his turn to die, we sat imprisoned by the limitations of Claire's body, waiting for her turn to live.

So don't judge me, unless you've fallen asleep on a couch with your ill child, thinking this night might be her last.

Ask instead: would you do it?

Would you give up your vengeance against someone you hate if it meant saving someone you love?

Would you want your dreams to come true if it meant granting your enemy's dying wish?

Maggie

In school, I was the kind of kid who crossed her *t*'s and dotted her *i*'s. I made sure to right-justify my papers, so that the type didn't look ragged. I'd craft elaborate covers—a tiny, two-dimensional working guillotine for my essay on *A Tale of Two Cities*; a science lab on prisms with the header rainbowed in multiple colors; a scarlet letter for . . . well, you get the picture.

To that end, putting together a letter to the commissioner of corrections reminded me a little of my days as a student. There were multiple parts involved: the transcript of Shay Bourne attesting that he wanted to donate his heart to the sister of his victim; an affidavit from Claire Nealon's cardiac surgeon, stating that she did indeed need a heart to survive. I had made a call to facilitate a medical visit for Shay, to see if he was a match for Claire; and I had spent an hour on the phone with a UNOS coordinator, to confirm that if Shay gave up his heart, he could pick the recipient. I fastened all these letters together with a shiny silver butterfly clip and then turned back to the computer to finish my note to Commissioner Lynch.

As evidenced by the letter from the defendant's spiritual advisor, Father Michael Wright, execution by lethal injection will not only prevent the defendant from his intention of donating his heart to Claire Nealon—it also interferes with his practice of religion—a blatant violation of his First Amendment rights. Therefore, under the New Hampshire criminal code 630:5, subsection XIV, it would be impractical for the commissioner of corrections to carry out the punishment

of death by lethal injection. A sentence of death carried out by hanging, however, would not only be allowed by the criminal code, but also would allow the defendant to practice his religion up to the moment of his execution.

I could imagine, at this moment, the commissioner's jaw dropping as he realized that I had managed to piece together two disparate laws in a way that would make the next few weeks a living hell.

Furthermore, this office would be pleased to work in conjunction with the commissioner of corrections to facilitate what needs to be done, as there are tissue matches and medical testing to be completed prior to the donation, and because time is of the essence during the organ harvest.

Not to mention—I don't trust you.

It is imperative to settle this matter swiftly, for obvious reasons.

We don't have a lot of time to work this out. Because neither Shay Bourne nor Claire Nealon have a lot of time left, period.

Sincerely,
Maggie Bloom, Attorney

I printed out the letter and slipped it into a manila envelope I'd already addressed. As I licked the envelope, I thought: *Please make this work.*

Who was I talking to?

I didn't believe in God. Not anymore.

I was an atheist.

Or so I told myself, even if there was a secret part of me that hoped I'd be proven wrong.

Lucius

||||||||||||||||||||||||||||||||||||||||||||||||||||||||||||||||||||||||||||||||||||||||||||||||||||||||||||||||||

People always think they know what they'd miss the most if they had to trade places with me in this cell. Food, fresh air, your favorite pair of jeans, sex—believe me, I've heard them all, and they're all wrong. What you miss the most in prison is choice. You have no free will: your hair is cut in one style, like everyone else's. You eat what's being served when it is given to you. You are told when you can shower, shit, shave. Even our conversations are prescribed: If someone bumps into you in the real world, he says "Excuse me." If someone bumps into you in here, you say "What the fuck, motherfucker" before he

can even speak. If you *don't* do this, you become a mark.

The reason we have no choice now is because we made a bad one in the past—
which is why we were all energized by Shay's
attempt to die on his own terms. It was still
an execution, but even that tiny sliver of pref-
erence was more than we had on a daily
basis. I could only imagine how my world
would change if we were given an option to
choose between orange scrubs and yellow
ones; if we were asked whether we'd like a
spoon or a fork with our meal trays, instead
of the universal plastic "spork." But the more
animated we got at the possibility of, well,
possibility . . . the more depressed Shay
grew.

"Maybe," he said to me one afternoon
when the air-conditioning had broken and we
were all wilting in our cells, "I should just let
them do what they want."

The officers, in an act of mercy, had
opened the door that led to the exercise cell.
It was supposed to afford us a breeze, but
that hadn't happened. "Why would you say
that?"

"Because it feels like I've started a war,"
Shay said.

"Well, imagine that," Crash laughed. "Since I'm over here practicing my shooting."

This afternoon Crash had been injecting Benadryl. Many of the inmates here had made their own points—homemade hypodermics that could be sharpened every few uses by scraping them against a matchbook. Benadryl was given out by the prison nurse; you could accumulate a stash and open up a capsule, then cook down the tiny beads of medicine in a spoon over a soda-can stove. It was a speed high, but the buffers used in the medicine would also make you crazy.

"Whaddya say, Mistah Messiah . . . you want a hit?"

"He most certainly does not," I answered.

"I don't think he was talking to *you*," Shay said. And then, to Crash: "Give it to me."

Crash laughed. "Guess you don't know him as well as you think you do, Liberace. Ain't that right, Death Row?"

Crash had no moral compass. He aligned himself with the Aryan Brotherhood when it suited his needs. He talked of terrorist attacks; he'd cheered when we were watching the news footage of the World Trade Center collapsing. He had a list of victims, should he ever get out. He wanted his kids to grow up to be addicts or dealers or whores, and said he would be disappointed if they turned out to be anything else. Once, I heard him describing a visit with his three-year-old daughter: he told her to punch another kid at school to make him proud, and not to come back till she did. Now I watched him fish Shay the hype kit, hidden neatly inside a dismantled battery, ready for a hit with the liquefied Benadryl inside it. Shay put the needle to the crook of his elbow, set his thumb on the plunger.

And squirted the precious drug onto the floor of the catwalk.

"What the fuck!" Crash exploded. "Gimme that back."

"Haven't you heard? I'm Jesus. I'm *supposed* to save you," Shay said.

"I don't want to be saved," Crash yelled. "I want my kit back!"

"Come and get it," Shay said, and he pushed the kit under his door, so that it landed square on the catwalk. "Hey, CO," he yelled. "Come see what Crash made."

As the COs entered to confiscate the hype kit—and write him a ticket that would include a stay in solitary—Crash slammed his hand against the metal door. "I swear, Bourne, when you least expect it . . ."

He was interrupted by the sound of Warden Coyne's voice out in the courtyard. "I just bought a goddamn death gurney," the warden cried, conversing with someone we could not see. "What am I supposed to do with *that*?" And then, when he stopped speaking, we all noticed something—or the lack of something. The incessant hammering and sawing that had been going on outside for months, as the prison built a death chamber to accommodate Shay's sentence, had fallen silent. All we heard was a simple, blissful quiet.

"... you're gonna wind up dead," Crash finished, but now we were starting to wonder if that would still be true.

MICHAEL

The Reverend Arbogath Justus preached at the Drive-In Church of Christ in God in Heldratch, Michigan. His congregation arrived in their cars on Sunday mornings and received a blue flyer with the day's scripture, and a note to tune in to AM 1620 in order to hear the good reverend when he took the pulpit— formerly the snack bar, when it was a movie theater. I would have ridiculed this, but his flock was six hundred strong, which led me to believe that there were enough people in this world who wanted to tuck their prayer requests beneath windshield wipers to be collected, and to receive Communion from altar girls on roller skates.

I suppose it wasn't a big stretch to go from the movie screen to the small one, which is why Reverend Justus ran a television ministry site, too, on a cable station called SOS (Save Our Souls). I'd caught it a few times, while I was flipping through channels. It was fascinating to me, in the same way Shark Week was fascinating on the Discovery Channel—I was curious to learn more, but from a nice, secure distance. Justus wore eyeliner on television, and suits in a range of lollipop colors. His wife played the accordion when it came time to sing hymns. It all seemed like a parody of what faith was supposed to be—quiet and heart-settling, not grandiose and dramatic—which is why I always eventually changed the channel.

One day, when I went to visit Shay, my car was stopped in traffic leading to the prison. Shiny, scrubbed Midwestern faces worked their way from car to car. They were wearing green T-shirts with the name of Justus's church on the back, scrawled above a rudimentary drawing of a '57 Chevy convertible. When one girl approached, I unrolled the window. "God bless you!" she said, and offered me a slip of yellow paper.

There was a picture of Jesus, arms outstretched and palms raised, floating in the oval of a sideview car mirror. The caption read: OBJECTS IN MIRROR ARE CLOSER THAN THEY APPEAR.

And then below it: *Shay Bourne: A Wolf in Sheep's Clothing? Don't Let a False Prophet Lead You Astray!*

The line of cars chugged forward, finally, and I turned into the parking lot. I had to pull my car onto the grass; it was that crowded. The throngs of people waiting for Shay, and the media covering his story, had not dissipated.

However, by the time I came close to the prison, I realized that the attention of most of these people was not held by Shay at that moment, but by a man in a three-piece lime-green suit, wearing a clerical collar. I got close enough to see the pancake makeup and the eyeliner, and realized that Reverend Arbogath Justus had now moved into the realm of satellite ministries . . . and had chosen the prison as his first stop. "Miracles mean nothing," Justus announced. "The world is full of false prophets. In Revelations, we're told of a beast that uses miracles to fool men into worshipping it. Do you know what happens to that beast on Judgment Day? He and the people who were fooled are all thrown into a lake of fire. Is that what you want?"

A woman fell forward from the cliff-edge of the crowd. "No," she sobbed. "I want to go with God."

"Jesus can hear you, sister," Reverend Justus said. "Because He's here, with us. Not inside that prison, like the false prophet Shay Bourne!"

There was a roar from his converts. But just as quickly, it was matched by those who hadn't given up on Shay. "How do we know *you're* not the false prophet?" one young man called out.

Beside me, a mother tucked her sick child into her arms more tightly. She looked at my collar and frowned. "Are you with him?"

"No," I said. "Definitely not."

She nodded. "Well, I'm not taking advice from a man whose church has a concession stand."

I started to agree, but was distracted by a burly man who grabbed the reverend from his makeshift pulpit and yanked him into the crowd.

The cameras, of course, were all rolling.

Without thinking twice about what I was doing, or that I was doing it on film, I pushed forward and rescued Reverend Arbogath Justus from the clutches of the mob. He wrapped his arms around me, gasping, as I pulled us both up onto a granite ledge that ran along the edge of the parking lot.

In retrospect, I didn't know why I had chosen to play the hero. And I *really* didn't know why I said what I did next. Philosophically, Reverend Justus and I were on the same team—even if we pitched religion with very different styles. But I also knew that Shay was—maybe for the first time in his life— attempting to do something honorable. He didn't deserve to be slandered for that.

I might not believe *in* Shay—but I believed him.

I felt the wide, white eye of a television camera swing toward me, and a herd of others followed. "Reverend Justus came here, I'm sure, because he thinks he's telling you the truth. Well, so does Shay Bourne. He wants to do one thing in this world before he leaves it: save the life of a child. The Jesus *I* know would endorse that, I think. And," I said, turning to the reverend, "the Jesus *I*

know wouldn't send people to some fiery
hell if they were trying to atone for their
sins. The Jesus *I* know believed in second
chances."

As Reverend Justus realized that I might
have saved him from the mob to sacrifice
him all over again, his face reddened. "There's
one true word of God," he proclaimed in his
camera-ready voice, "and Shay Bourne isn't
speaking it."

Well, I couldn't argue with that. In all the
time I'd been with Shay, he had never quoted
the New Testament. He was far more likely
to swear or go off on a tangent about Hanta
virus and government conspiracy. "You're
absolutely right," I said. "He's trying to do
something that's never been done before.
He's asking questions of the status quo.
He's trying to suggest another way—a
better way. And he's willing to die for it to
happen." I raised a brow. "Come to think of
it, I bet Jesus might find a lot in common
with a guy like Shay Bourne."

I nodded, stepped down from the granite
ledge, and shoved my way through the crowd
to the security partition, where a correctional
officer let me through. "Father," he said, shaking his head, "you got no idea how big a pile

of you-know-what you just stepped into." And as if I needed proof, my cell phone rang: Father Walter's angry summons back to St. Catherine's, immediately.

I sat in the front pew of the church as Father Walter paced in front of me. "What if I blamed it all on being moved by the Holy Spirit?" I offered, and received a withering glare.

"I don't understand," Father Walter said. "Why would you say something like that . . . on live television, for the love of God—"

"I didn't mean to—"

"—when you had to know that it was going to bring the heat down on St. Catherine's?" He sank down beside me and tipped his head back, as if he were praying to the carved statue of Jesus on the Cross that rose above us. "Michael, seriously, what were you thinking?" he said softly. "You're a young, handsome, smart, straight guy. You could write your ticket in the Church—get your own parish, wind up in Rome . . . be whatever you want. And instead, I get a copy of an affidavit from the attorney general's office, saying that as Shay Bourne's spiritual advisor you believe in salvation through organ donation? And then I turn on the midday news and see you on a soapbox, sounding like some kind of . . . some kind of . . ."

"What?"

He shook his head, but stopped short of calling me a heretic. "You've read Tertullian," he said.

We all had, in seminary. He was a famous orthodox Christian historian whose text *The Prescription Against Heretics* was a forerunner of the Nicene Creed. Tertullian had coined the idea of a deposit of faith—that we take what Christ taught and believe it as is, without adding to or taking away from it.

"You want to know why Catholicism's been around for two thousand years?" Father Walter said. "*Because* of people like Tertullian, who understood that you can't mess around with truth. People were upset with the changes of Vatican II. The Pope's even reinstated the Latin Mass."

I took a deep breath. "I thought being a spiritual advisor meant doing what Shay Bourne needs to face his death with peace—not what *we* need him to do, as a good Catholic."

"Good Lord," Father Walter said. "He's conned you."

I frowned. "He hasn't conned me."

"He's got you eating out of the palm of his hand! Look at you—you practically acted like his press secretary today on the news—"

"Do you think Jesus died for a reason?" I interrupted.

"Of course."

"Then why shouldn't Shay Bourne be allowed to do the same?"

"Because," Father Walter said, "Shay Bourne is not dying for anyone's sins, except his own."

I flinched. Well, didn't I know that better than anyone else?

Father Walter sighed. "I don't agree with the death penalty, but I understand this sentence. He murdered two people. A police officer, and a little girl." He shook his head. "Save his soul, Michael. Don't try to save his life."

I glanced up. "What do you think would have happened if just one of the apostles had stayed awake in the garden with Jesus? If they'd kept Him from being arrested? If they'd tried to save *His* life?"

Father Walter's mouth dropped open. "You don't *really* think Shay Bourne is Jesus, do you?"

I didn't.

Did I?

Father Walter sank down onto the pew and took off his glasses. He rubbed his eyes. "Mikey," he said, "take a couple weeks off. Go somewhere and pray. Think about what you're doing—what you're *saying*." He looked up at me. "And in the meantime, I don't want you going to the prison on behalf of St. Catherine's."

I looked around this church, which I had grown to love—with its polished pews and the spatter of light from the stained glass, the whispering silk of the chalice veil, the dancing flames on the candles lit in offering. *Where your treasure is, there your heart will be.*

"I won't go to the prison on behalf of St. Catherine's," I said, "but I will go on behalf of Shay."

I walked down the aisle, past the holy water, past the bulletin board with the information about the young boy from Zimbabwe the congregation supported with their donations. When I stepped outside the double doors of the church, the world was so bright that for a moment, I couldn't see where I was headed.

Maggie

There were four ways to hang someone. The short drop involved a prisoner falling just a few inches; their body weight and physical struggling tightened the noose and caused death by strangulation. Suspension hanging required the prisoner to be raised upward and strangled. Standard drop hanging—popular in America in the late nineteenth and twentieth centuries—meant the prisoner fell four to six feet, which might or might not break his neck. Long drop hanging was a more personal execution: the distance the prisoner fell was determined by weight and body type. The body was still accelerating due to gravity at the end of the drop, but the head was restricted by the noose—which broke the neck and ruptured the spinal cord, rendering instant unconsciousness, and a quick death.

I'd learned that next to shooting, hanging was the world's most popular form of execution. It was introduced in Persia twenty-five hundred years ago for male criminals (females were strangled at the stake, because it was less indecent)—a nice alternative to the blood and guts of a typical beheading, with all the same punch as any public spectacle.

It was not, however, foolproof. In 1885, a British murderer named Robert Goodale was hanged, but the force of the drop decapitated him. Most recently, Saddam Hussein's half brother had suffered the same grisly fate in Iraq. This was a legal conundrum: if the sentence of death was to be carried out by hanging, then the prisoner could not be decapitated, or the sentence wasn't fulfilled.

I had to do my homework—which explained why I was reading the Official Table of Drops and estimating Shay Bourne's weight when Father Michael came into my office. "Oh, good," I said, motioning to the seat across from my desk. "If the noose is positioned right—there's something about a brass eyelet—the fall causes an instant fracture of the C2 vertebra. It says here brain death occurs in six minutes, and whole-body death within ten to fifteen minutes. That means we've got a four-minute window to get him back on a respirator before the heart stops beating and oh, I almost forgot—I heard back from the AG's office. They denied our request to have Shay hanged instead of executed with lethal injection. They even included the original sentence, as if I haven't read it a bazillion times, and told me if I wanted to challenge it, I had to file the appropriate motions. Which," I said, "I did five hours ago."

Father Michael didn't even seem to hear me. "Listen," I said gently, "it's easier if you think about this hanging business as science . . . and stop connecting it personally to Shay."

"I'm sorry," the priest said, shaking his head. "It's just—it's been a pretty bad day."

"You mean the showdown you had with the televangelist?"

"You saw that?"

"You're the talk of the town, Father."

He closed his eyes. "Great."

"I'm sure Shay saw it, too, if that's any consolation."

Father Michael looked up at me. "Thanks to Shay, my supervising priest thinks I'm a heretic."

I thought about what my father would say if a member of his congregation came to him to ease his soul. "Do *you* think you're a heretic?"

"Does *any* heretic?" he said. "Honestly, I'm the last person who ought to be helping you win Shay's case, Maggie."

"Hey," I said, trying to boost his spirits. "I was just about to go to my parents' house for dinner. It's a standing engagement on Friday nights. Why don't you come with me?"

"I couldn't impose—"

"Believe me, there's always enough food to feed a third world country."

"Well, then," the priest said, "that would be great."

I switched off my desk lamp. "We can take my car," I said.

"Can I leave my motorcycle parked in the lot here?"

"You're allowed to ride a motorcycle, but you can't eat meat on Friday?"

He still looked as if the world had been

pulled out from beneath him. "I guess the Church forefathers found it easier to abstain from beef than Harleys."

I led him through the maze of file cabinets in the ACLU office and headed outside. "Guess what I found out today," I said. "The trapdoor from the old gallows at the state prison is in the chaplain's office."

When I glanced at Father Michael, I was pretty sure I saw the ghost of a smile.

June

|||||||||||||||||||||||||||||||||||||||||||||||||||||||||||||||||||||||||||||||||||||||||||||||||||||||||||||

One of the things I liked about Dr. Wu's office was the wall of pictures. An enormous cork-board held photographs of patients who had beaten the odds after having Dr. Wu operate on their failing hearts. There were babies propped up on pillows, Christmas card portraits, and boys wielding Little League bats. It was a mural of success.

When I'd first come to tell Dr. Wu about Shay Bourne's offer, he listened carefully and then said that in his twenty-three years of practice, he had yet to see a grown man's heart that would be a good match for a child. Hearts grew to fit the needs of their host body—which was why every other potential organ that had been offered to Claire for transplant had come from another child. "I'll examine him," Dr. Wu promised, "but I don't want you to get your hopes up."

Now I watched Dr. Wu take a seat and flatten his palms on the desk. I always marveled at the fact that he walked around shaking hands and waving as if the appendages were totally normal, instead of miraculous. Those ridiculous celebrities who insured their breasts and their legs had nothing on Dr. Wu and his hands. "June . . ."

"Just say it quickly," I said, full of false cheer.

Dr. Wu met my gaze. "He's a perfect match for Claire."

I had already gathered the strap of my purse in my fist, planning to thank him hastily and beat a retreat out of the office before I started crying again over yet another lost heart; but these words rooted me to my seat. "I . . . I'm sorry?"

"They have the same blood type—B positive. The tissue cross-match we did of their blood was nonreactive. But—here's the remarkable part—his heart is just the right size."

I knew they looked for a donor who was within 20 percent of the patient's weight—which for Claire meant anyone between sixty and a hundred pounds. Shay Bourne was a small man, but he was still an adult. He had to weigh 120 or 130 pounds.

"Medically, it doesn't make sense. Theoretically, his heart is too tiny to be doing the job his own body needs . . . and yet he seems to be healthy as a horse." Dr. Wu smiled. "It looks like Claire's got herself a donor."

I stilled. This was supposed to be wonderful news—but I could barely breathe. How would Claire react if she knew the circumstances behind the donation? "You can't tell her," I said.

"That she's going to have a transplant?"

I shook my head. "Where it came from."

Dr. Wu frowned. "Don't you think she'll find out? This is all over the news."

"Organ donations are always done anonymously. Plus, she doesn't want a boy's heart. She always says that."

"That's not really the issue here, is it?" The cardiologist stared at me. "It's a muscle, June. Nothing more, and nothing less. What makes a heart worthy for transplant has nothing to do with the donor's personality."

I looked up at him. "What would you do, if she was your daughter?"

"If she was my daughter," Dr. Wu replied, "I would already have scheduled the surgery."

Lucius

I tried to tell Shay that he was the topic on *Larry King Live* that night, but either he was asleep or he just didn't feel like answering me. Instead, I took out my stinger from where it was hidden behind a cement block in the wall and heated up some water for tea. The guests that night were the nutcase reverend that Father Michael had sparred with outside the prison, and some stuffed-shirt academic named Ian Fletcher. It was hard to tell who had the more intriguing backstory—Reverend Justus with his drive-in church, or Fletcher—who'd been a television atheist until he'd run across a little girl who could apparently perform miracles and raise the dead. He wound up marrying the girl's single mother, which in my opinion, greatly diluted the credibility of his commentary.

Still, he was a better speaker than Reverend Justus, who kept rising out of his seat as if he were filled with helium. "There's an old proverb, Larry," the reverend said. "You can't keep trouble from coming, but you don't have to make out a place card."

Larry King tapped his pen on the desk twice. "And by that you mean . . . ?"

"Miracles don't make a man into God. Dr. Fletcher ought to know that better than anyone."

Unrattled, Ian Fletcher smiled. "The more you think you're right, the likelier you are to be wrong. That's a proverb Reverend Justus probably hasn't encountered yet."

"Tell us about being a television atheist," Larry said.

"Well, I used to do what Jerry Falwell did, except instead of saying there's a God, I said there wasn't one. I went around debunking claims of miracles all over the country. Eventually, when I found one that I couldn't discredit, I started wondering if it was really God I objected to . . . or just the sense of entitlement that seems to be part of affiliating with a religious group. Like the way you'll hear that a person is a good Christian—well, who says Christians corner the market on virtue? Or when the president ends a speech with 'God bless the United States of America' . . . why just us?"

"Are you still an atheist?" King asked.

"Technically, I suppose you'd call me an agnostic."

Justus scoffed. "Splitting hairs."

"Not true; an atheist's got more in common with a Christian, since he believes you can know whether or not God exists—but where a Christian says absolutely, the atheist says absolutely not. For me, and any other agnostic—the jury's still out. Religion is intriguing, but in a historical sense. A man should live his life a certain way not because of some divine authority, but because of a personal moral obligation to himself and others."

Larry King turned to Reverend Justus. "And you, sir, your congregation meets in a former drive-in movie theater? Don't you think that takes some of the pomp and circumstance out of religion?"

"What we've found, Larry, is that for some

people the obligation of getting up and going to church is too overwhelming. They don't like having to see or be seen by others; they don't enjoy being indoors on a beautiful Sunday; they prefer to worship in private. Coming to the Drive-In Church allows a person to do whatever it is he needs to do while communing with God—whether that's wearing pajamas, or eating an Egg McMuffin, or dozing off during my sermon."

"Now, Shay Bourne isn't the first person to come along and stir the pot," King said. "Few years back, a Florida State football quarterback was found lying in the street, claiming to be God. And a fellow in Virginia wanted his driver's license changed to reflect that he was a resident of the Kingdom of Heaven. What do you think it is about Shay Bourne that makes people believe he might be the real deal?"

"As far as I understand," Fletcher said, "Bourne's not claiming to be the Messiah or Mary Poppins or Captain America—it's the people supporting him who have christened him, no pun intended. Ironically, that's very similar to what we see in the Bible—Jesus doesn't go around claiming to be God."

" '*I am the way, the truth, and the life; no*

man cometh unto the Father, but by me,'" Justus quoted. "John, 14:6."

"There's also evidence in the gospels that Jesus appeared in different forms to different people," Fletcher said. "The apostle James talks about seeing Jesus standing on the shore in the form of a child. He points it out to John, who thinks he's nuts, because the person on the shore isn't a child but a handsome young man. They go to investigate, and although one sees an old, bald man, the other sees a young guy with a beard."

Reverend Justus frowned. "I can quote the Gospel of John forward and backward," he said, "and that's *not* in there."

Fletcher smiled. "I never said it was from the Gospel of John. I said it was from *a* gospel. A Gnostic one, called the *Acts of John*."

"There's no Acts of John in the Bible," Justus huffed. "He's making this up."

"The reverend's right—it's not in the Bible. And there are dozens of others like it. Through a series of editorial decisions, they were excluded—and considered heresy by the early Christian church."

"That's because the Bible is the Word of God, period," Justus said.

"Actually, Matthew, Mark, Luke, and John weren't even written by the apostles Matthew, Mark, Luke, and John. They were written in Greek, by authors who had a modicum of education—unlike Jesus's fishermen disciples, who were illiterate, like ninety percent of the population. Mark is based on the apostle Peter's preaching. Matthew's author was probably a Jewish Christian from Antioch, Syria. The Gospel of Luke was allegedly written by a doctor. And the author of the Gospel of John never mentions his own name . . . but it was the latest of the four synoptic gospels to be written, roughly around A.D. 100. If the apostle John *was* the author, he would have been extremely old."

"Smoke and mirrors," Reverend Justus said. "He's using rhetoric to distract us from the basic truth here."

"Which is?" King asked.

"Do you truly believe that if the Lord chose to grace us with his earthly presence again —and that is a big *if*, in my humble opinion —he would willingly choose to inhabit a convicted murderer, two times over?"

My hot water started to boil, and I disconnected the stinger. Then I turned off the television without hearing Fletcher's answer. Why would God choose to inhabit *any* of us?

What if it was the other way around . . . if we were the ones who inhabited God?

MICHAEL

During the drive to Maggie's parents' home, I wallowed in various degrees of guilt. I had let down Father Walter and St. Catherine's. I'd made a fool of myself on TV. And although I'd started to tell Maggie that Shay and I had some history between us that he didn't know about—I had chickened out. Again.

"So here's the thing," Maggie said, distracting me from my thoughts as we pulled into the driveway. "My parents are going to be a little excited when they see you in my car."

I glanced around at the quiet, wooded retreat. "Don't get much company here?"

"Don't get many *dates* is more like it."

"I don't want to burst your bubble, but I'm not exactly boyfriend material."

Maggie laughed. "Yeah, thanks, but I'd like to think even *I'm* not that desperate. It's just that my mother's got radar or something—she can sniff out a Y chromosome from miles away."

As if Maggie had conjured her, a woman stepped out of the house. She was petite and blond, with her hair cut into a neat bob and pearls at her neck. Either she'd just come home from work, or she was headed out—my mother, on a Friday night, would have been wearing one of my dad's flannel shirts with the sleeves rolled up, and what she called her Weekend Fat Jeans. She squinted, glimpsing me through the windshield. "Maggie!" she cried. "You didn't tell us you were bringing a *friend* for dinner."

Just the way she said the word *friend* made me feel a rush of sympathy for Maggie.

"Joel!" she called into the house behind her. "Maggie's brought a guest!"

I stepped out of the car and adjusted my collar. "Hello," I said. "I'm Father Michael."

Maggie's mother's hand went to her throat. "Oh, God."

"Close," I replied, "but no cigar."

At that moment, Maggie's father came hurrying out the front door, tucking in his dress shirt. "Mags," he said, folding her into a bear hug, which was when I noticed his yarmulke. Then he turned to me and held out a hand. "I'm Rabbi Bloom."

"You could have *told* me your father was a rabbi," I whispered to Maggie.

"You didn't *ask*." She looped her arm through her father's. "Daddy, this is Father Michael. He's a heretic."

"Please tell me you're not dating him," Mrs. Bloom murmured.

"Ma, he's a priest. Of course I'm not." Maggie laughed as they headed toward the house. "But I bet that street performer who asked me out is starting to look a lot more palatable to you . . ."

That left two of us, men of God, standing awkwardly on the driveway. Rabbi Bloom led the way into the house, toward his study. "So," he said. "Where's your congregation?"

"Concord," I said. "St. Catherine's."

"And you met my daughter how?"

"I'm Shay Bourne's spiritual advisor."

He glanced up. "That must be unnerving."

"It is," I said. "On many levels."

"So is he or isn't he?"

"Donating his heart? That's going to be up to your daughter, I think."

The rabbi shook his head. "No, no. Maggie, she could move a mountain if she wanted to, one molecule at a time. I meant is he or isn't he Jesus?"

I blinked. "I never figured I'd hear that question from a rabbi."

"Jesus *was* a Jewish man, after all. Just look at the evidence: he lived at home, went into his dad's business, thought his mother was a virgin, and his mother thought he was God." Rabbi Bloom grinned, and I started to smile.

"Well, Shay's not preaching what Jesus did."

The rabbi laughed. "And you were around the first time to know this for sure?"

"I know what it says in scripture."

"I never understood people—Jewish *or* Christian—who read the Bible as if it were hard evidence. Gospel means good *news*. It's a way to update the story, to fit the audience you're telling it to."

"I don't know if I'd say that Shay Bourne's here to update the story of Christ for the modern generation," I replied.

"It makes you wonder, then, why so many people have jumped on his bandwagon. It's almost like who he is matters less than what all of them need him to be." Rabbi Bloom began to scour his bookshelves, finally lighting on one dusty tome, which he skimmed through until he found a certain page. *"Jesus said to his disciples, 'Compare me to someone and tell me whom I am like.' Simon Peter said to him, 'You are like a righteous angel.' Matthew said to him, 'You are like a wise philosopher.' Thomas said to him, 'Master, my mouth is wholly incapable of saying whom you are like.' Jesus said, 'I am not your master. Because you have drunk, you have become intoxicated from the bubbling spring which I have measured out.'"*

He snapped the book shut again as I tried to place the scripture. "History's always written by the winners," Rabbi Bloom said. "This was one of the losers." He handed me the book just as Maggie poked her head into the room.

"Dad, you're not trying to pawn off another copy of *The Best Jewish Knock-Knock Jokes,* are you?"

"Unbelievably, Father Michael already has a signed copy. Is dinner ready?"

"Yes."

"Thank goodness. I was beginning to think your mother had cremated the tilapia." As Maggie ducked back into the kitchen, Rabbi Bloom turned to me. "Well, in spite of how Maggie introduced you, you don't seem like a heretic to me."

"It's a long story."

"I'm sure you already know that *heresy* comes from the Greek word for *choice*." He shrugged. "Makes you wonder. What if the ideas that have always been considered sacrilegious aren't sacrilegious at all—just ideas we haven't come across before? Or ideas we haven't been *allowed* to come across?"

In my hands, the book the rabbi had given me felt as if it were burning. "You hungry?" Bloom asked.

"Starving," I admitted, and I let him lead the way.

June

When I was pregnant with Claire, I was told that I had gestational diabetes. I still don't think that was true, frankly—an hour before I had the test, I'd taken Elizabeth to McDonald's and finished her orange Hi-C drink, which is enough to put anyone into a sugar coma. However, when the obstetrician told me the results, I did what I had to do: stuck to a strict diet that left me hungry all the time, got blood drawn twice a week, held my breath at every visit while my doctor checked the baby's growth.

The silver lining? I was treated to numerous ultrasounds. Long after most momsto-be had gotten their twenty-week preview of the baby inside them, I continued to get updated portraits. It got to be so commonplace for Kurt and I to see our baby that he stopped coming to the weekly OB visits. He'd watch Elizabeth while I drove to the hospital, lifted up my shirt, and let the wand roll over my belly, illuminating on a monitor a foot, an elbow, the slope of this new child's nose. By then, in my eighth month, the picture wasn't the stick-figure skeleton you see at twenty weeks—you could see her hair, the ridges on her thumb, the curve of her cheek. She looked so real on the ultrasound screen that sometimes I'd forget she was still inside me.

"Not much longer," the technician had said to me that last day as she wiped the gel off my belly with a warm washcloth.

"Easy for you to say," I told her. "You're not the one chasing around a seven-year-old in your eighth month."

"Been there done that," she said, and she reached beneath the screen to hand me that day's printout of the baby's face.

When I saw it, I drew in my breath: that's how much this new baby looked like Kurt—completely unlike me, unlike Elizabeth. This new baby had his wide-set eyes, his dimples, the point of his chin. I folded the picture into my purse so that I could show it to him, and then I drove home.

There were cars backed up on the street leading to mine. I assumed it was construction; they'd been repaving the roads around here. We sat in a line, idling, listening to the radio. After five minutes, I started to worry— Kurt was on duty today, and had taken his lunch break early so that I could go to the ultrasound without dragging Elizabeth along. If I didn't get home soon, he'd be late for work.

"Thank God," I said when the traffic slowly began to move. But as I drew closer, I saw the detour signs set up at the end of my block, the police car sprawled sideways across the street. I felt that small tumble in my heart, the way you do when you see a fire engine racing toward the general vicinity of your home.

Roger, an officer I knew only marginally, was diverting traffic. I unrolled my window. "I live here," I said. "I'm married to Kurt Nea—"

Before I could finish, his face froze, and that was how I knew something had happened. I'd seen Kurt's face do the same thing when he'd told me that my first husband had been killed in the car wreck.

I snapped off my seat belt and pushed my way out of the car, ungainly and awkward in my pregnancy. "Where is she?" I cried, the car still running. "Where's Elizabeth?"

"June," Roger said as he wrapped an arm around me firmly. "Why don't you just come with me?"

He walked me down the road where I lived, until I could see what I hadn't been able to from the crossroads: the glare of police cruiser lights, blinking like a holiday. The yawning mouths of the ambulances. The door to my house wide open. One officer held the dog in his arms; when Dudley saw me, he began to bark like mad.

"Elizabeth!" I yelled, and I shoved away from Roger, running as fast as I could given my shape and size. "Elizabeth!!"

I was intercepted by someone who knocked the breath from me—the chief of police. "June," he said softly. "Come with me."

I struggled against Irv—scratching, kicking, pleading. I thought maybe if I put up a fight, it would keep me from hearing what he was about to say. "Elizabeth?" I whispered.

"She's been shot, June."

I waited for him to say *But she'll be just fine*, except he didn't. He shook his head. Later, I would remember that he had been crying.

"I want to see her," I sobbed.

"There's something else," Irv said, and as I watched, a brace of paramedics wheeled Kurt out on a stretcher. His face was white, leached of blood—all of which seemed to be soaking the makeshift bandage around his midsection.

I reached for Kurt's hand, and he turned toward me, his eyes glassy. "I'm sorry," he choked out. "I'm so sorry."

"What happened?" I shrieked, frantic. "Sorry for what? What happened to her!"

"Ma'am," a paramedic said, "we've got to get him to a hospital."

Another paramedic pulled me back. I watched them take Kurt away from me.

As Irv led me to the steps of another ambulance, he spoke, words that at the time felt as solid and square as bricks, layered sentence upon sentence to build a wall between life as I'd known it and the one I would now be forced to lead. *Kurt gave us a statement . . . found the carpenter sexually abusing Elizabeth . . . standoff . . . shots were fired . . . Elizabeth got in the way.*

Elizabeth, I used to say, when she was following me around the tiny kitchen as I cooked dinner, *I'm tripping over you.*

Elizabeth, your father and I are trying to have a conversation.

Elizabeth, not now.

Never.

My legs were numb as Irv led me into a second ambulance. "She's the mother," he said as one of the paramedics came forward. A small form lay on a stretcher in the central cavity of the ambulance, covered with a thick gray blanket. I reached out, shaking, and pulled the cloth down. As soon as I saw Elizabeth, my knees gave out; if not for Irv, I would have fallen.

She looked like she was sleeping. Her hands were tucked on either side of her body; her cheeks were flushed.

They'd made a mistake, that was all.

I leaned over the stretcher, touching her face. Her skin was still warm. "Elizabeth," I whispered, the way I did on school days to wake her. "Elizabeth, time to get up."

But she didn't stir; she didn't hear me. I broke down over her body, pulling her against me. The blood on her chest was garish. I tried to draw her closer, but I couldn't—this baby inside me was in the way. "Don't go," I whispered. "Please don't go."

"June," Irv said, touching my shoulder. "You can ride with them if you want, but you'll have to put her down."

I did not understand the great hurry to take her to a hospital; later, I would learn that only a doctor could pronounce Elizabeth dead, no matter how obvious it was.

The paramedics gently strapped Elizabeth to the gurney and offered me a seat beside it. "Wait," I said, and I unclasped a barrette from my hair. "She doesn't like her bangs in her eyes," I murmured, and I clipped them back. I left my hand on her forehead for a moment, a benediction.

On the interminable ride to the hospital, I looked down at my shirt. It was stained with blood, a Rorschach of loss. But I was not the only one who had been marked, permanently changed. It was no surprise when a month later I gave birth to Claire—an infant who looked nothing like her father, as she had that day at the ultrasound, but who instead was the spitting image of the sister she would never meet.

Maggie

Oliver and I were enjoying a glass of Yellow Tail and a TiVo'd *Grey's Anatomy* when there was a knock on the door. Now, this was alarming on several counts:

1. It was Friday night, and no one ever stopped by on Friday night.
2. People who ring the doorbell at ten p.m. are either
   a. stranded with a dead battery in their car
   b. serial killers
   c. all of the above
3. I was in my pajamas.

4. The ones with a hole on the butt, so that my underwear showed.

I looked at the rabbit. "Let's not get it," I said, but Oliver hopped off my lap and began to sniff around the bottom of the door.

"Maggie?" I heard. "I know you're in there."

"Daddy?" I got off the couch and unlocked the door to let him in. "Shouldn't you be at services?"

He took off his coat and hung it on an antique rack that my mother had given me for my birthday one year, and that I really hated, but that she looked for every time she came to my house (*Oh, Maggie, I'm so glad you've still got this!*). "I stayed for the important parts. Your mother's kibitzing with Carol; I'll probably make it home before she will."

Carol was the cantor—a woman with a voice that made me think of falling asleep in the summertime sun: strong, steady, utterly relaxing. When she wasn't singing, she collected thimbles. She went to conventions as far away as Seattle to trade them, and had one entire forty-foot wall of her house divvied up by a contractor into minuscule display shelves. Mom said that Carol had more than five thousand thimbles. I didn't think I had five thousand of anything, except maybe daily calories.

He walked into the living room and glanced at the television. "I wish that skinny girl would just ditch McDreamy."

"You watch *Grey's Anatomy*?"

"Your mother watches. I absorb by osmosis." He sat down on the couch, while I mulled over the fact that I actually did have something in common with my mother.

"I liked your friend the priest," my father said.

"He's not my friend. We work together."

"I can still like him, can't I?"

I shrugged. "Something tells me you didn't come all the way here to tell me how fabulous Father Michael is."

"Well, in part. How come you brought him over tonight?"

"Why?" I bristled. "Did Mom complain?"

"Will you just stop with the Mom thing?" My father sighed. "I'm asking you a question."

"He had a hard day. Being on Shay's side isn't easy for him."

My father looked at me carefully. "How about for you?"

"You told me to ask Shay what he wanted,"

I said. "He doesn't want his life saved. He wants his death to mean something."

My father nodded. "A lot of Jews think you can't donate organs, because it violates Jewish law—you're not supposed to mutilate the body after death; you're supposed to bury it as soon as possible. But *pikkuah nefesh* takes precedence over that. It says that the duty to save life trumps everything. Or in other words—a Jew is *required* to break the law, if it means saving a life."

"So it's okay to commit murder in order to save someone else?" I asked.

"Well, God's not stupid; He sets parameters. But if there's any karmic *pikkuah nefesh* in the world—"

"To mix metaphors, no less religions . . ."

"—then the fact that you can't stop an execution is at least balanced by the fact that you'll be saving a life."

"At what cost, Daddy? Is it okay to kill someone who's a criminal, someone society really doesn't want around anymore, so that a little girl can live? What if it wasn't a little girl who needed that heart? What if it was some other criminal? Or what if it wasn't Shay who had to die in order to donate his organs? What if it was *me*?"

"God forbid," my father said.

"It's semantics."

"It's morality. You're doing good."

"By doing bad."

My father shook his head. "There's something else about *pikkuah nefesh* . . . it clears the slate of guilt. You can't feel remorse about breaking the law, because ethically, you're obligated to do it."

"See, that's where you're wrong. I *can* feel remorse. Because we're not talking about not fasting on Yom Kippur since you happen to be sick . . . we're talking about a man dying."

"And saving your life."

I looked up at him. "*Claire's* life."

"Two birds with one stone," my father said. "Maybe it's not literal in your case, Maggie. But this lawsuit—it's fired you up. It's given you something to look forward to." He looked around my home—the place setting for one, the bowl of popcorn on the table, the rabbit cage.

I suppose there was a point in my life when I wanted the package deal—the chuppah, the husband, the kids, the carpools—but somewhere along the line, I'd just stopped hoping. I had gotten used to living alone, to saving the other half of the can of soup for the next night's dinner, to only changing the pillowcases on my side of the bed. I had become overly comfortable with myself, so much so that anyone else would have felt like an intrusion.

Pretending, it turned out, took much less effort than hoping.

One of the reasons I loved my parents— and hated them—is that they still thought I had a chance at all that. They only wanted me to be happy; they didn't see how on earth I could be happy by myself. Which, if you read between the lines, meant they found me just as lacking as I did.

I could feel my eyes filling with tears. "I'm tired," I said. "You should go now."

"Maggie—"

When he reached for me, I ducked away. "Good night."

I punched buttons on the remote control until the television went black. Oliver crept out from behind my desk to investigate, and I scooped him up. Maybe this was why I chose to spend my free time with a rabbit: he didn't offer unwanted advice. "You forgot one little detail," I said. "*Pikkuah nefesh* doesn't apply to an atheist."

My father paused in the act of taking his

coat from the world's ugliest coat rack. He slipped it over his arm and walked toward me. "I know it sounds strange for a rabbi," he said, "but it's never mattered to me what you believe in, Mags, as long as you believe in yourself as much as I do." He settled his hand on top of Oliver's back. Our fingers brushed, but I didn't look up at him. "And that's not semantics."

"Daddy—"

He held up a hand to shush me and opened the door. "I'll tell your mother to get you new pajamas for your birthday," he said, pausing at the threshold. "Those have a hole in the butt."

MICHAEL

|||||||||||||||||||||||||||||||||||||||||||||||||||||||||||||||||||||||||||||||||||||||||||||||||||||||||||||||||||||

In 1945, two brothers were digging beneath cliffs in Nag Hammadi, Egypt, trying to find fertilizer. One—Mohammed Ali—struck something hard as he dug. He unearthed a large earthenware jug, covered with a red dish. Afraid that a jinn would be inside it, Mohammed Ali didn't want to open the jar. Finally, the curiosity of finding gold instead led him to break it open—only to find thirteen papyrus books inside, bound in gazelle leather.

Some of the books were burned for firewood. The others made their way to religious scholars, who dated them to have been written around A.D. 140, about thirty years after the New Testament—and deciphered them to find the names of gospels not found in the Bible, full of sayings that were in the New Testament . . . and many that weren't. In some, Jesus spoke in riddles; in others, the Virgin birth and bodily resurrection were dismissed. They came to be known as the Gnostic gospels, and even today, they are given short shrift by the Church.

In seminary, we learned about the Gnostic gospels. Namely, we learned that they were heresy. And let me tell you, when a priest hands you a text and tells you this is what *not* to believe, it colors the way you read it. Maybe I skimmed the text, saving the careful close analysis for the Bible. Maybe I whiffed completely and told the priest who was teaching that course that I'd done my homework when in fact I didn't. Whatever the excuse, that night when I cracked open Joel Bloom's book, it was as if I'd never seen the words before, and although I planned to only read the foreword by the scholar who'd compiled the texts—a man named Ian Fletcher—I found myself devouring the pages as if it were the latest Stephen King novel and not a collection of ancient gospels.

The book had been earmarked to the

Gospel of Thomas. Any mentions of Thomas I knew from the Bible certainly weren't flattering: He doesn't believe Lazarus will rise from the dead. When Jesus tells His disciples to follow Him, Thomas points out that they don't know where to go. And when Jesus rises after the crucifixion, Thomas isn't even *there*—and won't believe it until he can touch the wounds with his own hands. He's the very definition of faithless—and the origin of the term *doubting Thomas*.

Yet in Rabbi Bloom's book, this page began:

These are the secret words which the living Jesus spoke, and the twin, Didymos Judas Thomas, wrote them down.

Twin? Since when did Jesus have a twin?

The rest of the "gospel" was not a narrative of Jesus's life, like Matthew, Mark, Luke, and John, but a collection of quotes by Jesus, all beginning with the words *Jesus said*. Some were lines similar to those in the Bible. Others were completely unfamiliar and sounded more like logic puzzles than any scripture:

If you bring forth what is within you, what is within you will save you. If you don't bring forth what is within you, what is within you will destroy you.

I read the line over twice and rubbed my eyes. There was something about it that made me feel as if I'd heard it before.

Then I realized where.

Shay had said it to me the first time I'd met with him, when he'd explained why he wanted to donate his heart to Claire Nealon.

I kept reading intently, hearing Shay's voice over and over again:

The dead aren't alive, and the living won't die.

We come from the light.

Split a piece of wood; I am there. Lift up the stone; you will find me there.

The first time I had gone on a roller coaster, I felt like this—like the ground had been pulled out from beneath my feet, like I was going to be sick, like I needed something to grab hold of.

If you asked a dozen people on the street if they'd ever heard of the Gnostic gospels, eleven would look at you as if you were crazy. In fact most people today couldn't even recite the Ten Commandments. Shay Bourne's religious training had been minimal and fragmented; the only thing I'd ever seen him "read" was the *Sports Illustrated* Swimsuit Issue. He couldn't write; he could barely follow a thought through to the end of one sentence. His formal schooling ended at a GED he'd gotten while at the juvenile detention facility.

How, then, could Shay Bourne have memorized the Gospel of Thomas? Where would he even have stumbled across it in his lifetime?

The only answer I could come up with was that he hadn't.

It could have been coincidence.

I could have been remembering the conversations incorrectly.

Or—maybe—I could have been wrong about him.

The past three weeks, I had pushed past the throngs of people camped out in front of the prison. I had turned off the television when yet another pundit suggested that Shay might be the Messiah. After all, I knew better. I was a priest; I had taken vows; I understood that there was one God. His message had been recorded in the Bible, and above all else, when Shay spoke, he did *not* sound like Jesus in any of the four gospels.

But here was a fifth. A gospel that hadn't made it into the Bible but was equally as ancient. A gospel that espoused the beliefs of at least *some* people during the birth of Christianity. A gospel that Shay Bourne had quoted to me.

What if the Church forefathers had gotten it wrong?

What if the gospels that had been dismissed and debunked were the real ones, and the ones that had been picked for the New Testament were the embellished versions? What if Jesus had actually said the quotations listed in the Gospel of Thomas?

It would mean that the allegations being made about Shay Bourne might not be that far off the mark.

And it would explain why a Messiah might return in the guise of a convicted murderer—to see if this time, we might get it right.

I got out of my chair, folding the book by my side, and started to pray.

Heavenly Father, I said silently, *help me understand.*

The telephone rang, making me jump. I glanced at the clock—who would call after three in the morning?

"Father Michael? This is CO Smythe, from the prison. Sorry to disturb you at this hour, but Shay Bourne had another seizure. We thought you'd want to know."

"Is he all right?"

"He's in the infirmary," Smythe said. "He asked for you."

At this hour, the vigilant masses outside the prison were tucked into their sleeping bags and tents, underneath the artificial day created by the enormous spotlights that flooded the front of the building. I had to be buzzed in; when I entered the receiving area, CO Smythe was waiting for me. "What happened?"

"No one knows," the officer said. "It was Inmate DuFresne who alerted us again. We couldn't see what happened on the security cameras."

We entered the infirmary. In a distant, dark corner of the room, Shay was propped up in a bed, a nurse beside him. He held a cup of juice that he sipped through a straw; his other hand was cuffed to the bed's railing. There were wires coming out from beneath his medical johnny. "How is he?" I asked.

"He'll live," the nurse said, and then, realizing her mistake, blushed fiercely. "We hooked him up to monitor his heart. So far, so good."

I sat down on a chair beside Shay and looked up at Smythe and the nurse. "Can we have a minute?"

"That's about all you've got," the nurse said. "We just gave him something to knock him out."

They moved to the far side of the room, and I leaned closer to Shay. "Are you okay?"

"You wouldn't believe it if I told you."

"Oh, try me," I said.

He glanced over to make sure no one else was listening. "I was just watching TV, you know? This documentary on how they make movie theater candy, like Dots and Milk Duds. And I started to get tired, so I went to turn it off. But before I could push the button, all the light in the television, it shot into me like electricity. I mean, I could feel those things inside my blood moving around, what are they called again, corporals?"

"Corpuscles."

"Yeah, right, those. I hate that word. Did you ever see that *Star Trek* where those aliens are sucking the salt out of everything? I always thought they should be called corpuscles. You say the word, and it sounds like you're eating a lemon . . ."

"Shay. You were talking about the light."

"Oh, right, yeah. Well, it was like I started boiling inside, and my eyes, they were going to jelly, and I tried to call out but my teeth were wired shut and then I woke up in here, feeling like I'd been sucked dry." He looked up at me. "By a *corpuscle.*"

"The nurse said it was a seizure. Do you remember anything else?"

"I remember what I was thinking," Shay said. "This was what it would feel like."

"What?"

"Dying."

I took a deep breath. "Remember when you were little, a kid—and you'd fall asleep in the car? And someone would carry you out and put you into bed, so that when you woke up in the morning, you knew automatically you were home again? That's what I think it's like to die."

"That would be good," Shay said, his voice deeper, groggy. "It'll be nice to know what home looks like."

A phrase I'd read just an hour ago slipped into my mind like a splinter: *The Father's kingdom is spread out upon the earth, and people don't see it.*

Although I knew it wasn't the right time, although I knew I was supposed to be here for Shay, instead of the other way around, I leaned closer, until my words could fall into the shell of his ear. "Where did you find the Gospel of Thomas?" I whispered.

Shay stared at me blankly. "Thomas who?" he said, and then his eyes drifted shut.

As I drove away from the prison, I heard Father Walter's voice: *He's conned you.* But when I'd mentioned the Gospel of Thomas, I hadn't seen even the slightest flicker of recognition in Shay's eyes, and he'd been drugged—it would have been awfully hard to keep dissembling.

Was this what it had felt like for the Jews who met Jesus and recognized him as more than just a gifted rabbi? I had no point of comparison. I'd grown up Catholic; I'd become a priest. I could not remember a time that I hadn't believed Jesus was the Messiah.

I knew someone, though, who could.

Rabbi Bloom didn't have a temple, because it had burned down, but he did rent office space close to the school where services were held. I was waiting in front of the locked door when he arrived just before eight a.m.

"Wow," he said, taking in the vision in front of him—a red-eyed, rumpled priest clutching a motorcycle helmet and the Nag Hammadi texts. "I would have let you borrow it longer than one night."

"Why don't Jews believe Jesus was the Messiah?"

He unlocked the door to the office. "That's going to take at least a cup and a half of coffee," Bloom said. "Come on in."

He started brewing a pot and offered me a seat. His office looked a lot like Father Walter's at St. Catherine's—inviting, comfortable. A place you'd want to sit and talk. Unlike Father Walter's, though, Rabbi Bloom's plants were the real thing. Father Walter's were plastic, bought by the Ladies' Aid, when he kept killing everything from a ficus to an African violet.

"It's a wandering Jew," the rabbi said when he saw me checking out the flowerpot. "Maggie's little idea of a joke."

"I just got back from the prison. Shay Bourne had another seizure."

"Did you tell Maggie?"

"Not yet." I looked at him. "You didn't answer my question."

"I haven't had my coffee." He got up and poured us each a cup, putting milk and sugar in mine without asking first. "Jews don't think Jesus was the Messiah because

he didn't fulfill the criteria for a Jewish messiah. It's really pretty simple, and it's all laid
out by Maimonides. A Jewish *moshiach* will
bring the Jews back to Israel and set up a
government in Jerusalem that's the center
of political power for the world, for both Jews
and Gentiles. He'll rebuild the Temple and
reestablish Jewish law as the governing law
of the land. He'll raise the dead—all of the
dead—and usher in a great age of peace,
when everyone believes in God. He'll be a
descendant of David, a king and a warrior, a
judge, and a great leader . . . but he'll also
be firmly, unequivocally *human*." Bloom set
the cup down in front of me. "We believe
that in every generation, a person's born
with the potential to become the *moshiach*.
But if the messianic age doesn't come and
that person dies, then that person isn't
him."

"Like Jesus."

"Personally, I've always seen Jesus as a
great Jewish patriot. He was a good Jew,
who probably wore a yarmulke and obeyed
the Torah, and never planned to start a new
religion. He hated the Romans and wanted
to get them out of Jerusalem. He got
charged with political rebellion, sentenced

to execution. Yes, a Jewish high priest carried it out—Caiaphas—but most Jews back then hated Caiaphas anyway because he was the henchman for the Romans." He looked up at me over the edge of his coffee mug. "Was Jesus a good guy? Yeah. Great teacher? Sure. Messiah? Dunno."

"A lot of the Bible's predictions for the messianic era *were* fulfilled by Jesus—"

"But were they the crucial ones?" Rabbi Bloom asked. "Let's say you didn't know who I was and I asked you to meet me. I told you I'd be standing outside the Steeplegate Mall at ten o'clock wearing a Hawaiian shirt and that I'd have curly red hair and be listening to Outkast on my iPod. And at ten o'clock, you saw someone standing outside the Steeplegate Mall who had curly red hair and was wearing a Hawaiian shirt and listening to Outkast on an iPod . . . but it was a woman. Would you still think it was me?"

He stood up to refill his coffee. "Do you know what I heard on NPR on the way over here today? Another bus blew up in Israel. Three more kids from New Hampshire died in Iraq. And the cops just arrested some guy in Manchester who shot his ex-wife in front of their two kids. If Jesus ushered in the messianic era, and the world I hear about on the news is one of peace and redemption . . . well, I'd rather wait for a different *moshiach*." He glanced back at me. "Now, if you don't mind me asking *you* a question . . . what's a priest doing at a rabbi's office at eight in the morning asking questions about the Jewish Messiah?"

I got up and began to walk around the little room. "The book you loaned me—it got me thinking."

"And that's a bad thing?"

"Shay Bourne has said things, verbatim, that I read last night in the Gospel of Thomas."

"Bourne? He's read Thomas? I thought Maggie said he—"

"—has no religious training to speak of, and a minimal education."

"It's not like the Gideons leave the Gospel of Thomas in hotel rooms," Rabbi Bloom said. "Where would he have—"

"Exactly."

He steepled his fingers. "Huh."

I placed the book he'd loaned me on his desk. "What would you do if you began to second-guess everything you believed?"

Rabbi Bloom leaned forward and riffled through his Rolodex. "I would ask more questions," he said. He scribbled down something on a Post-it and handed it to me.

Ian Fletcher, I read. *603-555-1367.*

Lucius

‖‖‖

The night Shay had his second seizure, I was awake, gathering ink that I planned to use to give myself another tattoo. If I do say so myself, I'm rather proud of my homemade tattoos. I had five—my rationale being that my body, up until three weeks ago, wasn't worth much more than being a canvas for my art; plus the threat of getting AIDS from a dirty needle was obviously a moot point. On my left ankle was a clock, with the hands marking the moment of Adam's death. On my left shoulder was an angel, and below it an African tribal design. On my right leg was a bull, because I was a Taurus; and swimming beside it was a fish, for Adam, who was a Pisces. I had grand plans for this sixth one, which I planned to put right on my chest: the word BELIEVE, in Gothic letters. I'd practiced the art in reverse multiple times in pencil and pen, until I felt sure that I could replicate it with my tattoo gun as I worked in the mirror.

My first gun had been confiscated by the COs, like Crash's hype kit. It had taken me six months to amass the parts for the new one. Making ink was hard to do, and harder to get away with—which was why I had chosen to work on this during the deadest hours of the night. I had lit a plastic spoon on fire, keeping the flame small so I could catch the smoke in a plastic bag. It stank horribly, and just as I was getting certain the COs would literally get wind of it and shut down my operation, Shay Bourne collapsed next door.

This time, his seizure had been different. He'd screamed—so loud that he woke up the whole pod, so loud that the finest dust of plaster drifted down from the ceilings of our cells. To be honest, Shay was such a mess when he was wheeled off I-tier that none of us were sure whether or not he'd be returning—which is why I was stunned to see him being led back to his cell the very next day.

"Po-lice," Joey Kunz yelled, just in time for me to hide the pieces of my tattoo gun underneath the mattress. The officers locked Shay into his cell, and as soon as the door to I-tier shut behind them, I asked Shay how he was feeling.

"My head hurts," he said. "I have to go to sleep."

With Crash still off the tier after the hype kit transgression, things were quieter. Calloway slept most days and stayed up nights with his bird; Texas and Pogie played virtual poker; Joey was listening to his soaps. I waited an extra few minutes to make sure the officers were otherwise occupied out in the control booth and then I reached underneath my mattress again.

I had unraveled a guitar string to its central core, a makeshift needle. This was inserted into a pen whose ink cartridge had been removed—and a small piece of its tip sawed off and attached to the other end of the needle, which was attached to the motor shaft of a cassette player. The pen was taped to a toothbrush bent into an L shape, which let you hold the contraption more easily. You could adjust the needle length by sliding the pen casing back and forth; all that was left was plugging in the AC adapter of the cassette player, and I had a functional tattoo gun again.

The soot I'd captured the previous night had been mixed with a few drops of shampoo to liquefy it. I stood in front of the stainless steel panel that served as a mirror, and scrutinized my chest. Then, gritting my teeth against the pain, I turned on the gun. The needle moved back and forth in an elliptical orbit, piercing me hundreds of times per minute.

There it was, the letter *B*.

"Lucius?" Shay's voice drifted into my house.

"I'm sort of busy, Shay."

"What's that noise?"

"None of your business." I lifted it to my skin again, felt the needle working against me, a thousand arrows striking.

"Lucius? I can still hear that noise."

I sighed. "It's a tattoo gun, Shay, all right? I'm giving myself a tattoo."

There was a hesitation. "Will you give me one?"

I had done this for multiple inmates when I was housed on different tiers—ones that had a bit more freedom than I-tier, which offered twenty-three rollicking hours of lockdown. "I can't. I can't reach you."

"That's okay," Shay said. "I can reach *you*."

"Yeah, whatever," I said. I squinted back into the mirror and set the tattoo gun against my skin. Holding my breath, I carefully formed the curves and flourishes around the letters *E* and *L*.

I thought I heard Shay whimpering when I started on the letter *I*, and surely he cried out when I tattooed the *V*. My gun must not have been helping his headache any. Shrugging off his moans, I stepped closer to the mirror and surveyed my handiwork.

God, it was gorgeous. The letters moved with every breath I took; even the angry red swelling of my skin couldn't take away from the clean lines of the letters.

"B-believe," Shay stammered.

I turned around, as if I could see him through the wall between our cells. "What did you say?"

"It's what *you* said," Shay corrected. "I read it right, didn't I?"

I had not told anyone of my plans for my sixth tattoo. I hadn't shared the prototype art-work. I knew for a fact that Shay, from where he stood, could not have seen into my cell as I worked.

Fumbling behind the brick that served as my safe, I took out the shank that I used as a portable mirror. I stepped up to the front of my cell and angled it so that I could see Shay's beaming face in the reflection. "How did you know what I was writing?"

Shay smiled wider, and then raised his fist. He unfolded his fingers, one at a time.

His palm was red and inflamed, and printed across it, in Gothic script, was the same exact tattoo I'd just given myself.

MICHAEL

Shay paced his cell in figure eights. "Did you see him?" he asked, wild-eyed.

I sank down on the stool I'd dragged in from the control booth. I was sluggish today—not only was my head buzzing with questions about what I'd read, but I was also—for the first time in a year—not officiating at this evening's midnight Mass. "See who?" I replied, distracted.

"Sully. The new guy. Next door."

I glanced into the other cell. Lucius Du-Fresne was still on Shay's left; on his right, the formerly empty cell now had someone occupying it. Sully, however, wasn't there. He was in the rec yard, repeatedly running full tilt across the little square yard and leaping up against the far wall, hands splayed, as if hitting it hard enough meant he'd go right through the metal.

"They're going to kill me," Shay said.

"Maggie's working on writing a motion at this very—"

"Not the state," Shay said. "One of *them*."

I did not know anything about prison politics, but there was a fine line between Shay's paranoia and what might pass for the truth. Shay was receiving more attention than any other inmate at the prison, as a result of his lawsuit and the media frenzy. There was every chance he might be targeted by the general prison population.

Behind me, CO Smythe passed in his flak jacket, carrying a broom and some cleaning supplies. Once a week, the inmates were required to clean their own cells. It was one-at-a-time, supervised cleaning: after an inmate came in from rec, the supplies would be waiting for him in his cell, and a CO would stand guard at the doorway until the work was finished—close by, because even Windex could become a weapon in here. I watched the empty cell door open, so that Smythe could leave the spray bottles and the toweling and the broom; then he walked to the far end of the tier to get the new inmate from the rec yard. "I'll talk to the warden. I'll make sure you're protected," I told Shay, which seemed to mollify him. "So," I said, changing the subject, "what do you like to read?"

"What, you're Oprah now? We're having a book club?"

"No."

"Good, because I'm not reading the Bible."

"I know that," I said, seizing this inroad. "Why not?"

"It's lies." Shay waved a hand, a dismissal.

"What do you read that *isn't* a lie?"

"I don't," he replied. "The words get all knotted up. I have to stare at a page for a year before I can make sense of it."

" '*There's light inside a person of light*,' " I quoted, " '*and it shines on the whole world*.' "

Shay hesitated. "Can you see it, too?" He held his hands up in front of his face, scrutinizing his fingertips. "The light from the television—the stuff that went into me—it's still there. It glows, at night."

I sighed. "It's from the Gospel of Thomas."

"No, I'm pretty sure it came from the television . . ."

"The *words*, Shay. The ones I just said. They came from a gospel I was reading last night. And so does a lot of stuff you've been saying to me."

His eyes met mine. "What do you know," he said softly, and I couldn't tell if it was a statement or a question.

"I *don't* know," I admitted. "That's why I'm here."

"That's why we're *all* here," Shay said.

If you bring forth what is within you, what is within you will save you. It was one of Jesus's sayings in the Gospel of Thomas; it was one of the first things Shay Bourne had ever told me, when he was explaining why he needed to donate his heart. Could it really be this simple? Could salvation be not a passive acceptance, like I'd been led to believe, but an active pursuit?

Maybe it was saying the rosary, for me, and receiving Holy Communion, and serving God. Maybe for Maggie's father, it was meeting with a bunch of die-hard congregants who wouldn't let the lack of a physical temple dissuade them from prayer. Maybe for Maggie, it was mending whatever kept her focused on her faults instead of her strengths.

Maybe for Shay, maybe it was offering his heart—literally and figuratively—to the mother who'd lost hers years ago because of him.

Then again, Shay Bourne was a killer; his sentences curled like a puppy chasing its tail; he thought he had something phosphorescent coursing through his veins because a television had zapped him in the middle of the night. He did not sound messianic—just delusional.

Shay looked at me. "You should go," he said, but then his attention was distracted by the sound of the rec yard door being opened. Officer Smythe led the new inmate back onto I-tier.

He was an enormous tower of muscle with a swastika tattooed on his scalp. His hair, sprouting out from a buzz cut, grew over it like moss.

The inmate's cell door was closed, and his handcuffs removed. "You know the drill, Sully," the officer said. He stood in the doorway as Sully slowly picked up the spray bottle and washed down his sink. I heard the squeak of paper toweling on metal.

"Hey, Father—you watch the game last night?" CO Smythe said, and then he rolled his eyes. "Sully, what are you doing? You don't need to sweep the—"

Suddenly the broom in Sully's hands was no longer a broom but a broken spear that he jutted into the officer's throat. Smythe grabbed his neck, gurgling. His eyes rolled back in his head; he stumbled toward Shay's cell. As he fell beside me, I clasped my hands over the wound and screamed for help.

The tier came to life. The inmates were all clamoring to see what had happened; CO Whitaker was suddenly there and hauling me to my feet, taking my place as another officer started CPR. Four more officers ran past me with pepper spray and shot it into Sully's face. He was dragged out of the tier shrieking as the closest physician arrived—a psychiatrist I'd seen around the prison. But by now, Smythe had stopped moving.

No one seemed to notice that I was there; there was far too much happening, too much at stake. The psychiatrist tried to find a pulse in Smythe's neck, but his hand came away slick with blood. He lifted the CO's wrist and, after a moment, shook his head. "He's gone."

The tier had gone absolutely silent; the inmates were all staring in shock at the body in front of them. Blood had stopped flowing from Smythe's neck; he was perfectly still. To my right, I could see an argument going on in the control booth—the EMTs who'd arrived too late and were trying to gain admission to the tier. They were buzzed in, still shrugging into their flak jackets, and knelt beside Smythe's body, repeating the same ineffective tests that the psychiatrist had.

Behind me, I heard weeping.

I turned around to find Shay crouched on the floor of his cell. His face was streaked with tears and blood; his hand slipped beneath his cell door so that his fingers brushed Smythe's.

"You here for last rites?" one of the medics asked, and for the first time, everyone seemed to realize I was still present.

"I, uh—"

"What's he doing here?" CO Whitaker barked.

"Who the hell *is* he?" another officer said. "I don't even work this tier."

"I can go," I said. "I'll . . . just go." I glanced once more at Shay, who was curled into a ball, whispering. If I hadn't known better, I would have thought he was praying.

As the two EMTs got ready to move the body onto a stretcher, I prayed over Smythe. "In the Name of God the Father Almighty who created you . . . in the Name of Jesus Christ who redeemed you; in the Name of the Holy Spirit who sanctifies you. May your rest be this day in peace, and your dwelling place in the Paradise of God. Amen."

I made the sign of the cross and started to get to my feet.

"On three," the first EMT said.

The second one nodded, his hands on the slain officer's ankles. "One, two . . . holy *shit*," he cried as the dead man began to struggle against him.

||||||||||||||||||||||||||||||||||||||||||||||||||||||||||||||||||||||||||||||||||||||||

"One of the proofs of the immortality
of the soul is that myriads have believed it.
They also believed the world was flat."

—*MARK TWAIN*, NOTEBOOK

June

Claire would be cut in half, her sternum buzzed open with a saw and held open with a metal spreader so that she could be made, literally, heartless—and this was not what terrified me the most.

No, what scared me to death was the idea of cellular memory.

Dr. Wu had said that there was no scientific evidence that the personality traits of heart donors transferred to their recipients. But science could only go so far, I figured. I'd read the books and done the research, and I didn't see why it was such a stretch to think that living tissue might have the ability to remember. After all, how many of us had tried to forget something traumatic . . . only to find it printed on the back of our eyelids, tattooed on our tongues?

There were dozens of cases. The baby with a clubfoot who drowned and gave his heart to another infant, who began to drag her left leg. The rapper who started playing classical music, and then learned his donor had died clutching a violin case. The cattle rancher who received the heart of a sixteen-year-old vegetarian, and could not eat meat again without getting violently ill.

Then there was the twenty-year-old organ donor who wrote music in his spare time. A year after he died, his parents found a CD of a love song he'd recorded, about losing his heart to a girl named Andi. His recipient, a twenty-year-old girl, was named Andrea. When the boy's parents played the song for her, she could complete the chorus, without ever having heard it.

Most of these stories were benign—a strange coincidence, an intriguing twist. Except for one: a little boy received the heart of another boy who'd been murdered. He began to have nightmares about the man who killed his donor—with details about the clothing the man wore, how he'd abducted the boy, where the murder weapon had been stashed. Using this evidence, the police caught the killer.

If Claire received Shay Bourne's heart, it would be bad enough if she were to harbor thoughts of murder. But what would absolutely wreck me was if, with that heart in her, she had to *feel* her own father and sister being killed.

In that case, better to have no heart at all.

Maggie

Today, I decided, I was going to do everything right. It was Sunday, and I didn't have to go to work. Instead, I got up and unearthed my *One Minute Workout* video (which was not nearly as slacker as it sounds—you could add minutes to your own liking, and no one was here to notice if I chose the four-minute option over the more grueling eight-minute one). I picked Focus on Abs, instead of the easier Upper Arm. I sorted my recyclables and flossed and shaved my legs in the shower. Downstairs, I cleaned Oliver's cage and let him have the run of the living room while I made myself scrambled egg whites for breakfast.

With *wheat germ.*

Well. I lasted forty-seven minutes, anyway, before I had to break out the Oreos that I hid in the box with my skinny jeans, a last-ditch attempt at utter guilt before I ripped open the package and indulged.

I gave Oliver an Oreo, too, and was starting my third cookie when the doorbell rang.

As soon as I saw the bright pink T-shirt of the man standing on the porch, with the words JOYOUS FOR JESUS printed boldly across it, I knew this was my punishment for falling off the wagon into the snack foods.

"If you're not gone in the next ten seconds, I'm calling 911," I said.

He grinned at me, a big platinum orthodontically enhanced grin. "I'm not a stranger," he said. "I'm a friend you haven't met yet."

I rolled my eyes. "Why don't we just cut to the chase—you give me the pamphlets, I politely refuse to talk to you, and then I close the door and throw them in the trash."

He held out his hand. "I'm Tom."

"You're *leaving*," I corrected.

"I used to be bitter, too. I'd go to work in the mornings and come home to an empty house and eat half a can of soup and wonder why I had even been put on this earth. I thought I had no one, but myself—"

"And then you offered Jesus the rest of your soup," I finished. "Look, I'm an atheist."

"It's not too late to find your faith."

"What you really mean is that it's not too late for me to find *your* faith," I answered, scooping up Oliver as he made a mad dash for the open door. "You know what I believe? That religion served its historical purpose—it was a set of laws to live by, before we had a justice system. But even when it starts out with the best of intentions, things get screwed up, don't they? A group bands together because they believe the same things, and then somehow that gets perverted so that anyone who doesn't believe those things is wrong. Honestly, even if there was a religion founded on the principle of doing good for other people, or helping them with their personal rights, like I do every day, I wouldn't join . . . because it would still be a *religion*."

I had rendered Tom speechless. This was probably the most heated debate he'd had in months; mostly, he'd have doors closed in his face. Inside my house, the phone began to ring.

Tom pushed a pamphlet into my hand and

beat a hasty retreat off my porch. As I closed the door behind him I glanced down at the cover.

GOD + YOU = ∞

"If there's any math to religion," I muttered, "it's division." I slipped the pamphlet onto the liner of newspaper beneath Oliver's cage as I hurried to the phone, which was on the verge of rolling over to the answering machine. "Hello?"

The voice was unfamiliar, halting. "Is Maggie Bloom there?"

"Speaking." I geared up for a zinger to put a telemarketer in her place for disturbing me on a Sunday morning.

As it turned out, she wasn't a telemarketer. She was a nurse at Concord Hospital, and she was calling because I had been listed as Shay Bourne's emergency contact, and an emergency had occurred.

Lucius

You would not have believed it possible, but when CO Smythe came back to life, things actually got worse.

The remaining officers had to give statements to the warden about the stabbing. We were kept in lockdown, and the next day a team of officers who did not normally work on I-tier were brought in on duty. They started our one-hour rotations on the exercise yard and the shower, and Pogie was the first to go.

I hadn't showered since the stabbing, although the COs had given both Shay and me a fresh set of scrubs. We had gotten Smythe's blood on us, and a quick wash in our cell basins didn't go very far to making me feel clean. While we were waiting for our turns in the shower, Alma showed up to give us both blood tests. They tested anyone who came in contact with an inmate's blood, and since that included CO Smythe, *his* blood apparently was only one step removed from questionable. Shay was moved in handcuffs, ankle cuffs, and a belly chain to a holding room outside the tier, where Alma was waiting.

In the middle of all this, Pogie slipped in the shower. He lay there, moaning about his back. Two more COs dragged in the backboard and handcuffed Pogie to it, then carried him to a gurney so he could be transported all the way to Medical. But because they were not used to I-tier, and because COs are supposed to follow us, not lead, they did not realize that Shay was already being brought back to the tier at the same time Pogie was going out.

Tragedies happen in a split second in prison; that's all it took for Pogie to use the handcuff key he'd hidden to free himself, jump off the backboard, grab it, and slam it into Shay's skull, so that he flew face-first into the brick wall.

"Weiss macht!" Pogie yelled—*White pride!*—

which was how I realized Crash—from where he was still being kept in solitary—had used his connections to order a hit on Shay in retaliation for ratting him out and giving his hype kit to the COs. Sully's attack on CO Smythe had just been collateral damage, meant to shake up the staffing on our tier so that part two of the plan could be carried out. And Pogie—a probate—had jumped at the chance to earn his bones by carrying out a murder sanctioned by the Aryan Brotherhood.

Six hours after this fiasco, Alma returned to finish drawing my blood. I was taken to the holding cell and found her still shaken by what had happened, although she would not tell me anything—except that Shay had been taken to the hospital.

When I saw something silver winking at me, I waited until Alma drew the needle from my arm. Then I put my head down between my knees.

"You all right, sugar?" Alma asked.

"Just feeling a little dizzy." I let my fingers trail along the floor.

If magicians are the best at sleight of hand, then inmates have to be a close second. As soon as I was back in my cell, I pulled my booty out of the seam in my scrubs where I'd hidden it. Pogie's handcuff key was tiny, shiny, formed from the fastener of a manila envelope.

I crawled beneath my bunk and wriggled the loose brick that concealed my prized possessions. In a small cardboard box were my bottles of paint and my Q-tip brushes. There were packets of candy, too, that I planned to extract pigment from in the future—a half-empty pack of M&M's, a roll of LifeSavers, a few loose Starbursts. I unwrapped one of the Starbursts, the orange one that tasted like St. Joseph children's aspirin, and kneaded the square with my thumbs until the taffy became pliable. I pressed the handcuff key into the center, then reshaped a careful square and folded it into its original wrapping.

I did not like the thought of profiting in some way from an incident that had hurt Shay so badly, but I was also a realist. When Shay ran out of his nine lives and I was left alone, I would need all the help I could get.

Maggie

Even if I hadn't been listed as Shay Bourne's emergency contact, I would have found him quickly enough at the hospital: he was the only patient with armed guards standing outside his door. I glanced at the officers, then turned my attention to the nurse at the desk. "Is he all right? What happened?"

Father Michael had called me after the attack on CO Smythe and told me Shay hadn't been hurt. Somewhere between now and then, however, something must have gone drastically wrong. I had tried calling the priest now, but he wasn't answering his

cell—I assumed he was on his way, that
he'd been called, too.

If Shay hadn't been treated at the prison
hospital, whatever had happened must've
been pretty awful. Inmates weren't moved
off-site unless absolutely necessary, because
of cost and security. With the hoopla Shay
had generated outside the prison walls, it
must have been a matter of life or death.

Then again, maybe *everything* was when
it came to Shay. Here I was literally shaking
over the news that he'd been seriously injured, when I had spent yesterday filing motions that would streamline his execution.

The nurse looked up at me. "He's just
come back from surgery."

"Surgery?"

"Yes," said a clipped British voice behind
me. "And no, it wasn't an appendectomy."

When I turned around, Dr. Gallagher was
standing there.

"Are you the *only* doctor who works
here?"

"It certainly feels that way sometimes. I'm
happy to answer your questions. Mr. Bourne
is my patient."

"He's my client."

Dr. Gallagher glanced at the nurse and at the armed officers. "Why don't we go somewhere to talk?"

I followed him down the hall to a small family waiting lounge that was empty. When the doctor gestured for me to take a seat, my heart sank. Doctors only made you sit down when they delivered bad news.

"Mr. Bourne is going to be fine," Dr. Gallagher said. "At least in terms of this injury."

"*What* injury?"

"I'm sorry, I thought you knew—apparently, it was an inmate fight. Mr. Bourne sustained a severe blow to the maxillary sinus."

I waited for him to translate.

"His maxilla's broken," Dr. Gallagher said, and he leaned forward, touching my face. His fingers brushed over the bone below my eye socket, tracing toward my mouth. "Here," he said, and I absolutely, positively stopped breathing. "There was a bit of a trauma during the operation. As soon as we saw the injuries we knew that the anesthesia would be intravenous, instead of inhalational. Needless to say, when Mr. Bourne heard the anesthesiologist say that she'd begun Sodium Pentothal drip, he grew quite agitated." The doctor looked up at me. "He asked if this was a dry run for the real thing."

I tried to imagine how it would feel to be Shay—hurt, aching, and confused—whisked away to an unfamiliar place for what seemed to be a prelude to his own execution. "I want to see him."

"If you can tell him, Ms. Bloom, that if I'd realized who he was—what his circumstances are, I mean—well, I would never have allowed the anesthesiologist to use that drug, much less an IV tube. I'm deeply sorry for putting him through that."

I nodded and stood up.

"One more thing," Dr. Gallagher said. "I really admire you. For doing this sort of thing."

I was halfway to Shay's room when I realized that Dr. Gallagher had remembered my name.

It took several cell phone calls to the prison before I was allowed in to see Shay, and even then, the warden insisted that the officer inside the room would have to stay. I walked inside, acknowledged the CO, and sat down on the edge of Shay's bed. His eyes were blackened, his face bandaged. He was asleep, and it made him look younger.

Part of what I did for a living meant championing the causes of my clients. I was the strong arm, fighting on their behalf, the bullhorn broadcasting their voices. I could feel the angry discomfort of the Abenaki boy whose school team was called the Redskins; I could identify with the passion of the teacher who'd been fired for being Wiccan. Shay, though, had sent me reeling. Although this was arguably the most important case I would ever bring to court, and although—as my father pointed out—I hadn't been this motivated in my career in ages, there was an inherent paradox. The more I got to know him, the better chance I had of winning his organ donation case. But the more I got to know him, the harder it would be for me to see him executed.

I dragged my cell phone out of my purse. The officer's eyes flicked toward me. "You're not supposed to use that in here—"

"Oh, piss off," I snapped, and for the hundredth time I dialed Father Michael, and reached his voice mail. "I don't know where you are," I said, "but call me back *immediately.*"

I had left the emotional component of Shay Bourne's welfare to Father Michael, figuring

(a) my talents were better put to use in a courtroom, and (b) my interpersonal relationship skills had grown so rusty I needed WD--40 before employing them. But now, Father Michael was MIA, Shay was hospitalized, and I was here, for better or for worse.

I stared at Shay's hands. They were cuffed at the wrist to the metal bars of the hospital gurney. The nails were clean and clipped, the tendons ropy. It was hard to imagine the fingers curled around a pistol, pulling a trigger twice. And yet, twelve jurors had been able to picture it.

Very slowly, I reached across the knobby cotton blanket. I threaded my fingers with Shay's, surprised at how warm his skin was. But when I was about to pull away, his grip tightened. His eyes slitted open, another shade of blue amid the bruising. "Gracie," he said, in a voice that sounded like cotton caught on thorns. "You came."

I did not know who he thought I was. "Of *course* I came," I said, squeezing his hand. I smiled at Shay Bourne and pretended that I was the person he needed me to be.

MICHAEL

Dr. Vijay Choudhary's office was filled with statues of Ganesha, the Hindu deity with a potbellied human body and an elephant's head. I had to move one in order to sit down, in fact. "Mr. Smythe was extremely lucky," the doctor said. "A quarter inch to the left, and he wouldn't have survived."

"About that . . ." I took a deep breath. "A doctor at the prison pronounced him dead."

"Between you and me, Father, I wouldn't trust a psychiatrist to find his own car in a parking lot, much less a hypotensive victim's pulse. Reports of Mr. Smythe's death were, as they say, greatly exaggerated."

"There was a lot of blood—"

"Many structures in the neck can bleed a great deal. To a layman, a pool of blood may look like a huge quantity, even when it's not." He shrugged. "What I imagine happened was a vasovagal reaction. Mr. Smythe saw blood and passed out. The body compensates for shock due to blood loss. Blood pressure lowers, and vasoconstriction occurs, and both tend to stop the bleeding. They also lead to a loss of palpable pulses in the extremities—which is why the psychiatrist couldn't find one in his wrist."

"So," I said, pinkening. "You don't think it's possible that Mr. Smythe was . . . well . . . resurrected?"

"No," he chuckled. "Now, in medical school, I saw patients who'd frozen to death, in the vernacular, come back to life when they were warmed up. I saw a heart stop beating, and then start up by itself again. But in neither of those cases—or in Mr. Smythe's—did I consider the patient clinically dead before his or her recovery."

My phone began to vibrate, as it had every ten minutes for the past two hours. I'd turned the ringer off when I came into the hospital, as per their policy. "Nothing miraculous, then," I said.

"Perhaps not by your standards . . . but I think that Mr. Smythe's family might disagree."

I thanked him, set the statue of Ganesha back on my chair, and left Dr. Choudhary's office. As soon as I exited the hospital building, I turned on my cell phone to see fifty-two messages.

Call me right back, Maggie said on her message. *Something's happened to Shay.* Beep.

Where are you?? Beep.

Okay, I know you probably don't have your phone on but you have to call me back immediately. Beep.

Where the fuck are you? Beep.

I hung up and dialed her cell phone. "Maggie Bloom," she whispered, answering.

"What happened to Shay?"

"He's in the hospital."

"What?! *Which* hospital?"

"Concord. Where are you?"

"Standing outside the ER."

"Then for God's sake, get up here. He's in room 514."

I ran up the stairs, pushing past doctors

and nurses and lab technicians and secre-
taries, as if my speed now could make up for
the fact that I had not been available for Shay
when he needed me. The armed officers at
the door took one look at my collar—a free
pass, especially on a Sunday afternoon—
and let me inside. Maggie was curled up on
the bed, her shoes off, her feet tucked underneath her. She was holding Shay's hand, although I would have been hard-pressed to
recognize the patient as the man I'd talked to
just yesterday. His skin was the color of fine
ash; his hair had been shaved in one patch
to accommodate stitches to close a gash.
His nose—broken, from the looks of it—was
covered with gauze, and the nostrils were
plugged with cotton.

"Dear God," I breathed.

"From what I can understand, he came
out on the short end of a prison hit," Maggie
said.

"That's not possible. I was *there* during the
prison hit—"

"Apparently, you left before Act Two."

I glanced at the officer who stood like a
sentry in the corner of the hospital room.
The man looked at me and nodded in confirmation.

"I already called Warden Coyne at home to give him hell," Maggie said. "He's meeting me at the prison in a half hour to talk about additional security measures that can be put in place to protect Shay until his execution— when what he really means is 'What can I do to keep you from suing?' " She turned to me. "Can you sit here with Shay?"

It was a Sunday, and I was utterly, absolutely lost. I was on an unofficial leave of absence from St. Catherine's, and although I had always known I'd feel adrift without God, I had underestimated how aimless I would feel without my church. Usually at this time, I would be hanging my robes after celebrating Mass. I would go with Father Walter to have lunch with a parishioner. Then we'd head back to his place and watch the preseason Sox game on TV, have a couple of beers. What religion did for me went beyond belief—it made me part of a community.

"I can stay," I answered.

"Then I'm out of here," Maggie said. "He hasn't woken up, not really, anyway. And the nurse said he'll probably have to pee when he does, and that we should use this torture device." She pointed at a plastic jug with a long neck. "I don't know about you, but I'm not getting paid enough for that." She paused in the doorway. "I'll call you later. Turn on your damn phone."

When she left, I pulled a chair closer to Shay's bed. I read the plastic placard about how to raise and lower the mattress, and the list of which television channels were available. I said an entire rosary, and still Shay didn't stir.

At the edge of the bed, Shay's medical chart hung on a metal clip. I skimmed through the language that I didn't understand—the injury, the medications, his vital statistics. Then I glanced at the patient name at the top of the page:

I. M. Bourne

Isaiah Matthew Bourne. We had been told this at his trial, but I had forgotten that Shay was not his Christian name. "I. M. Bourne," I said aloud. "Sounds like a guy Trump would hire."

I am born.

Was this a hint, another puzzle piece of evidence?

There were two ways of looking at any situation. What one person sees as a prisoner's babble, another might recognize as words from a long-lost gospel. What one person sees as a medically viable stroke of luck, another might see as a resurrection. I thought of Lucius being healed, of the water into wine, of the followers who had so easily believed in Shay. I thought of a thirty-three-year-old man, a carpenter, facing execution. I thought of Rabbi Bloom's idea—that every generation had a person in it capable of being the Messiah.

There is a point when you stand at the edge of the cliff of hard evidence, look across to what lies on the other side, and step forward. Otherwise, you wind up going nowhere. I stared at Shay, and maybe for the first time, I didn't see who he was. I saw who he might be.

As if he could feel my gaze, he began to toss and turn. Only one of his eyes could slit open; the other was swollen shut. "Father," he rasped in a voice still cushioned with medication. "Where am I?"

"You were hurt. You're going to be all right, Shay."

In the corner of the room, the officer was staring at us. "Do you think we could have a minute alone? I'd like to pray in private with him."

The officer hesitated—as well he should have: what clergyman isn't accustomed to praying in front of others? Then he shrugged. "Guess a priest wouldn't do anything funny," he said. "Your boss is tougher than mine."

People anthropomorphized God all the time—as a boss, as a lifesaver, as a justice, as a father. No one ever pictured him as a convicted murderer. But if you put aside the physical trappings of the body—something that all the apostles had had to do after Jesus was resurrected—then maybe anything was possible.

As the officer backed out of the room, Shay winced. "My face . . ." He tried to lift up his hand to touch the bandages, but found that he was handcuffed to the bed. Struggling, he began to pull harder.

"Shay," I said firmly, "don't."

"It hurts. I want drugs . . ."

"You're already on drugs," I told him. "We only have a few minutes till the officer comes back in, so we have to talk while we can."

"I don't want to talk."

Ignoring him, I leaned closer. "Tell me," I whispered. "Tell me who you are."

A wary hope lit Shay's eyes; he'd probably never expected to be recognized as the Lord.

He went very still, never taking his eyes off mine. "Tell me who *you* are."

In the Catholic Church, there were lies of commission and lies of omission. The first referred to telling an outright falsehood, the second to withholding the truth. Both were sins.

I had lied to Shay since before the moment we met. He'd counted on me to help him donate his heart, but he'd never realized how black mine was. How could I expect Him to reveal Himself when I hadn't done the same?

"You're right," I said quietly. "There's something I haven't told you . . . about who I used to be, before I was a priest."

"Let me guess . . . an altar boy."

"I was a college student, majoring in math. I didn't even go to church until after I served on the jury."

"What jury?"

I hesitated. "The one that sentenced you to death, Shay."

He stared at me for a long minute, and then he turned away. "Get out."

"Shay—"

"Get the fuck away from me!" He flailed against his handcuffs, yanking at the bonds

so that his skin rubbed raw. The sound he made was wordless, primordial, the noise that had surely filled the world before there was order and light.

A nurse came running in, along with the two officers who were standing outside. "What happened?" the nurse cried, as Shay continued to thrash, his head whipping from side to side on the pillow. The gauze in his nose bloomed with fresh blood.

The nurse pushed a call button on the panel behind Shay's head, and suddenly the room was filled with people. A doctor yelled at the officers to unlock his damn hands, but as soon as they did, Shay began swatting at everything he could reach. An aide plunged a hypodermic into his arm. "Get him out of here," someone said, and an orderly pulled me out of the room; the last thing I saw was Shay going boneless, sliding away from the people who were desperately trying to save him.

June

Claire was standing in front of a full-length mirror, naked. Her chest was crisscrossed with black ribbon, like the lacing on a football. As I watched, she untied the bow, unraveled the ribbons, and peeled back both halves of her chest. She unhooked a tiny brass hinge on her rib cage and it sprang open.

Inside, the heart was beating sure and strong, a clear sign that it wasn't hers. Claire lifted a serving spoon and began to carve at the organ, trying to sever it from the veins and arteries. Her cheeks went pale; her eyes were the color of agony—but she managed to pull it free: a bloody, misshapen mass that she placed in my outstretched hand. "Take it back," she said.

I woke up from the nightmare, sweat-soaked, pulse racing. After speaking with Dr. Wu about organ compatibility, I'd realized he was right—what was at issue here was not where this heart came from, but whether it came at all.

But I still hadn't told Claire a donor heart had become available. We had yet to go through the legal proceedings, anyway—and although I told myself I didn't want to get her hopes up until the judge ruled, another part of me realized that I just didn't want to have to tell her the truth.

After all, it was *her* chest that would be hosting this man's heart.

Even a long shower couldn't get the nightmare of Claire out of my mind, and I realized that we had to have the conversation I had been so studiously avoiding. I dressed and hurried downstairs to find her eating a bowl of cereal on the couch and watching television. "The dog needs to go out," she said absently.

"Claire," I said, "I have to talk to you."

"Let me just see the end of this show."

I glanced at the screen—it was *Full House*,

and Claire had watched this episode so often that even *I* could have told you Jesse came home from Japan realizing being a rock star was not what it was cracked up to be.

"You've seen it before," I said, turning off the television.

Her eyes flashed, and she used the remote to turn the show back on.

Maybe it was a lack of sleep; maybe it was just the weight of the imminent future on my shoulders—for whatever reason, I snapped. I whirled around and yanked the cable feed out of the wall.

"What is *wrong* with you?" Claire cried. "Why are you being such a bitch!"

Both of us fell silent, stunned by Claire's language. She'd never called me that before; she'd never really even argued with me. *Take it back*, I thought, and I remembered that image of Claire, holding out her heart.

"Claire," I said, backpedaling. "I'm sorry. I didn't mean to—"

I broke off as Claire's eyes rolled back in her head.

I'd seen this before—too often. The AICD in her chest was firing: when Claire's heart skipped a beat, or several, it automatically defibrillated her. I caught her as she collapsed, settling her on the couch, waiting for her heart to restart, for Claire to come to.

Except this time, she didn't.

On the ambulance ride to the hospital, I counted all the reasons I hated myself: For picking a fight with Claire. For accepting Shay Bourne's offer to donate his heart, without asking her first. For turning off *Full House* before the happy ending.

Just stay with me, I begged silently, and you can watch TV twenty-four hours a day. I will watch it with you. Don't give up, we've come so close.

Although the EMTs had gotten Claire's heart beating again by the time we reached the hospital, Dr. Wu had admitted her, with the unspoken agreement that this was her new home until a new heart arrived—or hers gave out. I watched him check Claire, who was fast asleep in the oceanic blue light of the darkened room. "June," he said, "let's talk outside."

He closed the door behind us. "There's no good news here."

I nodded, biting my lip.

"Obviously, the AICD isn't functioning correctly. But in addition, the tests we've done show her urine output decreasing and her creatinine levels rising. We're talking about renal failure, June. It's not just her heart that's giving out—her whole body is shutting down."

I looked away, but I couldn't stop a tear from rolling down my cheek.

"I don't know how long it's going to take to get a court to agree to that heart donation," the doctor said, "but Claire can't wait around for the docket to clear."

"I'll call the lawyer," I said softly. "Is there anything else I can do?"

Dr. Wu touched my arm. "You should think about saying good-bye."

I held myself together long enough for Dr. Wu to disappear into an elevator. Then, I rushed down the hallway and blindly plunged into a doorway that stood ajar. I fell to my knees and let the grief bleed out of me—one great, low keening note.

Suddenly I felt a hand on my shoulder. I blinked through my tears to find the priest who was Shay Bourne's ally staring at me. "June? Is everything all right?"

"No," I said. "No, everything is most definitely *not* all right."

I could see then what I hadn't noticed when

I first came into the room—the gold cross on the long dais in the front of the room, one flag with the star of David, another with a Muslim crescent moon: this was the hospital chapel, a place to ask for what you wanted the most.

Was it wrong to wish for someone's death so that Claire could have his heart sooner?

"Is it your daughter?" the priest asked.

I nodded, but I couldn't look him in the eye.

"Would it be all right—I mean, would you mind if I prayed for her?"

Although I did not want his assistance—had not *asked* for his assistance—this one time, I was willing to put aside how I felt about God, because Claire could use all the help she could get. Almost imperceptibly, I nodded.

Beside me, Father Michael's voice began to move over the hills and valleys of the simplest of prayers: *"Our Father, who art in heaven, hallowed be thy name. Thy kingdom come, thy will be done, on earth as it is in heaven."*

Before I realized what I was doing, my own mouth had started to form the words, a muscle memory. And to my surprise, instead

of it feeling false or forced, it made me relieved, as if I had just passed the baton to
someone else.

**"Give us this day our daily bread and
lead us not into temptation. Forgive us
our trespasses, as we forgive others who
trespass against us; and lead us not into
temptation, but deliver us from evil."**

It felt like putting on flannel pajamas on a
snowy night; like turning on your blinker for
the exit that you know will take you home.

I looked at Father Michael, and together
we said "Amen."

MICHAEL

Ian Fletcher, former tele-atheist and current academic, lived in New Canaan, New Hampshire, in a farmhouse on a dirt road where the mailboxes were not numbered. I drove up and down the street four times before turning down one driveway and knocking on the door. When I did, no one answered, although I could hear strains of Mozart through the open windows.

I had left June in the hospital, still shaken by my encounter with Shay. Talk about irony: just when I allowed myself to think that I *might* be in God's company, after all—He flatly rejected me. The whole world felt off-kilter; it is an odd thing to start questioning the frame-work that's ordered your life, your career, your expectations—and so I had placed a phone call to someone who'd been through it before.

I knocked again, and this time the door swung open beneath my fist. "Hello? Anyone home?"

"In here," a woman called out.

I stepped into the foyer, taking note of the colonial furniture, the photo on the wall that showed a young girl shaking hands with Bill Clinton and another of the girl smiling beside the Dalai Lama. I followed the music to a room off the kitchen, where the most intricate dollhouse I'd ever seen was sitting on a table, surrounded by bits of wood and chisels and glue gun sticks. The house was made of bricks no bigger than my thumbnail, the win-dows had miniature shutters that could be louvered to let in light; there was a porch with Corinthian columns. "Amazing," I murmured, and a woman stood up from behind the doll-house, where she'd been hidden.

"Oh," she said. "Thanks." Seeing me, she did a double take, and I realized her eyes were focused on my clerical collar.

"Bad parochial school flashback?"

"No . . . it's just been a while since I've had a priest in here." She stood up, wiping her hands on a white butcher's apron. "I'm Mariah Fletcher," she said.

"Michael Wright."

"*Father* Michael Wright."

I grinned. "Busted." Then I gestured to her handiwork. "Did you make this?"

"Well. Yeah."

"I've never seen anything like it."

"Good," Mariah said. "That's what the client's counting on."

I bent down, scrutinizing a tiny door knocker with the head of a lion. "You're quite an artist."

"Not really. I'm just better at detail than I am at the big picture." She turned off the CD player that was trilling *The Magic Flute*. "Ian said I was supposed to keep an eye out for you. And— Oh, shoot." Her eyes flew to the corner of the room, where a stack of blocks had been abandoned. "You didn't come across two hellions on your way in?"

"No . . ."

"That's not a good sign." Pushing past me, she ran into the kitchen and threw open a pantry door. Twins—I figured them to be about four years old—were smearing the white linoleum with peanut butter and jelly.

"Oh, God," Mariah sighed as their faces turned up to hers like sunflowers.

"You told us we could finger-paint," one of the boys said.

"Not on the floor; and not with food!" She glanced at me. "I'd escort you, but—"

"You have to take care of a sticky situation?"

She smiled. "Ian's in the barn; you can just head down there." She lifted each boy and pointed him toward the sink. "And you two," she said, "are going to clean up, and then go torture Daddy."

I left her washing the twins' hands and walked down the path toward the barn. Having children was not in the cards for me—I knew that. A priest's love for God was so all-encompassing that it should erase the human craving for a family—my parents, brothers, sisters, and children were *all* Jesus. If the Gospel of Thomas was right, however, and we were more *like* God than *unlike* Him, then having children should have been mandatory for everyone. After all, God had a son and had given Him up. Any parent whose child had gone to college or gotten married or moved away would understand this part of God more than me.

As I approached the barn, I heard the most unholy sounds—like cats being dismembered, calves being slaughtered. Panicked—was Fletcher hurt?—I threw open the door to find him watching a teenage girl play the violin.

Really badly.

She took the violin from her chin and settled it into the slight curve of her hip. "I don't understand why I have to practice in the barn."

Fletcher removed a pair of foam earplugs. "What was that?"

She rolled her eyes. "Did you even hear my piece at *all*?"

Fletcher paused. "You know I love you, right?" The girl nodded. "Well, let's just say if God was hanging around here today, that last bit probably sent Her running for the hills."

"Tryouts for band are tomorrow," she said. "What am I going to *do*?"

"Switch to the flute?" Fletcher suggested, but he put his arm around the girl and hugged her as he spoke. As he turned, he noticed me. "Ah. You must be Michael Wright." He shook my hand and introduced the girl. "This is my daughter, Faith."

Faith shook my hand, too. "Did *you* hear me play? Am I as bad as he says I am?"

I hesitated, and Fletcher came to my rescue. "Honey, don't put the priest in a position where he's going to have to lie—he'll waste his whole afternoon at confession." He grinned at Faith. "I think it's your turn to watch the demon twins from hell."

"No, I remember very clearly that it's *your* turn. I was doing it all morning while Mom worked."

"Ten bucks," Ian said.

"Twenty," Faith countered.

"Done." She put her violin back in its case. "Nice to meet you," she said to me, and she slipped out of the barn, heading toward the house.

"You have a beautiful family," I said to Fletcher.

He laughed. "Appearances can be deceiving. Spending an afternoon with Cain and Abel is a whole new form of birth control."

"Their names are—"

"Not really," Fletcher said, smiling. "But that's what I call them when Mariah's not listening. Come on back to my office."

He walked me past a generator and a snowblower, two abandoned horse stalls, and through a pine door. Inside, to my surprise, was a finished room with paneled walls and two stories of bookshelves. "I have to admit," Fletcher said, "I don't get very many calls from the Catholic clergy. They aren't quite the prevalent audience for my book."

I sat down on a leather wing chair. "I can imagine."

"So what's a nice priest like you doing in the office of a rabble-rouser like me? Can I expect a blistering commentary in the *Catholic Advocate* with your byline on it?"

"No . . . this is more of a fact-finding mission." I thought about how much I should admit to Ian Fletcher. The confidentiality relationship between a parishioner and a priest was as inviolable as the one between a patient and his doctor, but was telling Fletcher what Shay had said breaking a trust if the same words were already in a gospel that had been written two thousand years ago? "You used to be an atheist," I said, changing the subject.

"Yeah." Fletcher smiled. "I was pretty gifted at it, too, if I do say so myself."

"What happened?"

"I met someone who made me question everything I was so sure I knew about God."

"That," I said, "is why I'm in the office of a rabble-rouser like you."

"And what better place to learn more about the Gnostic gospels," Fletcher said.

"Exactly."

"Well, then, the first thing is that you shouldn't call them that. It would be like calling someone a spic or a Hebe—the label Gnostic was made up by the same people who rejected them. In my circles, we call them noncanonical gospels. *Gnostic* literally means *one who knows*—but the people who coined the term considered its followers *know-it-alls*."

"That's what we pretty much learn in seminary."

Fletcher looked at me. "Let me ask you a question, Father—in your opinion, what's the purpose of religion?"

I laughed. "Wow, thank goodness you picked an easy one."

"I'm serious . . ."

I considered this. "I think religion brings people together over a common set of beliefs . . . and makes them understand why they matter."

Fletcher nodded, as if this was the answer he'd been expecting. "I think it's there to answer the really hard questions that arise when the world doesn't work the way it's supposed to—like when your child dies of leukemia, or you're fired after twenty years of hard work. When bad things happen to good people, and good things happen to bad people. The really interesting thing, to me, is that somehow religion stopped being about trying to find honest solutions . . . and started being about ritual. Instead of everyone searching for understanding on their own, orthodox religion came along and said, 'Do x, y, and z—and the world will be a better place.' "

"Well, Catholicism's been around for thousands of years," I replied, "so it must be doing something right."

"You have to admit, it's done a lot *wrong*, too," Fletcher said.

Anyone who'd had limited religious instruction or a thorough college education knew about the Catholic Church and its role in politics and history—not to mention the heresies that had been squelched over the centuries. Even sixth graders studied the Inquisition. "It's a corporation," I said. "And sure, there have been times when it's been staffed badly, with people who think ambition trumps faith. But that doesn't mean you throw the baby out with the bathwater. No matter how screwed up God's servants are in the Church, His message has managed to get through."

Fletcher tilted his head. "What do you know about the birth of Christianity?"

"Did you want me to start with the Holy Ghost visiting Mary, or skip ahead to the star in the East . . ."

"That's the birth of *Jesus*," Fletcher said. "Two very different things. Historically, after Jesus's death, his followers weren't exactly welcomed with open arms. By the second century A.D., they were literally dying for their beliefs. But even though they belonged to groups that called themselves Christians, the groups weren't unified, because they were all very different from one another. One of these groups was the so-called Gnostics. To them, being Christian was a good first step, but to truly reach enlightenment, you had to receive secret knowledge, or *gnosis*. You *started* with faith, but you *developed* insight—and for these people, Gnostics offered a second baptism. Ptolemy called it *apolutrosis*—the same word used when slaves were legally freed."

"So how did people get this secret knowledge?"

"There's the rub," Fletcher said. "Unlike the church, you couldn't be taught it. It had nothing to do with being told what to believe, and everything to do with figuring it out on your own. You had to reach inside yourself, understand human nature and its destiny, and at that moment you'd know the secret— that there's divinity in you, if you're willing to look for it. And the path would be different for everyone."

"That sounds more Buddhist than Christian."

"*They* called themselves Christians," Fletcher corrected. "But Irenaeus, who was the bishop of Lyons at the time, disagreed. He saw three huge differences between Orthodox Christianity and Gnosticism. In Gnostic texts, the focus wasn't on sin and repentance, but instead on illusion and enlightenment. Unlike in the Orthodox Church, you couldn't be a member simply by joining—you had to show evidence of spiritual maturity to be accepted. And— this was probably the biggest stumbling block for the bishop—Gnostics didn't think Jesus's resurrection was literal. To them, Jesus was never really human—he just appeared in human form. But that was just a technicality to the Gnostics, because unlike Orthodox Christians, they didn't see a gap between the human and the divine. To them, Jesus wasn't a one-of-a-kind savior—he was a guide, helping you find your individual spiritual potential. And when you reached it, you weren't redeemed by Christ—you *became* a Christ. Or in other words: you were *equal* to Jesus. Equal to God."

It was easy to see why, in seminary, this had been taught as heresy: the basis of Christianity was that there was only one God, and He was so different from man that the only way to reach Him was through Jesus. "The biggest heresies are the ones that scare the Church to death."

"Especially when the Church is going through its own identity crisis," Fletcher said. "I'm sure you remember how Irenaeus decided to unify the Orthodox Christian Church—by figuring out who was a true believer, and who was faking. Who was speaking the word of God, and who was speaking . . . well . . . just words?"

On a pad in front of him, Fletcher wrote GOD = WORD = JESUS, then spun it around so I could see. "Irenaeus came up with this little gem. He said that we can't be divine, because Jesus's life and death were so different from that of any man—which became the very beginning of Orthodox Christianity. What didn't fit this equation became heretical—if you weren't worshipping the right way, you were out. It was sort of the first reality show, if you want to think of it that way: who had the purest form of Christianity? He condemned the folks who got creative with faith, like Marcus and his followers, who spoke in prophecies and had visions of a feminine divinity clothed in the letters of the Greek alphabet. He condemned the groups that swore by only one gospel—like the Ebionites, who were attached to Matthew; or the Marcionites, who studied only Luke. Just as bad were the groups like the Gnostics, who had too *many* texts. Instead, Irenaeus decided that Matthew, Mark, Luke, and John should be the four cornerstone gospels of what to believe—"

"—because they all had a narrative of Christ's Passion in them . . . which the Church needed, in order for the Eucharist to mean something."

"Exactly," Fletcher said. "Then Irenaeus appealed to all those people who were trying to decide which Christian group was right for them. Basically, he said: 'We know how hard it is to figure out what's true, and what's not. So we're going to make it easy for you, and tell you what to believe.' People who did that were true Christians. People who didn't were not. And the things Irenaeus told people to believe became the foundation for the Nicene Creed, years later."

Every priest knew that what we were taught in seminary had a Catholic spin put on it—yet there was an incontrovertible truth behind it. I had always believed that the Catholic Church was evidence of religious survival of the fittest: the truest, most powerful ideas were the ones that had prevailed over time. But Fletcher was saying that the most powerful ideas had been *subjugated* . . . because they jeopardized the existence of the Orthodox Church. That the reason they'd had to be crushed was because—at one point—they'd been as or more popular than Orthodox Christianity.

Or in other words, the reason the Church had survived and flourished was not because its ideas were the most valid, but because it had been the world's first bully.

"Then the books of the New Testament were just an editorial decision someone once had to make," I said.

Fletcher nodded. "But what were those decisions based on? The gospels aren't the word of God. They're not even the apostles' firsthand accounts of the word of God. They're simply the stories that best supported the creed that the Orthodox Church wanted people to follow."

"But if Irenaeus hadn't done that," I argued, "chances are there would be no Christianity. Irenaeus united a whole mass of fragmented followers and their beliefs. When you're in Rome in A.D. 150 and you're being arrested because you confess Christ as your savior, you want to make sure that the people beside you aren't going to turn around at the last minute and say they believe something different. In fact, it's *still* important today to figure out who's a believer and who's just a nutcase—read any paper and you'll see how anger, prejudice, or ego are all routinely passed off as the Word of God, usually with a bomb strapped to it."

"Orthodoxy takes the risk away," Fletcher agreed. "We tell you what's real and what's not, so you don't have to worry about getting it wrong. The problem is that the minute you do it, you start separating people into groups. Some get favored, some don't. Some gospels get picked, others get hidden away underground for thousands of years." He looked at me. "Somewhere along the line, organized religion stopped being about faith, and started being about who had the power to *keep* that faith." Fletcher ripped off the sheet of paper with Irenaeus's equation, leaving a clear, blank slate beneath. He crumpled the paper, tossed it into his trash can. "You said that the purpose of religion was to bring people together. But does it, really? Or does it—knowingly, purposefully, and intentionally—break them apart?"

I took a deep breath. And then I told him everything I knew about Shay Bourne.

Lucius

None of us were getting any sleep, but it wasn't for lack of trying.

Crowds have their own pH, and the remarkable thing is that they can change in an instant. The people who had been camping out outside the prison—who were featured in a countdown every night on the local news (MR. MESSIAH: DAY 23)—had somehow gotten word that Shay had been hospitalized for an injury. But now, in addition to the camp that was holding a prayer vigil for Shay, there was a very vocal group of people who felt that this was a sign, that the reason Shay had been hurt so badly was because God decided he had it coming to him.

They got louder, for some reason, after dark. Insults were hurled, fights were picked, punches were thrown. Someone sent the National Guard down to patrol the perimeter of the prison and keep the peace, but no one could shut them up. Shay's supporters would sing gospel to drown out the chants of the disbelievers ("Jesus lives! Bourne dies!"). Even with headphones on, I could still hear them, a headache that wouldn't go away.

Watching the eleven o'clock news that night was surreal. To see the prison and hear the resonant shouts of the mob outside echoing the broadcast on my television—well, it was like déjà vu, except it was happening now.

There's only one God, people shouted.

They carried signs: JESUS IS MY HOMEBOY— NOT SATAN.

LET HIM DIE FOR *HIS* SINS.

NO CROWN OF THORNS FOR SHAY BOURNE.

They were separated from the Shay loyalists by armed guards toting guns, who walked the fault line of public opinion between them.

"As you can see," the reporter said, "senti-ment in support of Shay Bourne and his unprecedented case to donate his heart is waning in the wake of his hospitalization. A recent poll done by WNRK news shows only thirty-four percent of New Hampshire residents still convinced that the courts should allow Bourne to be an organ donor; and even less than that—sixteen percent—agree that his miracles are divinely inspired. Which means that an overwhelming eighty-four percent of the state agrees with Reverend Arbogath Justus, who's joining us again this evening. Reverend, you and the members of your church have been here for nearly a week now and have been instrumental in turning the tide of public opinion. What's your take on the Bourne hospitalization?"

The Reverend Justus was still wearing that green suit. "Ninety-nine percent of the state thinks you should burn that outfit," I said out loud.

"Janice," the reverend replied, "we at the Drive-In Church of Christ in God have of course been praying for Shay Bourne's speedy and full recovery in the wake of the prison attack. However, when we pray, we pray to the one and only Lord: Jesus Christ."

"Is there any message you have for those who still don't agree with you?"

"Why, yes." He leaned closer to the camera. "I *told* you so."

The reporter took back the microphone. "We've been told that Bourne will be released from the hospital in the next few hours, but doctors haven't commented on his condition . . ." Suddenly, a roar went up from both sides of the crowd, and the reporter covered her earpiece with one hand. "This is unconfirmed," she said over the din, "but apparently an ambulance has just driven into the rear entrance of the prison . . ."

On the screen, the camera swung past her to catch a man decking a woman in a purple caftan. The armed guards stepped in, but by then other fights had broken out between the camps. The line separating the two bled, until the guards had to call in reinforcements. The cameras captured a teenager being trampled, a man being smacked in the head by the butt of a guard's rifle and collapsing.

"Lights-out," a CO said over the loudspeaker. Lights-out never really meant lights-out—there was always some residual bulb shining somewhere in the prison. But I pulled off my headphones, lay down on my bunk— and listened to the riot going on outside the brick walls of the prison.

This is what it always comes down to, I realized. There are the ones who believe, and the ones who don't, and caught in the space between them are guns.

Apparently, I wasn't the only one being disturbed. Batman the Robin began to squawk, in spite of Calloway's efforts to hush him.

"Shut that freaking bird up already!" Texas yelled.

"*You* shut up," Calloway said. "Fucking Bourne. Wish he'd never come onto this fucking tier."

As if he'd been summoned, the door to I-tier opened, and in the half-light, Shay moved toward his cell, escorted by a flock of six officers. He had a bandage on his face, and two black eyes. Part of his scalp had been shaved. He did not look at any of us as he passed. "Hey," I murmured as he walked by my cell, but Shay didn't respond. He moved like a zombie, like someone in a sci-fi film whose frontal lobe has been removed by the mad scientist.

Five of the officers left. The sixth stood outside Shay's cell door, his own personal security guard. The presence of the CO prevented me from talking to Shay. In fact, the presence of the CO prevented any of us from talking, period.

I guess we were all so focused on his return that it took us several moments to realize that the quiet wasn't just a lack of conversation. Batman the Robin had fallen asleep in Calloway's breast pocket. And outside, that din—that god-awful din—had gone spectacularly, blissfully silent.

Maggie

America was founded on religious freedom, on the separation of church and state, and yet I will be the first to tell you that we're not much better off than those Puritans were in the 1770s over in England. Religion and politics get into bed with each other all the time: the first thing we do in a courtroom is swear on a Bible; public school classes begin with the Pledge of Allegiance, which declares us one nation under God; even our currency is stamped with the words *In God We Trust*. You'd think that of all people, a lawyer like me from the ACLU would be violently opposed to this on principle, but no. I had spent thirty minutes in the shower and another twenty driving downtown to the federal courthouse trying to figure out the best way to drag religion smack into the middle of a courtroom.

I was just determined to do it without offending the personal beliefs of the judge.

In the parking lot, I called the ChutZpah and reached my mother on the first try.

"What kind of name is Haig?"

"You mean like the general?"

"Yeah."

"Sounds German, maybe," she mused. "I don't know. Why?"

"I was talking religious affiliation."

"Is that what you think I do?" my mother said. "Judge people on their last names?"

"Does *everything* have to be an accusation? I just need to know before I go into chambers, so that I can tailor what I say to the justice sitting on the case."

"I thought the whole point of being a judge was being impartial."

"Right. Just like the whole point of being crowned Miss America is to promote world peace."

"I can't remember if Alexander Haig is Jewish. I know your father liked him because he supported Israel . . ."

"Well, even if he is, that doesn't mean that my judge is. Haig isn't quite as easy to figure out as someone named O'Malley or Hershkowitz."

"Your father once dated a Jewish girl named Barbara O'Malley, for your information," my mother said.

"Hopefully before he married you . . ."

"Very funny. I'm just saying that your theory isn't airtight."

"Well, you don't meet many Jewish O'Malleys."

My mother hesitated. "I think her grandparents had their surname legally changed from Meyer."

I rolled my eyes. "I've got to go. No matter what his religion is, no judge likes a lawyer who's late."

I had received a call from my secretary when I was meeting with Warden Coyne about Shay's protection in the prison— Judge Haig wanted to see counsel in federal court the very next morning, a mere four days after I'd filed my complaint there. I should have realized things were going to move blisteringly fast. Shay already had an execution date scheduled, so the court had put us on an expedited trial calendar.

As I turned the corner, I saw the AAG from the appellate division, Gordon Greenleaf, already waiting. I nodded at him, and then felt my cell phone vibrating in my purse with a text message.

GOOGLED HAIG-ROM CATH. XO MOM

I snapped the phone shut as the clerk arrived to lead us into Judge Haig's chambers.

The judge had thinning gray hair and a distance-runner's body. I peered at the collar of his shirt, but he was wearing a tie: for all I knew, he might be wearing a crucifix, a star of David, or even a rope of garlic to ward off vampires. "All right, boys and girls," he said, "who can tell us why we're here today?"

"Your Honor," I answered, "I'm suing the commissioner of corrections of the State of New Hampshire on behalf of my client, Shay Bourne."

"Yes, thank you, Ms. Bloom, I already breathlessly read your complaint from cover to cover. What I meant was that Mr. Bourne's impending execution is already a zoo. Why is the ACLU turning it into a bigger one?"

Gordon Greenleaf cleared his throat. He had always reminded me of Bozo the Clown, with his tufted red hair and allergies that left his nose red more often than not. "He's a death row inmate trying to delay the inevitable, Your Honor."

"He's not trying to delay anything," I argued. "He's just trying to make amends for his sins, and he believes this is the way he needs to die in order to reach salvation. He'd be the first to tell you you can execute him tomorrow, as long as it's by hanging."

"This is 2008, Ms. Bloom. We execute people by lethal injection. We're not going back to a more archaic form of execution," Judge Haig said.

I nodded. "But, Judge, with all due respect, if the Department of Corrections finds lethal injection impractical, the sentence may be carried out by hanging."

"The Department of Corrections doesn't have a problem with lethal injection!" Greenleaf said.

"It does when Mr. Bourne's First Amendment rights are being violated. He has the right to practice his religious beliefs, even in a prison setting—up to and including during the moment of his execution."

"What are you talking about?" Greenleaf exploded. "*No* religion insists on organ donation. Just because one individual gets some crazy set of rules into his head to live—or die—by, that doesn't qualify it as a religious belief."

"Gee, Gordon," I said. "Who died and left *you* God?"

"Counselors, back to your corners," Judge Haig said. He pursed his lips, deep in thought. "There are some factual issues here that need to be fleshed out," he began, "but the first of these is, Mr. Greenleaf, whether the state will agree to hang Mr. Bourne in lieu of giving him a lethal injection."

"Absolutely not, Judge. Preparations are already in place for the method of execution that was specified at his sentencing."

Judge Haig nodded. "Then we'll set this down for trial. Given the very real deadline we're working under, it will be an expedited hearing. We're going to pretend that there's no such thing as federal discovery; we're going to pretend that there's no such thing as summary judgment motions—we don't have time for them. Instead, I want witness lists on my desk in a week, and I want you prepared to go straight to trial in two weeks."

Gordon and I gathered our belongings and stepped outside chambers. "Do you have any idea how much money the taxpayers of New Hampshire have spent on that death chamber?"

"Take it up with the governor, Gordon," I said. "If the rich towns in New Hampshire have to pay for public education, maybe the poor towns can cough up the funds for future death row inmates."

He folded his arms. "What's the ACLU's game here, Maggie? You can't get the death penalty declared unconstitutional, so you use religion as a fallback position?"

I smiled at him. "You do if it *helps* you get the death penalty declared unconstitutional. See you in two weeks, Gordon," I said, and I walked off, leaving him staring after me.

Three times, I picked up the phone and dialed. Three times, I hung up just as the line connected.

I couldn't do this.

But I had to. I had two weeks to get the facts; and if I was going to fight on Shay's behalf to donate his heart, I needed to understand exactly how this was going to work—and be able to explain that in court.

When the hospital switchboard connected,

I asked to speak to Dr. Gallagher's office. I left my name and number with a secretary, fully anticipating the fact that it would take some time before he returned my call, during which I might actually develop the courage to speak to him. So when the phone rang almost as soon as I put down the receiver, I was shocked to hear his voice. "Ms. Bloom," he said. "What can I do for you?"

"You weren't supposed to call back this fast," I blurted out.

"Ah, I'm sorry. I really should be less punctual with my patients."

"I'm not your patient."

"Right. You were only masquerading as one." He was silent, and then said, "I believe you called me?"

"Yes. Yes, I did. I was wondering if you might be willing to meet with me—professionally, of course—"

"Of course."

"—to talk about hanging and organ donation."

"If only I had a dime for every time I've been asked to do that," Dr. Gallagher said. "I'd be delighted to meet with you. Professionally, of course."

"Of course," I said, deflated. "The catch is, I have to meet you fairly soon. My client's trial starts in two weeks."

"Well, then, Ms. Bloom, I'll pick you up at seven."

"Oh—you don't have to do that. I can meet you at the hospital."

"Yes, but I really prefer to not eat the cafeteria Jell-O on my days off."

"It's your day off?" *He called me back on his day off?* "Well, we can do it some other time . . ."

"Didn't you just tell me this was something that needed to be done quickly?"

"Well," I said. "Yeah."

"Then seven o'clock it is."

"Excellent," I said in my finest courtroom voice. "I look forward to it."

"Ms. Bloom."

"Yes?"

I held my breath, waiting for him to lay down the parameters of this meeting. Do not expect this to be any more than it is on the surface: two professionals doing business. Do not forget that you could have asked any number of doctors, even ones who don't have eyes the color of a moonless night and an accent that tugs like a fishing hook. Do not delude yourself into pretending this is a real date.

"I don't know where you live."

Whoever said that black makes you look thinner obviously did not have the same clothes that were hanging in *my* closet. First I tried on my favorite black pants, which were no longer my favorite because they only buttoned if I stopped breathing and didn't intend to sit at all during the meal. The black turtleneck that still had tags on it made me look like I had a double chin, and the black crochet shrug that had looked so cute in the catalog showed every inch of bra roll. *Red*, I thought. *I'll be bold and make a statement.* I tried on a crimson silk camisole, but the only statement I seemed to be sending was Frederick's of Hollywood. I sifted through wraps and cardigans and shells and blazers, A-line skirts and pleated ones and cocktail dresses, tossing them off one by one onto the floor as Oliver hopped away in vain, trying not to get trapped underneath. I tried on every single pair of trousers in my possession and decided that my ass was well on its way to being declared one of Saturn's moons. Then I marched myself to the bathroom mirror. "Here's the thing," I said to myself. "You don't have to look like Jennifer Aniston to discuss the best way to execute someone."

Although, I imagined, it probably helped.

Finally I decided on my favorite pair of jeans, and a flowing pale green tunic that I'd found for five dollars at an Asian boutique, so I always felt good about wearing it, even when I didn't look perfect. I twisted my hair up and stabbed it with a hair stick, hoping it looked artful and Grecian instead of just messy and out of time.

At exactly seven, the doorbell rang. I took one last look at myself in the mirror—the outfit clearly said casual, together, not trying too hard—and opened the door to find Dr. Gallagher wearing a coat and tie.

"I can change," I said quickly. "I didn't know we were going somewhere nice. Not that I wouldn't expect you to take me somewhere nice. Or that you're *taking* me. I mean, I'm taking myself. And you're taking you. We're just going in the same car."

"You look lovely," he said. "This is how I dress all the time."

"On your day off?"

"Well, I *am* British," he replied, an explanation; but he hooked his finger in his collar and slipped the tie from his shirt. He draped it over the inside knob of the front door.

"When I was in college and someone did that it meant—" I broke off, remembering what it did mean: don't enter, because your roommate is getting lucky. "It meant that, um, you were busy studying for a test."

"Really?" Dr. Gallagher said. "How strange. At Oxford it meant your roommate was inside having sex."

"Maybe we should go," I said quickly, hoping he didn't notice that I was blushing fiercely, or that I lived alone with a rabbit, or that my hips were so big that they probably wouldn't fit into the seat of the little sports car he'd parked in my driveway.

He opened the car door for me and didn't turn the ignition until my seat belt was fastened. As he sped off, he cleared his throat. "There's something I'd like to get out of the way before we go any further," he said. "I'm Christian."

I stared at him. Was he some kind of fundamentalist who limited his extracurricular conversations to people of the same faith? Did he think that I harbored some secret desire to elope, and was he giving me the lay of the land? (All right. So maybe that last one wasn't far off the mark.)

Well, whatever. I'd been eating, sleeping, breathing religion with Shay's case; I was even more sensitive now about religious tolerance than I'd been before I took up this mantle. And if religion was so vitally important to Gallagher that he had to bring it up as the first point of conversation, I could give as good as I got. "I'm an atheist," I said, "but you might as well know right now that my father's a rabbi, and if you have a problem with that I'm sure I can find another physician to talk to me, and I'd really appreciate it if you didn't make a joke right now about Jewish doctors."

I exhaled.

"Well," he said, and glanced at me. "Perhaps you'd rather call me Chris?"

I was pretty sure Emily Post wouldn't have covered this topic, but it seemed more discreet to wait until after we were served our main course to start talking about how to kill a man.

The restaurant was inside an old colonial home in Orford, with floorboards that rolled like the seas beneath my feet and a bustling kitchen off to one side. The hostess had a husky, mellifluous voice and greeted the doctor by name.

Christian.

The room we were sitting in had only six tables, covered with mismatched linen and dishes and glasses; candles burned in recycled wine bottles. On the wall were mirrors in every shape and size—my own personal version of the ninth circle of hell—but I hardly even noticed them. Instead, I drank water and wine and pretended that I did not want to spoil my appetite by eating the freshly baked bread they'd served us along with dipping oil—or by talking about Shay's execution.

Christian smiled at me. "I've always imagined one day I'd be forced to consider how one went about losing one's heart, but I must admit, I didn't think it would be quite so literal."

The waiter arrived with our plates. The menu had been full of the most delectable cuisine: Vietnamese bouillabaisse, escargot tortellini, chorizo dumplings. Even the descriptions of the entrées made me salivate: *Handmade to order, fresh Italian parsley pasta filled with fresh artichoke hearts, roasted eggplant, a medley of cheeses, and sweet roasted red and yellow pepper, tossed with a sun-dried tomato cream sauce. Slices of boneless chicken lined with thin slices of prosciutto filled with fresh spinach, Asiago cheese, and sweet onion rolled and served with fresh fettuccine and a tomato marsala wine reduction. Boneless breast of duck roasted, thinly sliced, served with a sun-dried cherry sauce and a wild rice pancake.*

In the wild hope that I might fool Christian into thinking my waist size was not what it seemed to be, I'd swallowed hard and or-dered an appetizer. I'd fervently wished that Christian would order the braised leg of lamb or the steak frites so that I could beg a taste, but when I explained I wasn't all that hungry (a colossal lie), he said an appetizer was all he really wanted, too.

"From what I imagine," Christian said, "the inmate would be hanged in such a way that the spine would be fractured at C2/C3, which would arrest all spontaneous respiration."

I was trying very hard to follow along. "You mean he'd break his neck and stop breathing?"

"Right."

"So then he's brain-dead?"

A couple at the next table glanced at me, and I realized I'd been talking too loudly. That some people didn't like to mix death with dinner.

"Well, not quite. It takes some time for anoxic changes to the brain to result in a loss of reflexes . . . which is how you test for brainstem function. The problem is that you can't leave your man hanging for a great period of time, or his heart will stop, and that disqualifies him as a donor."

"So what has to happen?"

"The state needs to agree that the fact that respiration's ceased is enough to justify taking the body down from the noose on likely suspicion of death, then intubate him so that the heart is protected, and *then* test for brain death."

"Intubating him isn't the same as resuscitating him, then?"

"No. It's the equivalent of someone braindead being on a ventilator. It preserves the organs, but there won't be any brain function once that spinal cord is severed and hypoxia sets in, no matter how much oxygen you pump into his system."

I nodded. "So how do you determine brain death?"

"There are multiple ways. You can do a physical exam first—check to make sure there are no corneal reflexes, no spontaneous respirations, no gag reflex—and then repeat it twelve hours later. But since time is of the essence, I'd recommend a transcranial Doppler test, which uses ultrasound to measure blood flow through the carotid arteries at the base of the brain. If there's no blood flow for ten minutes, you can legally declare brain death."

I imagined Shay Bourne—who could barely string together a coherent sentence, who bit his fingernails to the quick—being led to a gallows. I pictured the noose being drawn tight around his neck and felt the hair stand up on the back of my own.

"It's brutal," I said softly, and put down my fork.

Christian was quiet for a moment. "I was a resident in Philadelphia the first time I had to tell a mother her child had died. He was the victim of a gang shooting—eight years old. He'd gone to the corner store to get a quart of milk, and was in the wrong place at the wrong time. I will never forget the look in her eyes when I told her we weren't able to save her son. When a child is killed, two people die, I think. The only difference is that his mother still had to suffer a heartbeat." He looked up at me. "It will be brutal for Mr. Bourne. But it was brutal for June Nealon first."

I sat back in my chair. This, then, was the catch. You meet a well-educated, intensely gorgeous, charming Oxford-educated man, and he turns out to be so right-wing he's nearly pointed backward. "Then you're in favor of capital punishment?" I asked, trying to keep my voice level.

"I think it's easy to take the moral high road when it's all theory," Christian said. "As a physician, do I think it's right to kill someone? No. But then again, I don't have children yet. And I'd be lying if I said that when I do, this issue will still seem crystal clear to me."

I didn't have children yet, either; at the rate I was going, I might never have them. And the only time I'd seen June Nealon, face-to-face, we'd been at the restorative justice meeting and she had been so filled with righteous anger that I found it hard to look at her. I didn't know what it felt like to carry a child underneath my heart for nine months, to feel my body give way to make room for hers. I didn't know what it felt like to hold an infant and rock her to sleep, to find a lullaby in her breathing. But I knew what it was like to be the daughter.

My mother and I hadn't always argued. I could still remember wishing that I was as glamorous as she was—trying on her high-heeled shoes, pulling her sheer satin slips up to my armpits as if they were strapless dresses, diving into the wondrous mystery of her makeup bag. She had, at one point, been the person I wanted to grow up to be.

It was so damn hard to find love in this world, to locate someone who could make you feel that there was a reason you'd been put on this earth. A child, I imagined, was the purest form of that. A child was the love you didn't have to look for, didn't have to prove anything to, didn't have to worry about losing.

Which is why, when it happened, it hurt so badly.

Suddenly, I wanted to call my mother. I wanted to call June Nealon. I was on my first date since the dinosaurs had roamed the planet, a date that was really just a business dinner, and I felt like bursting into tears.

"Maggie?" Christian leaned forward. "Are

you all right?" And then he put his hand on top of mine.

Arrest all spontaneous respiration, he had said.

The waiter appeared at the side of the table. "I hope you've left room for dessert."

I had nothing *but* room; my appetizer had been a crab cake the size of my thumbnail. But I could feel the warmth of Christian's skin on mine, and it was like heat at the tip of a candle—only a matter of time before the rest of me melted, too. "Oh, I couldn't," I said. "I'm stuffed."

"Right," Christian said, and he slipped his hand away from mine. "I guess just the bill, then."

Something had changed in his features— and there was a chill to his voice that hadn't been there a moment before. "What's the matter?" I asked. He shook his head, dismissive, but I knew what it was: the death penalty. "You think I'm on the wrong side."

"I don't think there are sides," Christian said, "but that's not it."

"Then what did I do wrong?"

The waiter sidled over with the bill, tucked into a leather folder. Christian reached for it.

"My last steady girlfriend was a principal dancer for the Boston Ballet."

"Oh," I said feebly. "She must have been . . ."

Beautiful. Graceful. Skinny.

Everything I wasn't.

"Every time we went out for a meal I felt like some sort of . . . *glutton* . . . because I had an appetite, and she never ate a damn thing. I suppose I thought—well, *hoped*— that you'd be different."

"But I *love* chocolate," I blurted out. "And apple fritters and pumpkin pie and mousse and tiramisu and I probably would have eaten everything on this menu if I didn't think it would make me look like a pig. I was trying to be . . ." My voice trailed off.

". . . what you thought I was looking for?"

I focused my attention on the napkin on my lap. Leave it to me to ruin a date that wasn't even really one.

"What if all I was looking for," Christian asked, "was you?"

I lifted my head slowly as Christian summoned back our waiter. "Tell us about dessert," he said.

"We have a crème brûlée, a fresh blueberry tart, warm peach puff pastries with homemade ice cream and caramel sauce, and my personal favorite," the waiter said. "Chocolate French toast with a thin pecan crust, served with mint ice cream, and our own raspberry sauce."

"What shall we try?" Christian asked.

I turned to the waiter. "Maybe we could skip back to the main course first," I said, and smiled.

‖‖

"This is my simple religion.
There is no need for temples;
no need for complicated philosophy.
Our own brain, our own heart is our temple;
the philosophy is kindness."

—*HIS HOLINESS THE 14TH DALAI LAMA*

June

||||||||||||||||||||||||||||||||||||||||||||||||||||||||||||||||||||||||||||||||||||||||||||||||

As it turned out, in spite of the deathbed promises, I didn't tell Claire about her potential new heart when she first awakened after the episode that had brought us back to this hospital. Instead, I made a hundred excuses: When she wasn't running a temperature. When she had a little more energy. When we knew for sure that a judge was going to allow the donation to happen. The longer I put off the conversation, the more I was able to convince myself that Claire would have another hour, day, week with me in which to have it.

And in the meantime, Claire was failing. Not just her body, but her spirit. Dr. Wu told me every day that she was stable, but I saw changes. She didn't want me to read from *Teen People*. She didn't want to watch television. She lay on her side, staring at a blank wall.

"Claire," I said one afternoon, "want to play cards?"

"No."

"How about Scrabble."

"No thanks." She turned away. "I'm tired."

I smoothed her hair back from her face. "I know, baby."

"No," she said. "I mean I'm *tired,* Mom. I don't want to do this anymore."

"Well, we can take a walk—I mean, *I* can take a walk and push you in a wheelchair. You don't have to stay in bed—"

"I'm going to die in here. You and I both know it. Why can't I just go home and do it there, instead of hooked up to all of this stuff?"

I stared at her. Where was the child in that sentence, the one who had believed in fairies and ghosts and all sorts of impossible things? *But we're so close to fixing that*, I started to say, and then I realized that if I did, I would have to tell her about the heart that might or might not be coming.

And whose it was.

"I want to sleep in my own bed," Claire said, "instead of one with stupid plastic sheets and a pillow that crackles every time I move my head. I want to eat meat loaf, instead of chicken soup in a blue plastic cup and Jell-O—"

"You hate when I serve meat loaf."

"I know, and I want to get mad at you for cooking it again." She flopped onto her back and looked at me. "I want to drink from the orange juice container. I want to throw a tennis ball for my dog."

I hesitated. "Maybe I can talk to Dr. Wu," I said. "We can get your own sheets and pillow, I bet . . ."

Something in Claire's eyes dimmed. "Just forget it," she said, and that was how I realized she'd already begun to die, before I had a chance to save her.

As soon as Claire fell asleep that afternoon, I left her in the capable hands of the nursing staff and exited the hospital for the first time in a week. I was stunned to see how much the world had changed. There was a nip in the air that whispered of winter; the trees had begun to turn color, sugar maples first, their bright heads like torches that would light the rest of the woods on fire. My car felt unfamiliar, as if

I were driving a rental. And most shocking—
the road that led past the state prison had
been rerouted with policemen on traffic detail.
I inched through the cones, gaping at the
crowds that had been cordoned off by police
tape: SHAY BOURNE WILL BURN IN HELL, read one
sign. Another banner said SATAN IS ALIVE AND
KICKING ON I-TIER.

Once, when Claire was tiny, she'd raised the
blackout shade in her bedroom window when
she woke up. At the sight of the sunrise, with its
outstretched crimson fingers, she'd gasped.
Did I do that?

Now, looking at the signs, I had to wonder:
Could you believe something so fiercely that
it actually happened? Could your thoughts
change the minds of others?

Keeping my eyes on the road, I passed
the prison gates and continued toward my
house. But my car had other intentions—it
turned right, and then left, and into the cemetery where Elizabeth and Kurt were buried.

I parked and started walking to their shared
grave. It was underneath an ash tree; in the
light wind, the leaves shimmered like golden
coins. I knelt on the grass and traced my finger over the lettering on the headstone:
BELOVED DAUGHTER.

TREASURED HUSBAND.

Kurt had bought his plot after we'd been married for a year. *That's macabre*, I had said, and he had just shrugged it off; he saw the business of death and dying every day. *Here's the thing, though*, he had said. *There's room for you, if you want.*

He had not wanted to impose, because he didn't know if I'd want to be buried near my first husband. Even that tiny bit of consideration—the fact that he wanted me to choose, instead of making an assumption —had made me realize why I loved him. *I want to be with you*, I had told him. I wanted to be where my heart was.

After the murders, I would sleepwalk. I'd find myself the next morning in the gardening shed, holding a spade. In the garage, with my face pressed against the metal cheek of a shovel. In my subconscious, I was making plans to join them; it was only when I was awake and alert and felt Claire kicking me from within that I realized I had to stay.

Would she be the next one I'd bury here? And once I did, what would keep me from carrying things through to their natural conclusion, from putting my family back together in one place?

I lay down for a minute, prone on the grass. I pressed my face into the stubbled moss at the edge of the headstone and pretended I was cheek-to-cheek with my husband; I felt the dandelions twine through my fingers and pretended I was holding my daughter's hand.

In the elevator of the hospital, the duffel bag started to move itself across the floor. I crouched down, unzipped the top of it. "Good boy," I said, and patted the top of Dudley's head. I'd retrieved him from my neighbor, who had been kind enough to play foster parent while Claire was sick. Dudley had fallen asleep in the car, but now he was alert and wondering why I had zipped him into a piece of luggage. The doors opened and I hoisted him up, approaching the nurse's desk near Claire's room. I tried to smile normally. "Everything all right?"

"She's been sleeping like a baby."

Just then, Dudley barked.

The nurse's eyes flew up to mine, and I pretended to sneeze. "Wow," I said, shaking my head. "Is that pollen count something or *what*?"

Before she could respond, I hurried into Claire's room and closed the door behind me.

Then I unzipped the bag and Dudley shot out like a rocket. He ran a lap around the room, nearly knocking over Claire's IV pole.

There was a reason dogs weren't allowed in hospitals, but if Claire wanted *normal*, then she was going to get it. I wrapped my arms around Dudley and hoisted him onto Claire's bed, where he sniffed the cotton blanket and began to lick her hand.

Her eyes fluttered open, and when she saw the dog, a smile split her face. "He's not allowed in here," she whispered, burying her hands in the fur at his neck.

"Are you going to tell on me?"

Claire pushed herself to a sitting position and let the dog crawl into her lap. She scratched behind his ears while he tried to chew on the wire that ran from beneath Claire's hospital gown to the heart monitor.

"We won't have a lot of time," I said quickly. "Someone's going to—"

Just then, a nurse walked in holding a digital thermometer. "Rise and shine, missy," she began, and then she saw the dog on the bed. "*What* is that doing in here?"

I looked at Claire, and then back at the nurse. "Visiting?" I suggested.

"Mrs. Nealon, not even service dogs are

allowed onto this ward without a letter from the vet stating that the vaccinations are up to date and the stool's tested negative for parasites—"

"I was just trying to make Claire feel better. He won't leave this room, I swear."

"I'll give you five minutes," the nurse said. "But you have to promise you won't bring him in again before the transplant."

Claire, who had a death grip on the dog, glanced up. "Transplant?" she repeated. "*What* transplant?"

"She was being theoretical," I said quickly.

"Dr. Wu doesn't schedule theoretical transplants," the nurse said.

Claire blinked at me. "Mom?" There was a thread in her voice that had started to unravel.

The nurse turned on her heel. "I'm counting," she said, and left the room.

"Is it true?" Claire asked. "There's a heart for me?"

"We're not sure. There's a catch . . ."

"There's *always* a catch," Claire said. "I mean, how many hearts have turned out to not be as great as Dr. Wu expected?"

"Well, this one . . . it's not ready for transplant yet. It's sort of still being used."

Claire laughed a little. "What are you planning to do? *Kill* someone?"

I didn't answer.

"Is the donor really sick, or old? How could she even *be* a donor if she's sick or old?" Claire asked.

"Honey," I said. "We have to wait for the donor to be executed."

Claire was not stupid. I watched her put together this new information with what she'd heard on television. Her hands tightened on Dudley. "No *way*," she said quietly. "I am not taking a heart from the guy who killed my father and my sister."

"He wants to *give* it to you. He offered."

"This is sick," Claire said. "You're sick." She struggled to get up, but she was tethered to the bed with tubes and wires.

"Even Dr. Wu said that it's an amazing match for you and your body. I couldn't just say no."

"What about me? Don't *I* get to say no?"

"Claire, baby, you know donors don't come along every day. I *had* to do it."

"Then *undo* it," she demanded. "Tell them I don't want his stupid heart."

I sank down on the edge of the hospital bed. "It's just a muscle. It doesn't mean you'll be like him." I paused. "And besides, he *owes* this to us."

"He doesn't owe us anything! Why don't you get that?" Her eyes filled with tears. "You can't tie the score, Mom. You just have to start over."

Her monitors began to sound an alert; her pulse was rising, her heart pumping too hard. Dudley began to bark. "Claire, you have to calm down . . ."

"This isn't about him," Claire said. "This isn't even about me. It's about *you. You* need to get payment for what happened to Elizabeth. *You* need to make him pay for what he did. Where do *I* fit into that?"

The nurse flew into the room like a great white heron, fussing over Claire. "What's going on in here?" she said, checking the connections and tubes and drips.

"Nothing," we both said simultaneously.

The nurse gave me a measured glance. "I highly recommend you take that dog away and let Claire get some rest."

I reached for Dudley and wrestled him back into the duffel bag. "Just think about it," I pleaded.

Ignoring me, Claire reached into the bag and patted the dog. "Good-bye," she whispered.

MICHAEL

||||||||||||||||||||||||||||||||||||||||||||||||||||||||||||||||||||||||||||||||||||||||||||||||||||||||||||||||||||||||||||||||||||||||||||

I had gone back to St. Catherine's. I told Father Walter that I had not been seeing clearly, and that God had opened my eyes to the truth.

I just neglected to mention that God happened to be sitting on I-tier about three miles away from our church, awaiting an expedited trial that began this week.

Each night, I said three consecutive rosaries—penance for lying to Father Walter—but I *had* to be there. I had to do something constructive with my time, now that I wasn't spending it with Shay. Since I'd confessed to him at the hospital that I'd served on the jury that had convicted him, he'd refused to see me.

There was a part of me that understood his reaction—imagine how it would feel to know your confidant had betrayed you—but there was another part of me that spent hours trying to figure out why divine forgiveness hadn't kicked in yet. Then again, if the Gospel of Thomas was to be believed, no matter how much time and space Shay put between us, we were never really separate: mankind and divinity were flip sides of the same coin.

And so, every day at noon, I told Father Walter I was meeting a fictional couple at their house to try to guide them away from the path of divorce. But instead, I rode my Trophy to the prison, burrowed through the crowds, and went inside to try to see Shay.

CO Whitaker was called to escort me to I-tier after I'd passed through the metal detectors at the visitor's booth. "Hi, Father. You here to sell Girl Scout cookies?"

"You know it," I replied. "Anything exciting happen today?"

"Let's see. Joey Kunz got a medical visit for diarrhea."

"Wow," I said. "Sorry I missed that."

As I suited up in my flak jacket, Whitaker

went into I-tier to tell Shay I'd come. Again. But no more than five seconds had passed before he returned, a sheepish look on his face. "Not today, Father," he said. "Sorry."

"I'll try again," I replied, but we both knew that wasn't possible. We had run out of time: Shay's trial began tomorrow.

I left the prison and walked back to my motorcycle. All modesty aside, I was the closest thing Shay had to a disciple; and if that was true, it meant learning from the mistakes of history. At Jesus's crucifixion, His followers had scattered—except for Mary Magdalene, and his mother. So even if Shay didn't acknowledge me in court, I would still be there. I would bear witness for him.

For a long time, I sat on my bike in the parking lot, going nowhere.

In fairness, it wasn't like I wanted to spring this all on Maggie a few days before the trial. The truth of the matter was that if Shay didn't want me as his spiritual advisor anymore, I had no excuse for not telling Maggie that I'd been on the jury that convicted him. I'd tried to contact her several times over the past week, but she was either out of her office, not at home, or not answering her cell. And then, out of the blue, she called me. "Get your ass down here," she said. "You have some explaining to do."

In twenty minutes, I was sitting in her ACLU office. "I had a meeting with Shay today," Maggie said. "He said you'd lied to him."

I nodded. "Did he go into detail?"

"No. He said I deserved to hear it first-hand." She crossed her arms. "He also said he didn't want you testifying on his behalf."

"Right," I mumbled. "I don't blame him."

"Are you really a priest?"

I blinked at her. "Of course I am—"

"Then I don't care what you're lying about," Maggie said. "You can unburden your soul *after* we win Shay's case."

"It's not that simple . . ."

"Yes it is, Father. You are the only character witness we've got for Shay; you're credible because you're wearing that collar. I don't care if you and Shay had a fight; I don't care if you moonlight as a drag queen; I don't care if you have enough secrets to last a lifetime. It's don't ask, don't tell until the trial starts, okay? All I care about is that you wear that collar, get on the stand, and make Shay sound like a saint. If you walk, the whole case goes down the toilet. Is that simple enough for you?"

If Maggie was right—if my testimony was the only thing that would help Shay—then how could I tell her something now that would ruin the case? A sin of omission could be understandable if you were helping someone by holding back. I could not give Shay his life back, but I could make sure his death was what he wanted.

Maybe it would be enough for him to forgive me.

"It's normal to be a little freaked out about going to court," Maggie said, misreading my silence.

During my testimony, I was supposed to explain in layman's terms how donating a heart to Claire Nealon was one of Shay's spiritual beliefs. Having a *priest* say this was a stroke of genius on Maggie's part—who wouldn't believe a member of the clergy when it came to religion?

"You don't have to be worried about the cross-exam," Maggie continued. "You tell the judge that while a Catholic would believe that salvation comes solely through Jesus Christ, Shay believes organ donation's necessary for redemption. That's perfectly true, and I can promise you that lightning isn't going to crash through the ceiling when you say it."

My head snapped up. "I can't tell the court that Shay will find Jesus," I said. "I think he might *be* Jesus."

She blinked. "You think *what*?"

The words began to spill out of me, the way I always imagined it felt to be speaking in tongues: truths that tumbled before you even realized they'd left your mouth. "It makes perfect sense. The age, the profession. The fact that he's on death row. The miracles. And the heart donation—he's literally giving himself away for our sins, again. He's giving the part that matters the least—the body—in order to become whole in spirit."

"This is *way* worse than having cold feet," Maggie murmured. "You're crazy."

"Maggie, he's been quoting a gospel that was written two hundred years after Christ's death—a gospel that most people don't even know exists. Word for word."

"I've listened to his words, and frankly, they're unintelligible. Do you know what he was doing yesterday when I briefed him on his testimony? Playing tic-tac-toe. With himself."

"You have to read between the lines."

"Yeah, right. And I bet when you listen to Britney Spears records backward, you hear

'Sleep with me, I'm not too young.' For God's sake—no pun intended—you're a Catholic *priest*. Whatever happened to the Father, Son, and Holy Ghost? I don't remember Shay being part of the Trinity."

"What about everyone camped outside the prison? Are they all crazy, too?"

"They want Shay to cure their kid's autism or reverse their husband's Alzheimer's. They're in it for *themselves*," Maggie said. "The only people who think Shay Bourne is the Messiah are so desperate that they'd be able to find salvation beneath the lid of a two-liter bottle of Pepsi."

"Or through a heart transplant?" I countered. "You've worked up a whole legal theory based on individual religious beliefs. So how can you tell me, categorically, that I'm wrong?"

"Because it's not a matter of right or wrong. It's life or death—namely, Shay's. I'd say whatever I had to to win this case for him; it's my job. And it was supposed to be *yours*, too. This isn't about some revelation; it's not about who Shay might have been or might be in the future. It's about who he is right now: a convicted murderer who's going to be executed unless I can do something about it.

It doesn't matter to me if he's a vagrant or Queen Elizabeth or Jesus Christ—it just matters that we win this case for him, so that he can die on his own terms. That means that you will get on that damn stand and swear on that Bible—which, for all I know, might not even be relevant to you now that you've found Jesus on I-tier. And if you screw this up for Shay by sounding like a nut job when I question you, I will make your life miserable." By the time Maggie finished, she was red in the face and breathless. "This old gospel," she said. "Word for word?"

I nodded.

"How did you find out about it?"

"From your father," I said.

Maggie's brows rose. "I'm not putting a priest *and* a rabbi on the stand. The judge will be waiting for a punch line."

I looked up at her. "I have an idea."

Maggie

In the client-attorney conference room out-side I-tier, Shay climbed on the chair and started talking to flies. "Go left," he urged as he craned his neck toward the air vent. "Come on. You can do it."

I looked up from my notes for a moment. "Are they pets?"

"No," Shay said, stepping down from the chair. His hair was matted, but only on the left side, which made him look absentminded at best and mentally ill at worst. I wondered what I could say to convince him to let me brush it before we went out in front of the judge tomorrow.

The flies were circling. "I have a pet rabbit," I said.

"Last week, before I was moved to I-tier, I had pets," Shay said, then shook his head. "It wasn't last week. It was yesterday. I can't remember."

"It doesn't matter—"

"What's its name?"

"Sorry?"

"The rabbit."

"Oliver," I said, and took out of my pocket what I'd been holding for Shay. "I brought you a gift."

He smiled at me, his eyes piercing and suddenly focused. "I hope it's a key."

"Not quite." I passed him a Snack Pack butterscotch pudding. "I figured you don't get the good stuff in prison."

He opened the foil top, licked it, and then carefully folded it into his breast pocket. "Is there butter in it?"

"I don't know."

"What about Scotch?"

I smiled. "I truly doubt it."

"Too bad."

I watched him take the first bite. "Tomorrow's going to be a big day," I said.

In the wake of Michael's crisis of faith, I had

contacted the witness he recommended—
an academic named Ian Fletcher whom I
vaguely remembered from a television show
he used to host, where he'd go around debunking the claims of people who saw the
Virgin Mary in their toast burn pattern and
things like that. At first, putting him on the
stand seemed to be a sure way to lose a
case—but the guy had a PhD from the
Princeton Theological Seminary, and there
had to be some merit in putting a former
atheist on the stand. If Fletcher could be convinced there was a God—be it Jesus, Allah,
Yahweh, Shay, or none of the above—then
surely *any* of us could.

Shay finished his pudding and handed the
empty cup back to me. "I need the foil, too," I
said. The last thing I wanted was to find out a
few days from now that Shay had fashioned
a shank out of the aluminum and hurt himself
or someone else. He took it out of his pocket
meekly and handed it back to me. "You *do*
know what's happening tomorrow, right?"

"Don't *you*?"

"Well. About the trial," I began, "all you
have to do is sit patiently and listen. A lot of
what you'll hear probably won't make sense
to you."

He looked up. "Are you nervous?"

I was nervous, all right—and not just because this was a high-profile death penalty case that might or might not have found a constitutional loophole. I lived in a country where 85 percent of the residents called themselves Christians and about half went regularly to some form of church—religion was not about the individual to the average American; it was about the community of believers, and my whole case was about to turn that on its ear. "Shay," I said. "You understand that we might lose."

Shay nodded, dismissive. "Where is she?"

"Who?"

"The girl. The one who needs the heart."

"She's in the hospital."

"Then we have to hurry," he said.

I exhaled slowly. "Right. I'd better go get my game face on."

I stood up, summoning the CO to let me out of the conference room, but Shay's voice called me back. "Don't forget to say you're sorry," he said.

"To whom?"

By then, though, Shay was standing on the chair again, his attention focused on something else. And as I watched, seven flies landed in quick succession on the palm of his outstretched hand.

When I was five, all I wanted was a Christmas tree. My friends had them, and the menorah we lit at night paled in comparison. My father pointed out that we got eight presents, but my friends got even more than that, if you added up what was sitting underneath their tree. One cold December afternoon, my mother told my father we were heading to the movies, and instead, she drove me to the mall. We waited in line with little girls who had ribbons in their hair and fancy lace dresses, so that I could sit on Santa's lap and tell him I wanted My Pretty Pony. Then, with a candy cane fisted in my hand, we walked to the decoration display where there were fifteen Christmas trees set up—white ones with glass balls, fake balsam ones strung with red beads and bows, one that had Tinker Bell at the top and all the Disney characters dotted as ornaments. "Like this," my mother said, and right in the middle of the department store we lay down at a crossroads of the trees and gazed up at the blinking light displays. I thought it was the most beautiful thing I'd ever seen. "I won't tell Daddy," I promised, but she said that didn't matter. This wasn't about another religion, my mother explained. These were just the trappings. You could admire the wrapping, without ever taking out what was inside the box.

After I left Shay, I sat in my car and called my mother at the ChutZpah. "Hi," I said when she answered. "What are you doing?"

There was a beat of silence. "Maggie? What's wrong?"

"Nothing. I felt like calling you."

"Did something happen? Did you get hurt?"

"Can't I call my mother just because I feel like it?"

"You *can,*" she said, "but you *don't.*"

Well. There was just no arguing with the truth. I took a deep breath and forged ahead. "Do you remember the time you took me to see Santa?"

"Please don't tell me you're converting. It'll kill your father."

"I'm not converting," I said, and my mother sighed with relief. "I just was remembering it, that's all."

"So you called to tell me?"

"No," I said. "I called to say I'm sorry."

"For what?" My mother laughed. "You haven't done anything."

In that moment, I remembered us lying on the floor of the department store, gazing at the lit trees, as a security guard loomed over us. *Just give her another few minutes,* my mother had begged. June Nealon's face flashed before me. Maybe this was the job of a mother: to buy time for her child, no matter what. Even if it meant doing something she'd rather not; even if it left her flat on her back.

"Yes," I answered. "I know."

"Desiring religious freedom is nothing new," I said, standing up in front of Judge Haig at the opening of Shay Bourne's trial. "One of the most famous cases happened more than two hundred years ago, and it didn't take place in our country—namely, because there *was* no country. A group of people who dared to hold religious beliefs different from the status quo found themselves being forced to adopt the policies of the Church of England—and instead, they chose to strike off to an unknown place across the ocean. But the Puritans liked religious freedom so much they kept it all to themselves—often persecuting people who didn't believe what they did. This is precisely why the founders of the new nation of the United States decided to put an end to religious intolerance by making religious freedom a cornerstone of this country."

This was a nonjury trial, which meant that the only person I had to preach to was the judge; but the courtroom was still filled. There were reporters there from four networks the judge had preapproved, there were victim's rights advocates, there were death penalty supporters and death penalty opponents. The only party present in support of Shay— and my first witness—was Father Michael, seated just behind the plaintiff's table.

Beside me, Shay sat in handcuffs and ankle cuffs, linked to a belly chain. "Thanks to the forefathers who crafted the Constitution, everyone in this country has the freedom to practice his own religion—even a prisoner on death row in New Hampshire. In fact, Congress went so far as to pass a law about it. The Religious Land Use and Institutionalized Persons Act guarantees an inmate the opportunity to worship whatever he likes as long as it doesn't impede the safety of others in the prison or affect the running of the prison. Yet Shay Bourne's constitutional right to practice his religion has been denied by the State of New Hampshire."

I looked up at the judge. "Shay Bourne is

not a Muslim, or a Wiccan; he's not a secular humanist or a member of the Baha'i faith. In fact, his system of beliefs may not be familiar to any common world religion you can name off the top of your head. But they *are* a system of beliefs, and they include the fact that—to Shay—salvation depends on being able to donate his heart after his execution to the sister of his victim . . . an outcome that's not possible if the state uses lethal injection as a method of execution."

I walked forward. "Shay Bourne has been convicted of possibly the most heinous crime in the history of this state. He has appealed that conviction, and those appeals have been denied—yet he is not contesting that decision. He knows he is going to die, Your Honor. All he asks is that, again, the laws of this country be upheld—in particular, the laws that say anyone has the right to practice their religion, wherever, whenever, however. If the state agrees to his execution by hanging, and provides for the subsequent donation of his organs, the safety of other inmates isn't impeded; the running of the prison isn't affected—but it would offer a very significant personal outcome for Shay Bourne: to save a little girl's life, and in the process, to save his own soul."

I sat back down and glanced at Shay. He had a legal pad in front of him. On it, he'd doodled a picture of a pirate with a parrot on his shoulder.

At the defense table, Gordon Greenleaf was seated beside the New Hampshire commissioner of corrections, a man with both hair and complexion the color of a potato. Greenleaf tapped his pencil twice on the desk. "Ms. Bloom brought up the founding fathers of this country. Thomas Jefferson, in fact, coined a phrase in a letter in 1789—'a wall of separation between church and state.' He was explaining the First Amendment—in particular the clauses about religion. And his words have been used by the Supreme Court many times—in fact, the Lemon test, which the high court has used since 1971, says that for a law to be constitutional, it must have a secular purpose, must neither advance nor inhibit religion, and must not result in excessive government entanglement with religion. That last part's an interesting bit—since Ms. Bloom is both crediting the forefathers of this nation with the noble division of church and state . . . and yet simultaneously asking Your Honor to join them together."

He stood up, walking forward. "If you were

to take her claim seriously," Greenleaf said, "you'd see that what she's really asking for is a legally binding sentence to be massaged, because of a loophole called religion. What's next? A convicted drug dealer asking that his sentence be overturned because heroin helps him reach nirvana? A murderer insisting that his cell door face Mecca?" Greenleaf shook his head. "The truth is, Judge, this petition has been filed by the ACLU not because it's a valid and troublesome concern—but because it will purposefully create a three-ring circus during the state's first execution in sixty-nine years." He waved his arm around the crowded gallery. "And all of you are proof that it's already working."

Greenleaf glanced at Shay. "Nobody takes the death penalty lightly, least of all the commissioner of corrections in the State of New Hampshire. The sentence in Shay Bourne's case was death by lethal injection. That's exactly what the state has prepared and intends to carry out—with dignity and respect for all parties involved.

"Let's look at the facts here. No matter what Ms. Bloom says, there is no organized religion that mandates organ donation after death as a means of reaching the afterlife. According to his records, Shay Bourne was raised in foster homes, so he can't claim that he was reared in one religious tradition that fostered organ donation. If he's converted to some religion that is now claiming that organ donation is part of its tenets, we submit to this court that it's pure bunk." Greenleaf spread his hands. "We know you'll listen carefully to the testimony, Your Honor, but the reality is that the Department of Corrections is not required to submit to the whim of every misguided prisoner that comes through its doors—especially one who has committed the monstrous torture and murders of two New Hampshire citizens, a child and a police officer. Don't let Ms. Bloom and the ACLU take a grave matter and turn it into a spectacle. Allow the state to impose the penalty that was set forth by the court, in as civilized and professional a manner as possible."

I glanced at Shay. On his legal pad, he'd added his initials, and the logo for the band AC/DC.

The judge pushed his glasses up his nose and looked at me. "Ms. Bloom," he said, "you may call your first witness."

MICHAEL

As soon as I was asked to approach the witness stand, I locked my gaze on Shay's. He stared back at me, silent, blank. The clerk approached, holding a Bible. "Do you swear to tell the truth, the whole truth, and nothing but the truth, so help you God?"

The leather cover of the book was finely grained and black, worn smooth by the palms of thousands who'd recited a vow just like this one. I thought of all the times I'd held a Bible for comfort, a religious man's security blanket. I used to think it contained all the answers; now I wondered whether the right questions had even been asked. *So help me God,* I thought.

Maggie's hands were clasped lightly in front of her. "Can you state your name and address for the record?"

"Michael Wright," I said, clearing my throat. "Thirty-four twenty-two High Street, in Concord."

"How are you employed?"

"I'm a priest at St. Catherine's."

"How does one become a priest?" Maggie asked.

"You go to seminary for a certain number of years, and then you become a member of the transitional deaconate . . . learning the ropes under the guidance of a more experienced parish priest. Finally, you get ordained."

"How long ago did you take your vows, Father?"

"It's been two years," I said.

I could still remember the ordainment ceremony, my parents watching from the pews, their faces lit as if they had stars caught in their throats. I had been so certain, then, of my calling—of serving Jesus Christ, of who Jesus Christ was. Had I been wrong then? Or was it simply that there was more than one kind of *right*?

"As part of your duties at St. Catherine's, Father, have you been a spiritual advisor for an inmate named Shay Bourne?"

"Yes."

"And is Shay here in the courtroom today?"

"He is."

"In fact," Maggie said, "he's the plaintiff in this case who was sitting beside me at that table, isn't that correct?"

"Yes." I smiled at Shay, who looked down at the table.

"During the course of your training to become a priest, did you speak with parishioners about their religious beliefs?"

"Of course."

"Is it part of your duty as a priest to help others become familiar with God?"

"Yes."

"How about deepening their faith in God?"

"Absolutely."

She turned to the judge. "I'm going to offer up Father Michael as an expert on spiritual advice and religious beliefs, Your Honor."

The other attorney shot up. "Objection," he said. "With all due respect, is Father Michael an expert on Jewish beliefs? Methodist beliefs? Muslim ones?"

"Sustained," the judge said. "Father Michael may not testify as an expert on religious beliefs outside of the Catholic faith, except in his role as a spiritual advisor."

I had no idea what that meant, and from the looks on their faces, neither did either attorney. "What's the role of a spiritual advisor in the prison?" Maggie asked.

"You meet with inmates who would like a friend to talk to, or a voice to pray with," I explained. "You offer them counseling, direction, devotional materials. Basically, you're a priest making a house call."

"How was it that you were chosen to become a spiritual advisor?"

"St. Catherine's—my parish—received a request from the state prison."

"Is Shay Catholic, Father?"

"One of his foster mothers had him baptized Catholic, so in the eyes of the Church, yes, he is. However, he does not consider himself a practicing Catholic."

"How does that work, then? If you're a priest and he's not Catholic, how are you able to be his spiritual advisor?"

"Because my job isn't to preach to him, but to listen."

"When was the first time you met with Shay?" Maggie asked.

"March eighth of this year," I said. "I've seen him once or twice a week since then."

"At some point, did Shay discuss his desire to donate his heart to Claire Nealon, the sister of one of his victims?"

"It was the very first conversation we had," I replied.

"How many times since have you discussed with Shay his feelings about this transplant?"

"Maybe twenty-five, thirty."

Maggie nodded. "There are people here today who think that Shay's desire to become an organ donor has everything to do with buying himself time, and nothing to do with religion. Do you agree with that?"

"Objection," the other attorney said. "Speculation."

The judge shook his head. "I'll allow it."

"He'd die today, if you let him donate his heart. It's not time he wants; it's the chance to be executed in a way that would allow for a transplant."

"Let me play devil's advocate," Maggie

said. "We all know donating organs is self-less . . . but where's the link between dona-tion and salvation? Was there something that convinced you this wasn't just altruism on Shay's part . . . but part of his faith?"

"Yes," I said. "When Shay told me what he wanted to do, he said it in a very striking way. It almost sounded like a weird riddle: 'If I bring forth what's inside me, what's inside me will save me. If I don't bring forth what's inside me, what's inside me will destroy me.' I found out later that Shay's statement wasn't original. He was quoting someone pretty important."

"Who, Father?"

I looked at the judge. "Jesus Christ."

"Nothing further," Maggie said, and she sat back down beside Shay.

Gordon Greenleaf frowned at me. "Forgive my ignorance, Father. Is that from the Old Testament or the New Testament?"

"Neither," I replied. "It's from the Gospel of Thomas."

This stopped the attorney in his tracks. "Aren't all gospels *somewhere* in the Bible?"

"Objection," Maggie called out. "Father Mi-chael can't respond, because he's not a reli-gious expert."

"*You* offered him up as one," Greenleaf said.

Maggie shrugged. "Then you shouldn't have objected to it."

"I'll rephrase," Greenleaf said. "So, Mr. Bourne quoted something that is not actually in the Bible, but you're claiming it's proof that he's motivated by religion?"

"Yes," I said. "Exactly."

"Well, then, what religion does Shay practice?" Greenleaf asked.

"He doesn't label it."

"You said he's not a practicing Catholic. Is he a practicing Jew, then?"

"No."

"A Muslim?"

"No."

"A Buddhist?"

"No," I said.

"Is Mr. Bourne practicing any type of organized religion that the court might be familiar with, Father?"

I hesitated. "He's practicing a religion, but it isn't formally organized."

"Like what? Bourneism?"

"Objection," Maggie interrupted. "If Shay can't name it, why do we have to?"

"Sustained," Judge Haig said.

"Let me clarify," Greenleaf said. "Shay Bourne is practicing a religion you can't name, and quoting from a gospel that's not in the Bible . . . and yet somehow his desire to be an organ donor is grounded in the concept of religious salvation? Does that not strike you, Father, as the slightest bit *convenient* on Mr. Bourne's part?"

He turned, as if he hadn't really expected me to give an answer, but I wasn't going to let him off that easy. "Mr. Greenleaf," I said, "there are all sorts of experiences that we can't really put a name to."

"I beg your pardon?"

"The birth of a child, for one. Or the death of a parent. Falling in love. Words are like nets—we hope they'll cover what we mean, but we know they can't possibly hold that much joy, or grief, or wonder. Finding God is like that, too. If it's happened to you, you know what it feels like. But try to describe it to someone else—and language only takes you so far," I said. "Yes, it sounds convenient. And yes, he's the only member of his religion. And no, it doesn't have a name. But . . . I believe him." I looked at Shay until he met my gaze. "I believe."

June

When Claire was awake, which was less and less often, we did not talk about the heart that might be coming for her or whether or not she'd take it. She didn't want to; I was afraid to. Instead, we talked about things that didn't matter: who'd been voted off her favorite reality TV show; how the Internet actually worked; if I'd reminded Mrs. Walloughby to feed Dudley twice a day instead of three times, because he was on a diet. When Claire was asleep, I held her hand and told her about the future I dreamed of. I told her that we'd travel to Bali and live for a month in a hut perched over the ocean. I told her that I would learn to water-ski barefoot while she drove the boat, and then we'd swap places. How we would climb Mt. Katahdin, get our ears double pierced, learn how to make chocolate from scratch. I imagined her swimming up from the sandy bottom of unconsciousness, bursting through the surface, wading to where I was waiting onshore.

It was during one of Claire's afternoon drug-induced marathon naps that I began to learn about elephants. That morning, when I had gone down to the hospital cafeteria for a cup of coffee, I passed the same three retail establishments I'd passed every day for the past two weeks —a bank, a bookstore, a travel agency. Today, though, for the first time, I was magnetically drawn to a poster in the window. EXPERIENCE AFRICA, it said.

The bored college girl staffing the office was talking to her boyfriend on the phone when I walked inside, and was more than happy to send me on my way with a brochure, in lieu of actually telling me about the destination herself. "Where were we?" I heard her say as she picked up the phone again when I left the office, and then she giggled. "With your *teeth*?"

Upstairs in Claire's room, I pored over pictures of rooms with beds as wide as the sea, covered with crisp white linens and draped with a net of gauze. Of outside showers, exposed to the bush, so that you were as naked as the animals. Of Land Rovers and African rangers with phosphorescent smiles.

And oh, the animals—sleek leopards, with their Rorschach spots; a lioness with eyes like amber; the massive monolith of an elephant yanking a tree out of the ground.

Did you know, the brochure read, *that elephants live in a society much like ours?*

That they travel in matriarchal packs, and gestate for 22 months?

That they can communicate over a distance of 50 km?

Come track the amazing elephant in its natural habitat, the Tuli Block . . .

"What are you reading?" Claire squinted at the brochure, her voice groggy.

"Something on safaris," I said. "I thought maybe you and I might go on one."

"I'm not taking that stupid heart," Claire said, and she rolled on her side, closing her eyes again.

I would tell Claire about the elephants when she woke up, I decided. About a country where mothers and daughters walked side by side for years with their aunts and sisters. About how elephants were either right-handed or left-handed. How they could find their way home years after they'd left.

Here is what I wouldn't tell Claire, ever: That elephants know when they're close to dying, and they make their way to a riverbed for nature to take its course. That elephants bury their dead, and grieve. That naturalists have seen a mother elephant carry a dead calf for miles, cradled in her trunk, unwilling and unable to let it go.

Maggie

||||||||||||||||||||||||||||||||||||||||||||||||||||||||||||||||||||||||||||||||||||||||||||||||||||||||||||||||

Nobody wanted Ian Fletcher to testify, including me.

When I'd called an emergency meeting with the judge days earlier, asking to add Fletcher to my witness list as an expert on the history of religion, I thought Gordon Greenleaf would burst a blood vessel in chambers. "Hello?" he said. "Rule 26(c)?"

He was talking about the Federal Rules of Civil Procedure, which said that witnesses had to be disclosed thirty days before a trial, unless otherwise directed by the court. I was banking on that last clause. "Judge," I said, "we've only had two weeks to prepare for this

trial—neither of us disclosed *any* of our witnesses within thirty days."

"You don't get to sneak in an expert just
because you happened to stumble over one,"
Greenleaf said.

Federal court judges were notorious for trying to keep their cases on the straight and
narrow. If Judge Haig allowed Fletcher to testify, it opened up a whole can of worms—
Greenleaf would need to prepare his cross,
and would most likely want to hire a counter-
expert, which would delay the trial . . . and we
all knew that couldn't happen, since we had a
deadline in the strictest sense of the word.
But—here was the crazy thing—Father Michael had been right. Ian Fletcher's book
dovetailed so neatly with the hook I was using
to drag Shay's case to a victory that it would
have been a shame not to try. And even better
—it provided the one element I'd been lacking in this case: a historical precedent.

I had fully convinced myself that Judge
Haig would laugh in my face anyway when
I tried to include a new witness at the last
minute, but instead, he looked down at the
name. "Fletcher," he said, testing the word
in his mouth as if it were made of sharp
stones. "*Ian* Fletcher?"

"Yes, Your Honor."

"Is he the one who used to have a television show?"

I sucked in my breath. "I believe so."

"I'll be damned," the judge said. He said this in a voice that wasn't wish-I-had-his-autograph, but more he-was-like-a-train-wreck-I-couldn't-turn-away-from.

The good news was, I was allowed to bring in my expert witness. The bad news was that Judge Haig didn't like him very much—and had in the forefront of his mind my witness's former incarnation as an atheist showboat, when I really wanted him to be seen as a grave and credible historian. Greenleaf was furious that he'd only had days to figure out what tune Fletcher was singing these days; the judge regarded him as a curiosity, and me—well, I was just praying that my whole case didn't self-destruct in the next ten minutes.

"Before we begin, Ms. Bloom," the judge said, "I have a few questions for Dr. Fletcher."

He nodded. "Shoot, Judge."

"How does a man who was an atheist a decade ago convince a court that he's an expert on religion now?"

"Your Honor," I interjected. "I'm planning

on going through Dr. Fletcher's credentials . . ."

"I didn't ask *you*, Ms. Bloom," he said.

But Ian Fletcher wasn't rattled. "You know
what they say, Your Honor. Sinners make the
best reformed saints." He grinned, a slow and
lazy smile that reminded me of a cat in the
sunlight. "I guess finding God is like seeing a
ghost—you can be a skeptic until you come
face-to-face with what you said doesn't exist."

"So you're a religious man now?" the judge
asked.

"I'm a *spiritual* man," Fletcher corrected.
"And I do think there's a difference. But being
spiritual doesn't pay the rent, which is why I
have degrees from Princeton and Harvard,
three *New York Times* bestselling nonfiction
books, forty-two published articles on the origins of world religions, and positions on six
interfaith councils, including one that advises
the current administration."

The judge nodded, making notes; and
Greenleaf stipulated to the list of Fletcher's
credentials. "I might as well start with where
Judge Haig left off," I said, beginning the direct examination. "It's pretty rare for an atheist to get interested in religion. Did you just
sort of wake up one day and find Jesus?"

"It's not like you're vacuuming under the sofa cushions and bingo, there he is. My interest grew more from a historical standpoint, because these days, people act like faith grows in a vacuum. When you break down religions and look politically and economically and socially at what was going on during their births, it changes the way you think."

"Dr. Fletcher, do you have to be part of a group to be part of a religion?"

"Not only *can* religion be individualized— it *has* been, in the past. In 1945, a discovery was made in Egypt: fifty-two texts that were labeled gospels—and that weren't part of the Bible. Some of them were full of sayings that would be familiar to anyone who's gone to Sunday school . . . and some of them, to be honest, were really bizarre. They were scientifically dated from the second century, roughly thirty to eighty years younger than the gospels in the New Testament. And they belonged to a group called Gnostic Christians—a splinter group from Orthodox Christianity, who believed that true religious enlightenment meant undertaking a very personal, individual quest to know yourself, not by your socioeconomic status or profession, but at a deeper core."

"Hang on," I said. "After Jesus's death, there was more than one kind of Christian?"

"Oh, there were dozens."

"And they had their own Bibles?"

"They had their own *gospels,*" Fletcher corrected. "The New Testament—in particular, Matthew, Mark, Luke, and John—were the ones that the orthodoxy chose to uphold. The Gnostic Christians preferred texts like the Gospel of Thomas, and the Gospel of Truth, and the Gospel of Mary Magdalene."

"Did those gospels talk about Jesus, too?"

"Yes, except the Jesus they describe isn't the one you'd recognize from the Bible. *That* Jesus is very different from the humans he's come here to save. But the Gospel of Thomas—my personal favorite from Nag Hammadi—says Jesus is a guide to help you figure out all you have in *common* with God. So if you were a Gnostic Christian, you would have *expected* the road to salvation to be different for everyone."

"Like donating your heart to someone who needs it . . . ?"

"Exactly," Fletcher said.

"Wow," I said, playing dumb. "How come this stuff isn't taught in Sunday school?"

"Because the Orthodox Christian Church felt threatened by the Gnostics. They called their gospels heresy, and the Nag Hammadi texts were hidden for two thousand years."

"Father Wright said that Shay Bourne quoted from the Gospel of Thomas. Do you have any idea where he would have stumbled over that text?"

"Maybe he read my book," Fletcher said, smiling widely, and the people in the gallery laughed.

"In your opinion, Doctor, could a religion that only one person believes and follows still be valid?"

"An individual can have a religion," he said. "He can't have a religious *institution*. But it seems to me that Shay Bourne is standing in a tradition similar to the ones the Gnostic Christians did nearly two thousand years ago. He's not the first to say that he can't name his faith. He's not the first to find a path to salvation that is different from others you've heard about. And he's certainly not the first to mistrust the body—to literally want to give it away, as a means to finding divinity inside oneself. But just because he doesn't have a church with a white steeple over his head, or a temple with a six-pointed star surrounding him, doesn't mean that his beliefs are any less worthy."

I beamed at him. Fletcher was easy to listen to, interesting, and he didn't sound like a left-wing nutcase. Or so I thought, until I heard Judge Haig exhale heavily and say court was recessed until the next day.

Lucius

||||||||||||||||||||||||||||||||||||||||||||||||||||||||||||||||||||||||||||||||||||||||||||||||||||||||||||||||||||||||||||

I was painting when Shay returned from his first day of trial, huddled and withdrawn, as going to court made most of us. I'd been working on the portrait all day, and I was quite pleased with the way it was turning out. I glanced up when Shay was escorted past my cell, but didn't speak to him. Better to let him come back to us on his own time.

Not twenty minutes afterward, a long, low keen filled the tier. At first I thought Shay was crying, letting the stress of the day bleed from him, but then I realized that the sound was coming from Calloway Reece's cell. "Come on," he moaned. He started smacking his fists against the door of his cell. "Bourne," he called out. "Bourne, I need your help."

"Leave me alone," Shay said.

"It's the bird, man. I can't get him to wake up."

The fact that Batman the Robin had survived inside I-tier for several weeks on crusts of toast and bits of oatmeal was a wonder in its own right, not to mention the fact that he'd cheated death once before.

"Give him CPR," Joey Kunz suggested.

"You can't do fucking CPR on a bird," Calloway snapped. "They got *beaks.*"

I put down the makeshift brush I was using to paint—a rolled wad of toilet paper—and angled my mirror-shank out my door so that I could see. In his enormous palm, Calloway cradled the bird, which lay on its side, unmoving.

"Shay," he begged, "*please.*"

There was no response from Shay's cell. "Fish him to me," I said, and crouched down with my line. I was worried that the bird had grown too big to make it through the little slit at the bottom, but Calloway wrapped him in a handkerchief, roped the top, and sent the slight weight in a wide arc across the floor of the catwalk. I knotted my string

with Calloway's and gently drew the bird toward me.

I couldn't resist unwrapping the kerchief
to peek. Batman's eyelid was purple and
creased, his tail feathers spread like a fan.
The tiny hooks on the ends of his claws were
as sharp as pins. When I touched them, the
bird did not even twitch. I placed my forefinger beneath the wing—did birds have hearts
where we did?—and felt nothing.

"Shay," I said quietly. "I know you're tired.
And I know you've got your own stuff going
on. But please. Just take a look."

Five whole minutes passed, long enough
for me to give up. I wrapped the bird in the
cloth again and tied him to the end of my
fishing line, cast him onto the catwalk for
Calloway to retrieve. But before his line could
tangle with mine, another whizzed out, and
Shay intercepted the bird.

In my mirror, I watched Shay take Batman
from the kerchief, hold him in his hand. He
stroked the head with his finger; he gingerly
covered the body with his other hand, as if he
had caught a star between his palms. I held
my breath, watching for that flutter or feather
or the faintest cheep, but after a few moments
Shay just wrapped the bird up again.

"Hey!" Calloway had been watching, too. "You didn't *do* anything!"

"Leave me alone," Shay repeated. The air had gone bitter as almonds; I could barely stand to breathe it. I watched him fish back that dead bird, and all of our hopes along with it.

Maggie

||||||||||||||||||||||||||||||||||||||||||||||||||||||||||||||||||||||||||||||||||||||||||||||||||||||||||

When Gordon Greenleaf stood up, his knees creaked. "You've studied comparative world religions in the course of your research?" he asked Fletcher.

"Yes."

"Do different religions take a stand on organ donation?"

"Yes," Fletcher said. "Catholics believe only in transplants done after death—you can't risk killing the donor, for example, during the donation. They fully support organ donation, as do Jews and Muslims. Buddhists and Hindus believe organ donation is a matter of individual conscience, and they put high value on acts of compassion."

"Do any of those religions *require* you to donate organs as a means to salvation?"

"No," Fletcher said.

"Are there Gnostic Christians practicing today?"

"No," Fletcher said. "The religion died out."

"How come?"

"When you have a belief system that says you shouldn't listen to the clergy, and that you should continually ask questions, instead of accepting doctrine, it's hard to form a community. On the other hand, the Orthodox Christians were delineating the steps to being card-carrying members of the group—confess the creed, accept baptism, worship, obey the priests. Plus, *their* Jesus was someone the average Joe could relate to—someone who'd been born, had an overprotective mom, suffered, and died. That was a much easier sell than the Gnostic Jesus—who was never even human. The rest of the Gnostics' decline," Fletcher said, "was political. In A.D. 312, Constantine, the Roman emperor, saw a crucifix in the sky and converted to Christianity. The Catholic Church became part of the Holy

Roman Empire . . . and having Gnostic texts and beliefs were punishable by death."

"So, it's fair to say no one's practiced Gnostic Christianity for fifteen hundred years?" Greenleaf said.

"Not formally. But there are elements of Gnostic belief in other religions that have survived. For example, Gnostics recognized the difference between the reality of God, which was impossible to describe with language, and the image of God as we knew it. This sounds a lot like Jewish mysticism, where you find God being described as streams of energy, male and female, which pool together into a divine source; or God as the source of all sounds at once. And Buddhist enlightenment is very much like the Gnostic idea that we live in a land of oblivion, but can waken spiritually right here while we're still part of this world."

"But Shay Bourne can't be a follower of a religion that no longer exists, isn't that true?"

He hesitated. "From what I understand, donating his heart is Shay Bourne's attempt to learn who he is, who he wants to be, how he is connected to others. And in that very basic sense, the Gnostics would agree that he's found the part of him that comes closest to being divine." Fletcher looked up. "A Gnostic Christian would tell you that a man on death row is more like us than unlike us. And that—as Mr. Bourne seems to be trying to suggest—he still has something to offer the world."

"Yeah. What*ever.*" Greenleaf raised a brow. "Have you ever even *met* Shay Bourne?"

"Actually," Fletcher said, "no."

"So for all you know, he doesn't have any religious beliefs at all. This could all be some grand plan to delay his execution, couldn't it?"

"I've spoken with his spiritual advisor."

The lawyer scoffed. "You've got a guy practicing a religion by himself that seems to hearken back to a religious sect that died out thousands of years ago. Isn't it possible that this is a bit too . . . easy? That Shay Bourne could just be making it all up as he goes along?"

Fletcher smiled. "A lot of people thought that about Jesus."

"Dr. Fletcher," Greenleaf said, "are you telling this court that Shay Bourne is a messiah?"

Fletcher shook his head. "Your words, not mine."

"Then how about your stepdaughter's words?" Greenleaf asked. "Or is this some kind of family trait you all have, running into God in state prisons and elementary schools and Laundromats?"

"Objection," I said. "My witness isn't on trial here."

Greenleaf shrugged. "His ability to discuss the history of Christianity is—"

"Overruled," Judge Haig said.

Fletcher narrowed his eyes. "What my daughter did or didn't see has no bearing on Shay Bourne's request to donate his heart."

"Did you believe she was a fake when you first met her?"

"The more I spoke with her, the more I—"

"When you *first* met her," Greenleaf interrupted, "did you believe she was a fake?"

"Yes," Fletcher admitted.

"And yet, with no personal contact, you were willing to testify in a court of law that Mr. Bourne's request to donate his organs could be massaged to fit your loose definition of a religion." Greenleaf glanced at him. "I guess, in your case, old habits die fairly easy."

"Objection!"

"Withdrawn." Greenleaf started back to his seat, but then turned. "Just one more question,

Dr. Fletcher—this daughter of yours. She was seven years old when she found herself at the center of a religious media circus not unlike this one, correct?"

"Yes."

"Are you aware that's the same age of the little girl Shay Bourne murdered?"

A muscle in Fletcher's jaw twitched. "No. I wasn't."

"How do you think you'd feel about God if your stepdaughter was the one who'd been killed?"

I shot to my feet. *"Objection!"*

"I'll allow it," the judge answered.

Fletcher paused. "I think that kind of tragedy would test anyone's faith."

Gordon Greenleaf folded his arms. "Then it's not faith," he said. "It's being a chameleon."

MICHAEL

During the lunch recess, I went to see Shay in his holding cell. He was sitting on the floor, near the bars, while a U.S. marshal sat outside on a stool. Shay held a pencil and scrap of paper, as if he were conducting an interview.

"H," the marshal said, and Shay shook his head. "M?"

Shay scribbled something on the paper. "I'm down to your last toe, dude."

The marshal sucked in his breath. "K."

Shay grinned. "I win." He scrawled something else on the page and passed it through the bars—only then did I notice that it had been a game of hangman, and that this time around, Shay was the executioner.

Scowling, the marshal stared down at the paper. "*Szygszyg* isn't a real word."

"You didn't say that it had to be *real* when we started playing," Shay replied, and then he noticed me standing at the threshold of the door.

"I'm Shay's spiritual advisor," I told the marshal. "Can we have a minute?"

"No problem. I have to take a whiz." He stood up, offering me the stool he was vacating, and headed out of the room.

"How are you doing?" I said quietly.

Shay walked to the back of the cell, where he lay down on the metal bunk and faced the wall.

"I want to talk to you, Shay."

"Just because you want to talk doesn't mean I want to listen."

I sank down on the stool. "I was the last one on your jury to vote for the death penalty," I said. "I was the reason we deliberated so long. And even after I'd been convinced by the rest of the jury that this was the best sentence, I didn't feel good about it. I kept having panic attacks. One day, during one, I stumbled into a cathedral and started to pray.

The more I did it, the fewer panic attacks I had." I clasped my hands between my knees. "I thought that was a sign from God."

Still with his back to me, Shay snorted.

"I still think it's a sign from God, because it's brought me back into your life."

Shay rolled onto his back and flung one arm over his eyes. "Don't kid yourself," he said. "It's brought you back into my death."

Ian Fletcher was already standing at a urinal when I ran into the men's room. I had been hoping it would be empty. Shay's comment— the bald truth—had made me so sick to my stomach that I'd rushed out of the holding cell without explanation. I pushed into a stall, fell to my knees, and got violently ill.

No matter how much I wanted to fool myself—no matter what I said about atoning for my past sins—the bottom line was that for the second time in my life, my actions were going to result in the death of Shay Bourne.

Fletcher pushed the door of the stall open and put his hand on my shoulder. "Father? You all right?"

I wiped my mouth, slowly got to my feet. "I'm fine," I said, then shook my head. "No, actually, I'm awful."

I walked to the sink, turned on the faucet, and splashed water on my face as Fletcher watched. "Do you need to sit down or something?"

I dried my face with a paper towel he passed me. And suddenly, I wanted someone else to bear this burden. Ian Fletcher was a man who'd unraveled secrets from two thousand years ago; surely he could keep one of mine. "I was on his jury," I murmured into the recycled brown paper.

"I'm sorry?"

No, I am, I thought. I met Fletcher's gaze. "I was on the jury that sentenced Shay Bourne to death. Before I joined the priesthood."

Fletcher let out a long, low whistle. "Does he know?"

"I told him a few days ago."

"And his lawyer?"

I shook my head. "I keep thinking that this must be how Judas felt after turning Jesus in."

Fletcher's mouth turned up at the corners. "Actually, there's a recently discovered Gnostic gospel—the Gospel of Judas—and there's very little in there about betrayal. In fact, this gospel paints Judas as Jesus's confidant—the only one he trusted to make what needed to happen, happen."

"Even if it was an assisted suicide," I said, "I'm sure Judas felt like crap about it afterward. I mean, he *killed* himself."

"Well," Fletcher said, "there was *that*."

"What would you do if you were me?" I asked. "Would you carry through with this? Help Shay donate his heart?"

"I guess that depends on why you're helping him," Fletcher said slowly. "Is it to save him, like you said on the stand? Or are you really just trying to save yourself?" He shook his head. "If man had the answers for questions like those, there wouldn't be a need for religion. Good luck, Father."

I went back into the stall and closed the lid of the toilet, sat down. I slipped my rosary out of my pocket and whispered the familiar words of the prayers, sweet in my mouth like sucking candies. Finding God's grace wasn't like locating missing keys or the forgotten name of a 1940s pinup girl—it was more of a feeling: the sun breaking through an overcast morning, the softest bed sinking under your weight. And, of course, you couldn't find God's grace unless you admitted you were lost.

A bathroom stall at the federal courthouse might not be the most likely spot to find God's grace, but that didn't mean it couldn't be done.

Find God's grace.

Find Grace.

If Shay was willing to give up his heart, then the least I could do was make sure he'd be remembered in someone else's. Someone who—unlike me—had never condemned him.

That was when I decided to find Shay's sister.

June

It is not an easy thing to pick the clothes in which your child will be buried. I had been told by the funeral director, after the murders, to think about it. He suggested something that represented her, a beautiful girl—such as a nice little dress, one that opened up the back, preferably. He asked me to bring in a picture of her so that he could use makeup to match the blush of her cheek, the natural color of her skin, her hairstyle.

What I had wanted to say to him was: Elizabeth hated dresses. She would have worn pants without buttons, because they were frustrating, or possibly last year's Halloween costume, or the tiny set of doctors' scrubs she got for Christmas—I had, just days before, found her "operating" on an overgrown zucchini that was the size of a newborn. I would have told him that Elizabeth did not have a hairstyle, because you could not ground her long enough to brush it, much less braid or curl. And that I did not want him putting makeup on her face, not when I would never have that bonding moment between a mother and daughter in a bathroom before an elegant night on the town, when I could let her try the eye shadow, a smudge of mascara, pink lipstick.

The funeral director told me that it might be nice to have a table of mementos that meant something to Elizabeth—stuffed animals or family vacation photos, chocolate chip cookies. To play her favorite music. To let her school friends write messages to her, which could be buried in a silk satchel inside the coffin.

What I wanted to say to him was: Don't you realize that by telling me the same things you tell everyone else about how to make a meaningful funeral, you are making it meaningless? That Elizabeth deserved fireworks, an angel choir, the world turning backward on its axis.

In the end, I had dressed Elizabeth in a ballerina's tutu, one she somehow always wanted to wear when we went grocery shopping, and that I always made her take off before we left. I let the funeral director put makeup on her face for the first time. I gave her a stuffed dog, her stepfather, and most of my heart to take with her.

It was not an open-casket funeral; but before we left for the graveside service, the funeral director lifted the cover to make final adjustments. At that moment, I pushed him out of the way. *Let me,* I had said.

Kurt was wearing his uniform, as befitted a police officer killed in the line of duty. He looked exactly like he did every day, except for the fine white line around his finger where his wedding ring had been. That, I now wore on a chain around my neck.

Elizabeth looked delicate, angelic. Her hair was tied up in matching ribbons. Her arm was around her stepfather's waist.

I reached into the coffin, and the moment my hand brushed my daughter's cheek I shivered, because somehow I had still expected it to be warm—not this fake-flesh, this cool-to-the-touch skin. I tugged the ribbons out of her hair, gently lifted her head, fanned her hair on both sides of her face. I tugged the left leotard sleeve down a quarter inch, to match the one on the right.

I hope you're pleased, the funeral director had said.

It didn't look like Elizabeth, not one bit, because she was too perfect. My daughter would have been rumpled and untucked, her hands dirty from chasing frogs, her socks mismatched, her wrists ringed with bracelets she'd beaded herself.

But in a world where things happen that shouldn't, you find yourself saying and doing things that are the complete opposite of what you mean. So I had nodded, and watched him seal away the two people I loved most in this world.

Now I found myself in the same position I'd been in eleven years ago, standing in the middle of my daughter's bedroom and sifting through her clothes. I sorted through shirts and skirts and tights, jeans as soft as flannel and a sweatshirt that still smelled like the apple orchard where she last wore it. I chose a pair of flared black leggings and a long-sleeved tee that had Tinker Bell printed on it—clothes that I had seen Claire wear on the laziest of Sundays, when it was snow-ing and there was nothing to be done but read the Sunday paper and doze with your cheek pressed against the wall of heat thrown by the fireplace. I picked out a pair of underwear—SATURDAY, it read across the front, but I couldn't find any other days of the week scattered in the drawer. It was when I was looking that I found, wrapped in a red bandanna, the photograph. In a tiny silver oval frame, I thought at first it was one of Claire's baby pictures—and then I realized it was Elizabeth.

The frame used to sit on top of the piano that nobody played anymore, gathering dust. The fact that I never even noticed it was missing was a testament to the fact that I must have learned how to live again.

Which is why I collected the clothes and put them into a shopping bag to take to the hospital: an outfit in which I sincerely hoped I would not bury my daughter, but instead, bring her back home.

Lucius

||||||||||||||||||||||||||||||||||||||||||||||||||||||||||||||||||||||||||||||||||||||||||||||||||||||||||||||||||||||||||||||||

These nights, I slept well. There were no more sweats, no diarrhea, no fevers to keep me thrashing in my bunk. Crash Vitale was still in solitary, so his rants didn't wake me. From time to time, the extra officer who'd been assigned to Shay for protection would prowl through the tier, his boots a soft-soled shuffle on the catwalk.

I had been sleeping so well, in fact, that I was surprised I woke up to the quiet conversation going on in the cell next door to mine. "Will you just let me explain?" Shay asked. "What if there's another way?"

I waited to hear whom he was talking to, but there was no answer.

"Shay?" I said. "Are you okay?"

"I tried to give away my heart," I heard him say. "And look at what it turned into." Shay kicked at the wall; something heavy in his cell tumbled to the floor. "I know what you want. But do you know what *I* want?"

"Shay?"

His voice was just a braid of breath. "*Abba*?"

"It's me. Lucius."

There was a beat of silence. "You were listening to my conversation."

Was it a conversation if you were having a monologue in your own cell? "I didn't mean to . . . you woke me up."

"Why were you asleep?" Shay asked.

"Because it's three in the morning?" I replied. "Because that's what you're supposed to be doing?"

"What I'm supposed to be doing," Shay repeated. "Right."

There was a thud, and I realized Shay had fallen. The last time that had happened, he'd been having a seizure. I scrabbled underneath the bunk and pulled out the mirror-shank. "Shay," I called out. "Shay?"

In the reflection, I could see him. He was on his knees in the front of the cell, with his hands spread wide. His head was bowed, and he was bathed in sweat, which—from the dim crimson light on the catwalk—looked like beads of blood.

"Go away," he said, and I withdrew the mirror from the slats of my own door, giving him privacy.

As I hid away my makeshift mirror, I caught a glimpse of my own reflection. Like Shay's, my skin looked scarlet. And yet even that didn't stop me from noticing the familiar ruby sore that had opened up once again across my forehead—a scar, a stain, a planet's moving storm.

MICHAEL

||||||||||||||||||||||||||||||||||||||||||||||||||||||||||||||||||||||||||||||||||||||||||||||||||||||||||||||||||||||||||||||||||||||||||||||||||||

Shay's last foster mother, Renata Ledoux, was a Catholic who lived in Bethlehem, New Hampshire, and as I'd traveled up to meet with her, the irony of the name of the town where Shay had spent his teenage years did not escape me. I was wearing my collar and had on my gravest priest demeanor, because I was pulling out all the stops. I was going to say whatever was necessary to find out what had happened to Grace.

As it turned out, though, it hardly took any work at all. Renata invited me in for tea, and when I told her I had a message for Grace from a person in my congregation, she simply wrote out an address and handed it to me. "We're still in touch," she said simply. "Gracie was a good girl."

I couldn't help but wonder what she thought of Shay. "Didn't she have a brother?"

"That boy," Renata had said, "deserves to burn in hell."

It was ludicrous to believe that Renata had not heard about Shay's death sentence—the news would have reached up here, even in rural Bethlehem. I had thought, maybe, as his foster mother, she'd at least harbor some soft spot for him. But then again, the boy she'd raised had left her home to go to juvenile prison, and had grown up to become a convicted murderer. "Yes," I'd said. "Well."

Now, twenty minutes later, I was approaching Grace's house, and hoping for a better reception. It was the pink one with gray shutters and the number 131 on a carved stone at the end of the drive—but the shades were drawn, the garage door was closed. There were no plants hanging on the porch, no doors open for a breeze, no outgoing mail in the box—nothing to indicate that the inhabitant was home.

I got out of my car and rang the doorbell. Twice.

Well, I could leave a note and ask her to call me. It would take more time—time Shay did not really have—but if it was the best I could do, then so be it.

Just then the door opened just a crack. "Yes?" a voice inside murmured.

I tried to see into the foyer, but it was pitch-dark. "Does Grace Bourne live here?"

A hesitation. "That's me."

"I'm Father Michael Wright. I have a message for you, from one of the parishioners in my congregation."

A slender hand slipped out. "You can give it to me," Grace said.

"Actually, could I just come in for a bit— use your restroom? It's been a long drive from Concord . . ."

She hesitated—I suppose I would, too, if a strange man showed up at my door and I was a woman living alone, even if he was wearing a collar. But the door opened wide and Grace stepped back to let me in. Her head was ducked to the side; a long curtain of black hair hung over her face. I caught a glimpse of long dark lashes and a ruby of a mouth; you could tell, even at first glance, how pretty she must be. I wondered if she was agoraphobic, painfully shy. I wondered who had hurt her so much that she was afraid of the rest of the world.

I wondered if it was Shay.

"Grace," I said, reaching for her hand. "It's nice to meet you."

She lifted her chin then, and the screen of hair fell back. The entire left side of Grace Bourne's face was ravaged and pitted, a lava flow of skin that had been stretched and sewed to cover an extensive burn.

"Boo," she said.

"I . . . I'm sorry. I didn't mean . . ."

"Everyone stares," Grace said quietly. "Even the ones who try not to."

There was a fire, Shay had said. *I don't want to talk about it.*

"I'm sorry."

"Yeah, you said that already. The bathroom's down the hall."

I put a hand on her arm. There were patches of skin there, too, that were scarred. "Grace. That message—it's from your brother."

She took a step away from me, stunned. "You know Shay?"

"He needs to see you, Grace. He's going to die soon."

"What did he say about me?"

"Not a lot," I admitted. "But you're the only family he has."

"Do you know about the fire?" Grace asked.

"Yes. It was why he went to juvenile prison."

"Did he tell you that our foster father died in it?"

This time, it was my turn to be surprised. A juvenile record would be sealed, which is why I hadn't known during the capital murder trial what Shay had been convicted of. I'd assumed, when fire had been mentioned, that it was arson. I hadn't realized that the charges might have included negligent homicide, or even manslaughter. And I understood exactly why, now, Renata Ledoux might viscerally hate Shay.

Grace was staring at me intently. "Did he ask to see me?"

"He doesn't actually know I'm here."

She turned away, but not before I saw that she had started to cry. "He didn't want me at his trial."

"He probably didn't want you to have to witness that."

"You don't know anything." She buried her face in her hands.

"Grace," I said, "come back with me. Come see him."

"I can't," she sobbed. "I can't. You don't understand."

But I was beginning to: Shay had set the fire that had disfigured her. "That's all the more reason to meet with him. Forgive him, before it's too late."

"Forgive him? Forgive *him*?" Grace parroted. "No matter what I say, it won't change what happened. You don't get to do your life over." She glanced away. "I think . . . I just . . . you should go."

It was my dismissal. I nodded, accepting.

"The bathroom's the second door on the right."

Right—my ruse to get inside. I walked down the hall to a restroom that was floral, overpowering in a scent of air freshener and rose potpourri. There were little crocheted toilet paper holders, a crocheted bra for the toilet tank, and a crocheted cover for the Kleenex box. There were roses on the shower curtain, and art on the walls—framed prints of flowers, except for one of a child's drawing—a dragon, or maybe a lizard. The room felt like the kind of abode for an elderly lady who'd lost count of her cats. It was stifling;

slowly, Grace Bourne was suffocating herself to death.

If Shay knew that his sister forgave him for the fire, then maybe—even if he wasn't allowed to donate his heart—it would be enough to let him die in peace. Grace was in no condition to be convinced right now, but I could work on her. I'd get her phone number and call her, until I'd worn down her resistance.

I opened the sliding mirrored medicine cabinet, looking for a prescription with Grace's phone number so that I could copy it down. There were lotions and creams and exfoliants, toothpaste and floss and deodorant. There was also a medicine bottle of Ambien, with Grace's phone number across the top of the label. I wrote it on the inside of my palm with a pen and set the pills back on the shelf, beside a small pewter frame. Two tiny children sat at a table: Grace in a high chair with a glass of milk in front of her, and Shay hunched over a picture he was drawing. A dragon, or maybe a lizard.

He was smiling, so wide it looked like it might hurt.

Every inmate is someone's child. And so is every victim.

I walked out of the bathroom. Handing Grace a card with my name and number on it, I thanked her. "Just in case you change your mind."

"Mine was never the one that needed changing," Grace said, and closed the door behind me. Immediately I heard the bolt slide shut, the curtain in the front window rustle. I kept envisioning the dragon picture, which was carefully matted and framed in the bathroom. TO GRACIE, it had said in the upper left-hand corner.

I was all the way to Crawford Notch before I realized what had been niggling in my mind about that photo of Shay as a child. In it, he'd been holding a pen in his right hand. But in prison—when he ate, when he wrote—he was a lefty.

Could someone change so radically over a lifetime? Or could all of these changes in Shay—from his dominant hand to his miracles to his ability to quote the Gospel of Thomas—have come from some . . . possession? It sounded like some bad science fiction movie, but that wasn't to say it couldn't happen. If prophets could be overtaken by the Holy Spirit, why not a murderer?

Or, maybe it was simpler than that. Maybe

who we were in the past informed who we chose to be in the future. Maybe Shay had intentionally shifted his writing hand. Maybe he cultivated miracles, to make up for a sin as horrible as setting a fire that took the lives of two people—one literal, one meta-phorical. It struck me that even in the Bible, there was no record of Jesus's life between the ages of eight and thirty-three. What if he'd done something awful; what if his later years were a response to that?

You could do a horrible thing, and then spend your whole natural life trying to atone.

I knew that better than anyone.

Maggie

The last conversation I had with Shay Bourne, before putting him on the stand as a witness, had not gone well. In the holding cell, I'd reminded him what was going to happen in court. Shay didn't deal well with curves being thrown at him; he could just as likely become belligerent as curl up in a ball beneath the wooden stand. Either way, the judge would think he was crazy—and that couldn't happen.

"So after the marshal helps you into the seat," I had explained, "they're going to bring you a Bible."

"I don't need one."

"Right. But they need you to swear on it."

"I want to swear on a comic book," Shay had replied. "Or a *Playboy* magazine."

"You have to swear on a Bible," I'd said, "because we have to play by their rules before we're allowed to change the game."

Just then, a U.S. marshal had come to tell me that court was about to convene. "Remember," I had said to Shay, "focus only on me. Nothing else in that courtroom's important. It's just us, having a chat."

He had nodded, but I could see that he was jittery. And now, as I watched him being brought into the courtroom, everyone else could see it, too. He was bound at the ankles and the wrists, with a belly chain to link the others; the links rattled as he shuddered into his seat beside me. His head was ducked, and he was murmuring words no one but I could hear. He was actually cursing out one of the U.S. marshals who'd led him into the courtroom, but with any luck, people who watched his mouth moving silently would think he was praying.

As soon as I put him on the witness stand, a quiet pall fell over the people in the gallery. *You are not like us,* their silence seemed to say. *You never will be.* And there, without me asking a single question, was my answer: no amount of piousness could erase the stain on the hands of a murderer.

I walked in front of Shay and waited until he caught my eye. *Focus,* I mouthed, and he nodded. He gripped the front of the witness box railing, and his chains clinked.

Dammit. I'd forgotten to tell him to keep his hands in his lap. It would be less of a reminder to the judge and the gallery that he was a convicted felon.

"Shay," I asked, "why do you want to donate your heart?"

He stared right at me. Good boy. "I have to save her."

"Who?"

"Claire Nealon."

"Well," I said, "you're not the only person in the world who can save Claire. There are other suitable heart donors."

"I'm the one who took the most away from her," Shay said, just like we had practiced. "I have the most to give back to her."

"Is this about clearing your conscience?" I asked.

Shay shook his head. "It's about clearing the slate."

So far, I thought, *so good.* He sounded rational, and clear, and calm.

"Maggie?" Shay said just then. "Can I stop now?"

I smiled tightly. "Not quite yet, Shay. We've got a few more questions."

"The questions are bullshit."

There was a gasp in the rear of the gallery— probably one of the blue-haired ladies I'd seen filing in with their Bibles wrapped in protective quilted cozies, who hadn't stumbled across a cuss word since before menopause. "Shay," I said, "we don't use that language in court. Remember?"

"Why is it called court?" he asked. "It's not like a tennis court or a basketball court, where you're playing a game. Or maybe you are, and that's why there's a winner and a loser, except it has nothing to do with how well you make a three-point shot or how fast your serve is." He looked at Judge Haig. "I bet you play golf."

"Ms. Bloom," the judge said. "Control your witness."

If Shay didn't shut up, I was going to personally cover his mouth with my hand. "Shay, tell me about your religious upbringing as a child," I said firmly.

"Religion's a cult. You don't get to choose your own religion. You're what your parents tell you you are; it's not upbringing at all, just a brainwashing. When a baby's getting water poured over his head at a christening he can't say, 'Hey, man, I'd rather be a Hindu,' can he?"

"Shay, I know this is hard for you, and I know that being here is very distracting," I said. "But I need you to listen to the question I'm asking, and answer it. Did you go to church when you were a kid?"

"Part of the time. And part of the time I didn't go anywhere at all, except hide in the closet so I wouldn't get beat up by another kid or the foster dad, who'd try to keep everyone in line with a metal hairbrush. It kept us in line, all right, all the way down our backs. The whole foster care system in this country is a joke; it ought to be called foster *don't* care, don't give a shit except for the stipend you're getting from the—"

"Shay!" I warned him with a flash of my eyes. "Do you believe in God?"

This question, somehow, seemed to calm him down. "I *know* God," Shay said.

"Tell me how."

"Everyone's got a little God in them . . . and a little murder in them, too. It's how your life turns out that makes you lean to one side or the other."

"What's God like?"

"Math," Shay said. "An equation. Except when you take everything away, you get infinity, instead of zero."

"And where does God live, Shay?"

He leaned forward, lifted his chained hands so that the metal chinked. He pointed to his heart. "Here."

"You said you used to go to church when you were a kid. Is the God you believe in today the same God you were taught about at church?"

Shay shrugged. "Whatever road you take, the view is going to be the same."

I was nearly a hundred percent certain I'd heard that phrase before, at the one and only Bikram yoga class I'd attended, before I decided that my body wasn't meant to bend in certain ways. I couldn't believe Greenleaf wasn't objecting, on the grounds that channeling the Dalai Lama wasn't the same as answering a question. Then again, I *could* believe Greenleaf wasn't objecting. The more Shay said, the crazier he appeared. It was hard to take someone's claims about religion seriously when he sounded delusional; Shay was digging a grave big enough for both of us.

"If the judge orders you to die by lethal

injection, Shay, and you can't donate your
heart—will that upset God?" I asked.

"It'll upset me. So yeah, it'll upset God."

"Well, then," I said, "what is it about giving
your heart to Claire Nealon that will *please*
God?"

He smiled at me then—the sort of smile you
see on the faces of saints in frescoes, and
that makes you wish you knew their secret.
"My end," Shay said, "is her beginning."

I had a few more questions, but to be honest, I was terrified of what Shay might say.
He already was talking in riddles. "Thank
you," I replied, and sat down.

"I have a question, Mr. Bourne," Judge
Haig said. "There's a lot of talk about odd
things that have occurred at the prison. Do
you believe you can perform miracles?"

Shay looked at him. "Do *you*?"

"I'm sorry, but that's not how a courtroom
works. I'm not allowed to answer your question, but you still need to answer mine. So," the
judge said, "do you believe you can perform
miracles?"

"I just did what I was supposed to. You
can call that whatever you want."

The judge shook his head. "Mr. Greenleaf,
your witness."

Suddenly, a man in the gallery stood up. He unzipped his jacket, revealing a T-shirt that had been emblazoned with the numbers 3:16. He started yelling, his voice hoarse. "For God so loved the world that he gave his only son—" By then, two U.S. marshals had descended, hauling him out of his seat and dragging him up the alley, as the news cameras swiveled to follow the action. "His only son!" the man yelled. "*Only!* You are going to hell once they pump your veins full of—" The doors of the courtroom banged shut behind him, and then it was utterly silent.

It was impressive that this man had gotten into the court in the first place—there were checkpoints with metal detectors and marshals in place before you entered. But his weapon had been the fundamental fury of his righteousness, and at that moment, I would have been hard-pressed to decide whether he or Shay had come off looking worse.

"Yes," Gordon Greenleaf said, getting to his feet. "Well." He walked toward Shay, who rested his chained hands on the witness stand rail again. "You're the only person who subscribes to your religion?"

"No."

"No?"

"I don't belong to a religion. Religion's the reason the world's falling apart—did you see that guy get carted out of here? *That's* what religion does. It points a finger. It causes wars. It breaks apart countries. It's a petri dish for stereotypes to grow in. Religion's not about being holy," Shay said. "Just holier-than-thou."

At the plaintiff's table, I closed my eyes—at the very least, Shay had surely just lost the case for himself; at the most, I was going to wind up with a cross being burned on my lawn. "Objection," I said feebly. "It's not responsive."

"Overruled," the judge replied. "He's not your witness now, Ms. Bloom."

Shay continued muttering, more quietly now. "You know what religion does? It draws a big fat line in the sand. It says, 'If you don't do it my way, you're out.' "

He wasn't yelling, he wasn't out of control. But he wasn't *in* control, either. He brought his hands up to his neck, started scratching at it as the chains jangled down his chest. "These words," he said, "they're cutting my throat."

"Judge," I said immediately, alert to a rapidly approaching meltdown. "Can we take a recess?"

Shay started rocking back and forth.

"Fifteen minutes," Judge Haig said, and the U.S. marshals approached to remand Shay into custody. Panicking, Shay cowered and raised his arms in defense. And we all watched as the chains he was wearing—the ones that had secured him at the wrists and the ankles and the waist, the ones that had jangled throughout his testimony—fell to the floor with a clatter, as if they'd been no more substantial than smoke.

|||||||||||||||||||||||||||||||||||||||||||||||||||||||||||||||||||||||||||||||||||||||||||||||

"Religion often gets in the way of God."

**—BONO, AT THE NATIONAL PRAYER
BREAKFAST, FEBRUARY 2, 2006**

Maggie

Shay stood, his arms akimbo, looking just as surprised to be unshackled as we were to see him that way. There was a collective moment of disbelief, and then chaos exploded in the courtroom. Screams rang out from the gallery. One marshal dragged the judge off the bench and into his chambers while the other drew his weapon, yelling for Shay to put his hands up. Shay froze, only to have the marshal tackle and handcuff him. "Stop!" Father Michael cried behind me. "He doesn't know what's happening!" As the marshal pushed Shay's head against the wooden floor, he looked up at us, terrified.

I whipped around to face the priest. "What the hell's going on? He's gone from being Jesus to being Houdini?"

"This is the kind of thing he does," Father Michael said. Was it me, or did I hear a note of satisfaction in his voice? "I tried to tell you."

"Let me tell *you*," I shot back. "Our friend Shay just earned himself a one-way ticket to the lethal injection gurney, unless one of us can convince him to say something to Judge Haig to explain what just happened."

"You're his lawyer," Michael said.

"*You're* his advisor."

"Remember how I told you Shay won't talk to me?"

I rolled my eyes. "Could we just pretend we're not in seventh grade anymore, and do our jobs?"

He let his gaze slide away, and immediately I knew that whatever else this conversation had to hold, it wasn't going to be pleasant.

By now, the courtroom had emptied. I had to get to Shay and put a solitary, cohesive thought in his head, one that I hoped he could retain long enough to take to the witness stand. I didn't have time for Father Michael's confessions right now.

"I was on the jury that convicted Shay," the priest said.

My mother had a trick she'd employed since I was a teenager—if I said something that made her want to (a) scream, (b) whack me, or (c) both, she would count to ten, her lips moving silently, before she responded. I could feel my mouth rounding out the syllables of the numbers, and with some dismay I realized that finally, I *had* become my mother. "Is that all?" I asked.

"Isn't that *enough*?"

"Just making sure." My mind raced. I could get into a lot of trouble for not telling Greenleaf that fact in advance. Then again, I hadn't *known* in advance. "Is there a reason you waited so long to mention this?"

"Don't ask, don't tell," he said, parroting my own words. "At first I thought I'd just help Shay understand redemption, and then I'd tell you the truth. But Shay wound up teaching *me* about redemption, and you said my testimony was critical, and I thought maybe it was better you didn't know. I thought it wouldn't screw up the trial quite as much . . ."

I held up my hand, stopping him. "Do you support it?" I asked. "The death penalty?"

The priest hesitated before he spoke. "I *used* to."

I would have to tell Greenleaf. Even if Father Michael's testimony was stricken from the record, though, you couldn't make the judge forget hearing it; the damage had been done. Right now, however, I had more important things to do. "I have to go."

In the holding cell, I found Shay still distraught, his eyes squinched shut. "Shay?" I said. "It's Maggie. Look at me."

"I can't," he cried. "Turn the volume down."

The room was quiet; there was no radio playing, no sound at all. I glanced at the marshal, who shrugged. "Shay," I commanded, coming up to the bars of the cell. "Open your goddamn eyes."

One eye squinted open a crack, then the other.

"Tell me how you did it."

"Did what?"

"Your little magic act in there."

He shook his head. "I didn't do anything."

"You managed to get out of handcuffs," I said. "What did you do, make a key and hide it in a seam?"

"I don't have a key. I didn't unlock them."

Well, technically, this was true. What I'd

seen were the still-fastened cuffs, clattering
to the floor, while Shay's hands were somehow free of them. He certainly could have
unfastened the locks and snapped them shut
again—but it would have been noisy, something we all would have heard.

And we hadn't.

"I didn't do anything," Shay repeated.

I'd read somewhere of magicians who
learned to dislocate their shoulders to get
out of straitjackets; maybe this had been
Shay's secret. Maybe he could double-joint
his thumbs or resettle the bones of his fingers and slide out of the metal fittings without anyone being the wiser. "Okay. Whatever."
I exhaled heavily. "Here's the thing, Shay. I
don't know if you're a magician, or a messiah. I don't know very much about salvation,
or miracles, or any of those things that Father
Michael and Ian Fletcher talked about. I don't
even know if I believe in God. But what I *do*
know is the law. And right now, everyone in
that courtroom thinks you're a raving lunatic.
You have to pull it together." I glanced at
Shay and saw him looking at me with utter
focus, his eyes clear and shrewd. "You have
one chance," I said slowly. "One chance to
speak to the man who will decide how you

die, and whether Claire Nealon gets to live. So what are you going to tell him?"

Once, when I was in sixth grade, I let the most popular girl in the school cheat off my paper during a math test. "You know what," she said afterward, "you're not totally uncool." She let me sit with her at the lunch table and for one glorious Saturday, I was invited to the mall with her Gordian knot of friends, who spritzed perfume onto their wrists at department stores and tried on expensive skinny jeans that didn't even come in my size. (I told them I had my period, and I didn't ever shop for jeans when I was bloated—a total lie, and yet one of the girls offered to show me how to make myself throw up in the bathroom to take off that extra five.) It was when I was getting a makeover at the Clinique counter, with no intent of buying any of the makeup, that I looked in a mirror and realized I did not like the girl staring back. To be the person they wanted me to be, I'd lost myself.

Watching Shay take the witness stand again, I thought about that sixth-grade thrill I'd gotten when, for a moment, I'd been part of the in-crowd; I'd been popular. The gallery, hushed, waited for another outburst—but Shay was mild-mannered and calm, quiet to a fault. He was triple-chained, and had to hobble to the stand, where he didn't look at anyone and simply waited for me to address him with the question we had practiced. I wondered whether remaking him in the image of a viable plaintiff said more about who *he* was willing to be, or whom *I* had become.

"Shay," I said. "What do you want to tell this court?"

He looked up at the ceiling, as if he were waiting for the words to drift down like snow. "The Spirit of the Lord is on me, because he has anointed me to preach good news," he murmured.

"Amen," said a woman in the gallery.

I'll be honest, this was not quite what I had had in mind when I had told Shay he could make one final attempt to sway this court. To me, religious scripture sounded just as wacky and zealous as the diatribe Shay had given on the nature of organized religion. But maybe Shay was smarter than I was, because his quote made the judge purse his lips. "Is that from the Bible, Mr. Bourne?"

"I don't know," Shay replied. "I don't remember where it comes from."

A tiny paper airplane torpedoed over my shoulder to land in my lap. I opened it up, read Father Michael's hastily scrawled note. "Yes, Judge," I said quickly. "It is."

"Marshal," Judge Haig said, "bring me the Bible." He began to thumb through the onionskin pages. "Do you happen to know where, Ms. Bloom?"

I didn't know when or if Shay Bourne had been reading scripture. This quote could have come from the priest; it could have come from God; it could have been the only line he knew in the whole Old Testament. But somehow, he'd piqued the interest of Judge Haig, who was no longer dismissing my client outright, but instead tracing the pages of the Bible as if it were written in Braille.

I stood, armed with Father Michael's citation. "It's in Isaiah, Your Honor," I said.

During the lunch recess, I drove to my office. Not because I had such an inviolable work ethic (although technically I had sixteen other cases going at the same time as Shay's, my boss had given me his blessing to put them on the back burner of the largest metaphorical stove *ever*), but because I just needed to get away from the trial completely. The secretary at the ACLU office blinked when I walked through the door. "Aren't you supposed to be—"

"Yes," I snapped, and I walked through the maze of filing cabinets to my desk.

I didn't know how Shay's outburst would affect the judge. I didn't know if I'd already lost this case, before the defense had even presented its witnesses. I did know that I hadn't slept well in three weeks and was flat out of rabbit food for Oliver, and I was having a really bad hair day. I rubbed my hands down my face, and then realized I'd probably smeared my mascara.

With a sigh, I glanced at the mountain of paperwork on my desk that had been steadily growing without me there to act as clearing-house. There was an appeal that had been filed in the Supreme Court by the attorneys of a skinhead who'd written the word *towel-head* in white paint on the driveway of his employer, a Pakistani convenience store owner who'd fired him for being drunk on the job; some research about why the words *under God* had been added to the Pledge of Allegiance in 1954 during the McCarthy era; and a stack of mail equally balanced between desperate souls who wanted me to fight on their behalf and right-wing conservatives who berated the ACLU for making it criminal to be a white churchgoing Christian.

One letter sifted through my hands and dropped onto my lap—a plain envelope printed with the address of the New Hampshire State Prison, the Office of the Warden. I opened it and found inside a pressed white sheet of paper, still bearing its watermark.

It was an invitation to attend the execution of Isaiah Bourne. The guest list included the attorney general, the governor, the lawyer who originally prosecuted Shay's case, me, Father Michael, and several other names I didn't recognize. By law, there had to be a certain number of people present for an execution from both the inmate's and the victim's sides. In this, it was a bit like organizing a wedding. And just like a wedding, there was a number to call to RSVP.

It was fifteen days before Shay was scheduled to die.

Clearly, I was the only one who found it remotely hilarious that the first and only witness the defense called—the commissioner of corrections—was a man named Joe Lynch. He was a tall, thin man whose sense of humor had apparently dissipated along with the hair on his scalp. I was quite sure that when he took the job, he'd never dreamed that he would be faced with New Hampshire's first execution in more than half a century.

"Commissioner Lynch," the assistant attorney general said, "what preparations have been made for the execution of Shay Bourne?"

"As you're aware," Lynch said, "the State of New Hampshire was not equipped to deal with the death sentence handed down to Inmate Bourne. We'd hoped that the job could be done at Terre Haute, but found out that wasn't going to happen. To that end, we've had to construct a lethal injection chamber—which now occupies a good corner of what used to be our exercise yard at the state penitentiary."

"Can you give us a breakdown of the costs involved?"

The commissioner began to read from a ledger. "The architectural and construction fees for the project were $39,100. A lethal injection gurney cost $830. The equipment associated with lethal injection cost $684. In addition, the human cost included meeting with staff, training the staff, and attending hearings—totaling $48,846. Initial supplies were $1,361, and the chemicals cost $426. In addition to this, several physical improvements were made to the space where the execution would occur: vertical blinds in the witness area, a dimmer switch in the chamber, a tinted one-way mirror, air-conditioning and an emergency generator, a wireless microphone and amplifier into the viewing area, a mono plug phone jack. These ran up to $14,669."

"You've done the math, Commissioner. By your calculation, what do you estimate you've spent on Shay Bourne's execution so far?"

"$105,916."

"Commissioner," Greenleaf asked, "does the State of New Hampshire have a gallows that could be used if the court ordered Mr. Bourne to be hanged?"

"Not anymore," Lynch replied.

"Would it be correct to assume, then, that there would be an additional outlay for the taxpayers of New Hampshire if a new gallows had to be constructed?"

"That's correct."

"What specifications are needed to build a gallows?"

The commissioner nodded. "A floor height of at least nine feet, a crossbeam of nine feet, with a clearance of three feet above the inmate being executed. The opening in the trapdoor would have to be at least three feet to ensure proper clearance. There would have to be a means of releasing the trapdoor and stopping it from swinging after it has been opened, and a fastening mechanism for the rope with the noose."

In a few short sentences, Gordon Greenleaf had recentered this trial from the woo-woo touchy-feely freedom-of-religion aspect, to the inevitability of Shay's imminent death. I glanced at Shay. He had gone white as the blank sheet of paper framed between his chained hands.

"You're looking at no less than seventy-five hundred for construction and materials," the commissioner said. "In addition, there would be the investment of a body restraint."

"What's that, exactly?" Greenleaf asked.

"A waist strap with two wrist restraints, made of three-thousand-pound test nylon, and another leg restraint made from the same materials. We'd need a frame—basically, a human dolly that enables the officers to transport the inmate to the gallows in the event of a physical collapse—and a hood, and a mechanical hangman's knot."

"You can't just use rope?"

"Not if you're talking about a humane execution," the commissioner said. "This knot is

made from a Delran cylinder and has two
longitudinal holes and a steel U-clamp to fas-
ten the rope, as well as a noose sleeve, a
rope in thirty-foot lengths, knot lubricant . . ."

Even I was impressed at how much time
and thought had gone into the death of Shay
Bourne. "You've done a great deal of research," Greenleaf said.

Lynch shrugged. "Nobody wants to execute a man. It's my job to do it with as much
dignity as possible."

"What would be the cost of constructing
and purchasing all this equipment, Commissioner Lynch?"

"A bit less than ten thousand."

"And you said the State of New Hampshire
has already invested over a hundred thousand on the execution of Shay Bourne?"

"That's correct."

"Would it be a burden on the penitentiary
system if you were required to construct a
gallows at this time, in order to accommodate
Mr. Bourne's so-called religious preferences?"

The commissioner puffed out a long breath.
"It would be more than a burden. It would be
damn near impossible, given the date of the
execution."

"Why?"

"The law said we were to execute Mr. Bourne by lethal injection, and we are ready and able to do it, after much preparation. I wouldn't feel personally and professionally comfortable cutting corners to create a last-minute gallows."

"Maggie," Shay whispered, "I think I'm going to throw up."

I shook my head. "Swallow it."

He lay his head down on the table. With any luck a few sympathetic people would assume that he was crying.

"If you were ordered by the court to construct a gallows," Greenleaf asked, "how long would it delay Mr. Bourne's execution?"

"I'd say six months to a year," the commissioner said.

"A whole year that Inmate Bourne would live past his execution warrant date?"

"Yes."

"Why so long?"

"You're talking about construction going on inside a working penitentiary system, Mr. Greenleaf. Background checks have to be done before a crew can come to work inside our gates—they're bringing in tools from the outside, which can be security threats; we have to have officers standing guard to watch them to make sure they don't wander into insecure areas; we have to make sure they're not trying to pass contraband to the inmates. It would be a substantial burden on the correctional institution if we had to, well, start from scratch."

"Thank you, Commissioner," Greenleaf said. "Nothing further."

I rose from my seat and approached the commissioner. "Your estimate for constructing the gallows is about ten thousand dollars?"

"Yes."

"So in fact, the cost to hang Shay Bourne would be one-tenth the cost of executing him by lethal injection."

"Actually," the commissioner said, "it would be a hundred and ten percent. You can't get a lethal injection chamber at Nordstrom with a satisfaction guarantee, Ms. Bloom. I can't return what we've already built."

"Well, you needed to construct that chamber anyway, didn't you?"

"Not if Inmate Bourne isn't going to be executed that way."

"The Department of Corrections didn't have the lethal injection chamber available for any other death row prisoners, however."

"Ms. Bloom," the commissioner said, "New

Hampshire doesn't *have* any other death row prisoners."

I couldn't very well suggest that in the future we might—no one wanted to entertain that option. "Would executing Shay Bourne by hanging affect the safety of the other inmates in the prison?"

"No. Not during the actual process."

"Would it impinge on the safety of the officers there?"

"No."

"And in terms of the personnel—there would be, in fact, less manpower needed for an execution by hanging than an execution by lethal injection, correct?"

"Yes," the commissioner said.

"So there's no safety issue involved in changing Shay's method of execution. Not for staff, and not for inmates. The only thing you can point to as a burden on the Department of Corrections, really, is a cost of just under ten thousand dollars to construct a gallows. Ten thousand lousy bucks. Is that right, Commissioner?"

The judge caught the commissioner's eye. "Do you have that in the budget?"

"I don't know," Lynch said. "Budgets are always tight."

"Your Honor, I have here a copy of the budget of the Department of Corrections, to be entered into evidence." I handed it to Greenleaf, to Judge Haig, and finally, to Commissioner Lynch. "Commissioner, does this look familiar?"

"Yes."

"Can you read me the line that's highlighted?"

Lynch settled his spectacles on his nose. "Supplies for capital punishment," he said. "Nine thousand eight hundred and eighty dollars."

"By supplies, what did you mean?"

"Chemicals," the commissioner said. "And whatever else came along."

What he meant, I was sure, was a fudge line in the budget. "By your own testimony, chemicals would only cost four hundred and twenty-six dollars."

"We didn't know what else might be involved," Lynch said. "Police blocks, traffic direction, medical supplies, extra manpower on staff . . . this is our first execution in nearly seventy years. We budgeted conservatively, so that we wouldn't find ourselves short when it actually came to pass."

"If that money was going to be spent on

Shay Bourne's execution no matter what, does it really matter whether it's used to purchase Sodium Pentothal . . . or to construct a gallows?"

"Uh," Lynch stammered. "It's still not ten thousand dollars."

"No," I admitted. "You're a hundred and twenty dollars short. Tell me . . . is that worth the price of a man's soul?"

June

Someone once told me that when you give birth to a daughter, you've just met the person whose hand you'll be holding the day you die. In the days after Elizabeth was born, I would watch those minuscule fingers, the nail beds like tiny shells, the surprisingly firm grip she had on my index finger—and wonder if, years from now, I'd be the one holding on so tight.

It is unnatural to survive your child. It is like seeing an albino butterfly, or a bloodred lake; a skyscraper tumbling down. I had already been through it once; now I was desperate to keep from experiencing that again.

Claire and I were playing Hearts, and don't

think I didn't appreciate the irony. The deck of cards showcased Peanuts characters; my game strategy had nothing to do with the suit, and everything to do with collecting as many Charlie Browns as I could. "Mom," Claire said, "play like you mean it."

I looked up at her. "What are you talking about?"

"You're *cheating*. But you're doing it so you'll lose." She shuffled the remaining deck and turned over the top card. "Why do you think they're called clubs?"

"I don't know."

"Do you think it's the kind you want to join? Or the kind that you use to beat someone up?"

Behind her, on the cardiac monitor, Claire's failing heart chugged a steady rhythm. At moments like these, it was hard to believe that she was as sick as she was. But then, all I had to do was witness her trying to swing her legs over the bed to go to the bathroom, see how winded she became, to know that looks could be deceiving.

"Do you remember when you made up that secret society?" I asked. "The one that met behind the hedge?"

Claire shook her head. "I never did that."

"Of course you did," I said. "You were little, that's why you've forgotten. But you were absolutely insistent about who could and couldn't be a member of the club. You had a stamp that said CANCELED and an ink pad—you put it on the back of my hand, and if I even wanted to tell you dinner was ready I had to give a password first."

Across the room, my cell phone began to ring in my purse. I made a beeline for it—mobile phones were strictly verboten in the hospital, and if a nurse caught you with one, you would be given the look of death. "Hello?"

"June. This is Maggie Bloom."

I stopped breathing. Last year, Claire had learned in school that there were whole segments of the brain devoted to involuntary acts like digesting and oxygen intake, which was so evolutionarily clever; and yet, these systems could be felled by the simplest of things: love at first sight; acts of violence; words you did not want to hear.

"I don't have any formal news yet," Maggie said, "but I thought you'd want to know: closing arguments start tomorrow morning. And then, depending on how long the judge deliberates, we'll know if and when Claire will have the heart." There was a crackle of silence. "Either way, the execution will take place in fifteen days."

"Thank you," I said, and closed the clam-shell of the phone. In twenty-four hours, I might know if Claire would live or die.

"Who called?" Claire asked.

I slipped the phone into the pocket of my jacket. "The dry cleaner," I said. "Our winter coats are ready to be picked up."

Claire just stared at me; she knew I was lying. She gathered up the cards, although we were not finished with our game. "I don't want to play anymore," she said.

"Oh. Okay."

She rolled onto her side, turning her face away from me. "I never had stamps and an ink pad," Claire murmured. "I never had a se-cret club. You're thinking of Elizabeth."

"I'm not thinking of—" I said automatically, but then I broke off. I could clearly picture Kurt and I standing at the bathroom sink, grinning as we scrubbed off the temporary tattoos we'd been given, wondering if our daughter would speak to us at breakfast with-out that mark of faith. Claire could not have initiated her father into her secret world; she had never even met him.

"I told you so," Claire said.

Lucius

Shay was not on I-tier often, but when he was, he was transported to conference rooms and the infirmary. He'd tell me, when he came back, about the psych tests they ran on him; about the way they tapped at the crooks of his elbows, checking his veins. I supposed it was important for them to dot their *i*'s and cross their *t*'s before the Big Event, so that they didn't look stupid when the rest of the world was watching.

The real reason they kept shuttling Shay around for medical tests, though, was to get him out of the pod so that they could have their practice runs. They'd done a couple of

these in August. I'd been in the exercise cage
when the warden led a small group of COs to
the lethal injection chamber that was being
built. I watched them in their hard hats. "What
we need to figure out, people," Warden Coyne
had said, "is how long it'll take the victim's
witnesses to get from my office to the chamber. We can't have them crossing paths with
the inmate's witnesses."

Now that the chamber was finished, they
had even more to check and double-check:
if the phone lines to the governor's office
worked; if the straps on the gurney were secure. Twice now, while Shay was at Medical,
a group of officers—the special ops team,
who had volunteered to be part of the
execution—arrived on I-tier. I'd never seen
any of them before. I suppose that there is
humanity in not having the man who kills you
be the same guy who has brought you your
breakfast for the past eleven years. And likewise: it must be easier to push the plunger
on that syringe if you haven't had a conversation with the inmate about whether the Patriots would win another Super Bowl.

This time, Shay had not wanted to go to
Medical. He put up a fight, saying that he
was tired, that he didn't have any blood left

for them to draw. Not that he had a choice, of course—the officers would have dragged him there kicking and screaming. Eventually, Shay agreed to be chained so that he could make the trip off I-tier, and fifteen minutes after he was gone, the special ops team showed up. They put an officer pretending to be Shay into his cell, and then one of the other COs started a stopwatch. "We're rolling," he said.

I don't know how the mistake happened, to be honest. I mean, I suppose that was the whole point of a practice run—you were leaving room for human error. But somehow, just as the special ops team was escorting Fake-Shay off the pod as part of their training, the real Shay was entering I-tier again. For a moment, they hesitated at the door, gazing at one another.

Shay stared at his faux counterpart, until Officer Whitaker had to drag him through the door of I-tier, and even then, he craned his neck, trying to see where his future was heading.

In the middle of the night, the officers came for Shay. He was banging his head against the walls of his cell, speaking in a river of gibberish. Usually, I would have heard all of this—I was often the first to know that Shay was upset—but I had slept through it. I woke up when the officers arrived in their goggles and shields, swarming over him like a clot of black cockroaches.

"Where are you taking him?" I yelled, but the words sliced my throat to ribbons. I thought of the run-through and wondered if it was time for the real thing.

One of the officers turned to me—a nice one, but in that instant I could not grasp his name, although I had seen him every week for the past six years. "It's okay, Lucius," he said. "We're just taking him to an observation cell, so he doesn't hurt himself."

When they left, I lay down on my bunk and pressed my palm against my forehead. Fever: it was a school of fish swimming through my veins.

Once before, Adam had cheated on me. I found a note in his pocket when I went to take his shirts to the dry cleaner. *Gary,* and a phone number. When I asked him about it, he said it had only been one night, after a show at the gallery where he worked. Gary was one of the artists, a man who created miniature cities out of plaster of Paris. New

York was currently on display. He told me about the art-deco detail on the top of the Chrysler Building; the individual leaves that were hand-fastened to the trees on Park Avenue. I imagined Adam standing with Gary, their feet planted in Central Park, their arms around each other, monstrous as Godzilla.

It was a mistake, Adam had said. *It was just so exciting, for a minute, to know someone else was interested.*

I could not imagine how people would not be interested in Adam, with his pale green eyes, his mocha skin. I saw heads turn all the time, gay and straight, when we walked down the street.

It felt all wrong, he said, *because it wasn't you.*

I had been naive enough to believe then that you could take something toxic and poisonous, and contain it so that you'd never be burned by it again. You'd think, after all that happened later with Adam, I had learned my lesson. But things like jealousy, rage, and infidelity—they don't disappear. They lie in wait, like a cobra, to strike you again when you least expect it.

I looked down at my hands, at the dark blotches of Kaposi's sarcoma that had al-

ready begun to blend into one another, turning my skin as dark as Adam's, as if my
punishment were to reinvent myself in his
image.

"Please don't do this," I whispered. But I
was begging to stop something that had
already started. I was praying, although I
couldn't remember to whom.

Maggie

After court had adjourned for the weekend, I took a trip to the ladies' room. I was sitting in a stall when suddenly a microphone snaked underneath the metal wall from the cubicle beside mine. "I'm Ella Wyndhammer from FOX News," a woman said. "I wonder if you have a comment about the fact that the White House has given a formal statement about the Bourne trial and the separation of church and state?"

I hadn't been aware that the White House had given a formal statement; there was a part of me that shivered with a thrill to know that we'd attracted that much attention. Then

I considered what the statement most likely had been, and how it probably wouldn't help my case at all. And *then* I remembered that I was in the bathroom.

"Yeah, I've got a comment," I said, and flushed.

Because I didn't want to be ambushed by Ella Wyndhammer or any of the other hundred reporters crawling over the steps of the courthouse like lichen, I retreated into a foxhole—okay, an attorney-client conference room—and locked the door. I took out a legal pad and began to write my closing for Monday, hoping that by the time I finished, the reporters would have moved onto a fresher kill.

It was dark when I slipped on my heels again and packed away my notes. The lights had been turned off in the courthouse; distantly, I could hear a custodian buffing the floors. I walked through the lobby, past the dormant metal detectors, took a deep breath, and opened the door.

The majority of the media had packed up for the night. In the distance, though, I could see one tenacious reporter holding his microphone. He called out my name.

I forged past him. "No comment," I

muttered, and then I realized he wasn't a reporter, and he wasn't holding a microphone.

"It's about time," Christian said, and he handed me the rose.

MICHAEL

"You're his spiritual advisor," Warden Coyne said when he phoned me at three in the morning. "Go give him some advice."

I had tried to explain to the warden that Shay and I weren't quite on speaking terms, but he hung up before I got the chance. Instead, with a sigh, I dragged myself out of bed and rode to the prison. Instead of taking me to I-tier, however, the CO led me elsewhere. "He's been moved," the officer explained.

"Why? Did someone hurt him again?"

"Nah, he was doing a good job of that on his own," he said, and as we stopped in front of Shay's cell, I understood.

Bruises mottled most of his face. His knuckles were scraped raw. A trickle of blood ran down his left temple. He was chained at the wrists and ankles and belly, even though he was inside the cell. "Why haven't you called a doctor?" I demanded.

"He's been here three times," the CO said. "Our boy, here, keeps ripping off the bandages. That's why we had to cuff him."

"If I promise you that he'll stop doing whatever he's doing—"

"Slamming his head into the wall?"

"Right. If I give you my word, will you take off the handcuffs?" I turned to Shay, who was studiously avoiding me. "Shay?" I said. "How does that sound?"

He didn't react one way or another, and I had no idea how I was going to convince Shay to stop harming himself, but the CO motioned him toward the cell door and removed the cuffs from his wrists and ankles. The belly chain, however, stayed on. "Just in case," he said, and left.

"Shay," I said. "Why are you doing this?"

"Get the fuck away from me."

"I know you're scared. And I know you're angry," I said. "I don't blame you."

"Then I guess something's changed. Because you sure *did*, once. You, and eleven other people." Shay took a step forward. "What was it like, in that room? Did you sit around talking about what kind of monster would do those horrible things? Did you ever think that you hadn't gotten the whole story?"

"Then why didn't you tell it?" I burst out. "You gave us *nothing*, Shay. We had the prosecution's explanation of what had happened; we heard from June. But you didn't even stand up and ask us for a lenient sentence."

"Who would believe what I had to say, over the word of a dead cop?" he said. "My own lawyer didn't. He kept talking about how we ought to use my troubled childhood to get me off—not my story of what happened. He said I didn't look like someone the jury would trust. He didn't care about me; he just wanted to get his five seconds on the news at night. He had a *strategy*. Well, you know what his strategy was? First he told the jury I didn't do it. Then it comes time for sentencing and he says: 'Okay, he did it, but here's why you shouldn't kill him for it.' You might as well admit that pleading not guilty in the first place was a lie."

I stared at him; stunned. It had never occurred to me during the capital murder trial that all this might be whirling around in Shay's head; that the reason he did not get up and beg for clemency during sentencing was because in order to do that, it felt like he'd also be admitting to the crime. Now that I looked back on it, it *had* felt like the defense had changed their tune between the penalty phase and the sentencing phase of the trial. It *had* made it harder to believe anything they said.

And Shay? Well, he'd been sitting right *there*, with his unwashed hair and his vacant eyes. His silence—which I'd read as pride, or shame—might only have been the understanding that for people like him, the world did not work the way it should. And I, like the other eleven jurors, had judged him before any verdict was given. After all, what kind of man gets put on trial for a double murder? What prosecutor seeks the death penalty without good reason?

Since I'd become his spiritual advisor, he'd told me that what had happened in the past didn't matter now, and I'd taken that to mean that he wouldn't accept responsibility for what he'd done. But it could also have meant that in spite of his innocence, he knew he was still going to die.

I'd been present at that trial; I'd heard all

the testimony. To think Shay might not have deserved a death sentence seemed ridiculous, impossible.

Then again, so were miracles.

"But Shay," I said quietly, "I heard that evidence. I saw what you did."

"I didn't *do* anything." He ducked his head. "It was because of the tools. I left them at the house. No one came when I knocked on the door so I just went inside to get them . . . and then I saw her."

I felt my stomach turn over. "Elizabeth."

"She used to play with me. A staring game. Whoever smiled first, that was the loser. I used to get her every time, and then one day while we were staring she lifted up my screwdriver—I didn't even know she'd taken it—and waved it around like a maniac with a knife. I burst out laughing. *I got you*, she said. *I got you*. And she did—she had me, one hundred percent." His face twisted. "I never would have hurt her. When I came in that day, she was with *him*. He had his pants down. And she was—she was crying . . . he was supposed to be her *father*." He flung an arm up over his face, as if he could stop himself from seeing the memory. "She looked up at me, like it was a staring contest, but then she smiled. Except this time, it wasn't because she lost. It was because she knew she was going to win. Because I was there. Because I could rescue her. My whole life, people looked at me like I was a fuckup, like I couldn't do anything right—but she, it was like she believed in me," Shay said. "And I wanted—God, I wanted to believe her."

He took a deep breath. "I grabbed her and ran upstairs, to the room I was finishing. I locked the door. I told her we would be safe there. But then there was a shot, and the whole door was gone, and he came in and pointed his gun at me."

I tried to imagine what it would be like to be Shay—easily confused and unable to communicate well—and to suddenly have a pistol thrust in my face.

I would have panicked, too.

"There were sirens," Shay said. "He'd called them in. He said they were coming for me and that no cop would believe any story from a freak like me. She was screaming, 'Don't shoot, don't shoot.' He said, 'Get over here, Elizabeth,' and I grabbed the gun so he couldn't hurt her and we were fighting and both our hands were on it and it went off and went off again." He swallowed. "I caught her. The blood, it was everywhere; it was on me, it was on her. He kept calling her name but she wouldn't look at him. She stared at me, like we were playing our game; she stared at me, except it wasn't a game . . . and then even though her eyes were open, she stopped staring. And it was over even though I didn't smile." He choked on a sob, pressed his hand against his mouth. "I didn't smile."

"Shay," I said softly.

He glanced up at me. "She was better off dead."

My mouth went dry. I remembered Shay saying that same sentence to June Nealon at the restorative justice meeting, her storming out of the room in tears. But what if we'd taken Shay's words out of context? What if he truly believed Elizabeth's death was a blessing, after what she'd suffered at the hands of her stepfather?

Something snagged in the back of my mind, a splinter of memory. "Her underpants," I said. "You had them in your pocket."

Shay stared at me as if I were an idiot. "Well, that's because she didn't have a chance to put them back *on* yet, before everything else happened."

The Shay I had grown to know was a man who could close an open wound with a brush of his hand, yet who also might have a breakdown if the mashed potatoes in his meal platter were more yellow than the day before. That Shay would not see anything suspicious about the police finding a little girl's underwear in his possession; it would make perfect sense to him to grab them when he grabbed Elizabeth, for the sake of her modesty.

"Are you telling me the shootings were accidental?"

"I never said I was guilty," he answered.

The pundits who downplayed Shay's miracles were always quick to point out that if God were to return to earth, He wouldn't choose to be a murderer. But what if He hadn't? What if the whole situation had been misunderstood; what if Shay had not willfully, intentionally killed Elizabeth Nealon and her stepfather—but in fact had been trying to save her from him?

It would mean that Shay was about to die for someone else's sins.

Again.

"*Not* a good time," Maggie said when she came to the door.

"It's an emergency."

"Then call the cops. Or pick up your red phone and dial God directly. I'll give you a call tomorrow morning." She started to close the door, but I stuck my foot inside.

"Is everything all right?" A man with a British accent was suddenly standing beside Maggie, who had turned beet red.

"Father Michael," she said. "This is Christian Gallagher."

He held out his hand to me. "Father. I've heard all about you."

I hoped not. I mean, if Maggie was having a date, clearly there were better topics of conversation.

"So," Christian asked amiably. "Where's the fire?"

I felt heat rising to the back of my neck. In the background, I could hear soft music playing; there was half a glass of red wine in the man's hand. There was no fire; it was already burning, and I had just thrown a bucket of sand on it. "I'm sorry. I didn't mean—" I stepped backward. "Have a nice night."

I heard the door close behind me, but instead of walking to my bike, I sat down on the front stoop. The first time I'd met Shay, I'd told him that you can't be lonely if God is with you all the time, but that wasn't entirely true. *He's lousy at checkers*, Shay had said. Well, you couldn't take God out to a movie on a Friday night, either. I knew that I could fill the space a companion normally would with God; and it was more than enough. But that wasn't to say I didn't feel that phantom limb sometimes.

The door opened, and into the slice of light stepped Maggie. She was barefoot, and she had her power-suit coat draped over her shoulders. "I'm sorry," I said. "I didn't mean to ruin your night."

"That's okay. I should have known better than to assume all the planets had aligned for me." She sank down beside me. "What's up?"

In the dark, with her face lit in profile by the moon, she was as beautiful as any Renaissance Madonna. It struck me that God had chosen someone just like Maggie when He picked Mary to bear His Son: someone willing to take the weight of the world on her shoulders, even when it wasn't her own burden. "It's Shay," I said. "I think he's innocent."

Maggie

I was not particularly surprised to hear what Shay Bourne had told the priest.

No, what surprised me was how fervently he'd fallen for it—hook, line, and sinker.

"It's not about protecting Shay's rights anymore," Michael said. "Or letting him die on his own terms. We're talking about an innocent man being killed."

We had moved into the living room, and Christian—well, he was sitting on the other end of the couch pretending to do a Sudoku puzzle in the newspaper, but actually listening to every word we said. He'd been the one to come outside and invite me back into my own home. I fully intended to pop Father Michael's bubble of incensed righteousness and get back to the spot I'd been in before he arrived.

Which was flat on my back, with Christian's hand moving over my side, showing me where you made the incision to remove a gallbladder—something that, in person, was far more exciting than it sounds.

"He's a convicted murderer," I said. "They learn how to lie before they learn how to walk."

"Maybe he never should have been convicted," Michael said.

"*You* were on the jury that found him guilty!"

Christian's head snapped up. "You *were*?"

"Welcome to my life," I sighed. "Father, you sat through days of testimony. You saw the evidence firsthand."

"I know. But that was before he told me that he walked in on Kurt Nealon molesting his own stepdaughter; and that the gun went off repeatedly while he was struggling to get it out of Kurt's hand."

At that, Christian leaned forward. "Well. That makes him a bit of a hero, doesn't it?"

"Not when he still kills the girl he's trying to rescue," I said. "And why, pray tell, did he not gift his defense attorney with this information?"

"He said he tried, but the lawyer didn't think it would fly."

"Well, gee," I said. "Doesn't *that* speak volumes?"

"Maggie, you know Shay. He doesn't look like a clean-cut American boy, and he didn't back then, either. Plus, he'd been found with a smoking gun, and a dead cop and girl in front of him. Even if he told the truth, who would have listened? Who's more likely to be cast as a pedophile—the heroic cop and consummate family man . . . or the sketchy vagrant who was doing work in the house? Shay was doomed before he ever walked into a courtroom."

"Why would he take the blame for someone else's crime?" I argued. "Why not tell someone—anyone—in eleven years?"

He shook his head. "I don't know the answer to that. But I'd like to keep him alive long enough to find out." Father Michael glanced at me. "*You're* the one who says the legal system doesn't always work for everyone. It was an *accident*. Manslaughter, not murder."

"Correct me if I'm wrong," Christian interrupted. "But you can't be sentenced to death for manslaughter, can you?"

I sighed. "Do we have any new evidence?"

Father Michael thought for a minute. "He told me so."

"Do we have any *evidence*," I repeated.

His face lit up. "We have the security camera outside the observation cell," Michael said. "That's got to be recorded somewhere, right?"

"It's still just a tape of him telling you a story," I explained. "It's different if you tell me, oh, that there's semen we can link to Kurt Nealon . . ."

"You're an ACLU lawyer. You must be able to do *something* . . ."

"Legally, there's nothing we *can* do. We can't reopen his case unless there's some fantastic forensic proof."

"What about calling the governor?" Christian suggested.

Our heads both swiveled toward him.

"Well, isn't that what always happens on TV? And in John Grisham novels?"

"*Why* do you know so much about the American legal system?" I asked.

He shrugged. "I used to have a torrid crush on the Partridge girl from *L.A. Law.*"

I sighed and walked to the dining room table. My purse was slogged across it like an amoeba. I dug inside for my cell phone, punched a number. "This better be good," my boss growled on the other end of the line.

"Sorry, Rufus. I know it's late—"

"Cut to the chase."

"I need to call Flynn, on behalf of Shay Bourne," I said.

"Flynn? As in Mark Flynn the governor? Why would you want to waste your last appeal before you even get a verdict back from Haig?"

"Shay Bourne's spiritual advisor is under the impression that he was falsely convicted." I looked up to find Christian and Michael both watching me intently.

"Do we have any new evidence?"

I closed my eyes. "Well. No. But this is really important, Rufus."

A moment later, I hung up the phone and pressed the number I'd scrawled on a paper napkin into Michael's hand. "It's the governor's cell number. Go call him."

"Why me?"

"Because," I said. "He's Catholic."

"I have to leave," I had told Christian. "The governor wants us to come to his office right now."

"If I had a quid for every time a girl's used

that one on me," he said. And then, just as if it were the most normal thing in the world, he kissed me.

Okay, it had been a quick kiss. And one that could have ended a G-rated movie. And it had been performed in front of a priest. But still, it looked completely natural, as if Christian and I had been kissing at the ends of sentences for ages, while the rest of the world was still hung up on punctuation.

Here's where it all went wrong. "So," I had said. "Maybe we could get together tomorrow?"

"I'm on call for the next forty-eight hours," he'd said. "Monday?"

But Monday I was in court again.

"Well," Christian said. "I'll call."

I was meeting Father Michael at the statehouse, because I wanted him to go home and get clothing that was as priestly as possible—the jeans and button-down shirt in which he'd come to my door weren't going to win us any favors. Now, as I waited for him in the parking lot, I replayed every last syllable of my conversation with Christian . . . and began to panic. Everyone knew that when a guy said he'd call, it really meant that he wouldn't—he just wanted a swift escape.

Maybe it had been the kiss, which was the precursor to that whole line of conversation. Maybe I had garlic breath. Maybe he'd just spent enough time in my company to know I wasn't what he wanted.

By the time Father Michael rode into the parking lot, I'd decided that if Shay Bourne had cost me my first shot at a relationship since the Jews went to wander the desert, I would execute him *myself*.

I was surprised that Rufus had wanted me to go to meet Governor Flynn alone; I was even more surprised that he thought Father Michael should be the one to finesse the interview in the first place. But Flynn wasn't a born New Englander; he was a transplanted southern boy, and he apparently preferred informality to pomp and circumstance. *He'll be expecting you to come to him for a stay of execution after the trial,* Rufus had mused. *So maybe catching him off guard is the smartest thing you can do.* He suggested that instead of a lawyer putting through the call, maybe a man of the cloth should do it instead. And, within two minutes of conversation, Father Michael had discovered that Governor Flynn had heard him preach at last year's Christmas Mass at St. Catherine's.

We were let into the statehouse by a security guard, who put us through the metal detectors and then escorted us to the governor's office. It was an odd, eerie place after hours; our footsteps rang like gunshots as we hustled up the steps. At the top of the landing, I turned to Michael. "Do *not* do anything inflammatory," I whispered. "We get one shot at this."

The governor was sitting at his desk. "Come in," he said, getting to his feet. "Pleasure to see you again, Father Michael."

"Thanks," the priest said. "I'm flattered you remembered me."

"Hey, you gave a sermon that didn't put me to sleep—that puts you into a *very* small category of clergymen. You run the youth group at St. Catherine's, too, right? My college roommate's kid was getting into some trouble a year ago, and then he started working with you. Joe Cacciatone?"

"Joey," Father Michael said. "He's a good kid."

The governor turned to me. "And you must be . . . ?"

"Maggie Bloom," I said, holding out my hand. "Shay Bourne's attorney." I had never been this close to the governor before. I thought, irrationally, that he looked taller on television.

"Ah, yes," the governor said. "The infamous Shay Bourne."

"If you're a practicing Catholic," Michael said to the governor, "how can you condone an execution?"

I blinked at the priest. Hadn't I just told him *not* to say anything provocative?

"I'm doing my job," Flynn said. "There's a great deal that I don't agree with, personally, that I have to carry out professionally."

"Even if the man who's about to be killed is innocent?"

Flynn's gaze sharpened. "That's not what a court decided, Father."

"Come talk to him," Michael said. "The penitentiary—it's a five-minute drive. Come listen to him, and then tell me if he deserves to die."

"Governor Flynn," I interrupted, finally finding my voice. "During a . . . confession, Shay Bourne made some revelations that indicate there are details of his case that weren't revealed at the time—that the deaths occurred accidentally while Mr. Bourne was in fact trying to protect Elizabeth Nealon from her father's sexual abuse.

We feel that with a stay of execution, we'll have time to gather evidence of Bourne's innocence."

The governor's face paled. "I thought priests couldn't reveal confessions."

"We're obligated to, if there's a law about to be broken, or if a life is in danger. This qualifies on both counts."

The governor folded his hands, suddenly distant. "I appreciate your concerns—both religious and political. I'll take your request under advisement."

I knew a dismissal when I heard one; I nodded and stood. Father Michael looked up at me, then scrambled to his feet, too. We shook the governor's hand again and groveled our way out of the office. We didn't speak until we were outside, beneath a sky spread with stars. "So," Father Michael said. "I guess that means no."

"It means we have to wait and see. Which probably means no." I dug my hands into the pockets of my suit jacket. "Well. Seeing as my entire evening has been shot to hell, I'm just going to call it a night—"

"You don't believe he's innocent, do you?" Michael said.

I sighed. "Not really."

"Then why are you willing to fight so hard for him?"

"On December twenty-fifth, when I was a kid, I'd wake up and it would be just another day. On Easter Sunday, my family was the only one in the movie theater. The reason I fight so hard for Shay," I finished, "is because I know what it's like when the things you believe make you feel like you're on the outside looking in."

"I . . . I didn't realize . . ."

"How could you?" I said, smiling faintly. "The guys at the top of the totem pole never see what's carved at the bottom. See you Monday, Father."

I could feel his gaze on me as I walked to my car. It felt like a cape made of light, like the wings of the angels I'd never believed in.

My client looked like he'd been run over by a truck. Somehow, in the middle of trying to get me to save his life, Father Michael had neglected to mention that Shay had begun a course of self-mutilation. His face was scabbed and bloomed with bruises; his hands—cuffed tightly to his waist after last week's fiasco—were scratched. "You look like crap," I murmured to Shay.

"I'm going to look worse after they hang me," he whispered back.

"We have to talk. About what you said to Father Michael—" But before I could go any further, the judge called on Gordon Green-leaf to offer his closing argument.

Gordon stood up heavily. "Your Honor, this case has been a substantial waste of the court's time and the state's money. Shay Bourne is a convicted double murderer. He committed the most heinous crime in the history of the state of New Hampshire."

I glanced at Shay beneath my lashes. If what he'd said was true—if he'd seen Eliza-beth being abused—then the two murders became manslaughter and self-defense. DNA testing had not been in vogue when he was convicted—was it possible that there was some shred of carpet or couch fabric left that could corroborate Shay's account?

"He's exhausted all legal remedies at every level," Gordon continued. "State, first circuit, Supreme Court—and now he's desperately trying to extend his life by filing a bogus law-suit that claims he believes in some bogus religion. He wants the State of New Hamp-shire and its taxpayers to build him his own special gallows so that he can donate his heart to the victims' family—a group that he suddenly has feelings for. He certainly didn't have feelings for them the day he murdered Kurt and Elizabeth Nealon."

It was, of course, highly unlikely that there would still be evidence. By now, even the underwear that had been found in his pocket had been destroyed or given back to June Nealon—this was a case that had closed eleven years ago, in the minds of the investigators. And all the eyewitnesses had died at the scene—except for Shay.

"Yes, there is a law that protects the religious freedom of inmates," Greenleaf said. "It exists so that Jewish inmates can wear yarmulkes in prison, and Muslims can fast during Ramadan. The commissioner of corrections always makes allowances for religious activity in compliance with federal law. But to say that this man—who's had outbursts in the courtroom, who can't control his emotions, who can't even tell you what the name of his religion is—deserves to be executed in some special way to comply with federal law is completely inappropriate, and is not what our system of justice intended."

Just as Greenleaf sat down, a bailiff slipped

a note to me. I glanced at it and took a deep breath.

"Ms. Bloom?" the judge prompted.

"One hundred and twenty dollars," I said. "You know what you can do with one hundred and twenty dollars? You can get a great pair of Stuart Weitzman shoes on sale. You can buy two tickets to a Bruins game. You can feed a starving family in Africa. You can purchase a cell phone contract. Or, you can help a man reach salvation—and rescue a dying child."

I stood up. "Shay Bourne is not asking for freedom. He's not asking for his sentence to be overturned. He's simply asking to die in accordance with his religious beliefs. And if America stands for nothing else, it stands for the right to practice your own religion, even if you die in the custody of the state."

I began to walk toward the gallery. "People still flock to this country because of its religious freedom. They know that in America, you won't be told what God should look like or sound like. You won't be told there is one right belief, and yours isn't it. They want to speak freely about religion, and to ask questions. Those rights were the foundation of America four hundred years ago, and they're still the foundation today. It's why, in this country, Madonna can perform on a crucifix, and *The Da Vinci Code* was a bestseller. It's why, even after 9/11, religious freedom flourishes in America."

Facing the judge again, I pulled out all the stops. "Your Honor, we're not asking you to remove the wall between church and state by ruling in favor of Shay Bourne. We just want the law upheld—the one that promises Shay Bourne the right to practice his religion even in the state penitentiary, unless there's a compelling governmental interest to keep him from doing so. The only governmental interest that the state can point to here is one hundred and twenty dollars—and a matter of a few months." I walked back to my seat, slipped into it. "How do you weigh lives and souls against two months, and a hundred and twenty bucks?"

Once the judge returned to chambers to reach his verdict, two marshals came to retrieve Shay. "Maggie?" he said, getting to his feet. "Thanks."

"Guys," I said to the marshals, "can you give me a minute with him in the holding cell?"

"Make it quick," one of them said, and I nodded.

"What do you think?" Father Michael said, still seated in the gallery behind me. "Does he have a chance?"

I reached into my pocket, retrieved the note the bailiff had passed me just before I began my closing, and handed it to Michael. "You better hope so," I said. "The governor denied his stay of execution."

He was lying on the metal bunk, his arm thrown over his eyes, by the time I reached the holding cell. "Shay," I said, standing in front of the bars. "Father Michael came to talk to me. About what happened the night of the murders."

"It doesn't matter."

"It does matter," I said urgently. "The governor denied your stay of execution, which means we're up against a brick wall. DNA evidence is used routinely now to overturn capital punishment verdicts. There was some talk about sexual assault during the trial, wasn't there, before that charge was dropped? If that semen sample still exists, we can have it tested and matched to Kurt . . . I just need you to give me the details about what happened, Shay, so that I can get the ball rolling."

Shay stood up and walked toward me, resting his hands on the bars between us. "I can't."

"Why not?" I challenged. "Were you lying when you told Father Michael you were innocent?"

He glanced up at me, his eyes hot. "No."

I cannot tell you why I believed him. Maybe I was naive, because I hadn't been a criminal defense attorney; maybe I just felt that a dying man had very little left to lose. But when Shay met my gaze, I knew that he was telling me the truth—and that executing an innocent man was even more devastating, if possible, than executing a guilty one. "Well, then," I said, my head already swimming with possibilities. "You told Father Michael your first lawyer wouldn't listen to you—but I'm listening to you now. Talk to me, Shay. Tell me something I can use to convince a judge you were wrongly convicted. Then I'll write up the request for DNA testing, you just have to sign—"

"No."

"I can't do this alone," I exploded. "Shay, we're talking about overturning your conviction, do you understand that? About you walking out of here, free."

"I know, Maggie."

"So instead of trying, you're just going to die for a crime you didn't commit? You're okay with that?"

He stared at me and slowly nodded. "I told you that the first day I met you. I didn't want you to save me. I wanted you to save my heart."

I was stunned. "Why?"

He struggled to get the words out. "It was still my fault. I tried to rescue her, and I couldn't. I wasn't there in time. I never liked Kurt Nealon—I used to try to not be in the same room as him when I was working, so I wouldn't feel him looking at me. But June, she was so nice. She smelled like apples and she'd make me tuna fish for lunch and let me sit at the kitchen table like I belonged there with her and the girl. After Elizabeth . . . afterward . . . it was bad enough that June wouldn't have them anymore. I didn't want her to lose the past, too. Family's not a thing, it's a place," Shay said softly. "It's where all the memories get kept."

So he took the blame for Kurt Nealon's crimes, in order to allow the grieving widow to remember him with pride, instead of hate. How much worse would it have been for

June if DNA testing had existed back then—
if the alleged rape of Elizabeth had proved
Kurt as the perpetrator?

"You go looking for evidence now, Maggie,
and you'll rip her wide open again. This way—
well, this is the end, and then it's over."

I could feel my throat closing, a fist of tears.
"And what if one day June finds out the truth?
And realizes that you were executed, even
though you were innocent?"

"Then," Shay said, a smile breaking over
him like daylight, "she'll remember me."

I had gone into this case knowing that
Shay and I wanted different outcomes; I had
expected to be able to convince him that an
overturned conviction was a cause for celebration, even if living meant organ donation
would have to be put on hold for a while. But
Shay was ready to die; Shay *wanted* to die.
He wasn't just giving Claire Nealon a future;
he was giving one to her mother, too. He
wasn't trying to save the world, like me. Just
one life at a time—which is why he had a
fighting chance of succeeding.

He touched my hand, where it rested on
the bars. "It's okay, Maggie. I've never done
anything important. I didn't cure cancer or
stop global warming or win a Nobel Prize.

I didn't do anything with my life, except hurt people I loved. But dying—dying will be different."

"How?"

"They'll see their lives are worth living."

I knew that I would be haunted by Shay Bourne for a very long time, whether or not his sentence was carried out. "Someone who thinks like that," I said, "does not deserve to be executed. Please, Shay. Help me help you. You don't have to play the hero."

"Maggie," he said. "Neither do you."

June

Code blue, the nurse had said.

A stream of doctors and nurses flooded Claire's room. One began chest compressions.

I don't feel a pulse.

We need an airway.

Start chest compressions.

Can we get an IV access . . .

What rhythm is she in?

We need to shock her . . . put on the patches . . .

Charge to two hundred joules.

All clear . . . fire!

Hold compressions . . .

No pulse.

Give epi. Lidocaine. Bicarb.

Check for a pulse . . .

Dr. Wu flew through the door. "Get the mother out of here," he said, and a nurse grasped my shoulders.

"You need to come with me," she said, and I nodded, but my feet would not move. Someone held the defibrillator to Claire's chest again. Her body jackknifed off the bed just as I was dragged through the doorway.

I had been the one present when Claire flatlined; I was the one who'd run to the nurse's desk. And I was the one sitting with her now that she'd been stabilized, now that her heart, battered and ragged, was beating again. She was in a monitored bed, and I stared at the screens, at the mountainous terrain of her cardiac rhythm, sure that if I didn't blink we'd be safe.

Claire whimpered, tossing her head from side to side. The monitors cast her skin an alien green.

"Baby," I said, moving beside her. "Don't try to talk. You've still got a tube in."

Her eyes slitted open; she pleaded to me with her eyes and mimed holding a pen.

I gave her the white board Dr. Wu had

given me; until Claire was extubated tomorrow morning she would have to use this to communicate. Her writing was shaky and spiked. WHAT HAPPENED?

"Your heart," I said, blinking back tears. "It wasn't doing so well."

MOMMY, DO SOMETHING.

"Anything, honey."

LET GO OF ME.

I glanced down; I was not touching her.

Claire circled the words again; and this time, I understood.

Suddenly I remembered something Kurt had told me once: you could only save someone who wanted to be saved; otherwise, you'd be dragged down for the count, too. I looked at Claire, but she was asleep again, the marker still curled in her hand.

Tears slipped down my cheeks, onto the hospital blanket. "Oh, Claire . . . I'm so sorry," I whispered, and I was.

For what I had done.

For what I knew I had to do.

Lucius

||||||||||||||||||||||||||||||||||||||||||||||||||||||||||||||||||||||||||||||||||||||||||||||||||||||||||||||||||||||||

When I coughed it turned me inside out. I could feel the tendons tangle on the outside of my skin and the fever in my head steaming against the pillow. You put ice chips on my tongue and they vanished before I swallowed isn't it funny how now things come back that I was so sure I'd forgotten like this moment of high school chemistry. Sublimation that's the word the act of turning into something you never expected to become.

The room it was so white that it hurt the backs of my eyeballs. Your hands were like hummingbirds or butterflies *Stay with us Lucius* you said but it was harder and harder to hear you and I could only feel you instead your hummingfly hands your butterbird fingers.

They talk about white lights and tunnels and there was a part of me expecting to see oh I'll just say it outright Shay but none of that was true. Instead it was Him and He was holding out His hand and reaching for me. He was just like I remembered coffee skin ebony eyes five o'clock shadow that dimple too deep for tears and I saw how foolish I had been. How could I not have known it would be Him how could I not have known that you see God every time you look at the face of the person you love.

There were so many things I expected Him to say to me now when it counted the most. *I love you. I missed you.* But instead He smiled at me with those white teeth those white wolf's teeth and He said *I forgive you Lucius I forgive you.*

Your hands pounded and pumped at me your electricity shot through my body but you could not reclaim my heart it already belonged to someone else. He spread the fingers of His hand a star a beacon and I went to him. *I am coming I am coming.*

Wait for me.

Maggie

||||||||||||||||||||||||||||||||||||||||||||||||||||||||||||||||||||||||||||||||||||||||||||||||||||||||||||||||||||

"I wouldn't have called you in here on a Sunday, normally," Warden Coyne said to me, "but I thought you'd want to know . . ." He closed the door to his office for privacy. "Lucius DuFresne died last night."

I sank down into one of the chairs across from the warden's desk. "How?"

"AIDS-related pneumonia."

"Does Shay know?"

The warden shook his head. "We thought that might not be the best course of action at this moment."

What he meant, of course, was that Shay was already in an observation cell for slamming his own head into a wall—they didn't need to give him even more reason to be upset. "He could hear about it from someone else."

"That's true," Coyne said. "I can't stop rumors."

I remembered the reporters glorifying Lucius's initial cure—how would this turn the tide of public opinion against Shay even more? If he wasn't a messiah, then—by default—he was only a murderer. I glanced up at the warden. "So you asked *me* here so I could break the bad news to him."

"That's your call, Ms. Bloom. I asked you here to give you this." He reached into his desk and removed an envelope. "It was with Lucius's personal effects."

The manila envelope was addressed to Father Michael and me in shaky, spiderweb handwriting. "What is it?"

"I didn't open it," the warden said.

I unhinged the clasp of the envelope and reached inside. At first I thought I was looking at a magazine advertisement of a painting—the detail was that precise. But a closer look showed that this was a piece of card stock; that the pigment wasn't oil, but what seemed to be watercolor and pen.

It was a copy of Raphael's *Transfiguration*, something I only knew because of an art history course I'd taken when I fancied myself in love with the TA who ran the class sessions— a tall, anemic guy with ski-slope cheekbones who wore black, smoked clove cigarettes, and wrote Nietzsche quotes on the back of his hand. Although I didn't really care about sixteenth-century art, I'd gotten an A, trying to impress him—only to discover he had a live-in lover named Henry.

The *Transfiguration* was thought to be Raphael's last painting. It was left unfinished and was completed by one of his students. The upper part of the painting shows Jesus floating above Mt. Tabor with Moses and Elijah. The bottom part of the painting shows the miracle of the possessed boy, waiting for Jesus to cure him, along with the Apostles and the other disciples.

Lucius's version looked exactly like the painting I'd seen slides of in a darkened amphitheater—until you looked closely. Then you noticed that my face was superimposed where Moses's should have been. Father Michael was standing in for Elijah. The possessed boy—there, Lucius had drawn his self-portrait. And Shay rose in white robes above Mt. Tabor, his face turned upward.

I slipped the painting back into the envelope carefully and looked at the warden. "I'd like to see my client," I said.

Shay stepped into the conference room. "Did you get the verdict?"

"Not yet. It's still the weekend." I took a deep breath. "Shay, I have some bad news for you. Lucius died last night."

The light faded from his face. "Lucius?"

"I'm sorry."

"He was . . . getting better."

"I guess he wasn't, really. It only looked that way," I said. "I know you thought you helped him. I know you *wanted* to help him. But Shay, you couldn't have. He was dying from the moment you met him."

"Like me," Shay said.

He bent over, as if the hand of grief were pushing hard on him, and started to cry— and that, I realized, was going to be my undoing. Because when you got right down to it, what was different between Shay and everyone else in this world was not nearly as profound as what we had in common. Maybe my hair was brushed, and I could string words together to make a sentence. Maybe I hadn't been convicted of murder. But if someone told me that the only friend I really had in this world had left it, I'd sink to my knees, sobbing, too.

"Shay," I said, at a loss, approaching him. How come there were no words for this kind of comfort?

"Don't touch me," Shay growled, his eyes feral. I ducked at the last moment as he swung at me, and his fist punched through the double pane of glass that separated us from the officer standing watch. "He wasn't supposed to die," Shay cried, as his hand bled down the front of his prison scrubs like a trail of regret. A small army of officers rushed in to save me and secure him, and then haul him off to the infirmary for stitches, proof—as if either of us needed it—that Shay was not invincible.

One year in junior high, during a sex-ed unit, our teacher discussed the painfully obvious fact that some of us would not mature as quickly as our classmates. This was not a lesson you had to teach someone like me, whose waistline was larger than her bra size; or Cheryl Otenski, who had gotten her period in full view of every other sixth grader during an assembly where she happened to be wearing white pants. "Late bloomers," the teacher called it—that was close enough to my last name for me to be the butt of every joke for the remaining week.

I had told my mother I had the bubonic plague and refused to get out of bed for three days, spending most of it under the covers and wishing I could just miraculously skip ahead ten or fifteen years to when my life surely would be more pleasant.

After seeing Shay, I was sorely tempted to pull the same act. If I stayed in bed when the verdict was read, did that mean the plaintiff lost by default?

Instead of driving to my house, however, I found myself pointing in the opposite direction and turned into the emergency entrance of the hospital. I felt as if I'd been poleaxed, which surely qualified me for medical attention—but I didn't think that even the most gifted physician could cure a skeptic who'd come to see the light: I could not remain as emotionally unattached from my client as I'd believed. This wasn't, as I'd told myself, about the death penalty in America. It wasn't about my career as a litigator. It was about a man I'd been sitting next to—a man whose scent I could recognize (Head & Shoulders shampoo and pungent industrial soap); whose voice was familiar (rough as sandpaper, with words dropped like stepping-stones)—who would, very shortly, be dead. I did not know Shay Bourne well, but that didn't mean he would not leave a hole in my life when he exited his own.

"I need to see Dr. Gallagher," I announced to the triage nurse. "I'm a personal . . ."

What?

Friend?

*Girl*friend?

Stalker?

Before the nurse could rebuff me, however, I saw Christian coming down the hall with another doctor. He noticed me and—before I could even make a decision to go to him—he came to me. "What's wrong, sweetheart?"

No one except my father had ever called me that. For this reason, and a dozen others, I burst into tears.

Christian folded me into his arms. "Follow me," he said, and led me by the hand into an empty family waiting room.

"The governor denied Shay's stay of execution," I said. "And Shay's best friend died, and I was the one who had to tell him. And *he's* going to die, Christian, because he won't let me try to find new evidence to exonerate him." I drew away from him, wiping my eyes on my sleeve. "How do you do it? How do you let go?"

"The first patient who died on my table," Christian said, "was a seventy-six-year-old woman who came in complaining of abdominal pain after a meal at a posh London restaurant. A half hour into the surgery, she coded, and we couldn't bring her back." He looked up at me. "When I went into the family waiting area to speak with her husband, the man just kept staring at me. Finally, I asked him if he had any questions, and he said he'd taken his wife to dinner to celebrate their fiftieth wedding anniversary." Christian shook his head. "That night, I sat with her body in the morgue. Silly, I know, but I thought that on one's fiftieth anniversary, one didn't deserve to spend the night alone."

If I hadn't been swayed before by Christian's charm, good looks, or the way he called the trunk of his car a boot and the hood a bonnet, I was now completely smitten.

"Here's the thing," Christian added. "It doesn't get any easier, no matter how many times you go through it. And if it does—well,

I suspect that means you've lost some part of yourself that's critically important." He reached for my hand. "Let me be the attending physician at the execution."

"You can't," I said automatically. Killing a man was a violation of the Hippocratic oath; doctors were contacted privately by the Department of Corrections, and the whole event was kept secret. In fact, in the other executions I'd studied before Shay's trial, the doctor's name was never mentioned—not even on the death certificate.

"Let me worry about that," Christian said.

I felt a fresh wave of tears rising. "You would do that for Shay?"

He leaned forward and kissed me lightly. "I would do that for you," he said.

If this had been a trial, here were the facts I'd present to the jury:

1. Christian had suggested that he swing by my house after his shift, just to make sure I wasn't falling apart at the seams.
2. He was the one who brought the bottle of Penfolds.
3. It would have been downright rude to refuse to have a glass. Or three.

4. I truly could not establish the causal line between how we went from kissing on the couch to lying on the carpet with his hands underneath my shirt, and me worrying about whether or not I was wearing underwear that was a step above granny panties.

5. Other women—those who have sex with men more often than once during a senatorial term, for example—probably have a whole set of underwear just for moments like these, like my mother has a set of Sabbath china.

6. I was truly hammered if I had just thought of sex and my mother in the same sentence.

Maybe the details here weren't nearly as important as the outcome—I had a man in my bed, right now, waiting for me. He was even more beautiful without clothes on than he was in them. And where was I?

Locked in the bathroom, so paralyzed by the thought of my disgusting, white, fish-bellied body being seen by him that I couldn't open the door.

I had been discreet about it—lowering my lashes and murmuring something about changing. I'm sure Christian assumed I meant slipping into lingerie. Me, I was thinking more along the lines of morphing into Heidi Klum.

Bravely, I unbuttoned my blouse and stepped out of my jeans. There I was in the mirror, in my bra and panties, just like a bikini—except I wouldn't be caught dead in a bikini. *Christian sees a hundred bodies a day,* I told myself. *Yours can't be any worse than those.*

But. Here was the ripple of cottage cheese cellulite that I usually avoided by dressing in the dark. Here was the inch (or two) that I could pinch with my fingers, which vanished beneath a waistband. Here was my butt, large enough to colonize, which could so craftily be camouflaged by black trousers. Christian would take one look at the acoustic version of me and run screaming for the hills.

His voice came, muffled, through the bathroom door. "Maggie?" Christian said. "Are you all right in there?"

"I'm fine!" *I'm fat.*

"Are you coming out?"

I didn't answer that. I was looking inside the waistband of my pants. They were a twelve, but that didn't count, because this label had resized downward so that fourteens like me could feel better about themselves for being able to squeeze into the brand at all. But hadn't Marilyn Monroe been a size fourteen? Or was that back when a size fourteen was really an eight—which meant that comparatively, I was a behemoth compared to your average 1940s starlet?

Well, hell. I was a behemoth compared to your average 2008 starlet, too.

Suddenly I heard scratching outside the door. It couldn't have been Oliver—I'd put him in his cage when he kept sniffing around our heads as we'd rolled across the living room carpet having our *From Here to Eternity* moment. To my horror, the locked doorknob popped open and began to twist.

I grabbed my ratty red bathrobe from the back of the door and wrapped it around myself just in time to see the door swing open. Christian stood there, holding a wire hanger with its neck straightened.

"You can pick locks, too?" I said.

Christian grinned. "I do laparoscopic surgery through belly buttons," he explained. "This isn't dramatically different."

He folded his arms around me and met my gaze in the mirror. "I can't say come back to bed, because you haven't been in it yet."

His chin notched over my shoulder. "Maggie," he murmured, and at that moment he realized that I was wearing a robe.

Christian's eyes lit up and his hands slipped down to the belt. Immediately, I started to tug him away. "Please. Don't."

His hands fell to his sides, and he took a step back. The room must have cooled twenty degrees. "I'm sorry," Christian said, all business. "I must have misread—"

"No!" I cried, facing him. "You didn't misread anything. I want this. I want *you*. I'm just afraid that . . . that . . . you won't want *me*."

"Are you *joking*? I've wanted you since the moment I didn't get to examine you for appendicitis."

"Why?"

"Because you're smart. And fierce. And funny. And so beautiful."

I smiled wryly. "I almost believed you, until that last part."

Christian's eyes flashed. "You truly think you're not?" In one smooth motion, before I could stop him, he yanked the wide shawl collar of the robe down to my elbows, and my blouse along with it. My arms were trapped; I stood before him in my underwear.

"Look at you, Maggie," he said with quiet awe. "My God."

I could not look at myself in the mirror, so instead, I looked at Christian. He wasn't scrutinizing breasts that sagged or a waist that was too thick or thighs that rubbed together when the temperature climbed above eighty degrees. He was just staring at me, and as he did, his hands began to shake where they touched me.

"Let me show you what I see when I look at you," Christian said quietly. His fingers were warm as they played over me, as they coaxed me into the bedroom and under the covers, as they traced the curves of my body like a roller coaster, a thrill ride, a wonder. And somewhere in the middle of it all, I stopped worrying about sucking in my stomach, or if he could see me in the half-light of the moon, and instead noticed how seamlessly we fit together; how when I let go of me, there was only room for us.

Wow.

I woke up with the sun slicing the bed like a scalpel, and every muscle in my body feeling like I'd started training for a triathlon. Last night could effectively be classified as a workout, and to be honest, it was the first exercise routine I could see myself really looking forward to on a daily basis.

I smoothed my hand over the side of the bed where Christian had slept. In the bathroom, I heard the shower being turned off. The door opened, and Christian's head popped out. He was wearing a towel. "Hi," he said. "I hope I didn't knock you up."

"Well. I, uh, hope so, too . . ." Christian frowned, confused, and I realized that we were not speaking the same language. "Let me guess," I said. "Where you come from, that doesn't mean getting a girl pregnant?"

"Good God, no! It's, you know, rousing someone from their sleep."

I rolled onto my back and started laughing, and he sank down beside me, the towel slipping dangerously low. "But since I've knocked you up," he said, leaning down to kiss me, "maybe I could try my hand at knocking you up . . ."

I had morning breath and hair that felt like a rat had taken nest in it, not to mention a courtroom verdict to attend, but I wrapped my arms around Christian's neck and kissed him back. Which was about the same moment that a phone began to ring.

"Bloody hell," Christian muttered, and he swung over the far side of the bed to where he'd folded his clothes in a neat pile, his cell phone and pager resting on top. "It's not mine," he said, but by then I'd wrapped his discarded towel around me and hiked to my purse in the living room to dig out my own.

"Ms. Bloom?" a woman's voice said. "This is June Nealon."

"June," I said, immediately sobering. "Is everything all right?"

"Yes," she said, and then, "No. Oh, God. I can't answer that question." There was a beat of silence. "I can't take it," June whispered.

"I can't imagine how difficult all this waiting has been for you," I said, and I meant it. "But we should know definitively what's going to happen by lunchtime."

"I can't take it," June repeated. "Give it to someone else."

And she hung up the phone, leaving me with Shay's heart.

MICHAEL

There were only seven people attending Monday morning Mass, and I was one of them. I wasn't officiating—it was my day off, so Father Walter was presiding, along with a deacon named Paul O'Hurley. I participated in the Lord's Prayer and the sign of peace, and I realized these were the moments Shay had missed: when people came *together* to celebrate God. You might be able to find Him on your own spiritual journey, but it was a lonelier trip. Coming to church felt like validation, like a family where everyone knew your flaws, and in spite of that was still willing to invite you back.

Long after Father Walter finished Mass

and said his good-byes to the congregants, I was still sitting in a pew. I wandered toward the votive candles, watching the tongues of their flames wag like gossips. "I didn't think we'd see you today, with the verdict and all," Father Walter said, walking up to me.

"Yeah," I said. "Maybe that's why I needed to come."

Father Walter hesitated. "You know, Mikey, you haven't been fooling anyone."

I felt the hair stand up on the back of my neck. "No?"

"You don't have to be embarrassed about having a crisis of faith," Father Walter said. "That's what makes us human."

I nodded, not trusting myself to respond. I wasn't having a crisis of faith; I just didn't particularly think Father Walter was any more right in his faith than Shay was.

Father Walter reached down and lit one of the candles, murmuring a prayer. "You know how I see it? There's always going to be bad stuff out there. But here's the amazing thing— light trumps darkness, every time. You stick a candle into the dark, but you can't stick the dark into the light." We both watched the flame reach higher, gasping for oxygen, before settling comfortably. "I guess from my point of view, we can choose to be in the dark, or we can light a candle. And for me, Christ is that candle."

I faced him. "But it's not just candles, is it? There are flashlights and fluorescent bulbs and bonfires . . ."

"Christ says that there are others doing miracles in His name," Father Walter agreed. "I never said there might not be a million points of light out there—I just think Jesus is the one who strikes the match." He smiled. "I couldn't quite understand why you were so surprised when you thought God had showed up, Mikey. I mean, when *hasn't* He been here?"

Father Walter started to walk back down the church aisle, and I fell into step beside him. "You got time for lunch in the next few weeks?" he asked.

"Can't," I said, grinning. "I'll be doing a funeral." It was a joke between priests—you couldn't schedule anything when your plans were likely to be changed by the lives and deaths of your parishioners.

Except this time, as I said it, I realized it wasn't a joke. In days, I'd be presiding over Shay's funeral.

Father Walter met my gaze. "Good luck today, Mike. I'll be praying."

Out of the blue I remembered the Latin words that had been combined to create *religion*: *re + ligere*. I had always assumed they translated to *reconnect*. It was only when I was at seminary that I learned the correct translation was *to bind*.

Back then, I hadn't seen a difference.

When I first arrived at St. Catherine's, I was given the task of hosting a heart: St. Jean Marie Baptiste Vianney's, to be precise—a French priest who'd died in 1859, at the age of seventy-three. Forty-five years later, when his body was exhumed, the priest's heart had not decayed. Our parish had been chosen as the U.S. location for the heart's veneration; thousands of Catholics from the Northeast were expected to view the organ.

I remembered being very stressed out, and wondering why I had to battle police lines and roadblocks when I had turned to the priesthood to get *closer* to God. I watched Catholics file into our little church and disrupt our Mass schedule and our confession schedule. But after the doors were locked and the onlookers gone, I'd stare down at the glass case with the organ sealed inside. The real wonder, to me, was the course of events that had brought this ancient relic all the way across an ocean to be venerated. Timing was everything. After all, if they hadn't dug up the saint's body, they never would have known about his heart, or told others. A miracle was only a miracle if someone witnessed it, and if the story was passed along to someone else.

Maggie sat in front of me with Shay, her back straight as a poker, her wild mane of hair tamed into a bun at the base of her neck. Shay was subdued, shuffling, fidgety. I glanced down at my lap, which held a manila envelope Maggie had passed me—a piece of art left behind by Lucius DuFresne, who'd passed away over the weekend. There had also been a note on a piece of lined paper:

June has refused the heart. Have not told Shay.

If, on a long shot, we won this case—how would we break the news to Shay that we still could not give him what he so desperately wanted?

"All rise," a U.S. marshal called.

Maggie glanced at me over her shoulder and offered a tight smile, and the entire courtroom got to its feet while Judge Haig entered.

It was so quiet that I could hear the tiny electronic gasps of the video equipment as the judge began to speak. "This is a unique case in New Hampshire's history," Haig said, "and possibly a unique case in the federal court system. The Religious Land Use and Institutionalized Persons Act certainly protects the religious freedoms of a person confined to an institution such as Mr. Bourne, but that doesn't mean that such a person can simply claim that any of his beliefs constitutes a true religion. For example, imagine what would happen if a death row inmate announced that by the tenets of his religion, he had to die of old age. Therefore, when balancing the religious rights of inmates against the compelling governmental interest of the state, this court is mindful of more than just the monetary cost, or even the security cost to other inmates."

The judge folded his hands. "That being said . . . we are not in the habit in this country of allowing the government to define what a church is, or vice versa. And that puts us at a standstill—unless we can develop a litmus test for what religion really is. So how do we go about doing *that*? Well, all we have to work with is history. Dr. Fletcher posed similarities between Gnosticism and Mr. Bourne's beliefs. However, Gnosticism is not a flourishing religion in today's world climate—it's not even an *existing* religion in today's world climate. Although I don't presume to be the expert on the history of Christianity that Dr. Fletcher is, it seems to me a stretch to connect the belief system of an individual inmate in a New Hampshire state prison to a religious sect that's been dead for nearly two thousand years."

Maggie's hand slipped back through the slatted rails that separated the first row of the gallery from the plaintiff's table. I snatched the folded note she held between her fingers. *WE'RE SCREWED*, she had written.

"Then again," the judge continued, "some of Mr. Bourne's observations about spirituality and divinity seem awfully familiar. Mr. Bourne believes in one God. Mr. Bourne thinks salvation is linked to religious practice. Mr. Bourne feels that part of the contract between man and God involves personal sacrifice. All of these are very familiar concepts to the average American who is practicing a mainstream religion."

He cleared his throat. "One of the reasons religion *doesn't* belong in a courtroom is because it's a deeply personal pursuit. Yet, ironically, something Mr. Bourne said struck a chord with this court." Judge Haig turned to

Shay. "I am not a religious man. I have not attended a service for many years. But I do believe in God. My own practice of religion, you could say, is a nonpractice. I personally feel that it's just as worthy on a weekend to rake the lawn of an elderly neighbor or to climb a mountain and marvel at the beauty of this land we live in as it is to sing hosannas or go to Mass. In other words, I think every man finds his own church—and not all of them have four walls. But just because this is how I choose to fashion my faith doesn't mean that I'm ignorant about formal religion. In fact, some of the things I learned as a young man studying for his bar mitzvah resonate with me even now."

My jaw dropped. Judge Haig was Jewish?

"There's a principle in Jewish mysticism called *tikkun olam*," he said. "It means, literally, world repair. The idea is that God created the world by containing divine light in vessels, some of which shattered and got scattered all over. It's the job of humanity to help God by finding and releasing those shards of light— through good deeds and acts. Every time we do, God becomes more perfect—and we become a little more like God.

"From what I understand, Jesus promised

his believers entry into the Kingdom of Heaven—and urged them to prepare through love and charity. The bodhisattva in Buddhism promises to wait for liberation until all who suffer have been freed. And apparently, even those long-gone Gnostics thought that a spark of divinity was inside all of us. It seems to me that no matter what religion you subscribe to, acts of kindness are the stepping-stones to making the world a better place— because we become better people in it. And that sounds, to me, a bit like why Mr. Bourne wants to donate his heart."

Did it really matter whether you believed that Jesus spoke the words in the Bible or the words in the Gospel of Thomas? Did it matter whether you found God in a consecrated church or a penitentiary or even in yourself? Maybe not. Maybe it only mattered that you not judge someone else who chose a different path to find meaning in his life.

"I find under the Religious Land Use and Institutionalized Persons Act of 2000 that Shay Bourne has a valid and compelling religious belief that he must donate his organs at the time of his death," Judge Haig pronounced. "I further find that the State of New Hampshire's plan to execute Mr. Bourne by lethal injection imposes a substantial burden on the ability to exercise his religious practices, and that they therefore must comply with an alternate means of execution, such as hanging, that will allow organ donation to be medically feasible. Court's adjourned, and I want to see counsel in my chambers."

The gallery exploded in a riot of noise, as reporters tried to get to the attorneys before they left to meet with the judge. There were women sobbing and students punching their fists in the air, and in the back of the room, someone had begun to sing a psalm. Maggie reached over the bar to embrace me, and then quickly hugged Shay. "I gotta run," she said, and Shay and I were left staring at each other.

"Good," he said. "This is good."

I nodded and reached out to him. I had never embraced Shay before, and it was a shock to me—how strong his heart beat against my own chest, how warm his skin was. "You have to call her," he said. "You have to tell the girl."

How was I supposed to explain that Claire Nealon didn't want his heart?

"I will," I lied, the words staining his cheek like Judas's kiss.

Maggie

||||||||||||||||||||||||||||||||||||||||||||||||||||||||||||||||||||||||||||||||||||||||||||||||||||

Wait until I told my mother that Judge Haig was not Catholic, like Alexander, but Jewish. No doubt it would inspire her to give me the speech again about how, with time and perseverance, I could be a judge, too. I had to admit, I liked his ruling—and not just because it had come out in favor of my client. His words had been thoughtful, unbiased, not at all what I expected.

"All right," Judge Haig said, "now that the cameras aren't on us, let's just cut the crap. We all know that this trial wasn't about religion, although you found a lovely legal coatrack to hang your complaint on, Ms. Bloom."

My mouth opened and closed, sputtering. So much for thoughtful and unbiased; Judge Haig's spirituality, apparently, was the kind that made itself present only when the right people were there to see it.

"Your Honor, I firmly believe in my client's religious freedoms—"

"I'm sure you do," the judge interrupted. "But get off your high horse so we can settle this business." He turned to Gordon Greenleaf. "Is the state really going to appeal this for a hundred and twenty dollars?"

"Probably not, Judge, but I'd have to check."

"Then go make a phone call," Judge Haig said, "because there's a family out there who deserves to know what's going to happen, and when. Are we clear on that?"

"Yes, Judge," we both parroted.

I left Gordon in the hallway, hunched over his cell phone, and headed downstairs to the holding cell where Shay was most likely still incarcerated. With each step, I moved a little more slowly. What did you say to the man whose imminent death you'd just set in motion?

He was lying on the metal bench in the cell, facing the wall. "Shay," I said, "you okay?"

He rolled toward me and grinned. "You did it."

I swallowed. "Yeah. I guess I did." If I had gotten my client the verdict he wanted, why did I feel like I was going to be sick?

"Did you tell her yet?"

He was talking about June Nealon, or Claire Nealon—which meant that Father Michael had not had the guts to tell Shay the truth either, yet. I pulled up a chair and sat down outside the cell. "I spoke to June this morning," I said. "She said Claire's not going to be using your heart."

"But the doctor told me I was a match."

"It's not that she *can't* use it, Shay," I said quietly. "It's that she doesn't *want* to."

"I did everything you wanted!" Shay cried. "I did what you asked!"

"I know," I said. "But again, this doesn't have to be the end. We can try to see what evidence still exists from the crime scene and—"

"I wasn't *talking* to you," Shay said. "And I don't want you to do anything for me. I don't want that evidence reviewed. How many times do I have to tell you?"

I nodded. "I'm sorry. It's just . . . hard for

me to be riding on the coattails of your death wish."

Shay glanced at me. "No one asked you to," he said flatly.

He was right, wasn't he? Shay didn't ask me to take on his case; I'd swooped down like an avenging angel and convinced him that what I wanted to do could somehow help him do what he wanted to do. And I'd been right—I'd raised the profile of the nature of death penalty cases; I'd secured his right to be hanged. I just hadn't realized that winning would feel, well, quite so much like losing.

"The judge . . . he's made it possible for you to donate your organs . . . afterward. And even if Claire Nealon doesn't want them, there are thousands of people in this country who do."

Shay sank onto the bunk. "Just give it all away," he murmured. "It doesn't matter anymore."

"I'm sorry, Shay. I wish I knew why she changed her mind."

He closed his eyes. "I wish you knew how to change it back."

MICHAEL

‖‖‖

Priests get used to the business of death, but that doesn't make it any easier. Even now that the judge had ruled in favor of a hanging, that still meant there was a will to be written. A body to be disposed of.

As I stood in the prison waiting room, handing over my license so that I could visit Shay, I listened to the commotion outside. This was nothing new; the mob would grow at leaps and bounds through the date of Shay's execution. "You don't understand," a woman was pleading. "I have to see him."

"Take a number, sweetheart," the officer said.

I looked out the open window, trying to see the woman's face. It was obscured by a black scarf; her dress reached from ankle to wrist. I burst through the front door and stood behind the line of correctional officers. "Grace?"

She looked up, tears in her eyes. "They won't let me in. I have to see him."

I reached over the human barrier of guards and pulled her forward. "She's with me."

"She's not on Bourne's visitor list."

"That's because," I said, "we're going to see the warden."

I had no idea how to get someone who had not had a background check done into the prison, but I figured that rules would be relaxed for a death row prisoner. And if they weren't, I was willing to say what I had to to convince the warden.

In the end, Warden Coyne was more amenable than I expected. He looked at Grace's driver's license, made a call to the state's attorney's office, and then offered me a deal. I couldn't take Grace into the tier, but he was willing to bring Shay out to an attorney-client conference room, as long as he remained handcuffed. "I'm not going to let you do this again," he warned, but that hardly mattered.

We both knew that Shay didn't have time for that.

Grace's hands shook as she emptied her pockets to go through the metal detector. We followed the officer to the conference room in silence, but as soon as the door was closed and we were left alone, she started to speak. "I wanted to come to the courthouse," Grace said. "I even drove there. I just couldn't get out of the car." She faced me. "What if he doesn't want to see me?"

"I don't know what frame of mind he'll be in," I said honestly. "He won his trial, but the mother of the heart recipient doesn't want him to be the donor anymore. I'm not sure if his attorney's told him that yet. If he refuses to see you, that might be why."

Only a few minutes passed before two officers brought Shay into the room. He looked hopeful, his fists clenched tight. He saw my face, and then turned—expecting Maggie, most likely. He'd probably been told there were two visitors, and figured one of us had managed to change June's mind.

As he saw his sister, however, he froze. "Gracie? Is that you?"

She took a step forward. "Shay. I'm sorry. I'm so, so sorry."

"Don't cry," he whispered. He went to lift his hand to touch her, but he was handcuffed, and instead just shook his head. "You grew up."

"The last time I saw you I was only fifteen."

He smiled ruefully. "Yeah. I was fresh out of juvy jail, and you wanted nothing to do with your loser brother. I think your exact words were 'Get the hell away from me.' "

"That's because I didn't—I hadn't—" She was sobbing hard now. "I don't want you to die."

"I *have* to, Grace, to make things right . . . I'm okay with that."

"Well, *I'm* not." She looked up at him. "I want to tell someone, Shay."

He stared at her for a long moment. "All right," Shay said. "But only one person, and I get to pick. And," he added, "I get to do this." He reached for the tail of the veil wrapped around her face, which was level with his bound hands. Tugging, he unraveled it, until it fluttered to the ground between them.

Grace brought her hands up to cover her face. But Shay reached up as far as he could in his chains until Grace threaded her fingers with his. Her skin was pocked and puckered, a whirlpool in some places, too tight in others, a relief map of the topology of regret.

Shay ran his thumb over the spot where her eyebrow should have been, where her lip twisted, as if he could repaint her. The look on his face was so honest, so replete, that I felt like I was intruding. I had seen it before— I just couldn't place it.

And then it came to me. A Madonna. Shay was staring at his sister the same way Mary looked at Jesus in all the paintings, all the sculptures—a relationship carved out of not what they had, but what they'd been destined to lose.

June

||||||||||||||||||||||||||||||||||||||||||||||||||||||||||||||||||||||||||||||||||||||||||||||||||||||||||||||||||

I had never seen the woman who came into Claire's hospital room, but I'd never forget her. Her face was horribly disfigured—the kind that you're always telling your kids not to stare at in the grocery store, and yet, when push came to shove, you found yourself doing that very thing.

"I'm sorry," I said quietly, standing up from the chair I'd pulled beside Claire's bed. "I think you must have the wrong room." Now that I had agreed to Claire's wishes and given up the heart—now that she was dying by degrees—I kept a vigil, 24/7. I didn't sleep, I didn't eat, because years from now, I knew I would miss those minutes.

"You're June Nealon?" the woman asked, and when I nodded, she took a step forward. "My name is Grace. I'm Shay Bourne's sister."

You know how when you're driving and skid on ice, or just avoid hitting the deer, you find yourself with your heart racing and your hands shaking and your blood gone to ice? That's what Grace's words did to me. "Get out," I said, my jaw clenched.

"Please. Just hear me out. I want to tell you why I . . . why I look this way."

I glanced down at Claire, but who was I kidding? We could scream at the top of our lungs and not disturb her; she was in a med-ically induced haze. "What makes you think I want to listen?"

She continued, as if I hadn't spoken at all. "When I was thirteen, I was in a fire. So was my whole foster family. My foster father, he died." She took a step forward. "I ran in to try to get my foster father out. Shay was the one who came to save me."

"Sorry, but I can't quite think of your brother as a hero."

"When the police came, Shay told them he'd set the fire," Grace said.

I folded my arms. She hadn't said anything yet that surprised me. I knew that Shay Bourne had been in and out of the foster care system. I knew that he'd been sent to juvenile prison. You could throw ten thousand more excuses for a sorry childhood on his shoulders, and in my opinion, it still wouldn't negate the fact that my husband, my baby, had been killed.

"The thing is," Grace said, "Shay lied." She pushed her hand through her hair. "I'm the one who set the fire."

"My daughter is dying," I said tightly. "I'm sorry you had such a traumatic past. But right now, I have other things to focus on."

Undaunted, Grace kept speaking. "It would happen when my foster mom went to visit her sister. Her husband would come to my bedroom. I used to beg to leave my lights on at night. At first, it was because I was afraid of the dark; then later it was because I so badly wanted someone to see what was happening." Her voice trailed off. "So one day, I planned it. My foster mother was gone overnight, and Shay was—I don't know where, but not home. I guess I didn't think about the consequences until after I lit the match—so I ran in to try to wake my foster dad up. But someone dragged me back out— Shay. And as the sirens got closer I told him everything and he promised me he'd take care of it. I never thought he meant to take the blame—but he wanted to, because he hadn't been able to rescue me before." Grace glanced up at me. "I don't know what happened that day, with your husband, and your little girl, and my brother. But I bet, somehow, something went wrong. That Shay was trying to save her, the way he couldn't save me."

"It's not the same," I said. "My husband would never have hurt Elizabeth like that."

"My foster mother said that, too." She met my gaze. "How would you have felt if—when Elizabeth died—someone told you that you can't have her back, but that a part of her could still be somewhere in the world? You may not know that part; you may not ever have contact with it—but you'd know it was out there, alive and well. Would you have wanted that?"

We were both standing on the same side of Claire's bed. Grace Bourne was almost exactly my height, my build. In spite of her scars, it felt like looking into a mirror. "There's still a heart, June," she said. "And it's a good one."

We pretend that we know our children, because it's easier than admitting the truth—from the minute that cord is cut, they are strangers. It's far easier to tell yourself your daughter is still a little girl than to see her in a bikini and realize she has the curves of a young woman; it's safer to say you are a good parent who has all the right conversations about drugs and sex than to acknowledge there are a thousand things she would never tell you.

How long ago had Claire decided that she couldn't fight any longer? Did she talk to a friend, a diary, Dudley, because I didn't listen? And had I done this before: ignored another daughter, because I was too afraid to hear what she had to say?

Grace Bourne's words kept circling around my mind: *My foster mother said that, too.*

No. Kurt would *never.*

But there were other images clouding my mind, like flags thrown on a grassy field: the pair of Elizabeth's panties that I found inside a couch cushion liner when she was too little to know how to work a zipper. The way he often needed to search for something in the bathroom—Tylenol, an Ace bandage—when Elizabeth was in the tub.

And I heard Elizabeth, every night, when I tucked her in. "Leave the lights on," she'd beg, just like Grace Bourne had.

I had thought it was a phase she'd outgrow, but Kurt said we couldn't let her give in to her fears. The compromise he suggested was to turn off the light—and lie down with her until she fell asleep.

What happens when I'm asleep? she'd asked me once. *Does everything stop?*

What if that had not been the dreamy question of a seven-year-old still figuring out this world, but a plea from a child who wanted to escape it?

I thought of Grace Bourne, hiding behind her scarves. I thought of how you can look right at a person and not see them.

I realized that I might never know what had really happened between them—neither Kurt nor Elizabeth could tell. And Shay Bourne—well, no matter what he saw, his fingerprints had still been on that gun. After last time, I did not know if I could ever bear to face him again.

She was better off dead, he'd said, and I'd run away from what he was trying to tell me.

I pictured Kurt and Elizabeth together in that coffin, his arms holding her tight, and suddenly I thought I was going to throw up.

"Mom," Claire said, her voice thin and wispy. "Are you okay?"

I put my hand on her cheek, where there was a faint flush induced by the medicine— her heart was not strong enough to put a bloom on her face. "No, I'm not," I admitted. "I'm dying."

She smiled a little. "What a coincidence."

But it wasn't funny. I was dying, by degrees. "I have to tell you something," I said, "and you're going to hate me for it." I reached for her hand and squeezed it tightly. "I know it isn't fair. But you're the child, and I'm the parent, and I get to make the choice, even though the heart gets to beat in your chest."

Her eyes filled with tears. "But you said— you *promised*. Don't make me do this . . ."

"Claire, I cannot sit here and watch you die when I know that there's a heart waiting for you."

"But not just any heart." She was crying now, her head turned away from me. "Did you think at all what it will be like for me, after?"

I brushed her hair off her forehead. "It's all I think about, baby."

"That's a lie," Claire argued. "All you ever think about is yourself, and what *you* want, and what *you've* lost. You know, you're not the only one who missed out on a real life."

"That's exactly why I can't let you throw this one away."

Slowly, Claire turned to face me.

"I don't want to be alive because of him."

"Then stay alive because of *me*." I drew in my breath and pulled my deepest secret free. "See, I'm not as strong as you are, Claire. I don't think I can stand to be left behind again."

She closed her eyes, and I thought she had drifted back into sleep, until she squeezed my hand. "Okay," she said. "But I hope you realize I may hate you for the rest of my life."

The rest of my life. Was there any other phrase with so much music in it? "Oh, Claire," I said tightly. "That's going to be a long, long time."

‖‖‖

"God is dead: but considering the state Man
is in,
there will perhaps be caves, for ages yet,
in which his shadow will be shown."

—*FRIEDRICH NIETZSCHE,* THE GAY SCIENCE

MICHAEL

When inmates tried to kill themselves, they'd use the vent. They would string coaxial cables from their television sets through the louvers, wrap a noose around their necks, and step off the metal bunk. For this reason, one week before Shay's execution, he was transferred to an observation cell. There was a camera monitoring his every move; an officer was stationed outside the door. It was a suicide watch, so that a prisoner could not kill himself before the state had its turn.

Shay hated it—it was all he talked about as I sat with him for eight hours a day. I'd read from the Bible, and from the Gospel of Thomas, and from *Sports Illustrated*. I'd tell him about the plans I'd made for the youth group to host a Fourth of July pie auction, a holiday that he would not be around to celebrate. He would act like he was listening, but then he'd address the officer standing outside. "Don't you think I deserve some privacy?" he'd yell. "If you only had a week left, would you want someone watching you every time you cried? Ate? Took a piss?"

Sometimes he seemed resigned to the fact that he was going to die—he'd ask me if I really thought there was a heaven, if you could catch stripers or rainbows or salmon there, if fish even *went* to heaven in the first place, if fish souls were just as good eating as the real kind. Other times he sobbed so hard that he made himself sick; he'd wipe his mouth on the sleeve of his jumpsuit and lie down on the bunk, staring up at the ceiling. The only thing that got him through those darker times was talking about Claire Nealon, whose mother had reclaimed Shay's heart. He had a grainy newspaper photo of Claire, and by now, he'd run his hands over it so often that the girl's pale face had become a blank white oval, features left to the imagination.

The scaffold had been built; throughout the prison you could smell the sap of the pine, taste the fine sawdust in the air. Although there had indeed already been a trapdoor in the chaplain's office, it proved too costly to decimate the cafeteria below it, which accommodated the drop. Instead, a sturdy wooden structure went up beside the injection chamber that had already been built. But when editorials in the *Concord Monitor* and the *Union Leader* criticized the barbarism of a public execution (they speculated that any paparazzi capable of crashing Madonna's wedding in a helicopter would also be able to get footage of the hanging), the warden scrambled to conceal the scaffold. On short order, their best arrangement was to purchase an old big-top tent from a family-run Vermont circus that was going out of business. The festive red and purple stripes took up most of the prison courtyard. You could see its spire from Route 93: *Come one, come all. The greatest show on earth.*

It was a strange thing, knowing that I was going to see Shay's death. Although I'd witnessed the passing of a dozen parishioners; although I'd stood beside the bed while they took their last breaths—this was different. It wasn't God who was cutting the thread of this life, but a court order. I stopped wearing my watch and kept time by Shay's life instead. There were seventy-two hours left, forty-eight, and then twenty-four. I stopped sleeping, like Shay, choosing instead to stay up with him around the clock.

Grace continued to visit once a day. She would only tell me that what had separated them before was a secret—something that had apparently been resolved after she visited June Nealon—and that she was making up for the time she'd lost with her brother. They spent hours with their heads bent together, trading memories, but Shay was adamant that he didn't want Grace at the execution—he did not want that to be her last memory of him. Instead, Shay's designated witnesses would be me, Maggie, and Maggie's boss. When Grace came for her visit, I'd leave her alone with Shay. I would go to the staff cafeteria and grab a soda, or sit and read the newspaper. Sometimes I watched the news coverage of the upcoming execution—the American Medical Association had begun to protest outside the prison, with huge banners that read FIRST DO NO HARM. Those who still believed that Shay was, well,

more than just a murderer began to light
candles at night, thousands of them, spelling out a message that burned so brightly
airplane pilots departing from Manchester
could read it as they soared skyward: HAVE
MERCY.

Mostly, I prayed. To God, to Shay, to anyone who was willing to listen, frankly. And I
hoped—that God, at the last minute, would
spare Shay. It was hard enough ministering
to a death row inmate when I'd believed him
to be guilty, but it was far worse to minister to
an innocent man who had resigned himself
to death. At night, I dreamed of train wrecks.
No matter how loud I shouted for someone
to throw the switch to the rail, no one understood what I was saying.

On the day before Shay's execution, when
Grace arrived, I excused myself and wandered into the courtyard between buildings,
along the massive perimeter of the circus
tent. This time, however, the officers who
usually stood guard at the front entrance
were missing, and the flap that was usually
laced shut was pinned open instead. I could
hear voices inside:

**. . . don't want to get too close to the
edge . . .**

. . . thirty seconds from the rear entrance to the steps . . .

. . . two of you out in front, three in back.

I poked my head in, expecting to be yanked away by an officer—but the small group inside was far too busy to even notice me. Warden Coyne stood on a wooden platform, along with six officers. One was slightly smaller than the rest, and wore handcuffs, ankle cuffs, and a waist chain. He was sagging backward, a deadweight in the other officers' hands.

The gallows itself was a massive metal upright with a crossbeam, set on a platform that had a set of double trapdoors. Below the trap was an open area where you'd be able to see the body drop. Off to both the left and right of the gallows were small rooms with a one-way mirror in the front, so that you could look out, but no one could look in. There was a ramp behind the gallows, and two white curtains that ran the entire length of the tent— one above the gallows, one below it. As I watched, two of the officers dragged the smaller one onto the gallows platform in front of the open curtain.

Warden Coyne pushed a button on his stopwatch. "And . . . cut," he said. "That's seven minutes, fifty-eight seconds. Nicely done."

The warden gestured to the wall. "Those red phones are direct hookups to the governor's office and the attorney general—the commissioner will call to make sure there's been no stay of execution, no last-minute reprieve. If that's the case, then he'll come onto the platform and say so. When he exits, I come up and read the warrant of execution, blah blah blah, then I ask the inmate if he has any final words. As soon as he's finished, I walk off the platform. The minute I cross this taped yellow line, the upper curtain will close, and that's when you two secure the inmate. Now, I'm not going to close the curtains right now, but give it a try."

They placed a white hood over the smaller officer's head and fitted the noose around his neck. It was made of rough rope, wrapped with leather; the loop wasn't made from a hangman's knot, but instead passed through a brass eyelet.

"We've got a drop of seven feet seven inches," Warden Coyne explained as they finished up. "That's the standard for a hundred-and-twenty-six-pound man. You can see the adjusting bracket above—that gold mark is where it should be lined up, at the eye bolt. During the actual event, you three—Hughes, Hutchins, and Greenwald—will be in the chamber to the right. You'll have been placed a few hours ahead of time, so that you aren't seen coming into the tent at all. You will each have a button in front of you. As soon as I enter the control chamber and close the door, you will push that button. Only one of the three actually electromagnetically releases the trapdoor of the gallows; the other two are dummies. Which of the three buttons connects will be determined randomly by computer."

One of the officers interrupted. "What if the inmate can't stand up?"

"We have a collapse board outside his cell—modeled after the one used at Walla Walla in '94. If he can't walk, he'll be strapped onto it and wheeled up by gurney."

They kept saying "the inmate" as if they did not know who they were executing in twenty-four hours. I knew, though, that the reason they would not say Shay's name was that none of them were brave enough. That would make them accountable for murder—the very same crime for which they were hanging a man.

Warden Coyne turned to the other booth. "How's that work for you?"

A door opened, and another man walked out. He put his hand on the mock prisoner's shoulder. "I beg your pardon," he said, and as soon as he spoke I recognized him. This was the British man who'd been at Maggie's apartment when I barged in to tell her Shay was innocent—Gallagher, that was his name. He took the noose and readjusted it around the smaller man's neck, but this time he tightened the knot directly below the left ear. "You see where I've snugged the rope? Make sure it's here, not at the base of the skull. The force of the drop, combined with the position of the knot, is what's meant to fracture the cervical vertebrae and separate the spinal cord."

Warden Coyne addressed the staff again. "The court's ordered us to assume brain death based on the measured drop and the fact that the inmate has stopped breathing. Once the doctor gives us the signal, the lower curtains will close as well, and the body gets cut down immediately. It's important to remember that our job doesn't end with the drop." He turned to the doctor. "And then?"

"We'll intubate, to protect the heart and other organs. After that, I'll perform a brain perfusion scan to fully confirm brain death, and we'll re-move the body from the premises."

"After the criminal investigation unit comes in and clears the execution, the body will go to the medical examiner's staff—they'll have an unmarked white van behind the tent," the war-den said, "and the special operations unit will transport the body back to the hospital, along with them."

I noticed that the warden did not speak the doctor's name, either.

"The rest of the visitors will be exiting from the front of the tent," Warden Coyne said, pointing to the opened flaps of the doorway and spotting me for the first time.

Everyone on the gallows platform stared at me. I met Christian Gallagher's gaze and he nodded imperceptibly. Warden Coyne squinted, and as he recognized me, he sighed. "I can't let you in here, Father," he said, but before the officers could escort me out, I had already slipped from the tent and back into the building where Shay was even now wait-ing to die.

That night, Shay was moved to the death tent. They had built a single cell there, one that would be manned round the clock. At first, it was just like any other cell . . . but two hours into his stay there, the temperature began to plummet. Shay kept shivering, no matter how many blankets were piled upon him.

"The thermostat says it's sixty-six degrees," the officer said, smacking the bulb with his hand. "It's May, for chrissake."

"Well, does it *feel* like sixty-six degrees to you?" I asked. My toes were numb. There was an icicle hanging from the bottom rung of my stool. "Can we get a heater? Another blanket?"

The temperature continued to drop. I put on my coat and zipped it tight. Shay's entire body was racked with tremors; his lips had started to turn blue. Frost swirled on the metal door of the cell, like a white feathered fern.

"It's ten degrees warmer outside this building," the officer said. "I don't get it." He was blowing on his hands, a small exclamation of breath that hovered in the air. "I could call maintenance . . ."

"Let me into the cell," I ordered.

The officer blinked at me. "I can't."

"Why? I've been searched twice over. I'm not near any other inmates. And *you're* here. It's no different than a meeting in an attorney-client conference room, is it?"

"I could get fired for this . . ."

"I'll tell the warden it was my idea, and I'll be on my best behavior," I said. "I'm a priest. Would I lie to you?"

He shook his head and unlocked the cell with an enormous Folger Adam key. I heard the tumblers click into place as he secured me inside; as I entered Shay's six-by-six world. Shay glanced up at me, his teeth chattering.

"Move over," I said, and sat down on the bunk beside him. I draped a blanket over us and waited until the heat from my body conducted through the slight space between us.

"Why . . . is it so . . . cold?" Shay whispered.

I shook my head. "Try not to think about it."

Try not to think about the fact that it is subzero in this tiny cell. Try not to think about the fact that it backs up to a gallows from which you will swing tomorrow. Try not to think about the sea of faces you will see when you stand up there, about what you will say when you are asked to, about your heart pounding so fast with fear that you cannot hear the words you speak. Try not to think about that same heart being cut from your chest, minutes later, when you are gone.

Earlier, Alma the nurse had come to offer Shay Valium. He'd declined—but now I wished I'd taken her up on his behalf.

After a few minutes, Shay stopped shaking so violently—he was down to an occasional tremor. "I don't want to cry up there," he admitted. "I don't want to look weak."

I turned to him. "You've been on death row for eleven years. You've fought—and won—the right to die on your own terms. Even if you had to *crawl* up there tomorrow, there's not a single person who'd think of you as weak."

"Are they all still out there?"

By *they*, he meant the crowds. And they were—and were still coming, blocking the exits off 93 to get into Concord. In the end, and this *was* the end, it did not matter whether or not Shay was truly messianic, or just a good showman. It mattered that all of those people had someone to believe in.

Shay turned to me. "I want you to do me a favor."

"Anything."

"I want you to watch over Grace."

I had already assumed he'd ask that; an execution bound people together much like any other massive emotional moment—a birth, an armed robbery, a marriage, a divorce. I would be linked to the parties involved forever. "I will."

"And I want you to have all my things."

I could not imagine what this entailed—his tools, maybe, from when he was a carpenter? "I'd like that." I pulled the blanket up a little higher. "Shay, about your funeral."

"It really doesn't matter."

I had tried to get him a spot in the St. Catherine's cemetery, but the committee in charge had vetoed it—they did not want the grave of a murderer resting beside their loved ones. Private plots and burials were thousands of dollars—thousands that neither Grace nor Maggie nor I had to spend. An inmate whose family did not make alternate plans would be buried in a tiny graveyard behind the prison, a headstone carved only with his correctional facility number, not his name.

"Three days," Shay said, yawning.

"Three days?"

He smiled at me, and for the first time in hours, I actually felt warm to the core. "That's when I'm coming back."

At nine o'clock on the morning of Shay's execution, a tray was brought up from the kitchen. Sometime during the night, the frost had broken; and with it, the cement that had been poured for the base of the holding cell. Weeds from the courtyard sprouted in tufts and bunches; vines climbed up the metal wall of the cell door. Shay took off his shoes and socks and walked across the new grass bare-foot, a big smile on his face.

I had moved back to my outside stool, so that the officer watching over Shay would not get into trouble, but the sergeant who arrived with the food was immediately wary. "Who brought in the plants?"

"No one," the officer said. "They just sort of showed up overnight."

The sergeant frowned. "I'm going to tell the warden."

"Yeah," the officer said. "Go on. I'm sure he's got nothing else to think about right now."

At his sarcasm, Shay and I looked at each other and grinned. The sergeant left, and the officer handed the tray through the trapdoor. Shay uncovered the items, one by one.

Mallomars. Corn dogs. Chicken nuggets.

Kettle corn and cotton candy, s'mores.

Curly fries, ice cream crowned with a halo of maraschino cherries. Fry bread sprinkled with powdered sugar. A huge blue Slurpee.

There was more than one man could ever eat. And it was all the sort of food you got at a country fair. The sort of food you remembered from your childhood.

If, unlike Shay, you'd had one.

"I worked on a farm for a while," Shay said absently. "I was putting up a timber-frame barn. One day, I watched the guy who ran it empty the whole sack of grain out into the middle of the pasture for his steers, instead of just a scoop. I thought that was so cool—like Christmas, for them!—until I saw the butcher's truck drive up. He was giving them all they could eat, because by then, it didn't matter."

Shay rolled the French fry he'd been holding between his fingers, then set it back on the plate. "You want some?"

I shook my head.

"Yeah," he said softly. "I guess I'm not so hungry, either."

Shay's execution was scheduled for ten a.m. Although death penalty sentences used to be carried out at midnight, it felt so cloak-and-dagger that now they were staggered at all times of the day. The family of the inmate was allowed to visit up to three hours prior to the execution, although this was not an issue, since Shay had told Grace not to come. The attorney of record and the spiritual advisor were allowed to stay up to forty-five minutes prior to the execution.

After that, Shay would be alone, except for the officer guarding him.

After the breakfast tray was removed, Shay got diarrhea. The officer and I turned our backs to give him privacy, then pretended it had not happened. Shortly afterward, Maggie arrived. Her eyes were red, and she kept wiping at them with a crumpled Kleenex. "I brought you something," she said, and then she saw the cell, overrun with vegetation. "What's this?"

"Global warming?" I said.

"Well. My gift's a little redundant." Maggie emptied her pockets, full of grass, Queen Anne's lace, lady's slippers, Indian paintbrushes, buttercups.

She fed them to Shay through the metal mesh on the door. "Thank you, Maggie."

"For God's sake, don't *thank* me," Maggie said. "I wish this wasn't the way it ended, Shay." She hesitated. "What if I—"

"No." Shay shook his head. "It's almost over, and then you can go on to rescuing people who want to be rescued. I'm okay, really. I'm ready."

Maggie opened her mouth to speak, but then pressed her lips together and shook her head. "I'll stand where you can see me."

Shay swallowed. "Okay."

"I can't stay. I need to make sure that Warden Coyne's talked to the hospital, so that everything happens like it's supposed to."

Shay nodded. "Maggie," he said, "promise me something?"

"Sure, Shay."

He rested his head against the metal door. "Don't forget me."

"Not a chance," Maggie said, and she pressed her lips against the metal door, as if she could kiss Shay good-bye.

Suddenly, we were alone, with a half hour stretching between us.

"How are you doing?" I asked.

"Um," Shay said. "Never better?"

"Right. Stupid question." I shook my head. "Do you want to talk? Pray? Be by yourself?"

"No," Shay said quickly. "Not that."

"Is there anything I can do?"

"Yeah," he said. "Tell me about her again."

I hesitated. "She's at the playground," I

said, "pumping her legs on a swing. When she gets to the top, and she's sure her sneakers have actually kicked a cloud, she jumps off because she thinks she can fly."

"She's got long hair, and it's like a flag behind her," Shay added.

"Fairy-tale hair. So blond it's nearly silver."

"A fairy tale," Shay repeated. "A happy ending."

"It is, for her. You're giving her a whole new life, Shay."

"I'm saving her again. I'm saving her twice. Now with my heart, and once before she was ever born." He looked directly at me. "It wasn't just Elizabeth he could have hurt. She got in the way, when the gun went off . . . but the other . . . I had to do it."

I glanced over my shoulder at the officer standing watch, but he had moved to a far corner and was speaking into his walkie-talkie. My words were thick, rubbery. "Then you *did* commit capital murder."

Shay shrugged. "Some people," he said simply, "deserve to die."

I stood, speechless, as the officer approached. "Father, I'm really sorry," he said, "but it's time for you to leave."

At that moment, the sound of bagpipes

filled the tent, and an accompanying swell of voices. The people outside, maintaining their vigil, had begun to sing:

> **Amazing   Grace,   how   sweet   the
> sound . . .**
> **That saved a wretch like me.**
> **I once was lost, but now I'm found.**
> **Was blind, but now I see.**

I didn't know if Shay was guilty of murder, or innocent and misunderstood. I didn't know if he was the Messiah, or a savant who channeled texts he'd never read. I didn't know if we were making history, or only reliving it. But I did know what to do: I motioned Shay forward, closed my eyes, and made the sign of the cross on his forehead. "Almighty God," I murmured, "look on this your servant, lying in great weakness, and comfort him with the promise of life everlasting, given in the resurrection of your Son Jesus Christ our Lord. Amen."

I opened my eyes to find Shay smiling. "See you around, Father," he said.

Maggie

‖‖

As soon as I left Shay's cell, I stumbled out of the circus tent—that's what this was, you know, a *circus*—and threw up on the grass in the courtyard.

"Hey," a voice said, "you all right?" I felt an arm steadying me, and I glanced into the dizzying sunlight to find Warden Coyne, looking just as unhappy to see me as I was to see him.

"Come on," he said. "Let's get you a glass of water."

He led me through dark, dismal corridors—corridors far more suited to an execution, I thought, than the beautiful spring day outside, with its brilliant blue sky and tufted clouds. In the empty staff cafeteria, he pulled out a chair for me, then went to the cooler to get me something to drink. I finished the whole cup of water, and still could taste the bitterness in my throat.

"Sorry," I said. "Didn't mean to vomit on your parade."

He sat down in a chair beside me. "You know, Ms. Bloom, there's a hell of a lot about me you don't know."

"Nor do I want to," I said, standing.

"For example," Warden Coyne continued blithely, "I don't really believe in the death penalty."

I stared at him, snapped my mouth shut, and sank back into my chair.

"I used to, don't get me wrong. And I'll perform an execution if I have to, because it's part of my job. But that doesn't mean I condone it," he said. "Truth is, I've seen plenty of inmates for whom life in prison is just as well served. And I've seen inmates I *wish* would be killed—there are just some people you cannot find the good in. But who am I to decide if someone should be killed for murdering a child . . . instead of for murdering a drug addict during a deal that went bad . . . or even if we should be killing the inmate himself? I'm not smart enough to be able to say which life is worth more than the other. I don't know if anyone is."

"If you know it's not fair, and you still do this, how do you sleep at night?"

Warden Coyne smiled sadly. "I don't, Ms. Bloom. The difference between you and me is that *you* expect me to be able to." He got to his feet. "I trust you know where you go from here?"

I was supposed to wait at the Public Information Office, along with Father Michael, so that we could be brought to the tent apart from the witnesses for the state and the victim. But somehow, I knew that wasn't what Warden Coyne had meant.

And even more surprising . . . I think he knew that I knew that.

The inside of the circus tent was painted with blue sky. Artificial clouds rose into the peaks, above the black iron of the gallows that had been constructed. I wondered if Shay would look at it and pretend that he was outside.

The tent itself was divided by a line of correctional officers, who kept the witnesses for both sides separated, like a human dam. We had been warned about our behavior in the letters from the Department of Corrections: any name-calling or inappropriate actions would result in us being hauled out of the tent. Beside me, Father Michael was praying a rosary. On my other side sat Rufus Urqhart, my boss.

I was shocked to see June Nealon sitting quietly in the front row across from us.

Somehow I'd assumed she'd be with Claire, especially given the fact that Claire would be getting ready for her heart transplant. When she'd called to tell me she wanted Shay's heart, I hadn't asked any questions— I hadn't wanted to jinx it. Now I wished I could go over to her and ask whether Claire was all right, if everything was on schedule—but I would run the risk of the officers thinking I was harassing her; and truth be told, I was afraid to hear her answer.

Somewhere behind that curtain, Christian was checking to make sure the rope and noose were exactly as they should be to ensure as humane a hanging as possible. I knew this was supposed to comfort me, but to be honest, I had never felt more alone in my life.

It was a hard thing, accepting to myself

that I had befriended someone convicted of murder. Lawyers knew better than to become emotionally and personally involved with their clients—but that didn't mean it didn't happen.

At exactly ten o'clock, the curtains opened.

Shay seemed very small on the gallows platform. He wore a white T-shirt, orange scrub pants, and tennis shoes, and was flanked by two officers I'd never seen before. His arms were fastened behind him, and his legs were bound together with what looked like a strap of leather.

He was shaking like a leaf.

Commissioner Lynch walked onto the platform. "There has been no stay of execution," he announced.

I thought about Christian's hands checking the knot against Shay's neck. I knew the mercy of his touch; I was grateful that Shay's last physical contact with a human would be gentle.

The warden stepped onto the platform as Lynch exited, and he read the entire warrant aloud. The words slipped in and out of my mind:

. . . Whereas on the sixth day of March, 1997, Isaiah Matthew Bourne was duly

and legally convicted of two counts of the crime of capital murder . . .

. . . said court pronounced sentence upon Isaiah Matthew Bourne in accordance with said judgment fixing the time for the execution for ten a.m. on Friday, the twenty-third of May, 2008 . . .

. . . command you to execute the aforesaid judgment and sentence by hanging in a manner that produces brain death in said Isaiah Matthew Bourne . . .

When the warden finished, he faced Shay. "Inmate Bourne, do you have any final words?"

Shay squinted, until he found me in the front row. He kept his eyes on me for a long moment, and then drifted toward Father Michael. But then he turned to the side of the tent where the witnesses for the victim were gathered, and he smiled at June Nealon. "I forgive you," he said.

Immediately afterward, a curtain was drawn. It reached only to the floor of the gallows, and it was a translucent white. I didn't know if the warden had intended for us to see what was happening behind it, but we could, in macabre silhouette: the hood being placed over Shay's head, the noose being tightened against his neck, the two officers who'd secured him stepping backward.

"Good-bye," I whispered.

Somewhere, a door slammed, and suddenly the trap was open and the body plummeted, one quick firecracker snap as the weight caught at the end of the rope. Shay slowly turned counterclockwise with the unlikely grace of a ballerina, an October leaf, a snowflake falling.

I felt Father Michael's hand on mine, conveying what there were not words to say. "It's over," he whispered.

I don't know what made me turn toward June Nealon, but I did. The woman sat with her back straight as a redwood, her hands folded so tightly in her lap that I could see the half-moons her own nails were cutting in her skin. Her eyes were tightly squeezed shut.

After all this, she hadn't even watched him die.

The lower curtain closed three minutes and ten seconds after Shay had been hanged. It was opaque, and we could not see what was happening behind it, although the fabric fluttered with movement and activity. The officers in the tent didn't let us linger, though—they hustled us out separate doors to the courtyard. We were led out of the prison gates and immediately inundated with the press. "This is good," Rufus said, pumped up with adrenaline. "This is our moment." I nodded, but my attention was focused on June. I could see her only briefly, a tiny crow of a woman ducking into a waiting car.

"Mr. Urqhart," a reporter said, as twenty microphones were held up to his face, a bouquet of black roses. "Do you have any comment?"

I stepped back, watching Rufus in the limelight. I wished I could just vanish on the spot. I knew that Rufus didn't mean to use Shay as a pawn here, that he was only doing his job as the head of the ACLU—and yet, how did that make him different from Warden Coyne?

"Shay Bourne is dead," Rufus said soberly. "The first execution in this state in sixty-nine years . . . in the only first world country to still have death penalty legislation on the books."

He looked out over the crowd. "Some people say that the reason we have a death penalty in this country is because we need to punish certain inmates. It's said to be a deterrent—but in fact, murder rates are higher in death penalty jurisdictions than in those without it. It's said to be cheaper to execute a man than to keep him in prison for life—but in fact, when you factor in the cost of eleven years of appeals, paid for with public funds, it costs about a third more to execute a prisoner than to sentence him to life in prison. Some people say that the death penalty exists for the sake of the victims' family—that it offers closure, so that they can deal, finally and completely, with their grief. But does knowing that the death toll has risen above and beyond their family member really offer justice? And how do we explain the fact that a murder in a rural setting is more likely to lead to a death sentence than one that occurs in the city? Or that the murder of a white victim leads to the death penalty three and a half times more often than the murder of a black victim? Or that women are sentenced to death only two-thirds as often as men?"

Before I realized what I was doing, I had stepped into the tiny circle of space that the media had afforded to Rufus. "Maggie," he whispered, covering the mikes, "I'm working this here."

A reporter gave me my invitation. "Hey, weren't you his lawyer?"

"Yes," I said. "Which I hope means I'm qualified to tell you what I'm going to. I work for the ACLU. I can spout out all the same statistics that Mr. Urqhart just did. But you know what that speech leaves out? That I am truly sorry for June Nealon's loss, after all this time. And that today, *I* lost someone I cared about. Someone who'd made some serious mistakes—someone who was a hard nut to crack—but someone I'd made a place for in my life."

"Maggie," Rufus hissed, pulling at my sleeve. "Save the true confessional for your diary."

I ignored him. "You know why I think we still execute people? Because, even if we don't want to say it out loud—for the really heinous crimes, we want to know that there's a really heinous punishment. Simple as that. We want to bring society closer together—huddle and circle our wagons— and that means getting rid of people we think are incapable of learning a moral les- son. I guess the question is: Who gets to identify those people? Who decides what crime is so awful that the only answer is death? And what if, God forbid, they get it wrong?"

The crowd was murmuring; the cameras were rolling. "I don't have children. I can't say I'd feel the same way if one of them was killed. And I don't have the answers—believe me, if I did, I'd be a lot richer—but you know, I'm starting to think that's okay. Maybe instead of looking for answers, we ought to be asking some questions instead. Like: What's the lesson we're teaching here? What if it's different every time? What if justice isn't equal to due process? Because at the end of the day, this is what we're left with: a victim, who's become a file to be dealt with, instead of a little girl, or a husband. An inmate who doesn't want to know the name of a correctional officer's child because that makes the relationship too personal. A warden who carries out executions even if he doesn't think they should happen in principle. And an ACLU lawyer who's supposed to go to the office, close the case, and move on. What we're left with is death, with the humanity removed from it." I hesitated a moment. "So you tell me . . . did this execution really make you feel safer? Did it bring us all closer together? Or did it drive us farther apart?"

I pushed past the cameras, whose heavy heads swung like bulls to follow my path, and into the crowd, which carved a canyon for me to walk through. And I cried.

God, I cried.

I turned on my windshield wipers on the way home, even though it was not raining. But I was falling apart at the seams, and sobbing, and I couldn't see; somehow I thought this would help. I had upstaged my boss on what was arguably the most important legal outcome for the New Hampshire ACLU in the past fifty years; even worse—I didn't particularly care.

I would have liked to talk to Christian, but he was at the hospital by now, supervising the harvest of Shay's heart and other organs. He'd said he'd come over as soon as he could, as soon as he had word that the transplant was going to be a success.

Which meant that I was going home to a house with a rabbit in it, and not much else.

I turned the corner to my street and immediately saw the car in my driveway. My mother was waiting for me at the front door. I wanted to ask her why she was here, instead of at work. I wanted to ask her how she'd known I'd need her.

But when she wordlessly held out a blanket that I usually kept on the couch, one with fuzzy fleece inside, I stepped into it and forgot all my questions. Instead, I buried my face against her neck. "Oh, Mags," she soothed. "It's going to be all right."

I shook my head. "It was *awful*. Every time I blink, I can see it, like it's still happening." I drew in a shuddering breath. "It's stupid, isn't it? Up till the last minute, I was expecting a miracle. Like in the courtroom. That he'd slip out of the noose, or—I don't know—fly away or something."

"Here, sit down," my mother said, leading me into the kitchen. "Real life doesn't work that way. It's like you said, to the reporters—"

"You saw me?" I glanced up.

"On television. Every channel, Maggie. Even CNN." Her face glowed. "Four people already called me to say you were brilliant."

I suddenly remembered sitting in my parents' kitchen when I was in college, unable to decide on a career. My mother had sat down, propped her elbows on the table. *What do you love to do?* she had asked.

Read, I'd told her. *And argue.*

She had smiled broadly. *Maggie, my love, you were meant to become a lawyer.*

I buried my face in my hands. "I was an idiot. Rufus is going to fire me."

"Why? Because you said what nobody has the guts to say? The hardest thing in the world is believing someone can change. It's always easier to go along with the way things are than to admit that you might have been wrong in the first place."

She turned to me, holding out a steaming, fragrant bowl. I could smell rosemary, pepper, celery. "I made you soup. From scratch."

"*You* made me soup from scratch?"

My mother rolled her eyes. "Okay, I *bought* soup someone else made from scratch."

When I smiled a little, she touched my cheek. "Maggie," she said, "eat."

Later that afternoon, while my mother did the dishes and cleaned up in my kitchen, and with Oliver curled up at my side, I fell asleep on the living room couch. I dreamed that I was walking in the dark in my favorite Stuart Weitzman heels, but they were hurting me. I glanced down to discover I was not walking on grass, but on a ground that looked like tempered glass after it's been shattered, like the cracked, parched landscape of a desert. My heels kept getting stuck in the crevasses, and finally I had to stop to pull one free.

When I did, a clod of earth overturned, and beneath it was light, the purest, most liquid lava form of it. I kicked at another piece of the ground with my heel, and more beams spilled outward and upward. I poked holes, and rays shined up. I danced, and the world became illuminated, so bright that I had to shade my eyes; so bright that I could not keep them from filling with tears.

June

This, I had told Claire, the night before the surgery, is how they'll transplant the heart:

You'll be brought into the operating room and given general anesthesia.

Grape, she'd said. She liked it way better than bubble gum, although the root beer wasn't bad.

You'll be prepped and draped, I told her. Your sternum will be opened with a saw.

Won't that hurt?

Of course not, I said. You'll be fast asleep.

I knew the procedure as well as any cardiac resident; I'd studied it that carefully, and that long. *What comes next?* Claire had asked.

Sutures—stitches—get sewn into the aorta, the superior vena cava, and the inferior vena cava. Catheters are placed. Then you're put on the heart-lung machine.

What's that?

It works so you don't have to. It drains blue blood from the two cava, and returns red blood through the cannula in the aorta.

Cannula's a cool word. I like how it sounds on my tongue.

I skipped over the part about how her heart would be removed: the inferior and superior vena cava divided, then the aorta.

Keep going.

His heart (no need to say whose) is flushed with cardioplegia solution.

It sounds like something you use to wax a car.

Well, you'd better hope not. It's chock-full of nutrients and oxygen, and keeps the heart from beating as it warms up.

And after that?

Then the new heart goes to its new home, I had said, and I'd tapped her chest. First, the left atriums get sewn together. Then the inferior vena cava, then the superior vena cava, then the pulmonary artery, and finally, the aorta. When all the connections are set, the cross clamp on your aorta is removed, warm blood starts flowing into the coronaries, and . . .

Wait, let me guess: the heart starts beating.

Now, hours later, Claire beamed up at me from her hospital gurney. As the parent of a minor, I was allowed to accompany her to the OR, gowned and suited, while she was put under anesthesia. I sat down on the stool provided by a nurse, amid the gleaming instruments, the shining lights. I tried to pick out the familiar face of the surgeon from his kind eyes, above the mask.

"Mom," Claire said, reaching for my hand.

"I'm right here."

"I don't hate you."

"I know, baby."

The anesthesiologist fitted the mask to Claire's face. "I want you to start counting for me, hon. Backward, from ten."

"Ten," Claire said, looking into my eyes. "Nine. Eight."

Her lids dropped, half-mast. "Seven," she said, but her lips went slack on the last syllable.

"You can give her a kiss if you want, Mom," said a nurse.

I brushed my paper mask against the soft bow of Claire's cheek. "Come back to me," I whispered.

MICHAEL

Three days after Shay's death, and two after his funeral, I returned to the prison cemetery. The headstones formed a small field, each one marked with a number. Shay's grave didn't have one yet; it was only a small raw plot of earth. And yet, it was the only one with a visitor. Sitting on the ground, her legs crossed, was Grace Bourne.

I waved as she got to her feet. "Father," she said. "It's good to see you."

"You, too." I came closer, smiled.

"That was a nice service you did the other day." She looked down at the ground. "I know it didn't seem like I was listening, but I was."

At Shay's funeral, I hadn't read from the Bible at all. I hadn't read from the Gospel of Thomas, either. I had created my own gospel, the good news about Shay Bourne, and spoke it from the heart to the few people who'd been present: Grace, Maggie, Alma the nurse.

June Nealon had not come; she was at the hospital with her daughter, who was recovering from the heart transplant. She'd sent a spray of lilies to lay on Shay's grave; they were still here, wilting.

Maggie had told me that Claire's doctor had been thrilled with the outcome of the operation, that the heart had started beating like a jackrabbit. Claire would be leaving the hospital by the end of the week. "You heard about the transplant?" I said.

Grace nodded. "I know that wherever he is, he's happy about that." She dusted off her skirt. "Well, I was on my way out. I have to get back to Maine for a seven o'clock shift."

"I'll call you in a few days," I said, and I meant it. I had promised Shay that I would look after Grace, but to be honest, I think he wanted to be sure she'd be looking after me as well. Somehow, Shay had known that without the Church, I'd need a family, too.

I sat down, in the same spot where Grace had been. I sighed, leaned forward, and waited.

The problem was, I wasn't sure what I was waiting for. It had been three days since Shay's death. He had told me he was coming back—a resurrection—but he had also told me that he'd murdered Kurt Nealon intentionally, and I couldn't hold the two thoughts side by side in my mind.

I didn't know if I was supposed to be on the lookout for an angel, like Mary Magdalene had seen, to tell me that Shay had left this tomb. I didn't know if he'd mailed me a letter that I could expect to receive later that afternoon. I was waiting, I suppose, for a sign.

I heard footsteps and saw Grace hurrying toward me again. "I almost forgot! I'm supposed to give this to you."

It was a large shoe box, wrapped with a rubber band. The green cardboard had begun to peel away from the corners, and there were spots that were watermarked. "What is it?"

"My brother's things. The warden, he gave them to me. But there was a note inside from Shay. He wanted you to have them. I would have given it to you at the funeral, but the note said I was supposed to give it to you *today.*"

"You should have these," I said. "You're his family."

She looked up at me. "So were you, Father."

When she left, I sat back down beside Shay's grave. "Is this it?" I said aloud. "Is this what I was supposed to wait for?"

Inside the box was a canvas roll of tools, and three packages of Bazooka bubble gum.

He had one piece of gum, I heard Lucius say, *and there was enough for all of us.*

The only other item inside was a small, flat, newspaper-wrapped package. The tape had peeled off years ago; the paper was yellowed with age. Folded in its embrace was a tattered photograph that made me catch my breath: I held in my hands the picture that had been stolen from my dorm when I was in college: my grandfather and I showing off our day's catch.

Why had he taken something so worthless to a stranger? I touched my thumb to my grandfather's face and suddenly recalled Shay talking about the grandfather he'd never had—the one he'd imagined from this photo.

Had he swiped it because it was proof of what he'd missed in his life? Had he stared at it, wishing he was me?

I remembered something else: the photo had been stolen before I was picked for Shay's jury. I shook my head in disbelief. It was possible Shay had known it was me when he saw me sitting in the courtroom. It was possible he had recognized me again when I first came to him in prison. It was possible the joke had been on me all along.

I started to crumple up the newspaper that the photo had been wrapped in, but realized it wasn't newspaper at all. It was too thick for that, and not the right size. It was a page torn out of a book. *The Nag Hammadi Library*, it read across the top, in the tiniest of print. *The Gospel of Thomas*, first published 1977. I ran a fingertip along the familiar sayings. *Jesus said: Whoever finds the interpretation of these sayings will not experience death.*

Jesus said: The dead are not alive, and the living will not die.

Jesus said: Do not tell lies.

Jesus said.

And so had Shay, after having years to memorize this page.

Frustrated, I tore it into pieces and threw

them on the ground. I was angry at Shay; I was angry at myself. I buried my face in my hands, and then felt a wind stir. The confetti of words began to scatter.

I ran after them. As they caught against headstones, I trapped them with my hands. I stuffed them into my pockets. I untangled them from the weeds that grew at the edge of the cemetery. I chased one fragment all the way to the parking lot.

Sometimes we see what we want to, instead of what's in front of us. And sometimes, we don't see clearly at all. I took all of the bits I'd collected and dug a shallow bowl beneath the spray of lilies, covered them with a thin layer of soil. I imagined the yellowed paper dissolving in the rain, being absorbed by the earth, lying fallow under winter snow. I wondered what, next spring, would take root.

||||||||||||||||||||||||||||||||||||||||||||||||||||||||||||||||||||||||||||||||||||||||

"There are only two ways to live your life.
One is as though nothing is a miracle.
The other is as though everything is a mira-
cle."

—ALBERT EINSTEIN

EPILOGUE

Claire

‖‖‖

I have been someone different now for three weeks. It's not something you can tell by looking at me; it's not even something I can tell by looking at myself in the mirror. The only way I can describe it, and it's weird, so get ready, is like waves: they just crash over me and suddenly, even if I'm surrounded by a dozen people, I'm lonely. Even if I'm doing everything I want to, I start to cry.

My mother says that emotion doesn't get transplanted along with the heart, that I have to stop referring to it as *his* and start calling it *mine*. But that's pretty hard to do, especially when you add up all the stuff I have to take just to keep my cells from recognizing this intruder in my chest, like that old horror movie with the woman who has an alien inside her. Colace, Dulcolax, prednisone, Zantac, enalapril, CellCept, Prograf, oxycodone, Keflex, magnesium oxide, nystatin, Valcyte. It's a cocktail to keep my body fooled; it's anyone's guess how long this ruse might continue.

The way I see it, either my body wins and I reject the heart—or I win.

And become who he used to be.

My mother says that I'm going to work through all this, and that's why I have to take Celexa (oh, right, forgot that one) and talk to a shrink twice a week. I nod and pretend to believe her. She's so happy right now, but it's the kind of happy that's like an ornament made of sugar: if you brush it the wrong way, it will go to pieces.

I'll tell you this much: it's so good to be home. And to not have a lightning bolt zapping me from inside three or four times a day. And to not pass out and wake up wondering what happened. And to walk up the stairs—up*stairs*!— without having to stop halfway, or be carried.

"Claire?" my mother calls. "Are you awake?"

Today, we have a visitor coming. It's a

woman I haven't met, although apparently she's met me. She's the sister of the man who gave me his heart; she came to the hospital when I was totally out of it. I am *so* not looking forward to this. She'll probably break down and cry (I would if I were her) and stare at me with an eagle eye until she finds some shred of me that reminds her of her brother, or at least convinces herself she has.

"I'm coming," I say. I have been standing in front of the mirror for the past twenty minutes, without a shirt on. The scar, which is still healing, is the angriest red slash of a mouth. Every time I look at it, I imagine the things it might be yelling.

I resettle the bandage that I'm not supposed to peel off but do when my mother isn't there to see it. Then I shrug into a shirt and glance down at Dudley. "Hey, lazybones," I say. "Rise and shine."

The thing is, my dog doesn't move.

I stand there, staring, even though I know what's happened. My mother told me once, in her dump truck–load of fun facts about cardiac patients, that when you do a transplant the nerve that goes from the brain to the heart gets cut. Which means that it takes people like me longer to respond to situations that would normally freak us out. We need the adrenaline to kick in first.

You can hear this and think, *Oh, how nice to stay calm.*

Or you can hear this and think, *Imagine what it would be like to have a brand-new heart, and be so slow to feel.*

And then, boom, just like that it kicks in. I fall down to my knees in front of the dog. I'm afraid to touch him. I have been too close to death; I don't want to go there again.

By now the tears are here; they stream down my face and into my mouth. Loss always tastes like salt. I bend down over my old, sweet dog. "Dudley," I say. "Come on." But when I scoop him up—put my ear against his rib cage—he's cold, stiff, not breathing.

"No," I whisper, and then I shout it so loud that my mother comes scrambling up the stairs like a storm.

She fills my doorway, wild-eyed. "Claire? What's wrong?"

I shake my head; I can't speak. Because, in my arms, the dog twitches. His heart starts beating again, beneath my own two hands.

AUTHOR'S NOTE

For those wishing to learn more about the topics in this book, try these sites and texts, which were instrumental to me during this journey.

ABOUT THE DEATH PENALTY

Death Penalty Information Center: www. deathpenaltyinfo.org.

Death Row Support Project, PO Box 600, Liberty Mills, IN 46946. (Contact them if you want to write to a death row prisoner.)

Murder Victims' Families for Human Rights: www.mvfhr.org.

Murray, Robert W. *Life on Death Row*. Albert Publishing Co., 2004.

Prejean, Sister Helen. *Dead Man Walking*. New York: Vintage Books, 1993.

———. *The Death of Innocents*. New York: Random House, 2005.

Rossi, Richard Michael. *Waiting to Die*. London: Vision Paperbacks, 2004.

Turow, Scott. *Ultimate Punishment*. New York: Picador, 2003.

ABOUT THE GNOSTIC GOSPELS

Pagels, Elaine. *Beyond Belief: The Secret Gospel of Thomas*. New York: Random House, 2003.

———. *The Gnostic Gospels*. New York: Random House, 1979.

Robinson, James M., ed. *The Nag Hammadi Library*. Leiden, the Netherlands: E. J. Brill, 1978.

VOICES OF THE PAST

GRID SERIES IN ADVERTISING AND JOURNALISM

Consulting Editors
ARNOLD M. BARBAN, University of Illinois
DONALD W. JUGENHEIMER, University of Kansas

OTHER BOOKS IN THE GRID SERIES IN ADVERTISING AND JOURNALISM

VOICES OF THE PAST

Key Documents in the History of American Journalism

Calder M. Pickett

Grid Inc., Columbus, Ohio

I.S.B.N. 0-88244-127-2
Library of Congress Catalog Card Number
76-19674

1 2 3 4 5 6 ⊠ 2 1 0 9 8 7

CONTENTS

Canons of Journalism
The Manassa Matador and the Wild Bull of the Pampas
Babe Ruth in the 1923 World Series
A Classic Moment for a Classic Pitcher
A Young Man Dies in a Cave
Bryan Takes the Stand in Dayton
William Jennings Bryan
A Commentary on Sacco and Vanzetti
Darrow Pleads for Mercy
The Snyder-Gray Case
About a Witness Called "The Pig Woman"
Daddy Browning Tells His Story
A Hero Is Welcomed in Paris
The World—in the Fabulous 1920s
The End of the World
Wall Street Lays an Egg

FOREWORD

Many years ago, when I first began teaching a course called History of American Journalism, I became convinced that I wanted my students to have more than a standard textbook in the course. So I assembled a huge corollary reading list, and I had my students chasing books all over the campus and waiting in line in the reserve library. This reading list system didn't work very well, so I began to read excerpts aloud in class: a little of Joseph Addison, a little of Thomas Paine, a little of Bryant and Bennett and Greeley and Pulitzer, a little of Edward R. Murrow. This I rather enjoyed, but I was finding it increasingly difficult to pack it all into one semester. So I began to cut, and often I had to cut examples that seemed especially important.

Well, I kept the textbook, of course, but I also began to use an anthology of great reporting. American journalism has been more than great reporting, however, so that concept became unsatisfactory. I remembered, then, that early reading list, the one that included a piece of Milton's *Areopagitica,* some *Common Sense,* Bryant's "On the Right of Workmen to Strike," and Ernie Pyle's death of Captain Waskow. I began to assemble a master reading list that I came to think of as *Key Documents in the History of American Journalism.* That reading list—greatly changed, expanded, but also contracted—makes up the contents of this anthology.

It is an anthology that already, for me, is insufficient. My *ideal* anthology would be several times as long as this volume. As I assembled, listed, and wrote I eliminated selections and added others. I reluctantly told myself that something wasn't really a *key* document, even though I liked it very much. I found that certain celebrated pieces of writing were really labored and dull, and I knew that if *I* found them dull some students would find them impossible. I eliminated them, or I trimmed them back. I also realized, early in the game, that "key documents" is a deceptive term—though I maintain it in the title. For, as I suggest in the text, there is no way to include Joseph Rosenthal's flag-raising on Iwo Jima in a book of readings, no way to suggest the impact of Herbert Morrison's description of the explosion of the *Hindenburg,* no way to capture the drama and emotion of Edward R. Murrow talking about the death of his friend Jan Masaryk, no way to incorporate the magnificent journalism that was television's handling of the four days of November, 1963. All of these, too, are key documents, and will have to be looked for elsewhere. There are motion pictures (how I wish I could include Pare Lorentz's *The Plow That Broke the Plains*), recordings, photographs, and all can become part of a course in History of American Journalism—if the professor can persuade his school that the course is worth more than one semester, or, I am told, one quarter in some universities.

I anticipate certain criticisms. Some readers will feel that I have ignored important documents. Others will wonder why something is considered important. Others will be troubled because I have taken something—Horace Greeley's "Prayer of Twenty Millions" comes to mind—and cut it back. I accept the criticisms, and I know that were I called upon to review such a book, I would ask why certain things were done, or not done. After much soul-searching, I decided *not* to include many legal documents. These exist elsewhere, and the subject seemed for me almost unmanageable. There are few governmental reports, although some from recent years seemed necessary. There is not much in the way of press criticism, another huge area. And I freely confess that some of the things I include are trash, but there has been trash in our journalistic past.

One thing that limited me somewhat, and I might as well get to the matter right now, is the problem of copyright permissions. There are a good many things I wanted to include, or to use at greater length, but the financial demands seemed exorbitant, and I did not want to mortgage the old homestead just to get a book of readings in print, important as the book is to me. In some cases I have made substitutions, feeling that certain pieces of writings have acquired reputations a bit more extravagant than they warrant.

I dedicate this book to my students, especially those who care about history as I care about it. The book is for them—and for those I might be teaching were I on some other campus. May they enjoy what they read here (at least some of it), and may it be almost as important in their lives as the latest popular songs.

CALDER M. PICKETT
Lawrence, Kansas

VOICES OF THE PAST

A TRADITION FROM THE OLD WORLD

It was the age we call the Renaissance, and the age we call the Reformation. The beginnings of journalism, in the Anglo-American tradition, belong to both ages. It was a time of towering figures: Columbus and Cortez; Michelangelo, Leonardo, and Raphael; Shakespeare and Milton and Cervantes; Erasmus, Luther, and Calvin; Henry VIII, Elizabeth I, and Charles I; Cromwell and Thomas More. It was the age, too, of Johann Gutenberg and of William Caxton. They were the supreme figures in the early history of printing, and though commentators from Erasmus to Henry J. Raymond of the *New York Times* may have been extravagant in praising the invention of printing as the greatest of all inventions there is little doubt that it was at least among the greatest. We do not need to be told that printing, in some forms, already existed elsewhere before Gutenberg invented movable type; we do not need to be told that someone somewhere would have invented such type had Gutenberg not done so. The overpowering historical fact is that sometime about 1450 movable type did come about, and that all the journalism we have had since then, including the journalism of the electronic media of the twentieth century, owes something to a printer of Mainz, Germany, named Gutenberg.

The way in which printing and journalism relate to the Renaissance is in the spreading of knowledge, in the new demand for books, in the breaking away of learning from the exclusive domain of the church. And the word *church* suggests, too, the relationship of printing and journalism to the Reformation, for printing spread the frightening and revolutionary ideas of the German Luther and the French Calvin, and then of their followers elsewhere on the continent and in Great Britain.

This anthology is not a history of printing, but it is necessary that we begin with Gutenberg in examining the documents of our journalism, and the story moves from Germany to England, where in 1476 a man named William Caxton installed in Westminster the types and perhaps the press that he had brought back from Europe. Caxton had gone to Bruges, Belgium, as a merchant, and had visited Cologne, where he may have seen a printing press set up by one Ulrich Zell, who had learned the craft in Mainz. Back in Westminster, which is now part of modern-day London, Caxton began to do his printing, one of his notable publications being *The Noble Histories of King Arthur and of Certain of His Knights,* which had been written sixteen years earlier by Sir Thomas Malory. But Caxton did not found a newspaper; nor did other Englishmen for much more than a century.

This does not mean that no journalism existed. As long as one person can convey news—information, intelligence, maybe rumor—to another person, there will be journalism. The reporting of news existed in part in the form of newsletters sent from foreign cities back to England. It existed in the form of the ballad. But readers in the twentieth century must permit their minds and imaginations to move back to a time in which transportation was still incredibly slow, when communication in the modern sense of the word did not exist, when printing processes were slow and laborious, when learning was restricted to a tiny elite, when the cities of Europe were much smaller than those of today. The very word *newspaper* seems a misnomer when one compares a giant of the 1970s with those primitive news sheets that came into being in the time of James I, Charles I, and Cromwell.

It is likely that journalism students will be the main readers of the anthology, and such students, impatient with stilted style, wishing to move along more rapidly to the exciting reading of the 1960s and 1970s, may be a bit bored with some of the early documents that make up the Anglo-American tradition. It may come as a shock, in these days when we attempt to pay homage to so many different cultural traditions, that so much attention is paid to what is sometimes called the "mother country," but no story of our journalism can be told, no examination of our principal documents can be made, without taking time to see what journalism was like in England in the early days of printing. For the colonization of America coincided with the development of journalism in England, and the very presses and type and names of newspapers, the very makeup (if such a word can be used to describe these odd old publications), came to us from England.

So it is in England that the story must begin.

It must begin, in fact, with some sampling of how those founding fathers, and at least one mother, wrote in Old England. Though we are told that the first newspaper was not printed until December 2, 1620, that it bore no name, and was printed not even in England but in Holland, it is "ballad journalism," not print journalism, that is our first document. Such journalism was, really, a forerunner of the mass journalism we know today. Imagine the newsboys who stood on street corners in pre-television days and shouted out the news of the day (a kidnaped child, a dead president, a war declared); imagine the beatniks in the North Beach area of San Francisco who sold their poetry on the streets in the late 1950s; imagine singing out a melody in fifteenth or sixteenth century England, the kind that perhaps Joan Baez or Judy Collins sang in the 1960s. This is ballad journalism. Ballad journalism was on broadsheets, and these sheets had subject matter like that of today's tabloids—or of the Bible or Shakespeare or the *Morte d'Arthur*—crime, disaster, scandal, war, royal death, tournaments, witchcraft, plagues. As the English dramatist Thomas Middleton wrote in 1620, the ballad monger never lacked for a subject: "one hangs himself today, another drowns himself tomorrow, a sergeant stabbed next day; here a pettifogger a' the pillory, a bawd in the cart's nose, a pander in the tail; *hic mulier, haec vir,* fashions, fictions, felonies, fooleries;—a hundred havens has the ballad-monger to traffic at, and new ones still daily discovered." One of the ballad writers was William Elderton, who was performing in tavern and on the street in the last quarter of the sixteenth century.

† † †

MY LADIE MARQUES

By William Elderton, in Arundell Esdaile, "Autolycus Pack: The Ballad Journalism of the Sixteenth Century," reprinted in Edwin H. Ford and Edwin Emery, *Highlights in the History of the American Press* (Minneapolis: University of Minnesota Press, 1954).

Ladies, I think you marvell that
　I writ no mery report to you,
And what is the cause I court it not
　So merye as I was wont to doe;
Alas, I let you understand,
　It is no newes for me to show;
The fairest flower of my garland
　Was caught from Court a great while agoe.

For, under the roufe of sweete Saint Paull
　There lyeth my Ladie buried in claye,
Where I make memory for her soule
　With weepinge eyes once evere daye;
All other sights I have forgot
　That ever in court I joyed to see;
And that is the cause I court it not
　So mery as I was wont to be . . .

But sure I am, ther liveth yet
　In court a dearer frinde to mee,
Whome I to sarve am so unfit,
　I am sure the like will never bee;

For I with all that I can dooe,
Unworthie most maie seeme to bee,
To undoo the latchet of her shooe;
Yet will I come to courte and see.

Then have amongste ye once again;
Faint harts faire ladies never win:
*I trust ye will consider my payne
When any good venison cometh in.*

† † †

Histories of journalism record that it was in Holland, and not in England, that the first sheets of foreign news were printed in the English language. What is usually considered to be the first news-sheet in English appeared December 2, 1620, in Amsterdam, with neither title nor headline, but describing the battle of Weissenberg, near Prague, fought November 8 and resulting in the defeat of Frederick, Elector of the Palatinate and head of the Protestant Union. That defeat marked the start of the Thirty Years' War. Other news-sheets have survived from that period, bearing such names as *Corrant out of Italy, Germany, &c; Corante, or Newes from Italy, Germanie, Hungarie, Spaine and France; Courant Newes out of Italy, Germany, Bohemia, Poland, &c.* These sheets consisted entirely of foreign news, and they dealt largely with developments in the Thirty Years' War. The earliest extant prototype of the newspaper is described as a coranto, published by Nicholas Bourne, on September 24, 1621. The first page of a single-sheet coranto, printed in Amsterdam in July, 1621, contains such "intelligence" as the following:

† † †

CONTENTS OF A SINGLE-SHEET CORANTO

Corante, or, Newes from Italy, Germanie, Hungarie, Spaine and France, July, 1621.

FROM LYONS THE 6 OF JUNE 1621

Our King in person lies before S. *John Dengely,* wherein the Duke of Roans brother is governour; whereof the Towne issued out 2. mile towards their enemie: *First Beauneant* regiment, and after them a company of light horsemen, after that a truce for 8. dayes was made therein to intreate for peace; in the meane time preparation is made to besiege Rochell, and the Duke *de Guise* is gon to Marsellis, there to prepare an armie by Sea, to besiege Rochell by water. . . .

FROM VENICE THE 21 OF JUNE 1621

From Millane it is written, that although there hath 2. commillions already bin sent out of Spaine to restore Valtelnta again; the governour to the contrarie sends more men thether, . . .

FROM LENSSCH IN HUNGARIE THE 4. OF JUNE, 1621

Heere is great trouble, there are 400 Dutch souldiers in the Towne, and there shall 1200 more come, which will trouble us much. . . .

† † †

The student of today may observe the peculiarities of spelling and of punctuation, and would be confused by the letter s that looks like the letter f, and by the very printing processes themselves. Besides such news-sheets, other brands of journalism existed in those grand old days of the Tudors and the Stuarts, of Privy Council and Stationers' Company and Star Chamber, of kings beheaded and courts troubled, of royal wars and religious wars. Such brands of journalism existed concurrently. In 1622 one of those forms called the "newsbook" originated, the first of this curious species carrying the distinguished name of *Mercurius Gallobellicus,* with others having names similar to those we see on newspapers today: *Courant, Newes, Post, Gazette, Intelligencer.* The sample from a newsbook in this collection is from a heavy tome—heavy in language, at least—called *Mercurius Diutinus, Collector of the Affaires of Great Britaine: And Martiall Proceedings in Europe, From Wed. the. 3. of Feb. to Wed. the 10. of February, 1646* (and the spelling and punctuation come directly from the first page in this book). As a modern reader will readily guess, such a newsbook was not likely to reach the person who would listen with great interest to a ballad.

† † †

A NEWSBOOK OF THE SEVENTEENTH CENTURY

Mercurius Diutinus, February 3-10, 1646.

Scarres were valued the richest apparel, Mountaines the strongest fortifications and Ploughs the most healthfull exercise, by the old victorious Romans. This may be the glory of England, have we but the hearts to make use of the opportunity, and not suffer our selves to be distracted with Tiffany Curtizans. If the King and Parliament agree (which is hopefull) then (God giving a blessing) whom should we fear: and that is in a fair way.

We had this day this account from Newcastle, that on Saturday, January 30. the English Commissioners received the King into their charge; and according to their instructions had signified so much to the two Houses of Parliament. They had some consultations for the safe conduct of his Majesty to Holmby house, and concerning what convoy they should desire of Major General Skippon for that purpose: They displeased Mr. Murrey and divers others of the Kings Bedchamber and Priviechamber, who have taken up armes and are disaffected to the Parliament, and have placed those sent by the Parliament to wait on his Majesty to Holdenby house and suffer no Malignants or ill affected persons to come at the King. The Commissioners remove to Mr. Lyddles house, and both theirs and all his Majesties quarters to Holdenby, watch themselves by turne, some sharpe words his Majesty hath spoken to some of his new attendants, but I had rather sway the questions then repeat them....

✝ ✝ ✝

Such a newsbook appeared in a time of trouble, a time of controversy. The Stuarts, not greatly loved in England, did indeed sit upon an uneasy throne. The Separatists, who wanted complete separation from the Church of England, were fleeing Britain, some of them camping out in Holland, some landing on the Massachusetts coast in 1620. The Puritans, who wanted to "purify" the church that Henry VIII had created when he broke with Rome, were asserting themselves even more; some of them, too, would go to the new world, and others would establish themselves in control of the government during the Commonwealth, which came into being when Charles I was executed in 1649 and Oliver Cromwell began to exert his own form of despotism. In those days licensing was a common practice, licensing of printers and publishers, and one of the Puritans, the poet John Milton, took exception to the practice in 1644, when he published his *Areopagitica,* a work written in opposition to the practice of licensing, a document whose language, whose assertion of the principles of truth and free speech, has universal meaning. It is sad, then, to note that when the Puritans took over the government that none other than John Milton should become their chief censor. Let this not detract, however, from an appreciation of this excerpt from his deservedly famous document:

✝ ✝ ✝

AREOPAGITICA

By John Milton, 1644, in Henry Morley ed., *English Prose Writings of John Milton* (London: George Routledge and Sons, 1889), pp. 341-349.

... Truth indeed came once into the world with her divine master, and was a perfect shape most glorious to look on: but when he ascended, and his apostles after him were laid asleep, then straight arose a wicked race of deceivers, who as that story goes of the

Egyptian Typhon with his conspirators, how they dealt with the good Osiris, took the virgin Truth, hewed her lovely form into a thousand pieces, and scattered them to the four winds. From that time ever since, the sad friends of Truth, such as dare appear, imitating the careful search that Isis made for the mangled body of Osiris, went up and down gathering up limb by limb still as they could find them. We have not yet found them all, Lords and Commons, nor ever shall do, till her Master's second coming; he shall bring together every joint and member, and shall mold them into an immortal feature of loveliness and perfection. Suffer not these licensing prohibitions to stand at every place of opportunity forbidding and disturbing them that continue seeking, that continue to do our obsequies to the torn body of our martyred saint . . .

Methinks I see in my mind a noble and puissant nation rousing herself like a strong man after sleep, and shaking her invincible locks: Methinks I see her as an eagle mewing her mighty youth, and kindling her undazzled eyes at the full midday beam; purging and unscaling her long abused sight at the fountain itself of heavenly radiance, while the whole noise of timorous and flocking birds, with those also that love the twilight, flutter about, amazed at what she means, and in their envious gabble would prognosticate a year of sects and schisms.

What should ye do then, should ye suppress all this flowery crop of knowledge and new light sprung up and yet springing daily in this city, should ye set an oligarchy of twenty ingrossers over it, to bring a famine upon our minds again, when we shall know nothing but what is measured to us by their bushel? Believe it, Lords and Commons, they who counsel ye to such a suppressing, do as good as bid ye suppress yourselves; and I will soon show how. If it be desired to know the immediate cause of all this free writing and free speaking, there can not be assigned a truer than your own mild, and free, and human government: it is the liberty, Lords and Commons, which your own valorous and happy counsels have purchased us, liberty which is the nurse of all great wits; this is that which hath rarified and enlightened our spirits like the influence of heaven; this is that which hath enfranchised, enlarged and lifted up our apprehensions degrees above themselves. Ye can not make us now less capable, less knowing, less eagerly pursuing of the truth, unless ye first make yourselves, that made us so, less the lovers, less the founders of our true liberty. We can grow ignorant again, brutish, formal, and slavish, as ye found us; but ye then must first become that which ye can not be, oppressive, arbitrary, and tyrannous, as they were from whom ye have freed us. That our hearts are now more capacious, our thoughts more erected to the search and expectation of great and exact things, is the issue of your own virtue propagated in us; ye can not suppress that unless ye reinforce an abrogated and merciless law, that fathers may despatch at will their own children. And who shall then stick closest to ye, and excite others? not he who takes up arms for cote and conduct, and his four nobles of Danegelt. Although I dispraise not the defense of just immunities, yet love my

10

peace better, if that were all. Give me the liberty to know, to utter, and to argue freely according to conscience, above all liberties.

What would be best advised then, if it be found so hurtful and so unequal to suppress opinions for the newness, or the unsuitableness to a customary acceptance, will not be my task to say; I only shall repeat what I have learned from one of your own honorable number, a right noble and pious lord, who had he not sacrificed his life and fortunes to the church and commonwealth, we had not now missed and bewailed a worthy and undoubted patron of this argument. Ye know him I am sure; yet I for honor's sake, and may it be eternal to him, shall name him, the Lord Brook. He writing of episcopacy, and by the way treating of sects and schisms, left ye his vote, or rather now the last words of his dying charge, which I know will ever be of dear and honored regard with ye, so full of meekness and breathing charity, that next to his last testament, who bequeathed love and peace to his disciples, I can not call to mind where I have read or heard words more mild and peaceful. He there exhorts us to hear with patience and humility those, however they be miscalled, that desire to live purely, in such a use of God's ordinances, as the best guidance of their conscience gives them, and to tolerate them, though in some disconformity to ourselves. The book itself will tell us more at large being published to the world, and dedicated to the Parliament by him who both for his life and for his death deserves, that what advice he left be not laid by without perusal.

And now the time in special is, by privilege to write and speak what may help to the further discussion of matters in agitation. The temple of Janus with his two controversial faces might now not unsignificantly be set open. And though all the winds of doctrine were let loose to play upon the earth, so truth be in the field, we do injuriously by licensing and prohibiting to misdoubt her strength. Let her and falsehood grapple; who ever knew truth put to the worse, in a free and open encounter? Her confuting is the best and surest suppressing. He who hears what praying there is for light and clearer knowledge to be sent down among us, would think of other matters to be constituted beyond the discipline of Geneva, framed and fabricated already to our hands. Yet when the new light which we beg for shines in upon us, there be who envy, and oppose, if it come not first in at their casements. What a collusion is this, whenas we are exhorted by the wise man to use diligence, *to seek for wisdom as for hidden treasures early and late,* that another order shall enjoin us to know nothing but by statute. When a man hath been laboring the hardest labor in the deep mines of knowledge, hath furnished out his findings in all their equipage, drawn forth his reasons as it were a battle ranged, scattered and defeated all objections in his way, calls out his adversary into the plain, offers him the advantage of wind and sun, if he please; only that he may try the matter by dint and argument, for his opponents then to skulk, to lay ambushments, to keep a narrow bridge of licensing where the challenger should pass, though it be valor enough in soldiership, is but weakness and cowardice in the wars of truth. For who knows not that truth is strong next to the Almighty; she needs no policies, no stratagems, no licensings to make her victorious, those are the shifts and the defenses that error uses against her power: give her but room, and do not bind her when she sleeps, for then she speaks not true, as the old Proteus did, who spake oracles only when he was caught and bound, but then rather she turns herself into all shapes, except her own, and perhaps tunes her voice according to the time, as *Micaiah* did before Ahab, until she be adjured into her own likeness. Yet is it not impossible that she may have more shapes than one. What else is all that rank of things indifferent, wherein truth may be on this side, or on the other, without being unlike herself? What but a vain shadow else is the abolition of those *ordinances, that handwriting nailed to the cross,* what great purchase is this Christian liberty which *Paul* so often boasts of? His doctrine is, that he who eats or eats not, regards a day, or regards it not, may do either to the Lord. How many other things might be tolerated in peace, and left to conscience, had we but charity, and were it not the chief stronghold of our hypocrisy to be ever judging one another. . . .

† † †

We move from John Milton to a form surely more understandable to the modern-day reader—the newspaper. Again, it would be well to erase from the mind any impression of today's *New York Times* or even today's *Wall Street Journal* (whose makeup *is* a bit similar to that of early times). On November 16, 1665, there came the single-sheet, semi-weekly *Oxford Gazette,* the first truly modern newspaper in England, and one which became the *London Gazette,* official paper of the British court (the court had moved to Oxford because of the black plague, but then returned to its home base). Henry Muddiman was the editor, and he printed his paper on both sides of a half-sheet, with two columns to the page, and he used the word "paper" to distinguish the journal from a "book." This excerpt was in the *Gazette* in 1680, several years after the founding of the paper.

† † †

THE FIRST MODERN ENGLISH NEWSPAPER

London Gazette, June 14-17, 1680.

MOSCOW, APRIL 27

The person which this Court had sent privately to *Constantinople,* to learn the Sentiments of the Grand Signior and the Divan, concerning a Peace, is returned with an account, That according to the best Information he could get, the Grand Signior was resolved not to depart from his demand of having all the *Ukraine,* from the *Black Sea* to the *Boristkenes,* yielded to him; and that besides, he pretended satisfaction for the Charges of the War: Whereupon the Czar, after having consulted with his Principal Ministers and Officers, has resolved to send a second Embassy to Poland, to strengthen the Negotiation of the Ministers he has already at that Court, as likewise to send an Ambassador to *France,* to demand the Alliance of that King against the Turks, and in consideration thereof to offer his Subjects several advantageous Priviledges in their Commerce.

Warsaw, May 28. This Week arrived here an Express sent by the Resident of this Crown at *Constantinople,* to acquaint his Majesty, That he had good grounds to believe that the *Ottoman* Forces would Advance this Summer to the Frontiers of this Kingdom, That their Army would be much more considerable then was now believed, That Orders had been sent to *Mahomet Bassa,* who lyes encamped with an Army on the *Dannube,* to Detach 20000 men to joyn with the *Tartars,* That the Turks had Built two Bridges over the River *Niester* for the Passage of their Army; And that the Hospedar of *Walachia* did make great Provision of Victuals, which he sent to Caminiec to be kept in the Magazines there for the use of the Turkish Army. . . .

† † †

Foreign news clearly was a major commodity in those pioneering English journals. History pays special attention to the word "first," though one hesitates to use a word that seemingly is so irrefutable. Henry Muddiman's *London Gazette* was the first modern newspaper; Elizabeth Mallet's *Daily Courant* was the first English daily, started March 11, 1702. It was a single small sheet, printed on one side; the editor wrote, "This Courant (as the title shows) will be Publish'd Daily: being design'd to give all the Material News as soon as every Post arrives: and is confin'd to half the Compass, to save the Publick at least half the Impertinences, of ordinary News-Papers." Mrs. Mallet's time with her *Daily Courant* was brief, she having abandoned it after two weeks, with publication resumed by Samuel Buckley.

† † †

THE FIRST DAILY NEWSPAPER

The *Daily Courant,* March 11, 1702.

NAPLES, FEB. 22

On Wednesday last, our New Viceroy, the Duke of Escalona, arriv'd here with a Squadron of the Galleys of Sicily. He made his Entrance drest in a French habit; and to give us the greater Hopes of the King's coming hither, went to Lodge in one of the little Palaces, leaving the Royal one for his Majesty. The Marquis of Grigni is also arriv'd here with a Regiment of French.

ROME, FEB. 25

In a Military Congregation of State that was held here, it was Resolv'd to draw a Line from Ascoli to the Borders of the Ecclesiastical State, thereby to hinder the Incursions of the Transalpine Troops. Orders are sent to Civita Vecchia to fit out the Galleys, and to strengthen the Garrison of that Place. Signior Casali is made Governor of Perugia. The Marquis del Vasto, and the Prince de Caserta continue still in the Imperial Embassador's Palace, where his Excellency has a Guard of 50 Men every Night in Arms. The King of Purtugal has def[?] the Arch-Bishoprick of Lisbon, vacant by the Death of Cardinal Sousa, for the Infante his second Son, who is about 11 Years old. . . .

† † †

For another sampling of journalistic style in England, and one quite different from the foregoing, we turn to the editor of the best known of the essay papers—little magazines, really—Joseph Addison of *The Spectator*. In 1711 and 1712, and again in 1714, *The Spectator* was appearing, a publication that represented the flowering of thought in those opening years of what we now call the Enlightenment. It was a time in which journalistic style reached new heights, when social, moral, literary, political, economic, and religious ideas were bandied about in the taverns and coffeehouses of London, where gentlemen like Addison, his sometime partner Richard Steele, Daniel Defoe of *Robinson Crusoe* and Jonathan Swift of *Gulliver's Travels* gathered—to drink and argue and, by some accounts of the time, pursue the women a bit—"wenching," they called it in *Tom Jones*'s day. Our excerpt from *The Spectator* is dated Tuesday, January 22, 1712, and it may puzzle some readers that its impact could have been so considerable, but we must remember that the literary and journalistic tastes of the late twentieth century are somewhat different from those of almost three hundred years ago. So make an effort to understand why. "A Coquette's Heart" so enraptured readers, and so influenced writing style not only in England but in the colonies as well.

† † †

A COQUETTE'S HEART

The Spectator, No. 281, Tuesday, January 22, 1712.
Pectoribus inhians spirantia consulit exta.—Virgil's *Aenead* iv. 64.
Anxious the reeking entrails he consults.

Having already given an account of the dissection of a beau's head, with the several discoveries made on that occasion; I shall here, according to my promise, enter upon the dissection of a coquette's heart, and communicate to the public such particularities as we observed in that curious piece of anatomy.

I should perhaps have waived this undertaking, had not I been put in mind of my promise by several of my unknown correspondents, who are very importunate with me to make an example of the coquette, as I have already done of the beau. It is therefore, in compliance with the request of friends, that I have looked over the minutes of my former dream, in order to give the public an exact relation of it, which I shall enter upon without farther preface.

Our operator, before he engaged in this visionary dissection, told us that there was nothing in his art more difficult than to lay open the heart of a coquette, by reason of the many labyrinths and recesses which are to be found in it, and which do not appear in the heart of any other animal.

He desired us first of all to observe the pericardium, or outward case of the heart, which we did very attentively; and by the help of our glasses discerned in it millions of little scars, which seemed to have been occasioned by the points of innumerable darts and arrows, that from time to time had glanced upon the outward coat; though we could not discover the smallest orifice by which any of them had entered and pierced the inward substance.

Every smatterer in anatomy knows that this pericardium, or case of the heart, contains in it a thin reddish liquor, supposed to be bred from the vapours which exhale out of the heart, and being stopped here, are condensed into this watery substance. Upon examining this liquor, we found that it had in it all the qualities of that spirit which is made use of in the thermometer to show the change of weather.

Nor must I here omit an experiment one of the company assured us he himself had made with this liquor, which he found in great quantity about the heart of a coquette whom he had formerly dissected. He affirmed to us, that he had actually inclosed it in a small tube made after the manner of a weather-glass; but that, instead of acquainting him with the variations of the atmosphere, it showed him the qualities of those persons who entered the room where it stood. He affirmed also, that it rose at the approach of a plume of feathers, an embroidered coat, or a pair of fringed gloves; and that it fell as soon as an ill-shaped periwig, a clumsy pair of shoes, or an unfashionable coat came into his house. Nay, he proceeded so far as to assure us, that upon his laughing aloud when he stood by it, the liquor mounted very sensibly, and immediately sunk again upon his looking serious. In short, he told us that he knew very well by this invention, whenever he had a man of sense or a coxcomb in his room.

Having cleared away the pericardium, or the case, and liquor above mentioned, we came to the heart itself. The outward surface of it was extremely slippery, and the mucro, or point, so very cold withal, that upon endeavouring to take hold of it, it glided through the fingers like a smooth piece of ice.

The fibres were turned and twisted in a more intricate and perplexed manner than they are usually found in other hearts; insomuch that the whole heart was wound up together like a

Gordian knot, and must have had very irregular and unequal motions, while it was employed in its vital function.

One thing we thought very observable, namely, that upon examining all the vessels which came into it, or issued out of it, we could not discover any communication that it had with the tongue.

We could not but take notice likewise that several of those little nerves in the heart which are affected by the sentiments of love, hatred, and other passions, did not descend to this before us from the brain, but from the muscles which lie about the eye.

Upon weighing the heart in my hand, I found it to be extremely light, and consequently very hollow, which I did not wonder at, when, upon looking into the inside of it, I saw multitudes of cells and cavities running one within another, as our historians describe the apartments of Rosamond's bower. Several of these little hollows were stuffed with innumerable sorts of trifles, which I shall forbear giving any particular account of, and shall, therefore, only take notice of what lay first and uppermost, which, upon our unfolding it, and applying our microscopes to it, appeared to be a flame-coloured hood.

We are informed that the lady of this heart, when living, received the addresses of several who made love to her, and did not only give each of them encouragement, but made everyone she conversed with believe that she regarded him with an eye of kindness; for which reason we expected to have seen the impression of multitudes of faces among the several plaits and foldings of the heart; but to our great surprise not a single print of this nature discovered itself till we came into the very core and centre of it. We there observed a little figure, which, upon applying our glasses to it, appeared dressed in a very fantastic manner. The more I looked upon it, the more I thought I had seen the face before, but could not possibly recollect either the place or time; when at length one of the company, who had examined this figure more nicely than the rest, showed us plainly by the make of its face, and the several turns of its features, that the little idol which was thus lodged in the very middle of the heart was the deceased beau, whose head I gave some account of in my last Tuesday's paper.

As soon as we had finished our dissection, we resolved to make an experiment of the heart, not being able to determine among ourselves the nature of its substance, which differed in so many particulars from that in the heart of other females. Accordingly, we laid it into a pan of burning coals, when we observed in it a certain salamandrine quality, that made it capable of living in the midst of fire and flame, without being consumed or so much as singed.

As we were admiring this strange phenomenon, and standing round the heart in a circle, it gave a most prodigious sigh, or rather crack, and dispersed all at once in smoke and vapour. This imaginary noise, which methought was louder than the burst of a cannon, produced such a violent shake in my brain, that it dissipated the fumes of sleep, and left me in an instant broad awake.

† † †

Of surpassing importance is a final document drawn from the
"Anglo" part of Anglo-American journalism—one of those publications called *Cato's Letters*. These, written by John Trenchard and
Thomas Gordon, and signed "Cato," appeared weekly from 1720 to
1723, first in the *London Journal*, then in the *British Journal*, and
finally in newspapers in both England and America. Trenchard and
Gordon discussed theories of liberty and of representative government, and their letters were especially popular in the colonies, where
both James Franklin and John Peter Zenger, editors we shall
encounter shortly, gave them wide currency. There is little doubt
that the letters helped to synthesize the thinking that resulted in the
pre-Revolution pamphleteering and in the Declaration of Independence.

† † †

A DISCUSSION OF LIBELS

Cato's Letters, No. 32, as reprinted in the *New York Weekly Journal*,
February 28 and March 4, 1734, in Leonard W. Levy, ed., *Freedom
of the Press from Zenger to Jefferson* (Indianapolis: Bobbs-Merrill,
1966), pp. 14-17.

Mr. Zenger;

As Libeling seems at Present the Topick that is canvassed both at
Court and among the People, I must beg you will insert in your
weekly Journal, the following Sentiment of CATO, upon that
Subject, and you'll oblige

Your Humble Servant, &c,

A Libel is not the less a Libel for being true, this may seem a
contradiction; but it is neither one in Law, or in common Sense.
There are some Truths not fit to be told; where, for Example, the
Discovery of a finall Fault may do mischief; or where the Discovery
of a great Fault can do no good, there ought to be no discovery at all,
and to make Faults where there are none is still worse.

But this Doctrine only holds true as to private and personal
failings; and it is quite otherwise when the Crimes of Men come to
Affect the Publick. Nothing ought to be so dear to us as our Country,
and nothing ought to come in Competition with its Interests. Every
crime against the publick, is a great crime, tho' there be some greater
then others. Ignorance and Folly may be pleaded in Alleviation of
private Offences; but when they come to be publick Offences, they
loose all Benefit of such a Plea; we are then no longer to consider, to
what Causes they are owing, but what Evils they may produce, and
here we shall readily find, that Folly has overturned States, and
private Interest been the parent of publick Confusion.

The exposing therefore of publick Wickedness, as it is a Duty
which every Man owes to Truth and his Country, can never be a

Libel in the nature of things; and they who call it so, make themselves no Complement; he who is affronted at the reading of the Ten Commandments would make the Decalogue a Libel, if he durst, but he Tempts us at the same Time to form a Judgment of his Life and Morals, not at all to his Advantage: Whoever calls publick and necessary Truths Libels, does apprise us of his own Character, and Arms us with Caution against his Designs.

I have long thought, that the World are very much mistaken in their Idea and Distinction of Libels, it has been hitherto generally understood, that there was no other libels but those against Magistrates and those against private Men. Now to me there seems to be a Third sort of Libels, full as Destructive as any of the former can probably be, I mean Libels against the People. It was otherwise at Athens and Rome, where the particular Men, and even great Men, were often treated with much Freedom and Severity, when they deserved it; yet the People, the body of the People, were spoken of with the utmost Regard and Reverence. *The Sacred Priviledge of the People, the Inviolable Majesty of the People, the awful Authority of the People, and the unappealable Judgment of the People,* were phrases Common in these wise, great and free Cities.

Some will tell us, this is setting up the Mob for Statesmen, and for the censurers of States. The word Mob does not at all move me, on this Occasion, nor weaken the Ground I go upon, it is certain that the whole People, who are the Publick, are the best Judges, whether Things go ill or well, with the publick. It is true they can't all of them see distant Dangers, nor watch the Motions nor guess the designs of neighbouring States: But every Cobler can Judge as well as a Statesman, whether he can fit peaceably in his Stall; whether he is paid for his Work; whether the Market where he buys his Victuals is well provided; and whether a Dragoon, or a parish Officer comes to him for his Taxes, if he pays any.

In short the People often Judge better than their Superiors, and have not so many Biasses to Judge wrong, and Politicians often rail at the People, chiefly because they have given the People occasion to rail: Those Ministers who cannot make the People their Friends, it is to be shrewdly suspected, do not deserve their Friendship.

I have indeed often wondered that the Inveighing against the Interest of the People, and calling their Liberty in Question, as has been and is commonly done amongst us, by old Knaves, and young Fools, has never been made an Express Crime.

I must own, I know not what Reason is if sapping and betraying the Liberties of a People be not Treason, in the Eternal and Original Nature of Things: Let it be remembered for whose sake Government is, or could be appointed, and then let it be considered, who are more to be regarded, the Governours, or the governed. They indeed owe one another mutual Duties; but if there are any Transgressions committed, the Side that is most obliged ought Doubtless to bear the Most; and yet it is so far otherwise, that almost all over the Earth, the People for one Injury they do their Governors, receive Ten Thousand from them. Nay, in some Countries it is made Death and Damnation, not to bear all the Oppressions and Cruelties, which Men made Wanton by Power inflict upon those that gave it them.

The Truth is, if the People are suffered to keep their own, it is the most they Desire: But even this is a Happiness which in few Places falls to their Lot; they are frequently robbed by those whom they pay to protect them. I know it is a general Charge against the People, that they are *Turbulent, Restless, Fickle,* and *Unruly,* than which there be nothing more untrue; for they are only so when they are made so, as for their being Turbulent, it is false, since there is scarce an Example in a 100 Years of any Peoples giving Governours any Uneasiness, till their Governours had made them uneasy; Nay, for the most Part, they bear many Evils without returning one, and seldom throw off their Burthens so long as they can stand under them.

† † †

2

EARLY JOURNALISM IN A NEW LAND

Colonial journalism, to put it plainly, was not distinguished.

With, that is, an exception or so which shall be accounted for in due time.

Our founding fathers had things other than printing and journalism on their minds. They reached Virginia and Massachusetts—or what we call Virginia and Massachusetts today—and busied themselves with various pursuits: tilling the land, which in New England, at least, tended to be rocky; fighting disease and starvation; planting crops; building businesses and shipping fleets; fighting Indians. That irreverent latter-day journalist, H. L. Mencken, who was certainly no Puritan, wrote that "When the Pilgrim Fathers landed, they fell upon their knees—and then upon the aborigines."

And those founding fathers were paying homage to the Lord. Such was their major concern, and it bore importantly upon the letters and the journalism that came into being. If we seem to oversimplify, again, in stressing the English, it is that it was mainly the English tradition from which we drew. The Spaniards had been first in the new world, from Columbus on: the conquistadors, Cortez and Pizarro, who despoiled Mexico and Peru and destroyed mighty cultures; Balboa, who went to the Pacific; Magellan, who made it part way around the world; DeSoto, who discovered the Mississippi; Coronado, who explored the American Southwest—all these storied soldiers, with a few priests along, who seemed interested mainly in gold. The French had gone to what we now call the Midwest, and to Canada; and there were settlements of Dutch, of Swedes and Finns, and from 1619 on there were Negroes. These explorers and salvation-seeking souls spread out mainly along the eastern coast; a map of the American colonies on the eve of the Revolution shows thin settlement only, and we must once again adjust our thinking so that we do not see eighteenth century America in twentieth century terms.

Our English forefathers settled in Virginia in 1607, in present-day Massachusetts in 1620 and on through the decade, and then to other settlements in the century that followed. The point, so far as journalism in America is concerned, is that these settlers were not occupied with things like printing presses and newspapers, though a press was installed at Harvard College in Cambridge in 1639, and it, we may assume, ground out such things as the *New England Primer:* "In *Adam's* Fall/We sinned all," through "*Zacheus* he/Did climb the Tree/His Lord to see." Other presses followed, and of course our colonial printers did not know that far to the south, in Mexico City, printing was already in existence. Not until 1690, on Thursday, September 25, did the northern colonies have a newspaper, and that one was published for one day only, for its editor-publisher-printer, a gadfly named Benjamin Harris, had not obtained royal sanction. He was promptly suppressed, for his newspaper "contained Reflections of a very high nature" and "sundry doubtful and uncertain Reports." The twentieth century reader, thinking perhaps of the content of the underground newspapers of our time, will look into Harris's paper with some mystification, for it all seems so innocent, this little three-page journal that he called *Publick Occurrences, Both Forreign and Domestick.* Here is a bit of the trouble-maker named Benjamin Harris:

† † †

BENJAMIN HARRIS'S BRIEF EXPERIMENT

Publick Occurrences, Both Forreign and Domestick,
September 25, 1690.

The Christianized Indians in some parts of Plimouth, have newly appointed a day of Thanksgiving to God for his Mercy in supplying their extream and pinching Necessities under their late want of Corn, & for His giving them now a prospect of a very Comfortable Harvest. Their Example may be worth Mentioning.

Tis observed by the Husbandmen, that altho the With-draw of so great a strength from them, as what is in the Forces lately gone for Canada, made them think it almost impossible for them to get well through the Affairs of their Husbandry at this time of the year, yet the Season has been so unusually favourable that they scarce find any want of the many hundreds of hands, that are gone from them; which is looked upon as a Merciful Providence.

While the barbarous Indians were lurking about Chelmsford, there were missing about the beginning of this month a couple of Children belonging to a man of that Town, one of them aged about eleven, the other aged about nine years, both of them supposed to be fallen into the hands of the Indians.

A very Tragical Accident happened at Water-Town, the beginning of this Month, an Old man, that was of somewhat a Silent and Morose Temper, but one that had long enjoyed the reputation of a Sober and [illegible] Man, having newly buried his Wife, The Devil took advantage of the Melancholy which he therupon fell into, his Wives discretion and industry had long been the support of his Family, and he seemed hurried with an impertinent fear that he should now come to want before he dyed, though he had very careful friends to look after him who kept a strict eye upon him, least he should do himself any harm. But one evening escaping from them into the Cow-house, they there quickly followed him found him hanging by a Rope, which they had used to tye their Calves withal, he was dead with his feet near touching the Ground.

Epidemical Fevers and Agues grow very common, in some parts of the Country, whereof, tho' many dye, nor yet they are sorely unfitted for their imployments; but in some parts a more malignant Fever seems to prevail in such sort that it usually goes thro' a Family where it comes, and proves Mortal unto many.

The Small-pox which has been raging in Boston, after a manner very Extraordinary, is now very much abated. It is thought that far more have been sick of it than were visited with it, when it raged so much twelve years ago, nevertheless it has not been so Mortal. The number of them that have dyed in Boston by this last Visitation is about three hundred and twenty, which is not perhaps half so many as fell by the former. The Time of its being most General, was in the Months June, July, and August, then 'twas that sometimes in some one Congregation on a Lord's Day there would be Bills desiring prayers for above an hundred Sick. It seized upon all sorts of people that came in the way of it, it infected even Children in the bellies of Mothers that had themselves undergone the Disease many years ago; for some such were newborn full of the Distemper. 'Tis not easy to relate the Trouble and Sorrow that poor Boston has felt by this Epidemical Coming-on. But we hope it will be pretty nigh Extinguished, by that time twelve month when it first began to Spread. It now unhappily spreads in several other places, among which our Garrisons in the East are to be reckoned some of the greatest Sufferers.

† † †

Newspapers succeeded in those colonial days not always because they were good, but sometimes because they were merely stuffy. And the word *stuffy* describes John Campbell's *Boston News-Letter,* which was "published by authority"—it says so right there on the front page—and was brought into the world on April 24, 1704. John Campbell was for sure no Benjamin Harris; he was the royally appointed postmaster of Boston, and his paper grew out of some newsletters he had been sending to the governors of the New England colonies. A painstaking and dull sheet, the *Boston News-Letter* lasted for seventy-two years, eighteen of them under

Campbell, and so is our first real newspaper. Try again to think like a New Englander of the early eighteenth century as you read this sample from another truly historic publication:

† † †

OUR FIRST NEWSPAPER OF CONTINUOUS PUBLICATION

Boston News-Letter, April 24, 1704.

Letters from Scotland bring us the Copy of a Sheet lately Printed there, Instituted, *A Seasonable Alarm for Scotland. In a Letter from a Gentlemen in the City, to his Friend in the Country, concerning the present Danger of the Kingdom and of the Protestant Religion.*

This Letter takes Notice, That Papists swarm in that Nation, that they traffick more avowedly than formerly, and that of late many Scores of Priests and Jesuites are come thither from France, and gone to the North, to the Highlands and other places of the Country. That the Ministers of the Highlands and North gave in large Lists of them to the Committee of the General Assembly, to be laid before the Privy-Council.

It likewise observes, that a great Number of other ill-affected persons are come over from France, under pretence of accepting her Majesty's Gracious Indemnity but, in reality, to increase Divisions in the Nation, and to entertain a Correspondence with France: That their ill Intentions are evident from their talking big, their owning the Interest of the pretended King James VIII, their secret Cabals, and their buying up of Arms and Ammunition, wherever they can find them.

To this he adds the late Writings and Actings of some disaffected Persons, many of whom are for that Pretender, that several of them have declared they had rather embrace Popery than conform to the present Government; that they refuse to pray for the Queen, but use the ambiguous word Soveraign, and some of them pray in express Words for the King and Royal Family; and the charitable and generous Prince who has shew'd them so much Kindness. He likewise takes notice of Letters not long ago found in Cypher, and directed to a Person lately come thither from St. Germains:

He says that the greatest Jacobites, who will not qualify themselves by taking the Oaths to Her Majesty, do now with the Papists and their Companions from St. Germains set up for the Liberty of the Subject, contrary to their own Principles, but meerly to keep up a Division in the Nation. He adds, that they aggravate those things which the People complain of, as to England's refusing, to allow them a freedom of Trade, etc. and do all they can to foment Divisions betwixt the Nations, and to obstruct a Redress of those things complain'd of.

† † †

Boston rivaled Philadelphia and New York among the towns of colonial America, so it is not surprising that Boston should have been the setting of the earliest journalism worth special consideration. In 1719 there came a journal called the *Boston Gazette,* whose great age lay far in the future. Two years later, on August 7, 1721, there came another paper—the *New-England Courant* of James Franklin—and with James Franklin and his brother Benjamin we enter the great age of colonial journalism. The elder Franklin did battle with both royal and religious authority, getting himself into trouble for writing essays on hypocrites and for suggesting that the government had been lax in suppressing pirates along the coast; finding himself ranked against the Mather dynasty of Massachusetts for opposing the Mathers and their plan to solve the problem of smallpox epidemics by a practice called inoculation (the often-wrong Mathers may have been on the right side of an issue this time). James Franklin would have been forgotten, perhaps, had it not been for the fabulous younger brother, and we let that brother tell the story of James and the *Courant* from his *Autobiography.* He also talks some about himself; Ben seldom shied from talking about himself.

† † †

THE FRANKLINS AND THEIR BOSTON NEWSPAPER

By Benjamin Franklin, from *The Autobiography* (New York: Modern Library, 1944), pp. 23-26.

My Brother had in 1720 or 21, begun to print a Newspaper. It was the second that appear'd in America, and was called *The New-England Courant.* The only one before it, was the *Boston News-Letter.* I remember his being dissuaded by some of his Friends from the Undertaking, as not likely to succeed, one Newspaper being in their judgment enough for America.—At this time 1771 there are not less than five and twenty.—He went on however with the Undertaking, and after having work'd in composing the Types and printing off the Sheets, I was employ'd to carry the Papers thro' the Streets to the Customers.—He had some ingenious Men among his Friends who amus'd themselves by writing little Pieces for this Paper, which gain'd it Credit, and made it more in Demand; and these Gentlemen often visited us.—Hearing their Conversations, and their Accounts of the Approbation their Papers were receiv'd with, I was excited to try my Hand among them. But being still a Boy, and suspecting that my Brother would object to printing any Thing of mine in his Paper if he knew it to be mine, I contriv'd to disguise my Hand, and writing an anonymous Paper I put it in at Night under the Door of the Printing House. It was found in the Morning and communicated to his Writing Friends when they call'd in as usual. They read it, commented on it in my Hearing, and I had the exquisite Pleasure, of finding it met with their Approbation, and that in their different Guesses at the Author none were named but Men of some Character among us for Learning and Ingenuity.—I suppose now that I was rather lucky in my Judges: And that perhaps they were not really so very good ones as I then esteem'd them. Encourag'd however by this, I wrote and convey'd in the same Way to the Press several more Papers, which were equally approv'd, and I kept my Secret till my small Fund of Sense for such Performances was pretty well exhausted, and then I discovered it; when I began to be considered a little more by my Brother's Acquaintance, and in a manner that did not quite please him, as he thought, probably with reason, that it tended to make me too vain. And perhaps this might be one Occasion of the Differences that we began to have about this Time. Tho' a Brother, he considered himself as my Master, and me as his Apprentice; and accordingly expected the same Services from me as he would from another; while I thought he demean'd me too much in some he requir'd of me, who from a Brother expected more Indulgence. Our Disputes were often brought before our Father, and I fancy I was either generally in the right, or else a better Pleader, because the Judgment was generally in my favour: But my Brother was passionate and had often beaten me, which I took extreamly amiss; and thinking my Apprenticeship very tedious, I was continually wishing for some Opportunity of shortening it, which at length offered in a manner unexpected.

One of the Pieces in our Newspaper, on some political Point which I have now forgotten, gave Offence to the Assembly. He was taken up, censur'd and imprison'd for a Month by the Speaker's Warrant, I suppose because he would not discover his Author. I too was taken up and examin'd before the Council; but tho' I did not give them any Satisfaction, they contented themselves with admonishing me, and dismiss'd me; considering me perhaps as an Apprentice who was bound to keep his Master's Secrets. During my Brother's Confinement, which I resented a good deal, notwithstanding our private Differences, I had the Management of the Paper, and I made bold to give our Rulers some Rubs in it, which my Brother took very kindly, while others began to consider me in an unfavourable Light, as a young Genius that had a Turn for Libelling and Satyr. My Brother's Discharge was accompany'd with an Order of the House, (a very odd one) *that James Franklin should no longer print the Paper called the New-England Courant.* There was a Consultation held in our Printing-House among his Friends what he should do in this Case. Some propos'd to evade the Order by changing the Name of the Paper; but my Brother seeing Inconveniences in that, it was finally concluded on as a better Way, to let it be printed for the future under the Name of *Benjamin Franklin.* And to avoid the Censure of the Assembly that might fall on him, as still printing it by his Apprentice, the Contrivance was, that my old Indenture should be return'd to me with a full Discharge on the Back of it, to be shown on Occasion; but to secure to him the Benefit of my Service I was to sign new Indentures for the Remainder of the Term, which were to be kept private. A very flimsy Scheme it was, but however it was immediately executed, and the Paper went on accordingly under my Name for several Months. At length a fresh Difference arising between my Brother and me, I took upon me to assert my Freedom, presuming that he would not venture to produce the new Indentures. It was not fair in me to take this Advantage, and this I therefore reckon one of the first Errata of my life: But the Unfairness of it weighed little with me, when under the Impressions of Resentment, for the Blows his Passion too often urg'd him to bestow upon me. Tho' he was otherwise not an ill-natur'd Man: Perhaps I was too saucy and provoking.

When he found I would leave him, he took care to prevent my getting Employment in any other Printing-House of the Town, by going round and speaking to every Master, who accordingly refus'd to give me Work. I then thought of going to New York as the nearest Place where there was a Printer: and I was the rather inclin'd to leave Boston, where I reflected that I had already made myself a little obnoxious to the governing Party; and from the arbitrary Proceedings of the Assembly in my Brother's Case it was likely I might if I stay'd soon bring myself into Scrapes; and farther that my indiscrete Disputations about Religion began to make me pointed at with Horror by good People, as an Infidel or Atheist. I determin'd on the Point: but my Father now siding with my Brother, I was sensible that if I attempted to go openly, Means would be used to prevent me. My Friend Collins therefore undertook to manage a little for me. He agreed with the Captain of a New York Sloop for my Passage, under the Notion of my being a young Acquaintance of his that had got a naughty Girl with Child, whose Friends would compel me to marry her, and therefore I could not appear or come away publickly. So I sold some of my Books to raise a little Money, Was taken on board privately, and as we had a fair Wind, in three Days I found myself in New York near 300 Miles from home, a Boy of but 17, without the least Recommendation to or Knowledge of any Person in the Place, and with very little Money in my Pocket.

† † †

It seems almost platitudinous to talk about Benjamin Franklin; it is like offering a compliment to the moon for looking so lovely on a spring night. Franklin was a mighty physical, political, scientific, philosophical presence—our true universal man, a mountain alongside the foothills of his time, as someone phrased it. In journalism we see him first as printer, editor, essayist; but he, of course, was the inventor of a stove that bore his name; bifocal glasses, which may have been necessary to read the type faces of the time; a glass harmonica, for which Mozart composed; he was a flier of kites in electrical storms, and thereby chief propounder of modern-day ideas of electricity; inventor, then, of the lightning rod; founder of the University of Pennsylvania; promoter of public libraries and fire companies; author of the most famous *Autobiography* in our letters; friend of Voltaire and Priestley and Boswell; lover of many

26

women; designer of the first newspaper cartoon in America; envoy to both England and France; gentle orator who helped to bring about repeal of the Stamp Act; sufferer with the gout. He was not at all the pious bore that his *Autobiography* and some of the sanctimonious utterances in *Poor Richard* make him out to be. Gloriously, in our political history, he was there for both the Continental Congress that signed the Declaration and the convention that wrote the Constitution; and on the Fourth of July we honor him equally with Thomas Jefferson and John Adams. In our journalism there are several important Franklinian documents, for Franklin is said to have made colonial journalism truly respectable after he purchased the *Pennsylvania Gazette* from Samuel Keimer in 1729. The first of these documents is from the *New-England Courant;* it is one of those essays he slipped under the door of the *Courant* office, to the delight of his readers, to the enjoyment of posterity.

† † †

THE DOGOOD PAPERS, NO. 35

The *New-England Courant.*
From Monday March 26. to Monday April 2. 1722
To the Author of the New-England Courant.

SIR,

It may not be improper in the first Place to inform your Readers, that I intend once a Fortnight to present them, by the Help of this Paper, with a short Epistle, which I presume will add somewhat to their Entertainment.

And since it is observed, that the Generality of People, now a days, are unwilling either to commend or dispraise what they read, until they are in some measure informed who or what the Author of it is, whether he be *poor* or *rich, old* or *young,* a *Scollar* or a *Leather Apron Man,* &c., and give their Opinion on the Performance, according to the Knowledge which they have of the Author's Circumstances, it may not be amiss to begin with a short Account of my past Life and present Condition, that the Reader may not be at a Loss to judge whether or no my Lucubrations are worth his reading.

At the time of my Birth, my Parents were on Ship-board in their Way from *London* to *N. England.* My Entrance into this troublesome World was attended with the Death of my Father, a Misfortune, which tho' I was not then capable of knowing, I shall never be able to forget; for as he, poor Man, stood upon the Deck rejoycing at my Birth, a merciless Wave entered the Ship, and in one Moment carry'd him beyond Reprieve. Thus was the *first* day which I saw, the *last* that was seen by my Father; and thus was my disconsolate Mother at once made both a *Parent* and a *Widow.*

When we arrived at *Boston* (which was not long after) I was put to Nurse in a Country Place, at a small Distance from the Town, where I went to School, and past my Infancy and Childhood in Vanity and

Idleness, until I was bound out Apprentice, that I might no longer be a Charge to my Indigent Mother, who was put to hard Shifts for a Living.

My Master was a Country Minister, a pious good-natur'd young Man, & a Batchelor. He labour'd with all his Might to instil vertuous and godly Principles into my tender Soul, well knowing that it was the most suitable Time to make deep and lasting Impressions on the Mind, while it was yet untainted with Vice, free and unbiass'd. He endeavour'd that I might be instructed in all that Knowledge and Learning which is necessary for our Sex, and deny'd me no Accomplishment that could possibly be attained in a Country Place, such as all Sorts of Needle-work, Writing, Arithmetick, &c. and observing that I took a more than ordinary Delight in reading ingenious Books, he gave me the free Use of his Library, which tho' it was but small, yet it was well chose, to inform the Understanding rightly and enable the Mind to frame great and noble Ideas.

Before I had liv'd quite two Years with this Reverend Gentleman, my indulgent Mother departed this Life, leaving me as it were by my self, having no Relation on Earth within my Knowledge.

I will not abuse your patience with a tedious Recital of all the frivolous Accidents of my Life, that happened from this Time until I arrived to Years of Discretion, only inform you that I liv'd a chearful Country Life, spending my leisure Time either in some innocent Diversion with the neighbouring Females, or in some shady Retirement, with the best of Company, *Books*. Thus I past away the Time with a Mixture of Profit and Pleasure, having no Affliction but what was imaginary, and created in my own Fancy; as nothing is more common with us Women, than to be grieving for nothing, when we have nothing else to grieve for.

As I would not engross too much of your Paper at once, I will defer the Remainder of my Story until my next Letter; in the mean time desiring your Readers to exercise their Patience, and bear with my Humours now and then, because I shall trouble them but seldom, I am not insensible of the Impossibility of pleasing all, but I would not willingly displease any; and for those who will take Offence where none is intended, they are beneath the Notice of

Your Humble Servant,
SILENCE DOGOOD

† † †

Franklin began to publish his *Poor Richard's Almanack* in 1732, and it was quite like some almanacs of the present—an attempt to forecast an entire year, a gathering of advice and information, a bit of humor. This, which Franklin himself published, may be the Franklin who for some Americans has been a bit on the tedious side.

† † †

POOR RICHARD'S ALMANACK: HOW TO GET RICHES

By Benjamin Franklin, 1749, in *The Autobiography of Benjamin Franklin and Selections from His Writings* (New York: Modern Library, 1944 ed.,), pp. 208-209.

He that would be beforehand in the World, must be beforehand with his Business: It is not only ill Management, but discovers a slothful Disposition, to do that in the Afternoon, which should have been done in the morning.

Useful Attainments in your Minority will procure Riches in Maturity, of which Writing and Accounts are not the meanest.

Learning, whether Speculative or Practical, is, in Popular or Mixt Governments, the Natural Source of Wealth and Honour.

PRECEPT I

In Things of moment, on thy self depend,
Nor trust too far thy Servant or thy Friend:
With private views, thy Friend may promise fair,
And Servants very seldom prove sincere.

PRECEPT II

What can be done, with Care perform to Day,
Dangers unthought-of will attend Delay;
Your distant Prospects all precarious are,
And Fortune is as fickle as she's fair.

PRECEPT III

Nor trivial Loss nor trivial Gain despise;
Molehills if often heap'd, to Mountains rise:
Weigh every small Expence, and nothing waste,
Farthings long sav'd amount to Pounds at last. . . .

† † †

Many documents could be chosen to illustrate the life and accomplishments of Benjamin Franklin. Those of us in journalism have only a small claim to this man, but part of our claim is based on another document, his "Apology for Printers," published June 10, 1731, in the *Pennsylvania Gazette*.

† † †

AN APOLOGY FOR PRINTERS

By Benjamin Franklin, *Pennsylvania Gazette*, June 10, 1731.

Being frequently censur'd and condemn'd by different Persons for printing things which they say ought not to be printed, I have sometimes thought it might be necessary to make a standing Apology for my self, and publish it once a Year, to be read upon all Occasions of that Nature. Much Business has hitherto hindered the execution of this Design; but having very lately given extraordinary Offence by printing an Advertisement with a certain N.B. at the End of it, I find an Apology more particularly requisite at this Juncture, tho' it happens when I have not yet Leisure to write such a Thing in the proper Form, and can only in a loose manner throw those Considerations together which should have been the Substance of it.

I request all who are angry with me on the Account of printing things they don't like, calmly to consider these following Particulars.

1. That the Opinions of Men are almost as various as their Faces; an Observation general enough to become a common Proverb, *So many Men so many Minds.*
2. That the Business of Printing has chiefly to do with Mens Opinions; most things that are printed tending to promote some, or oppose others.
3. That hence arises the peculiar Unhappiness of that Business, which other Callings are no way liable to; they who follow Printing being scarce able to do any thing in their way of getting a Living, which shall not probably give Offence to some, and perhaps to many; whereas the Smith, the Shoemaker, the Carpenter, or the Man of any other Trade, may work indifferently for People of all Persuasions, without offending any of them: and the Merchant may buy and sell with Jews, Turks, Hereticks and Infidels of all sorts, and get Money by every one of them, without giving Offense to the most orthodox, of any sort; or suffering the least Censure or Ill will on the Account from any Man whatever.
4. That it is unreasonable in any one Man or Set of Men to expect to be pleas'd with every thing that is printed, as to think that nobody ought to be pleas'd but themselves.
5. Printers are educated in the Belief, that when Men differ in Opinion, both Sides ought equally to have the Advantage of being heard by the Publick; and that when Truth and Error have fair Play, the former is always an overmatch for the latter: Hence they chearfully serve all contending Writers that pay them well, without regarding on which side they are of the Question in Dispute.
6. Being thus continually employ'd in serving both Parties, Printers naturally acquire a vast Unconcernedness as to the right or wrong Opinions contain'd in what they print; regarding it only as the Matter of their daily labour: They print things full of Spleen and Animosity, with the utmost Calmness and Indifference, and without the least Ill-will to the Persons reflected on; who nevertheless unjustly think the Printer as much their Enemy as the Author, and join both together in their Resentment.

7. That it is unreasonable to imagine Printers approve of every thing they print, and to censure them on any particular thing accordingly; since in the way of their Business they print such great variety of things opposite and contradictory. It is likewise as unreasonable what some assert, "That Printers ought not to print any Thing but what they approve;" since if all of that Business should make such a Resolution, and abide by it, an End would thereby be put to Free Writing, and the World would afterwards have nothing to read but what happen'd to be the Opinions of Printers.

8. That if all Printers were determin'd not to print anything till they were sure it would offend no body, there would be very little printed.

9. That if they sometimes print vicious or silly things not worth reading, it may not be because they approve such things themselves, but because the People are so viciously and corruptly educated that good things are not encouraged. I have known a very numerous Impression of Robin Hood's Songs go off in this Province at 2s. per Book, in less than a Twelvemonth; when a small Quantity of David's Psalms (an excellent Version) have lain upon my Hands above twice the time.

10. That notwithstanding what might be urg'd in behalf of a Man's being allow'd to do in the Way of his Business whatever he is paid for, Yet Printers do continually discourage the Printing of great Numbers of bad things, and stifle them in the Birth. I my self have constantly refused to print any thing that might countenance Vice, or promote Immorality; tho' by complying such Cases, with the corrupt Taste of the Majority, I might have got much Money. I have also always refus'd to print such things as might do real Injury to any Person, how much soever I have been solicited and tempted with Offers of Great Pay; and how much soever I have by refusing got the Ill-will of those who would have employ'd me. I have hitherto fallen under the Resentment of large Bodies of Men, for refusing absolutely to print any of their Party or Personal Reflections. In this Manner I have made my self many Enemies, and the constant Fatigue of denying is almost insupportable. But the Publick being unacquainted with all this, whenever the poor Printer happens either through Ignorance or much Persuasion, to do any thing that is generally thought worthy of Blame, he meets with no more Friendship or Favour on the above Account, than if there were no Merit in't at all. Thus, as Waller says,

> Poets lose half the Praise they would have got
> Were it but known what they discreetly blot;

Yet are censur'd for every bad Line found in their Works with the utmost Severity.

I come now to the Particular Case of the N.B. above mention'd, about which there has been more Clamour against me, than ever before on any other Account.—In the Hurry of other Business an Advertisement was brought to me to be printed; it signified that such a Ship lying at such a Wharff, would sail for Barbadoes in such a Time, and that Freighters and Passengers might agree with the Captain at such a Place; so far is what's common: But at the Bottom this odd Thing was added, "N.B. No Sea Hens or Black Gowns will be admitted on any Terms." I printed it, and receiv'd my Money; and the Advertisement was stuck up round the Town as usual. I had not so much Curiosity at that time as to enquire the Meaning of it, nor did I in the least imagine it would give so much Offence. Several good Men are very angry with me on this Occasion; they are pleas'd to say I have too much Sense to do such things ignorantly; that if they were Printers they would not have done such a thing on any Consideration; that it could proceed from nothing but my abundant Malice against Religion and the Clergy. They therefore declare they will not take any more of my Papers, nor have any farther Dealings with me; but will hinder me of all the Custom they can. All this is very hard!

I believe it had been better if I had refused to print the said Advertisement. However, 'tis done, and cannot be revok'd. I have only the following few Particulars to offer, some of them in my behalf, by way of Mitigation, and some not much to the Purpose; but I desire none of them may be read when the Reader is not in a very good Humour.

1. That I really did it without the least Malice, and imagin'd the N.B. was plac'd there only to make the Advertisement star'd at, and more generally read.
2. That I never saw the Word Sea-Hens before in my Life; nor have I yet ask'd the meaning of it; and tho' I had certainly known that Black Gowns in that place signified the Clergy of the Church of England, yet I have that confidence in the generous good Temper of such of them as I know, as to be well satisfied such a trifling mention of their Habit gives them no Disturbance.
3. That most of the Clergy in this and the neighbouring Provinces, are my Customers, and some of them my very good Friends; and I must be very malicious indeed, or very stupid, to print this thing for a small Profit, if I had thought it would have given them just Cause of Offence.
4. That if I had much Malice against the Clergy, and withal much Sense; 'tis strange I never write or talk against the Clergy myself. Some have observed that 'tis a fruitful Topic, and the easiest to be witty upon of all others; yet I appeal to the Publick that I am never guilty this way, and to all my Acquaintances as to my Conversation.
5. That if a Man of Sense had Malice enough to desire to injure the Clergy, this is the foolishest Thing he could possibly contrive for that Purpose.
6. That I got Five Shillings by it.
7. That none who are angry with me would have given me so much to let it alone.

8. That if all the People of different Opinions in this Province would engage to give me as much for not printing things they don't like, as I can get by printing them, I should probably live a very easy Life; and if all Printers were everywhere so dealt by, there would be very little printed.

9. That I am oblig'd to all who take my Paper, and am willing to think they do it out of meer Friendship. I only desire they would think the same when I deal with them. I thank those who leave off, that they have taken it so long. But I beg they would not endeavour to dissuade others, for that will look like Malice.

10. That 'tis impossible any Man should know what he would do if he was a Printer.

11. That notwithstanding the Rashness and Inexperience of Youth, which is most likely to be prevail'd with to do things that ought not to be done; yet I have avoided printing such Things as usually give Offence either to Church or State, more than any Printer that has followed the Business in this Province before.

12. And lastly, That I have printed above a Thousand Advertisements which made not the least mention of *Sea-Hens* or *Black Gowns;* and this being the first Offence, I have the more Reason to expect Foregiveness.

I take leave to conclude with an old Fable, which some of my Readers have heard before, and some have not.

A certain well-meaning Man and his Son, were travelling towards a Market Town, with an Ass which they had to sell. The Road was bad; and the old Man therefore rid, but the Son went a-foot. The first Passenger they met, asked the Father if he was not ashamed to ride by himself, and suffer the poor Lad to wade along thro' the Mire; This induced him to take up his Son behind him: He had not travelled far, when he met others, who said, they are two unmerciful Lubbers to get both on the Back of that poor Ass, in such a deep Road. Upon this the old Man gets off, and let his Son ride alone. The next they met called the Lad a graceless, rascally young Jackanapes, to ride in that Manner thro' the Dirt, while his aged Father trudged along on Foot; and they said the old Man was a Fool, for suffering it. He then bid his Son come down, and walk with him, and they travell'd on leading the Ass by the Halter; 'till they met another Company, who called them a Couple of senseless Blockheads, for going both on Foot in such a dirty way, when they had an empty Ass with them, which they might ride upon. The old Man could bear no longer; My Son, said he, it grieves me much that we cannot please all these People. Let me throw the Ass over the next bridge, and be no further troubled with him.

Had the old Man been seen acting this last Resolution, he would probably have been called a Fool for troubling himself about the different Opinions of all that were pleas'd to find Fault with him: Therefore, tho' I have a Temper almost as complying as his, I intend not to imitate him in this last Particular. I consider the Variety of

Humors among Men, and despair of pleasing every Body; yet I shall not therefore leave off Printing. I shall continue my Business. I shall not burn my Press and melt my Letters.

† † †

John Peter Zenger was a German immigrant who came to New York in 1710 as an indentured servant, a 13-year-old boy working for the printer William Bradford. The name of Zenger is perhaps more a symbol than anything else, for Zenger did not write the articles that made him famous—but he did spend eight months in prison, and it is not likely that prisons in the eighteenth century, especially in the cold months, were pleasant places to spend one's time. Zenger's newspaper was called the *New York Weekly Journal,* established in late 1733 in avowed opposition to Governor William Cosby and his followers, and it was a paper that published inflammatory writings in a time when the law held "the greater the truth, the greater the libel." It was James Alexander and others who did the writing, but Zenger was arrested and imprisoned for the attacks made upon the governor. It is not a writing from the *Journal* that is offered here, but instead an even more important document, for it is the plea made in court by the retired Philadelphia lawyer, Andrew Hamilton, who was prevailed upon by Zenger's backers to come to New York and argue the case before a jury. This Hamilton did, contending that evidence as to the truth of the statements alleged to be libelous should be admitted in court. A verdict of not guilty was brought in, Zenger was freed, and the concept of truth as a defense in libel was at least symbolically established in the American tradition, though it took several generations for it to receive a more official sanction.

† † †

THE TRIAL OF JOHN PETER ZENGER

From Stanley Nider Katz, ed., *A Brief Narrative of the Case and Trial of John Peter Zenger,* by James Alexander (Cambridge, Mass.: Belknap Press of Harvard University Press, 1963), pp. 61-101.

Mr. Hamilton: May it please Your Honor; I am concerned in this cause on the part of Mr. Zenger, the defendant. The information against my client was sent me, a few days before I left home, with some instructions to let me know how far I might rely upon the truth of those parts of the papers set forth in the information and which are said to be libelous. And though I am perfectly of the opinion with the gentleman who has just now spoke, on the same side with me, as to the common course of proceedings, I mean in putting Mr. Attorney upon proving that my client printed and published those papers mentioned in the information; yet I cannot think it proper for me (without doing violence to my own principles) to deny the publication of a complaint, which I think is the right of every freeborn subject to make, when the matters so published can be supported with truth; and therefore I'll save Mr. Attorney the trouble of examining his witnesses to that point; and I do (for my client) confess that he both printed and published the two newspapers set forth in the information, and I hope in so doing he has committed no crime.

Mr. Attorney: Then if Your Honor pleases, since Mr. Hamilton has confessed the fact, I think our witnesses may be discharged; we have no further occasion for them.

Mr. Hamilton: If you brought them here, only to prove the printing and publishing of these newspapers, we have acknowledged that, and shall abide by it.

Mr. Chief Justice: Well, Mr. Attorney, will you proceed?

Mr. Attorney: Indeed, sir, as Mr. Hamilton has confessed the printing and publishing these libels, I think the jury must find a verdict for the King; for supposing they were true, the law says that they are not the less libelous for that; nay, indeed, the law says their being true is an aggravation of the crime.

Mr. Hamilton: Not so neither, Mr. Attorney, there are two words to that bargain. I hope it is not our bare printing and publishing a paper that will make it a libel. You will have something more to do before you make my client a libeler; for the words themselves must be libelous, that is, *false, scandalous, and seditious* or else we are not guilty.

Mr. Attorney: The case before the court is whether Mr. Zenger is guilty of libeling His Excellency the Governor of New York, and indeed the whole administration of the government. Mr. Hamilton has confessed the printing and publishing, and I think nothing is plainer than that the words in the information are *scandalous, and tend to sedition, and to disquiet the minds of the people of this province.* And if such papers are not libels, I think it may be said there can be no such thing as a libel.

Mr. Hamilton: May it please Your Honor; I cannot agree with Mr. Attorney; for though I freely acknowledge that there are such things as libels, yet I must insist at the same time that what my client is charged with is not a libel; and I observed just now that Mr. Attorney, in defining a libel, made use of the words *scandalous, seditious, and tend to disquiet the people;* but (whether with design or not I will not say) he omitted the word *false.*

Mr. Attorney: I think I did not omit the word *false.* But it has been said already that it may be a libel notwithstanding it may be true.

Mr. Hamilton: In this I must still differ with Mr. Attorney; for I depend upon it, we are to be tried upon this information now before the court and jury, and to which we have pleaded *Not Guilty,* and by it we are charged with printing and publishing a certain *false, malicious, seditious, and scandalous libel.* This word *false* must have some meaning, or else how came it there?

Mr. Chief Justice: You cannot be admitted, Mr. Hamilton, to give the truth of a libel in evidence. A libel is not to be justified; for it is nevertheless a libel that it is true.

Mr. Hamilton: I am sorry the court has so soon resolved upon that piece of law; I expected first to have been heard to that point. I have not in all my reading met with an authority that says we cannot be admitted to give the truth in evidence upon an information for a libel.

Mr. Chief Justice: The law is clear that you cannot justify a libel. [Hamilton then cites cases to support his contention that the truth of a libel is admissible in evidence.]

Here the court had the case under consideration a considerable time, and every one was silent.

Mr. Chief Justice: Mr. Hamilton, the court is of opinion you ought not to be permitted to prove the facts in the papers: these are the words of the book, *"It is far from being a justification of a libel that the contents thereof are true, or that the person upon whom it is made had a bad reputation, since the greater appearance there is of truth in any malicious invective so much the more provoking it is."*

Mr. Hamilton: These are Star Chamber cases, and I was in hopes that practice had been dead with the court.

Mr. Chief Justice: Mr. Hamilton, the court have delivered their opinion, and we expect you will use us with good manners; you are not to be permitted to argue against the opinion of the court.

Mr. Hamilton: With submission, I have seen the practice in very great courts, and never heard it deemed unmannerly to—

Mr. Chief Justice: After the court have declared their opinion, it is not good manners to insist upon a point in which you are overruled.

Mr. Hamilton: I will say no more at this time; the court, I see, is against us in this point; and that I hope I may be allowed to say.

Mr. Chief Justice: Use the court with good manners, and you shall be allowed all the liberty you can reasonably desire.

Mr. Hamilton: I thank Your Honor. Then, gentlemen of the jury, it is to you we must now appeal, for witnesses to the truth of the facts we have offered, and are denied the liberty to prove; and let it not seem strange that I apply myself to you in this manner. I am warranted so to do both by law and reason. The last supposes you to be *summoned out of the neighborhood where the fact is alleged to be committed;* and the reason of your being taken out of the neighborhood is *because you are supposed to have the best knowledge of the fact that is to be tried.* And were you to find a verdict against my client, you must take upon you to say the papers referred to in the information, and which we acknowledge we printed and published, are *false, scandalous, and seditious;* but of this I can have no apprehension. You are citizens of New York; you are really what the law supposes you to be, *honest and lawful men;* and according to my brief, the facts which we offer to prove were not committed in a corner; *they are notoriously known to be true;* and therefore in your justice lies our safety. And as we are denied the liberty of giving evidence, to prove the truth of what we have published, I will beg leave to lay it down as a standing rule in such cases *that the suppressing of evidence ought always to be taken for the strongest evidence;* and I hope it will have that weight with you.

It is true in times past it was a crime to speak truth, and in that terrible Court of Star Chamber many worthy and brave men suffered for so doing; and yet even in that court, and in those bad times, a great and good man durst say, what I hope will not be taken amiss of me to say in this place, *to wit, the practice of informations for libels is a sword in the hands of a wicked king, and an arrant coward to cut down and destroy the innocent; the one cannot, because of his high station, and the other dares not, because of his want of courage, revenge himself in another manner.*

Mr. Attorney: Pray, Mr. Hamilton, have a care what you say, don't go too far neither, I don't like those liberties.

Mr. Hamilton: Sure, Mr. Attorney, you won't make any applications; all men agree that we are governed by the best of kings, and I cannot see the meaning of Mr. Attorney's caution, my well-known principles, and the sense I have of the blessings we enjoy under his present Majesty, makes it impossible for me to err, and, I hope, even to be suspected, in that point of duty to my king. May it please Your Honor, I was saying that notwithstanding all duty and reference claimed by Mr. Attorney to men in authority, they are not exempt from observing the rules of common justice, either in their private or public capacities; the laws of our mother country know no exemption.

I hope to be pardoned, sir, for my zeal upon this occasion: it is an old and wise caution *that when our neighbor's house is on fire, we ought to take care of our own.* For though, blessed be God, I live in a government where liberty is well understood and freely enjoyed, yet experience has shown us all (I'm sure it has to me) that a bad precedent in one government is soon set up for an authority in another; and therefore I cannot but think it mine and every honest man's duty that (while we pay all due obedience to men in authority) we ought at the same time to be upon our guard against power, wherever we apprehend that it may affect ourselves or our fellow subjects.

I am truly very unequal to such an undertaking on many accounts. And you see I labor under the weight of many years, and am borne down with great infirmities of body; yet old and weak as I am, I should think it my duty, if required, to go to the utmost part of the land where my service could be of any use in assisting to quench the flame of prosecutions upon informations, set on foot by the government, to deprive a people of the right of remonstrating (and complaining too) of the arbitrary attempts of men in power. Men who injure and oppress the people under their administration provoke them to cry out and complain; and then make that very complaint the foundation for new oppressions and prosecutions. I wish I could say there were no instances of this kind.

But to conclude: the question before the court and you, gentlemen of the jury, is not of small nor private concern, it is not the cause of a poor printer, nor of New York alone, which you are now trying. No! It may in its consequence affect every freeman that lives under a British government on the Main of America. It is the best cause. It is the cause of liberty; and I make no doubt but your upright conduct this day will not only entitle you to the love and esteem of your fellow citizens; but every man who prefers freedom to a life of slavery will bless and honor you as men who have baffled the attempt of tyranny, and, by an impartial and uncorrupt verdict, have laid a noble foundation for securing to ourselves, our posterity, and our neighbors that to which nature and the laws of our country have given us a right—the liberty both of exposing and opposing arbitrary power (in these parts of the world, at least) by speaking and writing truth.

Mr. Chief Justice: Gentlemen of the jury. The great pains Mr. Hamilton has taken to show how little regard juries are to pay to the opinion of the judges, and his insisting so much upon the conduct of some judges in trials of this kind, is done, no doubt, with a design that you should take but very little notice of what I may say upon this occasion. I shall therefore only observe to you that, as the facts or words in the information are confessed: the only thing that can come in question before you is whether the words, as set forth in the information, make a libel. And that is a matter of law, no doubt, and which you may leave to the court. But I shall trouble you no further with anything more of my own, but read to you the words of a learned and upright judge in a case of the like nature:

"To say that corrupt officers are appointed to administer affairs is certainly a reflection on the government. If people should not be called to account for possessing the people with an ill opinion of the government, no government can subsist. For it is necessary for all governments that the people should have a good opinion of it. And nothing can be worse to any government than to endeavor to procure animosities; as to the management of it, this has been always looked upon as a crime, and no government can be safe without it be punished."

Mr. Hamilton: I humbly beg Your Honor's pardon; I am very much misapprehended if you suppose what I said was so designed.

Sir, you know I made an apology for the freedom I found myself under a necessity of using upon this occasion. I said there was nothing personal designed; it arose from the nature of our defense.

The jury withdrew, and in a small time returned, and being asked by the clerk whether they were agreed of their verdict, and whether John Peter Zenger was guilty of printing and publishing the libels in the information mentioned, they answered by Thomas Hunt, their foreman: *Not Guilty.* Upon which there were three huzzas in the hall, which was crowded with people, and the next day I was discharged from my imprisonment.

† † †

3

JOURNALISTS MAKE A REVOLUTION

A multitude of pictures fills our minds as we think of the American Revolution: British soldiers firing into a crowd in Boston, the famous "Massacre"; a man on horseback galloping out to Lexington and Concord in the middle of the night; "Don't shoot till you see the whites of their eyes!";"one if by land and two if by sea"; a fire destroying hated stamps; Tom Paine writing his *Crisis* papers and Washington reading them to his troops; Thomas Jefferson and the Declaration; Franklin as envoy to the mother country and to France; the treason of a noted general, hero of Quebec and Saratoga; starving, ragged men at Valley Forge; a sea battle between the *Bon Homme Richard* and the *Serapis*.

We see, too, little colonial presses—presses of wood, little better than the one used by Gutenberg—laboriously pounding out propaganda. We do not see *news accounts,* at least not news accounts in the twentieth century sense of the words; we see, instead, inflammatory propaganda. And such propaganda is the main theme of the documents in this segment, which treats the press and the American Revolution.

The American newspaper had advanced, though not materially, from the status it had had in the time of the Franklins and Zenger. The papers were weeklies; they were small, usually consisting of no more than four pages. They were hand-set, hand-printed; the shops were one-man operations in some cases, for the primary occupation of the editor was likely that of printer. Advertising was mixed in with the news, and news was mixed in with editorials and propaganda. Patriotic captions were common and they were flamboyant in language: "The United Voice of His Majesty's free and loyal subjects in America—liberty and property, and no stamps."

The time span under consideration is, roughly, 1763 to 1783; the American Revolution is difficult to define in any exact time sense. The French and Indian War, which ended in 1763, had left the British government of King George III in debt, and that government contended, perhaps rightly, that the colonists should help to pay for the war that had been fought. Accordingly, a series of measures was passed by Parliament: the Sugar Act, in 1764, with high duties on foreign refined sugar; the Quartering Act, in 1763, requiring civil authorities to provide barracks and supplies for troops and for quartering in inns, alehouses and the like; the Stamp Act, of 1765, designed to raise 60,000 pounds a year, a tax upon printed papers, such as newspapers, almanacs, and pamphlets; that group of acts called the Townshend Acts, in 1767, taxes on glass, lead, paints, paper, and tea. Thus came the protests, and that historic string of events: the Boston Massacre of 1770, the Boston Tea Party of 1773, the Quebec Act of 1774 and the convening of the First Continental Congress the same year, and then the battles at Lexington and Concord in 1775. These were the matters that stirred the propagandists—propagandists of several persuasions.

Properly speaking, we should be reading here, too, the propaganda uttered from the pulpit, from the courtroom, from the legislative chamber—the impassioned words of James Otis and Patrick Henry, among others. Our samples, however, are mainly from the colonial press and the pamphlets of the time.

Of the practitioners in revolutionary propaganda none surpassed Samuel Adams, a Bostonian who worked behind the scenes, forming his Committees of Correspondence and his Sons of Liberty and his Caucus Club, writing for the *Independent Advertiser* and the *Boston Gazette*, whispering insidious doctrine into the willing ears of John Hancock, stirring up the people of Massachusetts over stamps and taxes and tea. One looks in vain for words of fire from Adams, and then concludes that it was the force of his arguments, and his behind-the-scenes operations, that made him supreme. The resolutions he offered to the House of Representatives of Massachusetts on October 20, 1765—the year of the debate over stamps—are the first of our revolutionary documents.

† † †

SOME RESOLUTIONS BY SAMUEL ADAMS

House of Representatives, Massachusetts, October 20, 1765, in Harry R. Warfel, Ralph H. Gabriel and Stanley T. Williams, *The American Mind,* Vol. I (New York: American Book Co., 1937), pp. 138-139.

Whereas the just rights of his Majesty's subjects of this province, derived to them from the British Constitution, as well as the royal charter, have been lately drawn into question: in order to ascertain the same, this House do unanimously come into the following resolves:

1. *Resolved,* That there are certain essential rights of the British Constitution of government, which are founded in the law of God and nature, and are the common rights of mankind;— therefore,
2. *Resolved,* That the inhabitants of this Province are unalienably entitled to those essential rights in common with all men: and that no law of society can, consistent with the law of God and nature, divest them of those rights.
3. *Resolved,* That no man can justly take the property of another without his consent; and that upon this original principle, the right of representation in the same body which exercises the power of making laws for levying taxes, which is one of the main pillars of the British Constitution, is evidently founded.
4. *Resolved,* That this inherent right, together with all other essential rights, liberties, privileges, and immunities of the people of Great Britain, have been fully confirmed to them by Magna Charta, and by former and by later acts of Parliament.
5. *Resolved,* That his Majesty's subjects in America are, in reason and common sense, entitled to the same extent of liberty with his Majesty's subjects in Britain.
6. *Resolved,* That by the declaration of the royal charter of this Province, the inhabitants are entitled to all the rights, liberties, and immunities of free and natural subjects of Great Britain to all intents, purposes, and constructions whatever.
7. *Resolved,* That the inhabitants of this Province appear to be entitled to all the rights aforementioned by an act of Parliament, 13th of Geo. II.
8. *Resolved,* That those rights do belong to the inhabitants of this Province upon the principle of common justice; their ancestors having settled this country at their sole expense, and their posterity having approved themselves most loyal and faithful subjects of Great Britain.
9. *Resolved,* That every individual in the Colonies is as advantageous to Great Britain as if he were in Great Britain and held to pay his full proportion of taxes there; and as the inhabitants of this Province pay their full proportion of taxes for the support of his Majesty's government here, it is unreasonable for them to be called upon to pay any part of the charges of the government there.
10. *Resolved,* That the inhabitants of this Province are not, and never have been, represented in the Parliament of Great Britain; and that such a representation there as the subjects in Britain do actually and rightfully enjoy is *impracticable* for the subjects in America;—and further, that in the opinion of this House, the several subordinate powers of legislation in America were constituted upon the apprehensions of this *impracticability.*

11. *Resolved,* That the only method whereby the constitutional rights of the subjects of this Province can be secure, consistent with a subordination to the supreme power of Great Britain, is by the continued exercise of such powers of government as are granted in the royal charter, and a firm adherence to the privileges of the same.

12. *Resolved,*—as a just conclusion from some of the foregoing resolves,—That all acts made by any power whatever, other than the General Assembly of this Province, imposing taxes on the inhabitants, are infringements of our inherent and unalienable rights as men and British subjects, and render void the most valuable declarations of our charter.

13. *Resolved,* That the extension of the powers of the Court of Admiralty within this Province is a most violent infraction of the right of trials by juries,—a right which this House, upon the principles of their British ancestors, hold most dear and sacred; it being the only security of the lives, liberties, and properties of his Majesty's subjects here.

14. *Resolved,* That this House owe the strictest allegiance to his most sacred Majesty King George the Third; that they have the greatest veneration for the Parliament; and that they will, after the example of all their predecessors from the settlement of this country, exert themselves to their utmost in supporting his Majesty's authority in the Province, in promoting the true happiness of his subjects, and in enlarging the extent of his dominion.

Ordered, That all the foregoing resolves be kept in the records of this House, that a just sense of liberty and the firm sentiments of loyalty be transmitted to posterity.

† † †

Samuel Adams was the leader of the faction that called itself "patriot"—"rebels," some would call them. Adams had decided early in life that loyalty to authority was not among the important virtues (those words in his resolutions about "strictest allegiance to his most sacred Majesty" have a curious ring), and whether his motivations were economic we do not know; we do know that he was improvident, and that by some definitions of the word he was a failure. In the middle position of the arguments were the Whigs. Their chief spokesman was a Philadelphia lawyer named John Dickinson, a member of the Stamp Act Congress, a spokesman who sought rapport with the British in some of the positions he enunciated, especially his *Letters from a Farmer in Pennsylvania,* published in the colonial press in 1767-68. Dickinson wanted to bring the dispute with the British to an end, rather than exacerbate it, and he sought what today we would term "dominion status" for the colonies.

† † †

LETTERS FROM A FARMER IN PENNSYLVANIA

By John Dickinson, Letter III, in Harry R. Warfel, Ralph H. Gabriel
and Stanley T. Williams, *The American Mind,* Vol. I (New York:
American Book Co., 1937), pp. 142-143.

. . . Sorry I am to learn, that there are some few persons, who shake
their heads with solemn motion, and pretend to wonder, what can be
the meaning of these letters. *"Great-Britain,"* they say, "is too
powerful to contend with; she is determined to oppress us; it is in vain
to speak of right on one side, when there is power on the other; when
we are strong enough to resist, we shall attempt it; but now we are
not strong enough, and therefore we had better be quiet; it signifies
nothing to convince us that our rights are invaded, when we cannot
defend them; and if we should get into riots and tumults about the
late act, it will only draw down heavier displeasure upon us."
      What can such men design? What do their grave observations
amount to, but this—"That these colonies totally regardless of their
liberties, should commit them with humble resignation to *chance,
time,* and the tender mercies of *ministers."*
      Are these men ignorant that usurpations which might have been
successfully opposed at first, acquire strength by continuance, and
thus become irresistible? Do they condemn the conduct of the
colonies concerning the *Stamp-Act?* Or have they forgot its
successful issue? Ought the colonies at that time, instead of acting as
they did, to have trusted for relief to the fortuitous events of futurity?
If it is needless "to speak of *rights"* now, it was as needless then. If
the behaviour of the colonies was prudent and glorious then, and
successful too, it will be equally prudent and glorious to act in the
same manner now, if our rights are equally invaded, and may be as
successful.—Therefore it becomes necessary to enquire, whether
"our rights *are* invaded." To talk of "defending" them, as if they
could be no otherwise "defended" than by arms, is as much out of the
way, as if a man having a choice of several roads, to reach his
journey, and should prefer the worst, for no other reason but because
it *is* the worst.
      As to "riots and tumults," the gentlemen who are so apprehensive
of them, are much mistaken if they think, that grievances cannot be
redressed without such assistance.
      I will now tell the gentlemen what is "the meaning of these
letters." The meaning of them is, to convince the people of these
colonies that they are, at this moment, exposed to the most imminent
dangers; and to persuade them immediately, vigorously, unanimously to exert themselves, in the most firm, and most peaceable
manner, for obtaining relief.
      The cause of liberty is a "cause of too much dignity, to be sullied by
turbulence and tumults." It ought to be maintained in a manner
suitable to her nature. Those who engage in it, should breathe a

sedate yet fervent spirit, animating them to actions of prudence, justice, modesty, bravery, humanity and magnanimity. . . .

I hope, my dear countrymen, that you will in every colony be upon your guard against those who may at any time endeavour to stir you up, under pretences of patriotism, to any measures disrespectful to our sovereign and our mother-country. Hot, rash, disorderly proceedings injure the reputation of a people as to wisdom, valour, and virtue, without procuring them the least benefit. I pray GOD that he may be pleased to inspire you and your posterity to the latest ages with that spirit, of which I have an idea, but find a difficulty to express: To express in the best manner I can, I mean a spirit that shall so guide you, that it will be impossible to determine whether an *American's* character is most distinguishable for his loyalty to his sovereign, his duty to his mother-country, his love of freedom, or his affection for his native soil. . . .

To these reflections on this subject, it remains to be added, and ought forever to be remembered; that resistance in the case of colonies against their mother-country, is extremely different from the resistance of a people against their prince. A nation may change their kings, or race of kings, and retaining their ancient form of government, be gainers by changing. Thus *Great-Britain,* under the illustrious house of *Brunswick,* a house that seems to flourish for the happiness of mankind, has found a felicity, unknown in the reigns of the *Stuarts.* But if once *we* are separated from our mother-country, what new form of government shall we accept, or where shall we find another *Britain* to supply our loss? Torn from the body to which we are united by religion, liberty, laws, affections, relations, language and commerce, we must bleed at every vein.

In truth, the prosperity of these provinces is founded in their dependance on *Great-Britain;* and when she returns to "her old good humour, and old good nature," as Lord *Clarendon* expresses it, I hope they will always esteem it their duty and interest, as it most certainly will be, to promote her welfare by all the means in their power."

† † †

In some American historical passages John Dickinson is better known for the words of one of the more notable ballads of the patriots than for the *Letters.* He wrote "The Liberty Song," probably the first American patriotic song, in 1768, and the words were published immediately in that fiery journal called the *Boston Gazette.* The publication of this song, which then was put to music, started a "Battle of the Ballads" that preceded the actual beginning of hostilities.

† † †

THE LIBERTY SONG

By John Dickinson, 1768.

Come, join Hand in Hand, brave AMERICANS all,
And rouse your bold Hearts at fair LIBERTY'S Call;
No *tyrannous Acts* shall suppress your *just Claim,*
Or stain with *Dishonour* AMERICA'S Name.
    In FREEDOM we're BORN, and in FREEDOM we'll
      LIVE,
    Our Purses are ready,
    Steady, Friends, Steady,
    Not as SLAVES, but as FREEMEN our Money
      we'll give.

Our worthy *Forefathers*—let's give them a Cheer—
To *Climates unknown* did courageously steer,
Thro' *Oceans* to *Deserts* for *Freedom* they came,
And dying bequeath'd us their *Freedom* and Fame—
    In FREEDOM we're BORN, &C.

Their generous Bosoms all Dangers despis'd,
So *highly,* so *wisely,* their BIRTHRIGHTS they priz'd;
We'll keep what they gave, we will piously keep,
Nor frustrate their Toils on the Land and the Deep.
    In FREEDOM we're BORN, &C.

The TREE their own Hands had to LIBERTY rear'd,
They liv'd to behold growing strong and rever'd;
With Transport then cry'd, "now our Wishes we gain,
For our Children shall gather the Fruits of our Pain."
    In FREEDOM we're BORN, &C....

Then join Hand in Hand brave AMERICANS all,
By *uniting* we stand, by *dividing* we fall;
In SO RIGHTEOUS A CAUSE let us hope to succeed,
For Heaven approves of each generous Deed.
    In FREEDOM we're BORN, &C.

All Ages shall speak with *Amaze* and *Applause,*
Of the Courage we'll shew IN SUPPORT OF OUR LAWS;
To DIE we can *bear*—but to SERVE we *disdain*
For SHAME is to *Freemen* more dreadful than PAIN.
    In FREEDOM we're BORN, &C.

This Bumper I crown for our SOVEREIGN'S Health,
And this for BRITANNIA'S Glory and Wealth;
That Wealth and that Glory immortal may be,
If *she* is but *just*—and if *we* are but *free.*
    In FREEDOM we're BORN, &C.

† † †

Much name-calling, some of it pretty vicious, marked that Battle of the Ballads, and in one case the rebels turned a satirical British tune to their own purpose; that tune being "Yankee Doodle," of course. Another piece of ballad propaganda came from Francis Hopkinson, musician, writer, signer of the Declaration of Independence, delegate to the Continental Congress, and judge of the admiralty.

† † †

THE BATTLE OF THE KEGS

By Francis Hopkinson, 1778.

Gallants, attend, and hear a friend
    Trill forth harmonious ditty:
Strange things I'll tell, which late befell
    In Philadelphia city.

'Twas early day, as poets say,
    Just when the sun was rising,
A soldier stood on a log of wood
    And saw a thing surprising.

As in amaze he stood to gaze,
    The truth can't be denied, sir,
He spied a score of kegs or more
    Come floating down the tide, sir.

A sailor, too, in jerkin blue,
    This strange appearance viewing,
First damn'd his eyes, in great surprise,
    Then said, "Some mischief's brewing:

"These kegs, I'm told, the rebels hold
    Packed up like pickled herring;
And they're come down t'attack the town,
    In this new way of ferrying."

The soldier flew, the sailor too,
    And scared almost to death, sir,
Wore out their shoes to spread the news,
    And ran till out of breath, sir.

Now up and down throughout the town
    Most frantic scenes were acted;
And some ran here and others there,
    Like men almost distracted.

Some fire cried, which some denied,
    But said the earth had quaked;
And girls and boys, with hideous noise,
    Ran through the streets half naked.

Sir William, he, snug as a flea,
    Lay all this time a snoring,
Nor dreamed of harm, as he lay warm,
    In bed with Mrs. Loring.

Now in a fright he starts upright,
    Awak'd by such a clatter;
He rubs his eyes and boldly cries,
    "For God's sake, what's the matter?"

At his bedside he then espied
    Sir Erskine at command, sir:
Upon one foot he had one boot,
    And t'other in his hand, sir.

"Arise, arise!" Sir Erskine cries;
    "The rebels, more's the pity,
Without a boat are all afloat
    And rang'd before the city.

"The motley crew, in vessels new,
    With Satan for their guide, sir,
Packed up in bags, or wooden kegs,
    Come driving down the tide, sir.

"Therefore prepare for bloody war:
    These kegs must all be routed,
Or surely we despis'd shall be,
    And British courage doubted."

The royal band now ready stand,
    All ranged in dread array, sir,
With stomachs stout, to see it out,
    And make a bloody day, sir.

The cannons roar from shore to shore,
    The small arms make a rattle;
Since wars began, I'm sure no man
    Ere saw so strange a battle.

The rebel dales, the rebel vales,
    With rebel trees surrounded,
The distant woods, the hills and floods,
    With rebel echoes sounded.

The fish below swam to and fro,
　Attack'd from every quarter:
"Why sure," thought they, "the devil's to pay
　'Mongst folks above the water."

The kegs, 'tis said, though strongly made
　Of rebel staves and hoops, sir,
Could not oppose their powerful foes,
　The conquering British troops, sir.

From morn till night these men of might
　Display'd amazing courage,
And when the sun was fairly down
　Retir'd to sup their porridge.

An hundred men, with each a pen,
　Or more, upon my word, sir,
It is most true would be too few
　Their valor to record, sir.

Such feats did they perform that day
　Against those wicked kegs, sir,
That years to come, if they get home,
　They'll make their boasts and brags, sir.

† † †

Actual news accounts of the American Revolution are rare, and those that we have are more propaganda than news. No account published during the war quite rivals the story written by editor Isaiah Thomas in 1775. This was the Thomas who wrote a famous *History of Printing,* who set type for the *New England Primer,* who was invited to set up presses throughout colonies, and who *may* have been the man who climbed into the tower of the Old North Church to hang the lantern that signaled the start of Paul Revere's ride. Thomas was a printer who started his paper, the *Massachusetts Spy,* in 1770; it has been written that slogans on his masthead could provide almost a chronology of the events of the Revolution. Thomas was a moderate, but he found the events of the early 1770s pushing him into the patriot camp, and there is little doubt as to how he felt in this, his justly famous description of the battles at Lexington and Concord—April 19, 1775.

† † †

THE BATTLE OF LEXINGTON

By Isaiah Thomas, The *Massachusetts Spy,* May 3, 1775.

Americans! Forever bear in mind the BATTLE OF LEXINGTON!
—where British troops, unmolested and unprovoked, wantonly and

in a most inhuman manner, fired upon and killed a number of our countrymen, then robbed, ransacked, and burnt their houses! nor could the tears of defenseless women, some of whom were in the pains of childbirth, the cries of helpless babes, nor the prayers of old age, confined to beds of sickness, appease their thirst for blood!—or divert them from their DESIGN OF MURDER and ROBBERY!

The particulars of this alarming event will, we are credibly informed, be soon published by authority, as a Committee of the Provincial Congress have been appointed to make special inquiry and to take the depositions, on oath, of such as are knowing in the matter. In the meantime, to satisfy the expectations of our readers, we have collected from those whose veracity is unquestioned the following account, viz.

A few days before the battle, the Grenadier and Light-Infantry companies were all drafted from the several regiments in Boston; and put under the command of an officer, and it was observed that most of the transports and other boats were put together, and fitted for immediate service. This maneuver gave rise to a suspicion that a more formidable expedition was intended by the soldiery, but what or where the inhabitants could not determine. However, town watches in Boston, Charlestown, Cambridge, etc., were ordered to look well to the landing place.

About ten o'clock on the night of the eighteenth of April, the troops in Boston were disclosed to be on the move in a very secret manner, and it was found they were embarking on boats (which they had privately brought to the place in the evening) at the bottom of the Common; expresses set off immediately to alarm the country, that they might be on their guard. When the expresses got about a mile beyond Lexington, they were stopped by about fourteen officers on horseback, who came out of Boston in the afternoon of that day, and were seen lurking in by-places in the country till after dark. One of the expresses immediately fled, and was pursued two miles by an officer, who when he had got up with him presented a pistol, and told him he was a dead man if he did not stop, but he rode on till he came up to a house, when stopping of a sudden his horse threw him off, having the presence of mind to holloo to the people in the house, "Turn out! Turn out! I have got one of them!"

The officer immediately retreated and fled as fast as he had pursued. The other express, after passing through a strict examination, by some means got clear.

The body of the troops, in the meantime, under the command of Lieutenant Colonel Smith, had crossed the river and landed at Phipp's Farm. They immediately, to the number of 1,000, proceeded to Lexington, about six miles below Concord, with great silence. A company of militia, of about eighty men, mustered near the meetinghouse; the troops came in sight of them just before sunrise. The militia, upon seeing the troops, began to disperse. The troops then set out upon the run, hallooing and huzzaing, and coming within a few rods of them the commanding officer accosted the militia, in words to this effect,

"Disperse, you damn'd rebels! —Damn you, disperse!"

Upon which the troops again huzzaed and immediately one or two officers discharged their pistols, which were instantaneously followed by the firing of four or five of the soldiers; and then there seemed to be a general discharge from the whole body. It is to be noticed they fired on our people as they were dispersing, agreeable to their command, and that we did not even return the fire. Eight of our men were killed and nine wounded. The troops then laughed, and damned the Yankees, and said they could not bear the smell of gunpowder.

A little after this the troops renewed their march to Concord, where, when they arrived, they divided into parties, and went directly to several places where the province stores were deposited. Each party was supposed to have a Tory pilot. One party went into the jailyard and spiked up and otherwise damaged two cannon, belonging to the province, and broke and set fire to the carriages. Then they entered a store and rolled out about a hundred barrels of flour, which they unheaded and emptied about forty into the river. At the same time others were entering houses and shops, and unheading barrels, chests, etc., the property of private persons. Some took possession of the town house, to which they set fire, but was extinguished by our people without much hurt. Another party of the troops went and took possession of the North Bridge. About 150 provincials who mustered upon the alarm, coming toward the bridge, the troops fired upon them without ceremony and killed two on the spot! (Thus had the troops of Britain's king fired FIRST at two separate times upon his loyal American subjects, and put a period to two lives before one gun was fired upon them.) Our people THEN fired and obliged the troops to retreat, who were soon joined by their other parties, but finding they were still pursued the whole body retreated to Lexington, both provincials and troops firing as they went.

During this time an express from the troops was sent to General Gage, who thereupon sent out a reinforcement of about 1400 men, under the command of Earl Percy, with two fieldpieces. Upon the arrival of this reinforcement at Lexington, just as the retreating party had got there, they made a stand, picked up their dead, and took all the carriages they could find and put their wounded thereon. Others of them, to their eternal disgrace be it spoken, were robbing and setting houses on fire, and discharging their cannon at the meetinghouse.

The enemy, having halted about an hour at Lexington, found it necessary to make a second retreat, carrying with them many of their dead and wounded. They continued their retreat from Lexington to Charlestown with great precipitation. Our people continued their pursuit, firing till they got to Charlestown Neck (which they reached a little after sunset), over which the enemy passed, proceeded up Bunker's Hill, and the next day went into Boston, under the protection of the *Somerset,* man-of-war of sixty-four guns.

A young man, unarmed, who was taken prisoner by the enemy, and made to assist in carrying off their wounded, says that he saw a barber who lives in Boston, thought to be one Warden, with the troops and that he heard them say he was one of their pilots. He likewise saw the said barber fire twice upon our people and heard Earl Percy give the order to fire the houses. He also informs that several officers were among the wounded who were carried into Boston, where our informant was dismissed. They took two of our men prisoners in battle, who are now confined in barracks.

Immediately upon the return of the troops to Boston, all communication to and from the town was stopped by General Gage. The provincials, who flew to the assistance of their distressed countrymen, are posted in Cambridge, Charlestown, Roxbury, Watertown, etc., and have placed a guard on Roxbury Neck, within gunshot of the enemy. Guards are also placed everywhere in view of the town, to observe the motions of the King's troops. The Council of War and the different Committees of Safety and Supplies sit at Cambridge, and the Provincial Congress at Watertown. The troops in Boston are fortifying the place on all sides, and a frigate of war is stationed at Cambridge River, and a sixty-four-gun ship between Boston and Charlestown.

Deacon Joseph Loring's house and barn, Mrs. Mulliken's house and shop, and Mr. Joshua Bond's house and shop, in Lexington, were all consumed. They also set fire to several other houses, but our people extinguished the flames. They pillaged almost every house they passed by, breaking and destroying doors, windows, glass, etc., and carrying off clothing and other valuable effects. It appeared to be their design to burn and destroy all before them, and nothing but our vigorous pursuit prevented their infernal purposes from being put into execution. But the savage barbarity exercised upon the bodies of our unfortunate brethren who fell is almost incredible. Not content with shooting down the unarmed, aged, and infirm, they disregarded the cries of the wounded, killing them without mercy, and mangling their bodies in the most shocking manner.

We have the pleasure to say that notwithstanding the highest provocations given by the enemy, not one instance of cruelty that we have heard of was committed by our militia; but, listening to the merciful dictates of the Christian religion, they "breathed higher sentiments of humanity."

The public most sincerely sympathize with the friends and relations of our deceased brethren, who sacrificed their lives in fighting for the liberties of their country. By their noble intrepid conduct, in helping to defeat the force of an ungrateful tyrant, they have endeared their memories to the present generation, who will transmit their names to posterity with the highest honor.

† † †

One can stir up emotional feeling—from either political extreme, or from the center, for that matter—with little difficulty when the name and work and career of Thomas Paine are considered. Unlike Samuel Adams, his pamphleteer counterpart in Boston, Paine wrote in language that burns; his arguments may not always hold up logically, but as literature they have few rivals. He was an Englishman, who arrived in America in 1774 and produced his first important piece of propaganda in January 1776—in time for the events of that historic year and to help bring them about. Though Paine was scarcely the proletariat hero described in 1943 in Howard Fast's *Citizen Tom Paine,* he was a man of the people, even though his acquaintances in Britain included Edmund Burke and Oliver Goldsmith, even though his American friends included Jefferson and Franklin. *Common Sense* was that great document of 1776, and it is said that within a short time it was read by, or read to, virtually every inhabitant of the then British colonies in America. Paine's arguments were not original; he probably borrowed some from John Milton. But the excerpts that follow suggest not only the power of the arguments but also the power of the language, for had Paine presented his polemic in typical eighteenth century literary form it is doubtful that it would have had such a reception.

† † †

COMMON SENSE

By Thomas Paine, from *Common Sense,* 1776, in Howard Fast, ed., *The Selected Work of Tom Paine and Citizen Tom Paine* (New York: Modern Library, 1943), pp. 6-19.

ON THE ORIGIN AND DESIGN OF GOVERNMENT IN GENERAL, WITH CONCISE REMARKS ON THE ENGLISH CONSTITUTION.

Some writers have so confounded society with government, as to leave little or no distinction between them; whereas they are not only different, but have different origins. Society is produced by our wants, and government by our wickedness; the former promotes our happiness *positively* by uniting our affections, the latter *negatively* by restraining our vices. The one encourages intercourse, the other creates distinctions. The first is a patron, the last a punisher.

Society in every state is a blessing, but Government, even in its best state, is but a necessary evil; in its worst state an intolerable one: for when we suffer, or are exposed to the same miseries *by a Government,* which we might expect in a country *without Government,* our calamity is heightened by reflecting that we furnish the means by which we suffer. Government, like dress, is the badge of lost innocence; the palaces of kings are built upon the ruins of the bowers of paradise. For were the impulses of conscience clear, uniform, and irresistibly obeyed, man would need no other lawgiver; but that not being the case, he finds it necessary to surrender up a part of his property to furnish means for the protection of the rest; and this he is induced to do by the same prudence which in every other case advises him, out of two evils, to choose the least. Wherefore, security being the true design and end of government, it unanswerably follows that whatever form thereof appears most likely to ensure it to us, with the least expense and greatest benefit, is preferable to all others.

In order to gain a clear and just idea of the design and end of government, let us suppose a small number of persons settled in some sequestered part of the earth, unconnected with the rest; they will then represent the first peopling of any country, or of the world. In this state of natural liberty, society will be their first thought. A thousand motives will excite them thereto; the strength of one man is so unequal to his wants, and his mind so unfitted for perpetual solitude, that he is soon obliged to seek assistance and relief of another, who in his turn requires the same. Four or five united would be able to raise a tolerable dwelling in the midst of a wilderness, but one man might labour out the common period of life without accomplishing any thing; when he had felled his timber he could not remove it, nor erect it after it was removed; hunger in the mean time would urge him to quit his work, and every different want would call him a different way. Disease, nay even misfortune, would be death; for, though neither might be mortal, yet either would disable him from living, and reduce him to a state in which he might rather be said to perish than to die.

Thus necessity, like a gravitating power, would soon form our newly arrived emigrants into society, the reciprocal blessings of which would supercede, and render the obligations of law and government unnecessary while they remained perfectly just to each other; but as nothing but Heaven is impregnable to vice, it will unavoidably happen that in proportion as they surmount the first difficulties of emigration, which bound them together in a common cause, they will begin to relax in their duty and attachment to each other: and this remissness will point out the necessity of establishing some form of government to supply the defect of moral virtue.

Some convenient tree will afford them a State House, under the branches of which the whole Colony may assemble to deliberate on public matters. It is more than probable that their first laws will have the title only of Regulations and be enforced by no other penalty than public disesteem. In this first parliament every man by natural right will have a seat.

But as the Colony encreases, the public concerns will encrease likewise, and the distance at which the members may be separated, will render it too inconvenient for all of them to meet on every occasion as at first, when their number was small, their habitations near, and the public concerns few and trifling. This will point out the convenience of their consenting to leave the legislative part to be managed by a select number chosen from the whole body, who are supposed to have the same concerns at stake which those have who appointed them, and who will act in the same manner as the whole body would act were they present. If the colony continue encreasing, it will become necessary to augment the number of representatives, and that the interest of every part of the colony may be attended to, it will be found best to divide the whole into convenient parts, each part sending its proper number: and that the *elected* might never form to themselves an interest separate from the *electors,* prudence will point out the propriety of having elections often: because as the *elected* might by that means return and mix again with the general body of the *electors* in a few months, their fidelity to the public will be secured by the prudent reflection of not making a rod for themselves. And as this frequent interchange will establish a common interest with every part of the community; they will mutually and naturally support each other, and on this, (not on the unmeaning name of king,) depends the *strength of government, and the happiness of the governed.* . . .

England since the conquest hath known some few good monarchs, but groaned beneath a much larger number of bad ones: yet no man in his senses can say that their claim under William the Conqueror is a very honorable one. A French bastard landing with an armed Banditti and establishing himself king of England against the consent of the natives, is in plain terms a very paltry rascally original. It certainly hath no divinity in it. However it is needless to spend much time in exposing the folly of hereditary right; if there are any so weak as to believe it, let them promiscuously worship the Ass and the Lion, and welcome. I shall neither copy their humility, nor disturb their devotion. . . .

The Sun never shined ón a cause of greater worth. 'Tis not the affair of a City, a Country, a Province, or a Kingdom; but of a Continent—of at least one-eighth part of the habitable Globe. 'Tis not the concern of a day, a year, or an age; posterity are virtually involved in the contest, and will be more or less affected even to the end of time, by the proceedings now. Now is the seed-time of Continental union, faith, and honour. The least fracture now will be like a name engraved with the point of a pin on the tender rind of a young oak; the wound would enlarge with the tree, and posterity read in it full grown characters. . . .

† † †

Thomas Paine continued to write, and to write extensively, later producing *The Rights of Man,* a defense of the French Revolution, and *The Age of Reason,* an argument for deism. But in his role as propagandist of the American Revolution he is better remembered for the papers that followed *Common Sense* and that were known as *The American Crisis.* The first of these was produced in late 1776, after Paine himself had joined the army of Washington, after defeats and ill treatment by Congress had caused the army of 20,000 to fall off to a small band of hopeless, hungry soldiers. Legend attends the writing of the *Crisis* papers: it seems a splendid story indeed that Paine wrote by a campfire, on the head of a drum, with the tattered soldiers gathered about him. Let us keep the legend alive, for it is both harmless and glowing, and let us also savor some of the most powerful writing in the journalism of any country—the opening words of the *Crisis* papers.

† † †

THE TIMES THAT TRY MEN'S SOULS

By Thomas Paine, *The Crisis,* No. 1, in Howard Fast, ed., *The Selected Work of Tom Paine and Citizen Tom Paine* (New York: Modern Library, 1943), pp. 47-48.

These are the times that try men's souls. The summer soldier and the sunshine patriot will in this crisis, shrink from the service of his country; but he that stands it NOW, deserves the love and thanks of man and woman. Tyranny, like hell, is not easily conquered; yet we have this consolation with us, that the harder the conflict, the more glorious the triumph. What we obtain too cheap, we esteem too lightly; 'tis dearness only that gives everything its value. Heaven knows how to put a proper price upon its goods; and it would be strange indeed, if so celestial an article as FREEDOM should not be highly rated. Britain, with an army to enforce her tyranny, has declared that she has a right (*not only* to TAX) but "to BIND *us in* ALL CASES WHATSOEVER,*" and if being *bound in that manner,* is not slavery, then there is not such a thing as slavery upon earth. Even the expression is impious, for so unlimited a power can belong only to God.

Whether the independence of the continent was declared too soon, or delayed too long, I will not now enter into as an argument; my own simple opinion is, that had it been eight months earlier, it would have been much better. We did not make a proper use of last winter, neither could we, while we were in a dependent state. However, the fault, if it were one, was all our own; we have none to blame but ourselves. But no great deal is lost yet; all that Howe has been doing for this month past, is rather a ravage than a conquest, which the spirit of the Jerseys a year ago would have quickly repulsed, and which time and a little resolution will soon recover.

I have as little superstition in me as any man living, but my secret opinion has ever been, and still is, that God Almighty will not give up a people to military destruction, or leave them unsupportedly to perish, who have so earnestly and so repeatedly sought to avoid the calamities of war, by every decent method which wisdom could invent. Neither have I so much of the infidel in me, as to suppose that he has relinquished the government of the world, and given us up to the care of devils; and as I do not, I cannot see on what grounds the king of Britain can look up to heaven for help against us: a common murderer, a highwayman, or a house-breaker, has as good a pretence as he.

'Tis surprising to see how rapidly a panic will sometimes run through a country. All nations and ages have been subject to them: Britain has trembled like an ague at the report of a French fleet of flat-bottomed boats; and in the fourteenth century the whole English army, after ravaging the kingdom of France, was driven back like men petrified with fear; and this brave exploit was performed by a few broken forces collected and headed by a woman, Joan of Arc. Would that heaven might inspire some Jersey maid to spirit up her countrymen, and save her fair fellow sufferers from ravage and ravishment!

† † †

In the poet Philip Freneau the patriot cause had another powerful partisan, even though in his own behavior concerning the Revolution he seemed unsure. His most powerful words, it is interesting to note, were written after he was seized by the British while on his way to the West Indies. He was a New Jersey man, a graduate of the college that became Princeton, a classmate of James Madison and Aaron Burr and Hugh Henry Brackenridge, and, as we shall later see, a Jeffersonian editor in the 1790s. But poetry was his chief love, and his poetry appeared in such places as Brackenridge's *Pennsylvania Magazine.* He wrote extensively. We read briefly from "The British Prison Ship" and "In Memory of the Brave Americans," the one harsh and sometimes crude, the other gentle and moving, as befits this man who became the first American poet of nature.

† † †

THE BRITISH PRISON-SHIP

By Philip Freneau, in Evert A. Duyckinck, ed., *Philip Freneau's Poems Relating to the American Revolution* (New York: Crowell, 1865), p. 10.

Such food they sent to make complete our woes,—
It looked like carrion torn from hungry crows:
Such vermin vile on every joint were seen,
So black, corrupted, mortified, and lean,
That once we tried to move our flinty chief,
And thus addressed him, holding up the beef:
"See, Captain, see! what rotten bones we pick;
What kills the healthy cannot cure the sick;
Not dogs on such by Christian men are fed
And see, good master, see what lousy bread!
"Your meat or bread," this man of death replied,
"'Tis not my care to manage or provide—
But this, base rebel dogs, I'd have you know,
That better than your merit we bestow."

† † †

TO THE MEMORY OF THE BRAVE AMERICANS

By Philip Freneau, in Evert A. Duyckinck, ed., *Philip Freneau's Poems . . .*, pp. 134-135.

At Eutaw Springs the valiant died:
　　Their limbs with dust are cover'd o'er—
Weep on, ye spring, your tearful tide;
　　How many heroes are no more!

If in this wreck of ruin, they
　　Can yet be thought to claim a tear,
O smite thy gentle breast, and say
　　The friends of freedom slumber here!

Thou, who shalt trace this bloody plain,
　　If goodness rules thy generous breast,
Sigh for the wasted rural reign;
　　Sigh for the shepherds, sunk to rest!

† † †

American histories, those scores of books coming out of the minds of men and women since the Revolution, are loaded—understandably so. Most of these writers have identified with the patriot cause, and it is difficult to stir up enthusiasm for those known as the Tories, or as the Loyalists, or as the Royalists. Yet they, too, were Americans, and it is likely that they saw themselves as more patriotic than the Adamses, the Franklins, and the Jeffersons. Of the Tory editors the best known were Hugh Gaine, a turncoat who called his paper the *Gazette and Weekly Mercury,* and the mercurial and probably charming James Rivington—Jemmy Rivington, a Britisher, who founded in 1773 *Rivington's New York Gazetteer; or the Connecticut, New Jersey, Hudson's River and Quebec Weekly Advertiser.* Let us know it by its later name, the *Royal Gazette,* and reflect that, Tory or not, it was Rivington who penned those acid words about Isaiah Thomas and the "Join or Die" snake cartoon:

"Ye sons of sedition, how come it to pass,
That America's typ'd by a SNAKE—in the grass?"

Modern historical evidence suggests that James Rivington could be called by that exciting term of the recent age—a double agent. Maybe . . . It *is* believed that he changed letters, intercepted letters, took liberties with the truth. His style is conveyed in this paragraph.

† † †

A TORY ATTACK ON CONGRESS

By James Rivington, *Royal Gazette,* May 12, 1781.

The Congress is finally bankrupt! Last Saturday a large body of the inhabitants with paper dollars in their hats by way of cockades, paraded the streets of Philadelphia ... with a DOG TARRED, and instead of the usual appendage and ornament of feathers, his back was covered with the Congress' paper dollars. This example of disaffection, immediately under the eyes of the rulers of the revolted provinces, in solemn session at the State House assembled, was directly followed by the jailer, who refused accepting the bills in purchase of a glass of rum, and afterwards by the traders of the city, who shut up their shops, declining to sell any more goods but for gold or silver. It was declared also by the popular voice, that if the opposition to Great Britain was not in future carried on by solid money instead of paper bills, all further resistance to the mother country were vain, and must be given up.

† † †

James Rivington also carried moving social history, as in this statement made by a fleeing Tory:
"I leave America and every endearing connection, because I will not raise my hand against my Sovereign,—nor will I draw my sword against my Country; when I can conscientiously draw it in her favour, my life shall be cheerfully devoted to her service."
To indicate, too, the possible fate of those editors who disagreed with popular local opinion—and such editors were patriot, too, of course—there is a description from the *Pennsylvania Journal* in November 1775 of mob action directed against editor James Rivington:

† † †

A MOB ATTACKS A TORY EDITOR

Pennsylvania Journal, November, 1775, in Richard Wheeler, *Voices of 1776* (New York: Crowell, 1972), pp. 91-92.

On the twentieth of this month, sixteen respectable inhabitants of New Haven, Connecticut, in company with Captain Sears, set out from that place to East and West Chester, in the province of New York, to disarm the principal Tories there and secure the persons of Parson Seabury, Judge Fowler and Lord Underhill. On their way thither they were joined by Captains Richards, Sillick and Mead, with about eighty men. At Mamaroneck they burnt a small sloop which was ... [used] for the purpose of carrying provisions on board the *Asia.* At East Chester they seized Judge Fowler, then repaired to

West Chester and secured Seabury and Underhill. Having possessed themselves of these three caitiffs, they sent them to Connecticut under a strong guard.

The main body, consisting of seventy-five, then proceeded to New York, where they entered at noonday on horseback, bayonets fixed, in the greatest regularity, went down the main street and drew up in close order before the printing office of the infamous James Rivington. A small detachment entered it, and in about three-quarters of an hour brought off the principal part of his types. . . . They then faced and wheeled to the left and marched out of town to the tune of Yankee Doodle. A vast concourse of people assembled at the Coffee House, on their leaving the ground, and gave them three very hearty cheers.

On their way home they disarmed all the Tories that lay on their route, and yesterday arrived at New Haven escorted by a great number of gentlemen from the westward, the whole making a very grand procession. Upon their entrance into town they were saluted with the discharge of two cannon and received by the inhabitants with every mark of approbation and respect. . . .

4

EARLY YEARS IN A REPUBLIC

Thomas Jefferson and Alexander Hamilton—the mighty names of our early history as a nation, the men to whom we trace many currents and attitudes in our political systems. An understanding of the Jefferson-Hamilton dispute could possibly provide a basis for understanding much of our political history. Knowledge of these two famous men and their political positions is essential to an understanding of the documents in the 1783-1833 segment of our history: the early years of the republic, from Washington's time into Jackson's, from the party press up to what we call the penny press.

It oversimplifies Jefferson and Hamilton to treat them merely as opposites, and even Jefferson in his later years made considerable accommodation to what we think of as Hamiltonian attitudes. Jefferson was a Virginia aristocrat, at least on one side of his family, and he sometimes thought like an aristocrat. If he was philosophically attuned to the masses, it was not that he had come to such a view out of his own background; he was *not* a Thomas Paine. He dreamed of an America that would be like the Virginia he had known as a boy, the Virginia where he had built his Monticello, founded a state university, and served as governor. He was a southern planter, too, and recent writings recall some rumors that damaged the Jeffersonian reputation in his presidential days, especially rumors relating to his "arrangement" with a slave woman. Jefferson envisioned a democratic agrarian order based on the small individual—the farmer, the laborer, the artisan. He favored a broad spread of the wealth, and his European experience had persuaded him that we would be better if we were free from industrialism, urbanism, finance, and commerce. In a time when the creditor-debtor issue was important in politics he backed the debtor; in a time when states' rights belonged on the left of the political spectrum he opposed a centralized government. He believed that men, acting through representative institutions, and given some education, could be left to govern themselves.

Hamilton was *arriviste*, a man "on the make," a West Indian born illegitimate, and one who possibly felt the stigma of such a beginning. His background, then, was quite different from that of Jefferson. Hamilton performed ably during the American Revolution, and he amassed a dedicated following, rapidly demonstrating that his tendencies and attitudes were far more conservative and far more aristocratic than those of Jefferson. But his conservatism was not the traditionalism of an Edmund Burke or a John Adams; the kind of society he envisioned for America appalled Adams, and Hamilton and Adams definitely were not friends. Hamilton favored an economic order more balanced and diversified than the one dreamed of by Jefferson, and he thought that government should give active encouragement to certain sectors of the society— financial, industrial, commercial. His sympathy lay with the creditor; he advocated a strong national government under a strong executive; states' rights were not important to Alexander Hamilton. He distrusted the capacity of the people to govern; where Jefferson looked at history and emerged with an optimistic view, Hamilton looked at it and came out pessimistic. The best government, he believed, was that of an elite.

And the conflict between Jefferson and Hamilton both marked and marred the years that followed. It realized itself later in the Whig-Democratic disputes, in the quarreling over the "American System" of Henry Clay and the National Bank in the time of Andrew Jackson. It lay behind the frequently virulent party press that prevailed until the coming of penny journalism.

In the Revolution, propaganda had been the primary role of the press, in utterances from the three positions—patriot, Whig, loyalist. Propaganda remained the role of the press in the 1790s; not for more than a generation did the true *newspaper* emerge, the newspaper whose chief concern was news. In the 1780s the newspaper press led in stirring up the controversies, the arguments during that tenuous era in which the former colonies were governed by the Articles of Confederation—a structure that ultimately proved so unsatisfactory that demands began to grow for a stronger governmental organization. And so the Constitutional Convention met, again in historic Philadelphia, in 1787. On October 27 of that year a document was published in the *Independent Journal,* signed *Publius,* the signature that appeared on all subsequent articles of the series we know now as the *Federalist* papers. The series ran to April 1788, and the six final numbers appeared first in book form. It was revealed later that the authors were three of our most notable public men—James Madison, Alexander Hamilton, and John Jay. The first of these *Federalist* papers was written by Hamilton.

† † †

THE FEDERALIST NO. 1

Independent Journal, in Alexander Hamilton, James Madison and John Jay, *Selections from The Federalist* (New York: Appleton-Century-Crofts, 1949), pp. 1-3.

To the People of the State of New York:

After an unequivocal experience of the inefficiency of the subsisting federal government, you are called upon to deliberate on a new Constitution for the United States of America. The subject speaks its own importance; comprehending in its consequences nothing less than the existence of the UNION, the safety and welfare of the parts of which it is composed, the fate of an empire in many respects the most interesting in the world. It has been frequently remarked that it seems to have been reserved to the people of this country, by their conduct and example, to decide the important question, whether societies of men are really capable or not of establishing good government from reflection and choice, or whether they are forever destined to depend for their political constitutions on accident and force. If there be any truth in the remark, the crisis at which we are arrived may with propriety be regarded as the era in which the decision is to be made; and a wrong election of the part we shall act may, in this view, deserve to be considered as the general misfortune of mankind.

This idea will add the inducements of philanthropy to those of patriotism, to heighten the solicitude which all considerate and good men must feel for the event. Happy will it be if our choice should be directed by a judicious estimate of our true interests, unperplexed and unbiased by considerations not connected with the public good. But this is a thing more ardently to be wished than seriously to be expected. The plan offered to our deliberations affects too many particular interests, innovates upon too many local institutions, not to involve in its discussion a variety of objects foreign to its merits, and of views, passions and prejudices little favorable to the discovery of truth.

Among the most formidable of the obstacles which the new Constitution will have to encounter may readily be distinguished the obvious interest of a certain class of men in every State to resist all changes which may hazard a diminution of the power, emolument, and consequence of the offices they hold under the State establishments; and the perverted ambition of another class of men, who will either hope to aggrandize themselves by the confusions of their country, or will flatter themselves with fairer prospects of elevation from the subdivision of the empire into several partial confederacies than from its union under one government.

It is not, however, my design to dwell upon observations of this nature. I am well aware that it would be disingenuous to resolve indiscriminately the opposition of any set of men (merely because their situations might subject them to suspicion) into interested or ambitious views. Candor will oblige us to admit that even such men may be actuated by upright intentions; and it cannot be doubted that much of the opposition which has made its appearance, or may hereafter make its appearance, will spring from sources, blameless at least, if not respectable—the honest errors of minds led astray by preconceived jealousies and fears. So numerous indeed and so powerful are the causes which serve to give a false bias to the judgment, that we, upon many occasions, see wise and good men on the wrong as well as on the right side of questions of the first magnitude to society. This circumstance, if duly attended to, would furnish a lesson of moderation to those who are ever so much persuaded of their being in the right in any controversy. And a further reason for caution, in this respect, might be drawn from the reflection that we are not always sure that those who advocate the truth are influenced by purer principles than their antagonists. Ambition, avarice, personal animosity, party opposition, and many other motives not more laudable than these, are apt to operate as well upon those who support as those who oppose the right side of a question. Were there not even inducements to moderation, nothing could be more ill-judged than that intolerant spirit which has, at all times, characterized political parties. For in politics, as in religion, it is equally absurd to aim at making proselytes by fire and sword. Heresies in either can rarely be cured by persecution.

And yet, however just these sentiments will be allowed to be, we have already sufficient indications that it will happen in this as in all former cases of great national discussion. A torrent of angry and malignant passions will be let loose. To judge from the conduct of the opposite parties, we shall be led to conclude that they will mutually hope to evince the justness of their opinions, and to increase the number of their converts by the loudness of their declamations and the bitterness of their invectives. An enlightened zeal for the energy and efficiency of government will be stigmatized as the offspring of a temper fond of despotic power and hostile to the principles of liberty. An over-scrupulous jealousy of danger to the rights of the people, which is more commonly the fault of the head than of the heart, will be represented as mere pretence and artifice, the stale bait for popularity at the expense of the public good. It will be forgotten, on the one hand, that jealousy is the usual concomitant of love, and that the noble enthusiasm of liberty is apt to be infected with a spirit of narrow and illiberal distrust. On the other hand, it will be equally forgotten that the vigor of government is essential to the security of liberty; that, in the contemplation of a sound and well-informed judgment, their interest can never be separated; and that a dangerous ambition more often lurks behind the specious mask of zeal for the firmness and efficiency of government. History will teach us that the former has been found a much more certain road to the introduction of despotism than the latter, and that of those men who have overturned the liberties of republics, the greatest number have begun their career by paying an obsequious court to the people; commencing demagogues, and ending tyrants.

In the course of the preceding observations, I have had an eye, my fellow-citizens, to putting you upon your guard against all attempts, from whatever quarter, to influence your decision in a matter of the utmost moment to your welfare, by any impressions other than those which may result from the evidence of truth. You will, no doubt, at the same time, have collected from the general scope of them, that they proceed from a source not unfriendly to the new Constitution. Yes, my countrymen, I own to you that, after having given it an attentive consideration, I am clearly of opinion it is your interest to adopt it. I am convinced that this is the safest course for your liberty, your dignity, and your happiness. I affect not reserves which I do not feel. I will not amuse you with an appearance of deliberation when I have decided. I frankly acknowledge to you my convictions, and I will freely lay before you the reasons on which they are founded. The consciousness of good intentions disdains ambiguity. I shall not, however, multiply professions on this head. My motives must remain in the depository of my own breast. My arguments will be open to all, and may be judged of by all. They shall at least be offered in a spirit which will not disgrace the cause of truth. . . .

† † †

The lack of a "bill of rights" in the Constitution stirred numerous attacks upon the document and its authors. In *Federalist Paper LXXXIV,* Hamilton defended the absence of any explicit statement of rights, and he made reference in particular to the matter of freedom of the press.

† † †

THE FEDERALIST NO. LXXXIV

By Alexander Hamilton, James Madison and John Jay, *The Federalist,* in Frank Luther Mott and Ralph D. Casey, ed., *Interpretations of Journalism* (New York: Crofts, 1937), p. 39.

. . . On the subject of the liberty of the Press, as much has been said, I cannot forbear adding a remark or two. In the first place, I observe that there is not a syllable concerning it in the Constitution of this State; in the next, I contend that whatever has been said about it in that of any other State, amounts to nothing. What signifies a declaration, that "the liberty of the Press shall be inviolably preserved"? What is the liberty of the Press? Who can give it any definition which would not leave the utmost latitude for evasion? I hold it to be impracticable; and from this I infer, that its security, whatever fine declarations may be inserted in any Constitution respecting it, must altogether depend on public opinion, and on the general spirit of the people and of the Government. And here, after all, as intimated upon another occasion, must we seek for the only solid basis for all our rights. . . .

† † †

Immediate harmony among the former colonies did not follow publication of the *Federalist* papers. The press of editor Thomas Greenleaf of the *New York Journal* was wrecked, because the editor opposed ratification of the Constitution. And out of the dispute over the Constitution arose the parties that came to be known as Federalist and Anti-Federalist, that grew eventually into, our present-day Republican and Democratic parties, respectively, though the genealogical lineage is far from exact. Out of the parties arose the oft-virulent party newspapers of the 1790s, the newspapers of those good old days to which we so often refer—the age Frank Luther Mott called "the dark ages of partisan journalism." In Philadelphia, our national capital in the 1790s, the most important of the party papers were concentrated—the *Gazette of the United States* of John Fenno and the *National Gazette* of Philip Freneau. The first of these was a newspaper backed by Alexander Hamilton; the second was backed by Thomas Jefferson. John Fenno presented an aristocratic point of view that was derided by opposition editors.

† † †

AN EDITORIAL BY JOHN FENNO

Gazette of the United States, March, 1790, cited in Samuel Forman, *The Political Activities of Philip Freneau,* in the *Johns Hopkins University Studies in Historical and Political Science* (Baltimore: Johns Hopkins Press, 1902), p. 42.

Take away thrones and crowns from among men and there will soon be an end of all dominion and justice. There must be some adventitious properties infused into the government to give it energy and spirit, or the selfish, turbulent passions of men can never be controlled. This has occasioned that artificial splendor and dignity that are to be found in the courts of many nations. The people of the United States may probably be induced to regard and obey the laws without requiring the experiment of courts and titled monarchs. In proportion as we become populous and wealthy must the tone of the government be strengthened.

† † †

In his *National Gazette,* Philip Freneau, the poet of the Revolution, some of whose work we already have seen, offered his opinions, most of them in opposition to the sometimes aristocratic, if not monarchist, opinions of Fenno, whose point of view was similar to that of Benjamin Russell in the *Columbian Centinel* and Noah Webster in the *American Minerva.* Freneau was especially taken with the revolutionary experiment then going on in France, and his admiration proved his undoing. Freneau, in prose a bit heavy, offered a satire of what a page of news would be like in 1801 in the

Gazette of Fenno if that editor's monarchist ideal should come to pass.

† † †

AN EDITORIAL BY PHILIP FRENEAU

National Gazette, cited in Samuel Forman, *The Political Activities of Philip Freneau,* p. 44.

On Monday last arrived in this city in perfect health, His Most Serene Highness the Protector of the United States, who on Wednesday next will review the regular troops which compose the garrison.

Yesterday came on before the circuit court of the Protector, the trial of James Barefoot, laborer, for carelessly treading on the great toe of My Lord Ohio. The defendant was found guilty, but as the offense appeared quite accidental, and his lordship had already inflicted on him fifty lashes, the court fined him only 100 pounds and ordered him to be imprisoned six months. Considering the blood and rank of the prosecutor, the humanity of the sentence cannot be too highly extolled. His Lordship's toe is in a fair way of recovery, although one of his physicians thinks the nail is in danger.

† † †

Philip Freneau's party colleague, successor, and rival, too, was Benjamin Franklin Bache, grandson of the beloved Ben, an imperious young man who was laughingly referred to as "Lightning Rod Jr." He was not at all restrained in his language or in his support of the French, and he especially was taken with that envoy to America, Citizen Edmond Genêt. Like Freneau he loved to lampoon the Federalists, especially Adams and Hamilton, and like Freneau he lashed the already untouchable Father of Our Country. Among early-day editorials few have the force, or the cruelty, of Bache's exultant words on the occasion of Washington leaving the presidency, words that may have been inspired by what Bache saw as Washington's treatment of Franklin.

† † †

AN EDITORIAL BY BENJAMIN FRANKLIN BACHE

Philadelphia *Aurora,* March 6, 1797.

"Lord, now lettest thou thy servant depart in peace, for mine eyes have seen thy salvation," was the pious ejaculation of a man who beheld a flood of happiness rushing in upon mankind. If ever there was a time that would license the reiteration of the exclamation, that time is now arrived; for the man who is the source of all the misfortunes of our country, is this day reduced to a level with his fellow citizens, and is no longer possessed of power to multiply evils upon the United States. If ever there was a period for rejoicing, this is the moment—every heart in unison with the freedom and happiness of the people ought to beat high, with exultation that the name of Washington from this day ceases to give a currency to political iniquity, and to legalize corruption. A new era is opening upon us, a new era which promises much to the people; for public measures must now stand upon their own merits, and nefarious projects can no longer be supported by a name. When a retrospect is taken of the Washingtonian Administration for eight years, it is a subject of the greatest astonishment, that a single individual should have canceled the principles of republicanism in an enlightened people, and should have carried his designs against the public liberty so far, as to have put in jeopardy its very existence. Such, however, are the facts, and with these staring us in the face, this day ought to be a *jubilee* in the United States.

† † †

Both sides had their men of intemperate language and behavior in those troubled nineties, of course. One of these men came to America from England—William Cobbett, already disliked in his home country for the vitriol of his attacks, and he continued such attacks in America, where he founded a paper called *Porcupine's Gazette* in 1797. Cobbett had a strongly vituperative style, and he came to be almost as disliked within his own party, the Federalist, as within the Republican. He finally left America, and he had a later career in England, part of it marked by that strange episode in which he dug up the bones of Thomas Paine in New York state with the plan of putting them on exhibition in England. But long before he left these shores he showed the vigor of his style and the force of his invective in his aptly titled newspaper, and one of his targets was the very Benjamin Franklin Bache who was so rough on Washington.

† † †

WILLIAM COBBETT ON BACHE

Porcupine's Gazette, November 14, 1797.

This atrocious wretch (worthy descendant of old Ben) knows that all men of any understanding set him down as an abandoned liar, a tool and a hireling; and he is content that they should do so. He does not want to be thought anything else. As this *Gazette* is honored with many readers in foreign countries, it may not be improper to give them some little account of this miscreant.

If they have read the old hypocrite Franklin's will, they must have observed that part of his library, with some other things, are left to a certain *grandson;* this is the very identical Market-Street scoundrel.

He spent several years in hunting offices under the Federal Government, and being constantly rejected, he at last became its most bitter foe. Hence his abuse of General Washington, whom, at the time he was soliciting a place, he panegyrized to the third heaven.

He was born for a hireling, and therefore when he found that he could not obtain employ in one quarter, he sought it in another. The first effect of his paw being greased, appeared soon after Genet's arrival, and he has from that time to this been as faithful to the cutthroats of Paris, as ever dog was to his master.

He is an ill-looking devil. His eyes never get above your knees. He is of a sallow complexion, hollow-cheeked, dead-eyed, and has *a tout ensemble* just like that of a fellow who has been about a week or ten days on a gibbet.

† † †

Such language, intemperate and injudicious, had at least a little to do with that ugly episode in our history known as the Alien and Sedition Acts, a series of laws that were the chief manifestation of the Federalist-Republican controversy. These laws were passed in the administration of John Adams and were directed mainly against the Republican admirers of Thomas Jefferson. It must be remembered, too, that they were passed in a time when this young and feeble nation was in deep fear of war with either England or France. In opposition to the Alien and Sedition Acts two states adopted resolutions in their legislatures—the now-famous Virginia and Kentucky Resolutions, the first written by James Madison, the second by Jefferson, both arguing for a principle that in later times became known as nullification.

Public figures on both sides were the targets of the press, for attacks upon the presidency are far from being a modern-day invention. Jefferson especially suffered from attack; the *New-England Palladium,* a Federalist paper, said of him: "Should the Infidel Jefferson be elected to the Presidency, the seal of death is that moment set on our holy religion, our churches will be prostrated, and some infamous prostitute, under the title of the Goddess of Reason, will preside in the Sanctuaries now devoted to the Most High." Jefferson, it would appear, was able to rise above such attacks, though he himself seemed a bit enamored of overdone language in one of his most famous utterances.

† † †

LETTER TO EDWARD CARRINGTON

Paris, January 16, 1787, in Adrienne Koch and William Peden, eds., *The Life and Selected Writings of Thomas Jefferson* (New York: Modern Library, 1944), pp. 411-412.

. . . The people are the only censors of their governors; and even their errors will tend to keep these to the true principles of their institution. To punish these errors too severely would be to suppress the only safe-guard of the public of the public liberty. The way to prevent these irregular interpositions of the people is to give them full information of their affairs thro' the channel of the public papers, & to contrive that those papers should penetrate the whole mass of the people. The basis of our governments being the opinion of the people, the first object should be to keep that right; and were it left to me to decide whether we should have a government without newspapers or newspapers without a government, I should not hesitate to prefer the latter. But I should mean that every man should receive those papers & be capable of reading them. I am convinced that those societies (as the Indians) which live without government enjoy in their general mass an infinitely greater degree of happiness than those who live under the European governments. Among the former, public opinion is in the place of law, & restrains morals as powerfully as laws ever did anywhere. Among the latter, under pretence of governing they have divided their nations into two classes, wolves & sheep. I do not exaggerate. This is a true picture of Europe. Cherish therefore the spirit of our people, and keep alive their attention. Do not be too severe upon their errors, but reclaim them by enlightening them.

† † †

That letter written by Thomas Jefferson preceded his presidency, of course, and also the bitter feelings over war with England, the purchase of Louisiana, the Burr affair, and the moving of the capital to the District of Columbia. Jefferson's chief opponent in public life, Alexander Hamilton, also offered a viewpoint on the press, arguing in behalf of Harry Croswell, the editor of the *Wasp*, in Hudson, New York, who had libeled Jefferson. There is a basic right to criticize public men, said Hamilton, in anticipation of court holdings of the 1960s.

† † †

THE RIGHT TO CRITICIZE PUBLIC MEN

By Alexander Hamilton, in Frank Luther Mott and Ralph D. Casey, eds., *Interpretations of Journalism* (New York: Crofts, 1937), pp. 58-59.

... After these preliminary observations, and before I advance to the full discussion of this question, it may be necessary for the safety and accuracy of investigation, a little to define what this liberty of the press is, for which we contend, and which the present doctrines of those opposed to us, are, in our opinions, calculated to destroy.

The liberty of the press consists, in my idea, in publishing the truth, from good motives and for justifiable ends, though it reflect on government, on magistrates, or individuals. If it be not allowed, it excludes the privilege of canvassing men, and our rulers. It is in vain to say, you may canvass measures. This is impossible without the right of looking to men. To say that measures can be discussed, and that there shall be no bearing on those who are the authors of those measures, cannot be done. The very end and reason of discussion would be destroyed. Of what consequence to show its object? Why is it to be thus demonstrated, if not to show, too, who is the author? It is essential to say, not only that the measure is bad and deleterious, but to hold up to the people who is the author, that, in this our free and elective government, he may be removed from the seat of power. If this be not to be done, then in vain will the voice of the people be raised against the inroads of tyranny. For, let a party but get into power, they may go on from step to step, and, in spite of canvassing their measures, fix themselves firmly in their seats, especially as they are never to be reproached for what they have done. This abstract mode, in practice can never be carried into effect. But, if under the qualifications I have mentioned, the power be allowed, the liberty, for which I contend, will operate as a salutary check. In speaking thus for the freedom of the press, I do not say there ought to be an unbridled license; or that the characters of men who are good, will naturally tend eternally to support themselves. I do not stand here to say that no shackles are to be laid on this license.

I consider this spirit of abuse and calumny as the pest of society. I know the best of men are not exempt from the attacks of slander. Though it pleased God to bless us with the first of characters, and though it has pleased God to take him from us, and this band of calumniators, I say, that falsehood eternally repeated would have affected even his name. Drops of water, in long and continued succession, will wear out adamant. This, therefore, cannot be endured. It would be to put the best and the worst on the same level. . . .

Some observations have, however, been made in opposition to these principles. It is said, that as no man rises at once high into office, every opportunity of canvassing his qualities and qualifications is afforded, without recourse to the press; that his first election ought to stamp the seal of merit on his name. This, however, is to forget how often the hypocrite goes from stage to stage of public fame, under false array, and how often, when men attain the last object of their wishes, they change from that which they seemed to be; that men, the most zealous reverers of the people's rights, have, when placed on the highest seat of power, become their most deadly oppressors. It becomes, therefore, necessary to observe the actual conduct of those who are thus raised up. . . .

† † †

Of the papers that gave their support to Thomas Jefferson during his presidency, the most important was the *National Intelligencer,* established in 1800 by Samuel Harrison Smith. This editor was an able shorthand reporter. He deserves special attention because after some difficulty he obtained the right to sit in the chamber of the House of Representatives during debate, and he kept the only records of such debate for some time. His paper thereby achieved the distinction of being the journal on which all other papers based their news of government in the first quarter of the century. Smith had been advised by Jefferson to come to Washington from Philadelphia, and his newspaper became the official organ of the administration. It is not surprising, then, that an editorial reflecting on British behavior prior to the War of 1812 should have appeared in this newspaper, written by Smith.

† † †

AN EDITOR ATTACKS THE BRITISH

National Intelligencer, July 10, 1807.

We are pleased to observe the circumspection of the merchants. If they consult their own interests, or that of the country, they will for a time repress their spirit of adventure, and run as few risks as possible, until an explicit answer shall be given by the British Ministry. As yet it remains a point undetermined whether the late barbarous outrages have emanated directly from the British Cabinet, or are the acts exclusively of subordinate commanders. If they are directly authorized by the Cabinet, then we may calculate upon a scene of violence co-extensive with British power, and for another display of that perfidy so characteristic of its government. Every American vessel on the ocean will be seized and sent into some British port for adjudication, and the courts will take special care, if they do not forthwith proceed to condemnation, at any rate to keep the cases *sub judice.* Indeed, if the recent outrages do not emanate from the government, it is difficult to say whether they will not, notwithstanding, seize what they may consider a favorable opportunity to wreak their vengeance on this country. We know the hostility of the greater part of those who compose the British administration to our principles, and they may be Quixotic enough to imagine themselves able to crush these principles, or seriously arrest our commercial growth. They may, therefore, under some hollow pretext, refuse that satisfaction which we demand, the result of which will be war. There is indeed no small color of truth in the supposition that this outrage has flowed from the change in the British Ministry, connected with the fate the treaty has received from our government, and that without meaning or expecting war, they have virtually authorized aggressions on us, which they fancied we would tamely submit to; and that however astonished they may be with the manifestation they will soon receive of the temper of the nation, their pride may prevent them from retracting.

Everything is, and must for some time remain, uncertain. In the meantime, it becomes our duty to husband all our strength. But little injury can accrue to the merchant from a suspension of his export business for a few months, compared with the incalculable evils that might befall him from its active prosecution. He is, therefore, under a double obligation to pursue this course, arising not only from a regard to his own interest, but likewise from a love of his country. In the day of danger it will want all its resources, and all its seamen. Were Congress in session, it is extremely probable that their first step would be the imposition of an embargo. What they would do, were they sitting, it is the interest and duty of the merchant to do himself. We have no doubt that the intelligence of this order of men may on this occasion, as it has on all former occasions, be relied on.

† † †

Samuel Harrison Smith was succeeded on the *National Intelligencer* in 1810 by Joseph Gales Jr., son of the Englishman who had come to America and established himself as a printer of considerable success, as a reporter of congressional affairs, and as a sponsor of Smith himself. The younger Gales was joined in 1812 by W. W. Seaton, and the two became a powerful combination, covering both House and Senate. Their newspaper was distinctive; Allan Nevins wrote that it, more than any other, offered acute observations of American life in its editorial columns—such as these:

† † †

AN OPINION ON A RAILROAD

National Intelligencer, March 5, 1827.

A great Railway is spoken of in Baltimore, to extend from Baltimore to the Ohio, and many capitalists are said seriously to patronize the thought. They had better patronize the Ohio and Chesapeake Canal, which appears to us much more feasible than a railway *three hundred miles long.* We cannot conceive of the practicability of such work, as a regular everyday line of transportation. We shall, however, lay before our readers the arguments in favor of the measure, which we should be far from opposing from any mean motive of jealousy or envy, if the work is practicable. There would be trade enough to leave the road, whenever it found a water communication—at Cumberland, for example—to make the part of the road which crosses the mountain ridges a very important work to this District.

† † †

A VOTE AGAINST GENERAL JACKSON

National Intelligencer, August 4, 1827.

Of the seductiveness of military fame in popular governments, if we had ever doubted it, the last Presidential election has given us instructive illustration. Mr. Adams, Mr. Crawford, Mr. Clay, and Mr. Calhoun, all distinguished civilians, were familiarly spoken of as candidates for the Presidency before General Jackson was seriously announced. The moment he was brought forward, the soldiers whom he had led to battle rallied under his standard. It was by them, in fact, that he was formally presented as a candidate. The military fervor, created by the arrival and triumphal progress of the good Lafayette through the land, aided the spread of the contagion; and in some populous districts of the interior, the militia, exalted into enthusiasm by the militia victory at New Orleans, marched almost literally in embattled legions to the polls. Had the election taken place three months later, it is quite possible that the experiment would have been made, which we have been taught by all history to deprecate, of a successful general arriving, by means solely of a military achievement, at the highest station of the republic.

Such an experiment we deprecate, not because we have any apprehension for the form of our government from any leader, military or civil. The Constitution will be found strong enough to check the boldest and most daring attempt at usurpation. But we object to placing a military man in the chief authority because, having once tasted of the pleasure of absolute command, as on the field of battle, he may retain the relish for it, and is too likely, in the exercise of public duties, to substitute for the injunctions of law, or the suggestions of policy, his own sovereign will and pleasure. He cannot endanger the existence of the government, but he may endanger the public peace, at home as well as abroad. We object to such elevation of a military man especially when his military fame is the only argument in favor of it, and when his civil qualifications are either not inquired into, or not established.

† † †

Our early journalistic history was not restricted to the newspaper or the pamphlet. There had been a string of notable magazines, going back to such publications as Franklin's *General Magazine* in 1741 and the brilliant *American Magazine* of William Bradford in 1757-58; coming up through Robert Aitken's *Pennsylvania Magazine* of the Revolution, the one for which Thomas Paine wrote; Joseph Greenleaf's *Royal American Magazine,* patriot, despite its name; Hugh Henry Brackenridge's *United States Magazine;* another *American Magazine,* this one edited by Noah Webster; the distinguished *American Museum* of Matthew Carey; and into the early nineteenth century, when Joseph Dennie published his famous *Port Folio* in Philadelphia, Harvard people published the *North American Review,* and others began the *Saturday Evening Post.* As a repository of information and insights about early America, few publications, however, have the importance of the magazine called *Niles' Weekly Register,* started by Hezekiah Niles in Baltimore, in 1811. It was an excellent compendium of speeches, documents, governmental statements, and commentary. In 1820 the Missouri Compromise came onto the stage of history, heard by Jefferson as a "firebell in the night." Niles was opposed to slavery but supported the compromise.

† † †

HEZEKIAH NILES ON SLAVERY

Niles' Weekly Register, December 23, 1820.

It is established (so far as large majorities in both houses of Congress can establish it) that the power to check the progress of a slave population within the territories of the United States exists by the Constitution; but admitted that it was not expedient to exert that power in regard to Missouri and Arkansas. The latter depended on many considerations of no ordinary importance: the safety and feelings of the white population in several of the States appeared to be involved in it, and the rights and feelings of others were as deeply concerned in the subject at large. In this conflict of interests, among persons who possibly desired the same ultimate issue, though their views of it were diametrically opposed, a spirit of conciliation prevailed and a compromise was effected. The people of those sections of the country in which there are few or no slaves or persons of color, very imperfectly appreciate the wants, necessity, or general principle of others differently situated.

Collectively, the latter deprecate slavery as severely as the former, and deprecate its increase; but individual cupidity and rashness acts against the common sentiment, in the hope that an event which everybody believes must happen, will not happen in their day. It is thus that too many of us act about death; we are sure it must come, yet we commit wrong to acquire property, just as if we should hold and enjoy it forever. That the slave population will, at some certain period, cause the most horrible catastrophe, cannot be doubted; those who possess them act defensively in behalf of all that is nearest and dearest to them, when they endeavor to acquire all the strength and influence to meet that period which they can; and hence the political and civil opposition to these to the restriction which was proposed to be laid on Missouri. They *have* the offensive population, and no feasible plan has yet been contrived to rid them of it, if they were disposed to do so. Will the people of any of the States, so much alive to humanity, pass acts to encourage emancipation by agreeing to receive the emancipated? What will they do, what can they do, to assist the people of others to relieve themselves of their unfortunate condition? It is easy to use severe terms against the practise of slavery; but let us first tell the Southern people what they can safely do to abolish it, before we condemn them wholesale.

No one can hate slavery more than I do—it is a thing opposed to every principle that operates on my mind as an individual—and in my own private circle I do much to discourage it. I am also exceedingly jealous of it, so far as it affects my political rights as a citizen of the United States, entitled to be fairly and fully represented, and no more. But I can make great allowances for those who hold slaves in districts where they abound—where, in many cases, their emancipation might be an act of cruelty to them, and of most serious injury to the white population. Their difference of color is an insuperable barrier to their incorporation within the society; and the mixture of free blacks with slaves is detrimental to the happiness of both, the cause of uncounted crimes. Yet I think that some have urged their defensive character too far; without a proper respect for the rights and feelings of others, as applicable to an extension of the evil. But we advocated the compromise, as fixing certain points for the future government of all the parties concerned; believing that the moral and political evil of spreading slavery over Missouri and even in Arkansas was not greater than that which might have risen from restriction, though to restrict was right in itself. The harmony of the Union, and the peace and prosperity of the white population, most excited our sympathies. We did not fear the dreadful things which some silly folks talked of, but apprehended geographical oppositions which might lead to the worst of calamities. We had no pleasant feeling on the Compromise, for bad was the best that could be done. Nevertheless, we hoped that the contest was at an end, and that things would settle down and adapt themselves to the agreement which necessity imposed.

† † †

In 1801, Alexander Hamilton had founded another of the famous newspapers, the *New York Evening Post,* which was powerfully Federalist under editor William Coleman but became a Jacksonian Democratic, then Free Soil, then abolitionist Republican journal—all under the editorship of William Cullen Bryant. This editor was better known as a poet, of course, for a time perhaps the best-known poet of America, and one who maintained his popularity through much of the nineteenth century. As an adolescent he wrote the remarkable "Thanatopsis," and later "To a Waterfowl" and other pieces of nature poetry. As a man of nature, one who associated with the painters of the Hudson River School and liked to flee the heat and turmoil of New York, he ventured out into the still pastoral Manhattan island and was inspired to write one of his best editorials.

† † †

PROMOTING A PARK FOR NEW YORK

New York Evening Post, July 3, 1844.

The heats of summer are upon us, and while some are leaving the town for shady retreats in the country, others refresh themselves with short excursions to Hoboken and New Brighton, or other places among the beautiful environs of our city. If the public authorities who spend so much of our money in laying out the city would do what is in their power, they might give our vast population an extensive pleasure ground for shade and recreation in these sultry afternoons, which we might reach without going out of town.

On the road to Harlem, between Sixty-eighth Street on the south and Seventy-seventh on the north, and extending from Third Avenue to the East River, is a tract of beautiful woodland, comprising sixty or seventy acres, thickly covered with old trees, intermingled with a variety of shrubs. The surface is varied in a very striking and picturesque manner, with craggy eminences and hollows, and a little stream runs through the midst. The swift tides of the East River sweep its rocky shores, and the fresh breeze of the bay comes in, on every warm summer afternoon, over the restless waters. The trees are of almost every species that grows in our woods—the different varieties of ash, the birch, the beech, the linden, the mulberry, the tulip tree and others; the azalea, the kalmia, and other flowering shrubs are in bloom here in their season, and the ground in spring is gay with flowers. There never was a finer situation for the public garden of a great city. Nothing is wanting but to cut winding paths through it, leaving the woods as they now are, and introducing here and there a jet from the Croton aqueduct, the streams from which would make their own waterfalls over the rocks, and keep the brooks running through the place always fresh and full.

As we are now going on, we are making a belt of muddy docks all round the island. We should be glad to see one small part of the shore without them, one place at least where the tides may be allowed to flow pure, and the ancient brim of rocks which borders the waters left in its original picturesqueness and beauty. Commerce is devouring inch by inch the coast of the island, and if we would rescue any part of it for health and recreation, it must be done now.

All large cities have their extensive public grounds and gardens; Madrid and Mexico City their Alamedas, London its Regent's Park, Paris its Champs Elysees, and Vienna its Prater. There are none of them, we believe, which have the same natural advantages of picturesque and beautiful which belong to this spot. It would be easy access to the citizens, and the public carriages which now rattle in almost every street of this city would take them to its gates. The only objection which we can see to the plan would be the difficulty of persuading the owners of the soil to part with it—and this rich city can easily raise the means.

† † †

Bryant was one of the first editors of "personal journalism." Like some who were his contemporaries, and many who followed him, he was able to excite the interest of readers so that they were concerned more with what *he* had to say than with what his *newspaper* had to say. He was a man of old-fashioned sentiments, a pure romantic in an age of booming industrialism. One of his editorials shows his apparent obliviousness to the age in which he was living; he demonstrates no awareness that a new invention called the railroad would have much impact upon him personally or upon his newspaper.

† † †

THE RAILROAD VIEWED AS MATCHMAKER

New York Evening Post, November 9, 1833.

One would not readily perceive, at the first glance, any very intimate connexion between railroads and matrimony, or in what way, through the instrumentality of locomotives and steam engines, the bond of Hymen will assist in strengthening our political bond of Union. But there is one class of readers who receive particular delectation from perusing that department of our paper which contains the advertisements of marriages; and as this class is composed in a good measure of single ladies, it can hardly have escaped their observation that the introduction of steamboats, railroads, and locomotives has, among other happy effects, already had a very important influence in forwarding the designs of heaven—where, it is said, matches are always made, though hitherto, for the want of railroads, the parties meant for each other have not always been fortunate enough to meet. . . .

The chances of discovering the twin-mind, the partner whose soul was fashioned in the same mould with our own, are certainly very much increased now-a-days. Man has become more of a locomotive being, since he has had steam locomotives to assist him in his peregrinations. The American people are naturally of a migratory disposition, and their wandering habits have kept pace with the increase of facilities for travelling. . . .

† † †

If journalism history gives an important place to Bryant, it is as an editor of the age of Jackson. His admiration was not for Jackson the President so much as for the policies and programs of Jackson, and Bryant was fortunate in having an associate editor, William Leggett, whose heart really bled for the common people. The egalitarian position of Bryant in the age of Jackson is demonstrated especially in an editorial in which Bryant hit at the common belief of his time that labor unions had no right to exist, that workmen had no right to strike. The editorial is almost the quintessential expression of the era.

† † †

BRYANT PLEADS FOR THE WORKING MAN

New York Evening Post, June 13, 1836.

Sentence was passed on Saturday on the twenty "men who had determined not to work."—They have committed the crime of unanimously declining to go to work at the wages offered to them by their masters. They had said to one another, "Let us come out from the meanness and misery of our caste. Let us begin to do what every order more privileged and more honored is doing every day. By the means which we believe to be the best, let us raise ourselves and our families above the humbleness of our condition. We may be wrong, but we cannot help believing that we might do much if we were true brothers to each other, and would resolve not to sell the only thing which is our own, the cunning of our hands, for less than it is worth." What other things they may have done is nothing to the purpose; it was for this they were condemned; it is for this they are to endure the penalty of the law.

We call upon a candid and generous community to mark that the punishment inflicted upon these twenty "men who had determined not to work" is not directed against the offence of conspiring to prevent others by force from working at low wages, but expressly against the offence of settling by preconcert the compensation which they thought they were entitled to obtain. It is certainly superfluous to repeat, that this journal would be the very last to oppose a law levelled at any attempt to molest the labourer who chooses to work for less than the prices settled by the union. We have said, and to cut off cavil, we say it now and again, that a conspiracy to deter, by threats of violence, a fellow-workman from arranging his own terms with his employers, is a conspiracy to commit a felony—a conspiracy which, being a crime against liberty, we should be the first to condemn—a conspiracy which no strike should, for its own sake, countenance for a moment—a conspiracy already punishable by the statute, and far easier to reach than the one of which "the twenty" stood accused; but a conspiracy, we must add, that has not a single feature in common with the base and barbarous prohibition under which the offenders were indicted and condemned.

They were condemned because they had determined not to work for the wages that were offered them! Can anything be imagined more abhorrent to every sentiment of generosity or justice, than the law which arms the rich with the legal right to fix, by assize, the wages of the poor? If this is not SLAVERY, we have forgotten its definition. Strike the right of associating for the sale of labour from the privileges of a freeman, and you may as well at once bind him to a master, or ascribe him to the soil. If it be not in the colour of his skin, and in the poor franchise of naming his own terms in a contract for his work, what advantage has the labourer of the north over the bondsman of the south? Punish by human laws a "determination not to work," make it penal by any other penalty than idleness inflicts, and it matters little whether the taskmasters be one or many, an individual or an order, the hateful scheme of slavery will have gained a foothold in the land.

"Self-created societies," says Judge Edwards, "are unknown to the constitution and laws, and will not be permitted to rear their crest and extend their baneful influence over any portion of the community." If there is any sense in this passage, it means that self-created societies are unlawful, and must be put down by the courts. Down then with every literary, every religious, and every charitable association not incorporated!—Gather up then and sweep to the penitentiary all those who are confederated to carry on any business or trade in concert, by fixed rules, and see how many you would leave at large in this city. The members of every partnership in the place will come under the penalties of the law, and not only them, but every person pursuing any occupation whatever, who governs himself by a mutual understanding with others that follow the same occupation.

† † †

William Cullen Bryant, as an editor favoring the programs of Andrew Jackson, was located in the commercial center, New York; two other editors were in the national capital itself. These editors were Francis P. Blair and Amos Kendall; their newspaper was the *Washington Globe,* the chief organ of the Jackson administration. The *Globe* followed another newspaper as chief sponsor of Jackson; Duff Green of St. Louis had started the *United States Telegraph* in 1826. Green, a long-time promoter of Jackson, remained, briefly, the chief beneficiary, helping to elect Jackson in 1828 but then becoming involved with John C. Calhoun in the many controversies of the time. Blair and Kendall founded the *Globe* in 1830, Blair being a banker, editor, and plantation owner from Frankfort, Kentucky; Kendall being a polemicist of old and an associate of Blair on the *Argus of the Western World.* Both became part of the legendary kitchen cabinet, and some credit Kendall with being the founder of presidential public relations, as press secretary of sorts and propagandist for Jackson. Their *Globe* was a powerful journal and an authoritative one, and with their *Congressional Globe,* launched in 1834, they established a publication that became the nineteenth century forerunner of our present-day *Congressional Record.* One of the editorials in the *Washington Globe* favored a program that was favored by most Democratic editors in the 1840s.

† † †

THE GLOBE AND ANNEXATION OF TEXAS

Washington Globe, April 20, 1844.

Texas will come in at the right door, for she will be cordially received by the family to which she belongs. We have said before that we looked upon Texas, in right, as a territory of the Union. The guardian who once had the disposal of this fair patrimony in his hands made way with it wrongfully by throwing it into the arms of the Spanish potentate. A revolution made it the possession of another power on this continent—Mexico; another revolution makes it the appanage of a young branch of our own family. These children of the American Union now come forward and say: "The inheritance which was divorced from us by unworthy management has been honestly regained. It is ours and we are yours. We ask the annexation of Texas 'on a footing in all respects equal with the other States of the Union.'" Is there a State in the Union prepared to repel this fair proposal?—a proposal which brings to us innumerable benefits, and confers on them all the blessings of our glorious nation.

It is said that President Houston and the patriotic men who have redeemed Texas will, in yielding their acquisitions to us, make a conquest of the United States for themselves. This is a proud achievement, worthy of their ambition. The Roman citizens who gave new States to their country were indulged with a triumph at the seat of their empire. We should be glad to welcome, in the same way, the conquerors of Texas in the capital of the United States. And who will object, if they thus receive back their own country by winning for it again the fine regions dissevered by faithfulness? But we think the people of Texas will deserve more than a triumphant welcome for the services they have rendered. We would be glad to see an ample, nay a noble dowry put at the disposal of the State; one not only commensurate with its sacrifices and its sufferings, its expenditure of money and of blood, but sufficient to requite her for the full value of the lands she brings into the common stock, and to make some advance for the rich contributions which must be derived from imposts upon the consumption of her people.

† † †

Among the important documents of American journalism are two from foreign visitors, and these say much about our press. In the 1830s the Frenchman, Alexis de Tocqueville, came to America and wrote one of the world's most famous books, *Democracy in America.* Tocqueville, though not always pleased by the American experiment in democracy, seemed excited by it. He wrote of the "liberty of the press" in this country.

† † †

A FRENCHMAN COMMENTS ON
THE PRESS IN AMERICA

By Alexis de Tocqueville, in *Democracy in America* (Boston: John Allyn, 1876 ed.,), pp. 233-239.

. . . America is perhaps, at this moment, the country of the whole world which contains the fewest germs of revolution; but the press is not less destructive in its principles than in France, and it displays the same violence without the same reasons for indignation. In America, as in France, it constitutes a singular power, so strangely composed of mingled good and evil that it is at the same time indispensable to the existence of freedom, and nearly incompatible with the maintenance of public order. Its power is certainly much greater in France than in the United States; though nothing is more rare in the latter country than to hear of a prosecution having been instituted against it. The reason of this is perfectly simple: the Americans, having once admitted the doctrine of the sovereignty of the people, apply it with perfect consistency. It was never their intention to found a permanent state of things with elements which undergo daily modifications; and there is consequently nothing criminal in an attack upon the existing laws, provided it be not attended with a violent infraction of them. They are moreover of the opinion that courts of justice are unable to check the abuses of the press; and that as the subtilty of human language perpetually eludes the severity of judicial analysis, offences of this nature are apt to escape the hand which attempts to apprehend them. They hold that to act with efficacy upon the press it would be necessary to find a tribunal, not only devoted to the existing order of things, but capable of surmounting the influence of public opinion; a tribunal which should conduct its proceedings without publicity, which should pronounce its decrees without assigning its motives, and punish the intentions even more than the language of an author. Whosoever should have the power of creating and maintaining a tribunal of this kind would waste his time in prosecuting the liberty of the press; for he would be the supreme master of the whole community, and he would be as free to rid himself of the authors as of their writings. In this question, therefore, there is no medium between servitude and extreme license; in order to enjoy the inestimable benefits which the liberty of the press ensures, it is necessary to submit to the inevitable evils which it engenders. To expect to acquire the former and to escape the latter is to cherish one of those illusions which commonly mislead nations in their times of sickness, when, tired with faction and exhausted by effort, they attempt to combine hostile opinions and contrary principles upon the same soil. . . .

The personal opinions of the editors have no kind of weight in the eyes of the public; the only use of a journal is, that it imparts the knowledge of certain facts, and it is only by altering or distorting those facts that a journalist can contribute to the support of his own views.

But although the press is limited to these resources, its influence in America is immense. It is the power which impels the circulation of political life through all the districts of that vast territory. Its eye is constantly open to detect the secret springs of political designs, and to summon the leaders of all parties to the bar of public opinion. It rallies the interests of the community round certain principles, and it draws up the creed which factions adopt; for it affords a means of intercourse between parties which hear, and which address each other without ever having been in immediate contact. When a great number of the organs of the press adopt the same line of conduct, their influence becomes irresistible; and public opinion, when it is perpetually assailed from the same side, eventually yields to the attack. In the United States each separate journal exercises but little authority, but the power of the periodical press is only second to that of the people. . . .

†　†　†

The other European visitor—and many came to this country in the early nineteenth century—was Charles Dickens, already famous, and already frustrated and indignant that no international copyright law existed to keep American publishers from pirating his works, including a few publishers of newspapers. He arrived here in 1841, and from his travels he produced two books—the nonfictional *American Notes* and the novel *Martin Chuzzlewit*. It is the novel, depicting the young Martin arriving on "that noble and fast-sailing line-of-packet ship, the *Screw*, at the port of New York, in the United States of America," that offers a biting insight by this other traveler in America.

†　†　†

AN ENGLISHMAN VIEWS THE NEW YORK PRESS

By Charles Dickens, *Martin Chuzzlewit* (London: J. M. Dent, 1907 ed.), pp. 247-248.

Some trifling excitement prevailed upon the very brink and margin of the land of liberty; for an alderman had been elected the day before; and Party Feeling naturally running rather high on such an exciting occasion, the friends of the disappointed candidate had found it necessary to assert the great principles of Purity of Election and Freedom of Opinion by breaking a few legs and arms, and furthermore pursuing one obnoxious gentleman through the streets with the design of slitting his nose. These good-humoured little outbursts of the popular fancy were not in themselves sufficiently remarkable to create any great stir, after the lapse of a whole night; but they found fresh life and notoriety in the breath of the newsboys, who not only proclaimed them with shrill yells in all the highways and byways of the town, upon the wharves and among the shipping, but on the deck and down in the cabins of the steamboat; which, before she touched the shore, was boarded and overrun by a legion of those young citizens.

"Here's this morning's New York Sewer!" cried one. "Here's this morning's New York Stabber! Here's the New York Family Spy! Here's the New York Private Listener! Here's the New York Peeper! Here's the New York Plunderer! Here's the New York Keyhole Reporter! Here's the New York Rowdy Journal! Here's all the New York papers! Here's full particulars of the patriotic loco-foco movement yesterday, in which the whigs was so chawed up; and the last Alabama gouging case; and the interesting Arkansas dooel with Bowie knives; and all the Political, Commercial, and Fashionable News. Here they are! Here they are! Here's the papers, here's the papers!"

"Here's the Sewer!" cried another. Here's the New York Sewer! Here's some of the twelfth thousand of to-day's Sewer, with the best accounts of the markets, and all the shipping news, and four whole columns of country correspondence, and a full account of the Ball at Mrs. White's last night, where all the beauty and fashion of New York was assembled; with the Sewer's own particulars of the private lives of all the ladies that was there! Here's the Sewer! Here's some of the twelfth thousand of the New York Sewer! Here's the Sewer's exposure of the Wall Street Gang, and the Sewer's exposure of the Washington Gang, and the Sewer's exclusive account of a flagrant act of dishonesty committed by the Secretary of State when he was eight years old; now communicated, at a great expense, by his own nurse. Here's the Sewer!" . . .

† † †

5

NEWSPAPERS FOR THE PEOPLE

Truly historic dates, the kind the schoolchild once had to commit to memory, are many: 1066, 1215, 1492, 1588, 1620, 1776, 1787, as examples. For the student of American journalism 1833 is such a date—the year of the penny press. It seems apt that the penny press should have come into being in the very year in which Andrew Jackson was entering his second term of office, the year when Ralph Waldo Emerson was writing of individualism and self-reliance. For the penny press was so much a part of the age of Jackson, of democracy, of increasing individual opportunity. A new working class was on the rise; education and social advancement were spreading. And Benjamin Day founded the *New York Sun*—more properly just the *Sun.*

Day was a New Englander, 23 years old, a printer; he does not belong in the pantheon of great personal editors, but his *newspaper* was highly personal, written for the common people. It cost only a penny, instead of the prohibitive six pennies that had kept the common people from being much interested in such newspapers as Bryant's *Evening Post* and James Watson Webb's *Courier and Enquirer.* Day did not found his paper with any such intention as declaring a revolution; he wanted an enterprise that would help keep his printing office going in a time of economic distress. He had many imitators in the years that followed—James Gordon Bennett with the *Herald,* Horace Greeley with the *Tribune,* Henry J. Raymond with the *Times,* all following the *Sun* in New York. A team consisting of Arunah Abell, Azariah Simmons, and William Swain launched the *Philadelphia Public Ledger* and then the *Baltimore Sun,* though it was mainly Abell who ran the *Sun.* In New Orleans the penny paper of George W. Kendall was called the *Picayune;* in Chicago the penny paper was the *Tribune;* in the booming provincial town of Springfield, Massachusetts, it was the *Republican.* The movement spread to Cleveland and Cincinnati, to Pittsburgh and Detroit, and in the post-Civil War period a new group of penny journals (perhaps selling by this time for more than one penny) was coming into being.

What set these newspapers apart was their content, more than their price; their stress was on news and human interest more than on politics and religion—though it would be wrong to conclude, as some commentators seem to have concluded, that political matters, at least, were not part of the penny press. But it will become rapidly obvious that the materials in this section of the anthology are different from those in the preceding ones, for news and human interest become the main themes. It is the latter—human interest —that is especially pronounced in our first document of the penny press: a little story that appeared down in the corner of the righthand column of the first issue of the *Sun.*

† † †

A BOY WHO WHISTLED TOO MUCH

New York *Sun,* September 3, 1833.

A Whistler.—A boy in Vermont, accustomed to working alone, was so prone to whistling, that, as soon as he was by himself, he unconsciously commenced. When asleep, the muscles of his mouth, chest, and lungs were so completely concatenated in the association, he whistled with astonishing shrillness. A pale countenance, loss of appetite, and almost total prostration of strength, convinced his mother it would end in death, if not speedily overcome, which was accomplished by placing him in the society of another boy, who had orders to give him a blow as soon as he began to whistle.

† † †

Many modern-day readers will readily recognize the formula of human interest in such a story, and they probably will not be too troubled that we never learn the name of that unfortunate boy, or the town in Vermont in which he lived, or what finally happened to him. Editor Day was not concerned with such mundane matters. On that front page of the first *Sun* the lead article was this little sketch about highway robbers.

† † †

AN IRISH CAPTAIN

New York Sun, September 3, 1833.

"These are as sweet a pair of pistols as any in the three kingdoms;" said an officer, showing a pair to a young student of his acquaintance, "and have done execution before now; at the slightest touch, off they go, as sweet as honey, without either recoiling or dipping. I never travel without them."

"I never heard of highwaymen in this part of the country."

"Nor I," replied the officer, "and if I had I should not trouble myself to carry the pistols on their account—Highwaymen are a species of sharks who are not fond of attacking us lobsters; they know we are a little too hard to crack. No, my dear sir, highwaymen know that soldiers have not much money, and what they have they fight for."

"Since that is the case; how come you to travel always with pistols?"

"Because," answered the officer, "I find them very useful in accommodating any little differences I may accidentally have with a friend, or which one friend may chance to have with another."....

† † †

It was the good fortune of Benjamin Day, or at least the good fortune of penny journalism, that a man named George Wisner came on the scene, a printer who was out of work and who persuaded Day to let him cover the police news of the town in the way reporters in London had covered police news there. And so, instead of Day (or somebody) writing or rewriting stories that had appeared in the sixpenny papers, Wisner went to work. His approach to the news of the courts was refreshing, and much different from the staid accounts of late eighteenth century.

† † †

DIVORCE, NINETEENTH CENTURY STYLE

New York Sun, July 21, 1834.

GIVING A DIVORCE.—Yesterday morning a little curly-pated fellow, by the name of John Lawler was called up on a charge of kicking over the mead-stand of Mary Lawler, alias Miss Donohue, alias Mrs. Donohue.

MAGISTRATE (to the complainant): Mrs. Donohue, what were the circumstances of this affair?

COMPLAINANT: You will be so good, sir, if you please, as to call me Miss Donohue. It is my maiden name and I wish no other.

MAG.: Very good, Miss Donohue, how came he to kick over your stand and break your bottles and glasses?

COMP.: Aye, yes, now, I like that better. Every virtuous woman should be called by her own right and proper name.

MAG.: Well, let's hear your story. Do you know the boy?

COMP.: The boy, did you say. Indade, sir, divil a bit o'boy is there about the baste, nor man neither, barring he drinks brandy like a fish. (Loud laughter.)

MAG.: Did you ever see him before?

COMP.: Indade, I guess I did. Many years ago he was my husband, but your honor sees, I gave him a divorce. That is, ye see, I gave him a bit of paper stating that I wouldn't live with him no longer. (Laughter)

PRISONER: It's no sich thing, your honor. She used to go off with other men, and so I sold her for a gill of rum. . . .

† † †

If any stories gave a boost to the penny press it was those carried in the *Sun* beginning August 25, 1835, that we now call the "Moon Hoax." These stories were the work of a reporter with the distinguished name of Richard Adams Locke, the successor to George Wisner and one who knew that readers in the 1830s were quite interested in science, especially in the heavens and in astronomy. Locke's inspiration was to fashion a story that supposedly had appeared in the *Edinburgh Journal of Science,* one dealing with a real-life astronomer, Sir John Herschel, and the observatory he had set up near Cape Town in 1835 to make a complete survey of the visible heavens. Locke told the readers of the *Sun* what Sir John was seeing through his giant telescope. What Sir John was seeing was the moon, including life on the moon:

† † †

THE GREAT MOON HOAX

New York Sun, August 25-28, 1835.

. . . The specimen of lunar vegetation, however, which they had already seen, had decided a question of too exciting an interest to induce them to retard its exit. It had demonstrated that the moon has an atmosphere constituted similarly to our own, and capable of sustaining organized and, therefore, most probably, animal life.

"The trees," says Dr. Grant, "for a period of ten minutes were of one unvaried kind, and unlike any I have seen except the largest class of yews in the English churchyards, which they in some respects resemble. These were followed by a level green plain which, as measured by the painted circle on our canvas of forty-nine feet, must have been more than half a mile in breadth.". . .

. . . Then appeared as fine a forest of firs, unequivocal firs, as I have ever seen cherished in the bosom of my native mountains. Wearied with the long continuance of these, we greatly reduced the magnifying power of the microscope without eclipsing either of the reflectors, and immediately perceived that we had been insensibly descending, as it were, a mountainous district of highly diversified and romantic character, and that we were on the verge of a lake, or inland sea; but of what relative locality of extent, we were yet too greatly magnified to determine. . . .

. . . In the shade of the woods on the southeastern side we beheld continuous herds of brown quadrupeds, having all the external characteristics of the bison, but more diminutive than any species of the *bos genus* in our natural history. Its tail was like that of our *bos grunniens;* but in its semicircular horns, the hump on its shoulders, the depth of its dewlap, and the length of its shaggy hair, it closely resembled the species to which I have compared it . . . .

The next animal perceived would be classed on earth as a monster. It was of a bluish lead color, about the size of a goat, with a head and beard like him, and a *single horn,* slightly inclined forward from the perpendicular. The female was destitute of the horn and beard, but had a much longer tail. It was gregarious, and chiefly abounded on the acclivitous glades of the woods. . . .

. . . On examining the center of this delightful valley we found a large, branching river, abounding with lovely islands and water-birds of numerous kinds. A species of gray pelican was the most numerous, but black and white cranes, with unreasonably long legs and bill, were also quite common. . . . Near the upper extremity of one of these islands we obtained a glimpse of a strange amphibious creature of a spherical form, which rolled with great velocity across the pebbly beach, and was lost sight of in the strong current which set off from this angle of the island. . . .

. . . They averaged four feet in height, were covered, except on the face, with short and glossy copper-colored hair, and had wings composed of a thin membrane, without hair, lying snugly upon their backs, from the top of the shoulders to the calves of the legs. The face, which was a yellowish flesh-color, was a slight improvement upon that of the large orangutan, being more open and intelligent in its expression, and having a much greater expanse of forehead. . . .

† † †

Such stories, written in academic language that might have characterized the *Edinburgh Journal of Science,* astounded and entranced the readers of the *Sun.* Some scientists, we are told, were hoodwinked by the story, though some others, from Yale University, were skeptical enough to wish to see the actual copy of the *Journal* that carried the story. The other newspapers of the town were hoaxed, and it all may have gone on for some time had not Locke, over a drink in a saloon, told a friend that the story had originated in his fertile brain. But meanwhile the circulation of the *Sun* had soared, surpassing even that of the famous *Times* of London.

The age of collegiate tomfoolery was not over. One of the people who were touched by the Moon Hoax was that journeyman editor-reporter-poet-short story writer named Edgar Allan Poe, whose story of a moon trip, "The Unparalleled Adventure of One Hans Pfaall," published in the *Southern Literary Messenger,* was reduced in impact by Locke's yarn. Poe himself contributed something to the *Sun* on April 13, 1844, his story being one that the histories of journalism now treat on the same page as that of the moon tale. The excitement generated by this one was not quite of the scope generated by Locke's wild imaginings, but it was still quite a story.

† † †

AN OCEAN VOYAGE BY BALLOON

New York Sun, April 13, 1844.

. . .The great problem is at length solved! The air, as well as the earth and the ocean, has been subdued by science, and will become a common and convenient highway for mankind. *The Atlantic has been actually crossed in a Balloon!* and this too without difficulty—without any great apparent danger—with thorough control of the machine—and in the inconceivably brief period of seventy-five hours from shore to shore! By the energy of an agent at Charleston, S.C., we are enabled to be the first to furnish the public with a detailed account of this most extraordinary voyage, which was performed between Saturday, the 6th instant, at 11 A.M. and 2 P.M., on Tuesday, the 9th instant, by Sir Everard Bringhurst; Mr. Osborne, a nephew of Lord Bentinck's; Mr. Monck Mason and Mr. Robert Holland, the well-known aeronauts; Mr. Harrison Ainsworth, author of "Jack Sheppard," etc.; and Mr. Henson, the projector of the late unsuccessful flying machine—with two seamen from Woolwich—in all, eight persons. The particulars furnished below may be relied on as authentic and accurate in every respect, as, with a slight exception, they are copied *verbatim* from the joint diaries of Mr. Monck Mason and Mr. Harrison Ainsworth, . . .

† † †

The Moon Hoax and the Balloon Hoax provided excitement for readers of newspapers in the 1830s and the 1840s, but actual events were also exciting to read about. An example, also in the *Sun* of New York, was this story:

† † †

THE ANNIHILATION OF SPACE

New York Sun, May 27, 1844.

MAGNETIC TELEGRAPH.—The new invention is completed from Baltimore to Washington. The wire, perfectly secured against the weather by a covering of rope yarn and tar, is conducted on the top of posts about twenty feet high and one hundred yards apart. The nominations of the convention this day [Democratic national] are to be conveyed to Washington by this telegraph, where they will arrive in a few seconds. On Saturday morning the batteries were charged and the regular transmission of intelligence between Washington and Baltimore commenced. . . . At half past 11 A.M., the question being asked, what was the news at Washington, the answer was almost instantaneously returned: "Van Buren Stock is rising." This is indeed the annihilation of space!

† † †

So penny journalism continued. A writer named Paul Peebles tells us that on May 6, 1835, an editor "threw out upon the sidewalks of New York a bundle of detonating firecrackers, . . ." The editor was James Gordon Bennett, 40, a Scotsman, a failure, a genius of sorts. That bundle of firecrackers was called the *New York Herald,* and it was the second of the major penny papers of the big city. Its formula, like that of the *Sun,* was news and human interest, and in the realm of news Bennett outstripped every competitor in his time. In the early years he covered the big stories himself, meanwhile writing editorials of unbridled arrogance, and meanwhile insulting organized society, religion, and journalism, so that what came to be known as the "moral war" took place. The flavor of Bennett is quite marked in his prospectus.

† † †

THE MIGHTY MISSION OF A NEWSPAPER

New York Herald, May 6, 1835.

I mean to make the *Herald* the great organ of social life, the prime element of civilization, the channel through which native talent, native genius, and native power may bubble up daily, as the pure sparkling liquid of the Congress fountain at Saratoga bubbles up from the centre of the earth, till it meets the rosy lips of the fair. I shall mix together commerce and business, pure religion and morals, literature and poetry, the drama and dramatic purity, till the *Herald* shall outstrip everything in the conception of man. The age of trashy novels, of more trashy poems, of most trashy quarterly and weekly literature, is rapidly drawing to a close.

This is the age of the Daily Press, inspired with the accumulated wisdom of past ages, enriched with the spoils of history, and looking forward to a millennium of a thousand years, the happiest and most splendid ever yet known in the measured span of eternity!

† † †

One cannot truthfully say that James Gordon Bennett *originated* journalistic concepts, but he did give to certain kinds of stories a distinctive style and approach. One of these stories was the stock market report, what he called the "money article." Another was the disaster story, and few reports rival the highly personal but also quite commendable description Bennett gave his readers of the terrible fire that destroyed much of the Wall Street district in late 1835.

† † †

A REPORTER COVERS A GREAT FIRE

New York Herald, December 17-18, 1835.

TERRIBLE CONFLAGRATION.—Last evening, between eight and nine o'clock, a fire broke out in the store No. 25 Merchant, a narrow street that leads into Pearl and Exchange streets, near the post office, and one of the most terrible and destructive conflagrations took place that ever visited New York.

At ten o'clock, when we left the scene, probably thirty or forty of the most valuable and richest dry goods stores in the city were burned down or on fire.

It was expected that it would sweep away the whole of that section of the city, in its range through Pearl, Water and Front streets to the East river. Wall street for hours was as light as day.

The loss of property cannot be estimated—*probably several millions.*

The narrowness of the streets in that quarter aided the spread of the destructive element. The wind blew from the west, and the cold was extremely intense. . . .

POSTSCRIPT—ELEVEN O'CLOCK—Just come from the scene. From Wall street to Hanover Square, and from the Merchants' Exchange to the East River, all on fire. About 300 stores burned, and burning down—probably *five millions* of property lost. About 1000 merchants ruined, and several Insurance Companies gone. . .

Good God! in one night we have lost the whole amount for which the nation is ready to go to war with France! Gracious Heaven! is it a punishment for our madness? Forgive us our sins as we forgive those that sin against us!

We recorded in our paper of yesterday, the first stage of one of the most awful conflagrations that ever befell any city, in any age, or in any country. Talk not to us of the burning of Moscow—the property there lost, was nothing in comparison to that yesterday in New York. The great fire in London is equally unimportant.

The details, descriptions, sketches, anecdotes of this terrible calamity, will be found in our subsequent columns. . . .

The street was full of boxes and goods. I felt quite old.—I saw a large group of men stirring up a fire in the centre of Wall Street, between Water and Front, which is here wide. On going near to warm myself, I found the fire was made out of the richest merchandize and fine furniture from some of the elegant counting rooms.

† † †

James Gordon Bennett's newspaper was in competition, of course, with the lively *Sun,* and in covering the Wall Street fire Bennett had to compete personally with those who worked for Benjamin Day. Beginning in April, 1836, Bennett began to edify his readers with a story about a prostitute named Ellen Jewett, who had been murdered, the editor baldly said, by a man who had been "keeping her"—Richard Robinson. Bennett first worked to convict Robinson, and then he switched and worked to free him. One of his stories was obtained by the process of interviewing. It may be that Bennett conducted the first newspaper interview in America, and it is sad to report that such an interview was with a madame. These are fragments of the Jewett story.

† † †

BENNETT COVERS A CRIME OF PASSION

New York Herald, April 11-13, 1836.

MOST ATROCIOUS MURDER.—Our City was disgraced on Sunday, by one of the most foul and premeditated murders, that ever fell to our lot to record. The following are circumstances as ascertained on the spot.

Richard P. Robinson, the alleged perpetrator of this most horrid deed, had for some time been in the habit of keeping (as it is termed) a girl named Ellen Jewett, who has for a long period resided at No. 41 Thomas-street, in the house kept by Rosina Townsend.

Having, as he suspected, some cause for jealousy, he went to the house on Saturday night as appears, with the intention of murdering her, for he carried a hatchet with him. On going up into her room, quite late at night, he mentioned his suspicions, and expressed a determination to quit her, and demanded his watch and miniature together with some letters which were in her possession. She refused to give them up, and he then drew from beneath his cloak the hatchet, and inflicted upon her head three blows, either of which must have proved fatal, as the bone was cleft to the extent of three inches in each place.

She died without a struggle; and the cold blooded villain deliberately threw off his cloak, cast the lifeless body upon the bed *and set fire to that.* . . .

The excitement yesterday morning throughout the city, was extraordinary. Every body exclaimed "what a horrible affair"—"what a terrible catastrophe!" News was received from Texas, highly disastrous to the colonists, but the private tragedy of Ellen Jewett almost absorbed all public attention.

REFLECTIONS—WHO IS THE MURDERER?—The denouement of the tragedy of Ellen Jewett continues to agitate the public mind beyond any event that we ever heard of or saw in any city. Yesterday the excitement exceeded anything hitherto known to have sprung out of this awful drama. It is rapidly becoming a doubtful point, notwithstanding the startling circumstances, whether the poor, unfortunate girl was destroyed by the young man now in the custody of the public authorities. It is asked—Is it possible for a youth, hitherto unimpeached and unimpeachable in his character, to have engendered and perpetrated so diabolical an act as the death of Ellen Jewett was? Is it the character of crime to jump at once from the heights of virtue to the depths of vice? . . .

† † †

Self-exploitation was frequently Bennett's editorial theme. Modesty and humility were not his long suits, and one of the editorials that outraged a dignified metropolis readership was one published in 1840 about an important event that would stun much of the human race.

† † †

A MODEST ANNOUNCEMENT OF IMPENDING MARRIAGE

New York Herald, June 1, 1840.

To the Readers of the Herald—Declaration of Love—Caught At Last—Going to be Married— New Movement in Civilization.—I am going to be married in a few days. The weather is so beautiful; times are getting so good; the prospects of political and moral reform so auspicious, that I cannot resist the divine instinct of honest nature any longer; so I am going to be married to one of the most splendid women in intellect, in heart, in soul, in property, in person, in manner, that I have yet seen in the course of my interesting pilgrimage through human life.

. . . I cannot stop in my career. I must fulfill that awful destiny which the Almighty Father has written against my name, in the broad letters of life, against the wall of heaven. I must give the world a pattern of happy wedded life, with all the charities that spring from a nuptial love. In a few days I shall be married according to the holy rites of the most holy Christian church, to one of the most remarkable, accomplished, and beautiful young women of the age. She possesses a fortune. I sought and found a fortune—a large fortune. She has no Stonington shares or Manhattan stock, but in purity and uprightness she is worth half a million of pure gold. Can any swindling bank show as much? In good sense and elegance another half a million; in soul, mind, and beauty, millions on millions, equal to the whole specie of all the rotten banks in the world. Happily the patronage of the public to the Herald is nearly twenty-five thousand dollars per annum, almost equal to a President's salary. But property in the world's goods was never my object. Fame, public good, usefulness in my day and generation; the religious associations of female excellence; the progress of true industry—these have been my dreams by night and my desires by day.

In the new and holy condition into which I am about to enter, and to enter with the same reverential feelings as I would enter heaven itself, I anticipate some signal changes in my feelings, in my views, in my purposes, in my pursuits. What they may be I know not—time alone can tell. My ardent desire has been through life, to reach the highest order of human intelligence, by the shortest possible cut. Association, night and day, in sickness and in health, in war and in peace, with a woman of the highest order of excellence, must produce some curious results in my heart and feelings, and these results the future will develop in due time in the columns of the Herald.

† † †

Horace Greeley is perhaps most symbolic today of the editors of personal journalism, and his newspaper, the *New York Tribune,* is remembered as the most distinguished of the early penny journals, even though it was not as much a *mass* publication as its rivals, the *Sun* and the *Herald.* In his time Greeley became known as "Uncle Horace," editor of both a daily and weekly paper, a spokesman to laboring men and to farmers throughout the land, the chief promoter of both a homestead law and a transcontinental railroad. He was born in 1811 in New Hampshire, a poor boy who worked hard, made good, and became a leader not only in journalism but in politics. He came into prominence as editor of the Whig party paper, the *Log Cabin,* in 1840, and remained vigorous in the Whig party and then in its successor, the Republican, though it is easy to fancy him as a thorn in the side of some of the party leaders. Greeley did not admire the often raw and crude sensationalism of his competitors, even though he did not eschew crime news himself, and a famous Greeley editorial spoke to the question.

† † †

ON "SATANIC" NEWSPAPERS

New York Tribune, February 17, 1849.

The age we live in is remarkable for its multiplication and enlargement of all the agencies alike of good and evil. Life is more intense, more active, more eventful with us than it was with our grandfathers, and he who lives to see sixty years has really lived longer than the man who lived to eighty a century ago. Steamships, Railroads, Electric Telegraphs, Power-Presses, render communication so rapid that ideas circulate from mind to mind like the lightning, and are received in all the vivid energy of their fresh conception. . . . The moral world shares the new momentum of the intellectual and the physical, and transcendent virtues and revolting crimes are alike less rare than formerly. Philanthropy,

Charity, Religion impel their votaries to unvented exertion; so do Lechery, Selfishness and Impiety. And foremost among the instrumentalities of these last stands THE SATANIC PRESS. . . . [It] had its foreshadowings among the darkest days of atheistic butchery and terror in Revolutionary France. . . . [It is the] perverted product of a diseased Civilization wherein debauched and prurient appetites gloat upon the unripe and poisonous fruit of the Tree of Knowledge. . . . It has one sole aspiration—to achieve notoriety and coin gold for its director by pandering to whatever is vile and bestial in a corrupted and sensual populace.

† † †

As a Whig, as a man of the age of Manifest Destiny, as a reformer who saw no conflict between his oft-socialistic attitudes and the increasingly big business attitudes of both Whigs and Republicans, Horace Greeley sponsored two major ideas. First, as an agrarian, he was advising people to "go West," whether they were young or old, and he wished to free the industrial worker from the chains of life in city and factory. He saw the great plains as a safety valve that could serve as an alternative to strikes and hard times, and in the *Tribune* he long campaigned for what became the Homestead Act in 1862.

† † †

PROMOTING THE VIRGIN LANDS IN THE WEST

New York Tribune, February 18, 1854.

Make the Public Lands free in quarter-sections to Actual Settlers and deny them to all others, and earth's landless millions will no longer be orphans and mendicants; they can work for the wealthy, relieved from the degrading terror of being turned adrift to starve. When employment fails or wages are inadequate, they may pack up and strike westward to enter upon the possession and culture of their own lands on the banks of the Wisconsin, the Des Moines, or the Platte, which have been patiently awaiting their advent since creation. Strikes to stand still will be glaringly absurd when every citizen is offered the alternative to work for others or for himself, as to him shall seem most advantageous. The mechanic or labor who works for another will do so only because he can thus secure a more liberal and satisfactory recompense than he could by working for himself.

† † †

A second program of Horace Greeley for which he campaigned long was a railroad that would link East and West. This he also helped to bring about, though there were scoffers—his foe at the

Herald, James Gordon Bennett, being among them (Bennett once proposed a camel caravan to get goods across the Great American Desert). Here Greeley speaks about the railroad.

† † †

A PLAN TO JOIN EAST AND WEST

New York Tribune, December 2, 1852.

A direct Railroad from the Mississippi to California is the noblest Physical project of our age—and not without important Moral and Intellectual bearings. It ought to be speedily built, and when completed will bring the rich and populous East within six weeks of us, and place New-York on the main route from Western Europe to China. With a Railroad to California from some point on the Mississippi, . . .San Francisco will be within twenty days of London and ten days of this City, and such a Road, if this day in running order, would have business enough to pay a fair dividend on its cost even in 1853. . . .

† † †

During part of the 1840s and 1850s Greeley's associate editor was Charles A. Dana. Like Greeley a New Hampshireman, like him an idealist—at least in his younger days —he looked with great favor upon the socialistic and utopian experiments of the day, including the colony of Brook Farm, where Dana himself taught German for a time. He was a major editorial writer on Greeley's *Tribune,* and he also was a reporter, going to Europe during the revolutions of 1848 and 1849, supporting himself by filing letters to the *Tribune* and also to other newspapers. His report of revolution in Paris in 1848 may safely be described by that overworked word, "classic."

† † †

REVOLUTION IN THE STREETS OF PARIS

New York Tribune, July 24, 1848.

PARIS, JUNE 20, 1848— The public papers will give you lengthy details upon the terrible events which have just taken place in Paris. These events are so multiplied and varied in their character that it is impossible to grasp them in their totality and give any exact statement in regard to them. The most distorted and erroneous accounts are spreading in every direction, and each party will give its own coloring to what has taken place instead of seeking to discover the exact truth and making it known. I will not undertake to give you a history of the crisis through which this great capital has just passed. I doubt whether any one can do it at present, for, as I understand, the recent events are too varied to be summed up and reduced to order so soon after their occurrence. I will, therefore, simply state what I have seen myself and acts of which I can guarantee the authenticity. . . .

As we approached Paris all was perfectly quiet. The inhabitants in the little villages through which we passed did not seem unusually excited, and yet a desperate conflict was going on in the capital—the center and head of the nation. We arrived at length at Saint-Denis, about two leagues distant from Paris. Here the National Guards got out, formed into columns, and marched into Paris by some circuitous route. The part of the capital which the railroad entered was in the hands of the insurgents, and persons were placed at Saint-Denis to inform them of the danger. The insurgents would have attacked them, or any armed men, but not travelers without arms. . . .

As I had no other opportunity of seeing or conversing with the men engaged in the insurrection except on that evening and the next morning, I will enter into some details of what I heard and saw. It may give you some idea of the character of those engaged in the late outbreak and the spirit that animated them. From the public prints you cannot obtain any impartial information. The conservative papers will denounce the insurgents as a body of plunderers who wished merely to destroy and pillage, while the ultraradical papers are either suppressed or are silent.

At one of the tables sat a young man in a blouse, a workman, who had been engaged in the affray during the day. I entered into a conversation and asked him what his political principles were. "I am," said he, "a Socialist and Democratic Republican. I do not want that the rich should prey upon the poor; I want the association of labor and capital; that the laborer should have a share of the profits, and that the rich man should not take all the profits to himself and make a fortune out of the labor of the poor man.". . .

I was very desirous of entering the city, but not wishing to separate my party, I began to inquire the possibility of finding a more comfortable resting place. A workman in the cabaret said he had a lodging near by, with two beds in it, which he would give up to our party—that four could sleep there if we choose to lie two upon a bed. We had been told previously, upon inquiring as to the possibility of entering the city, that there was a barricade at the end of the street not far distant from the cabaret, and that if we passed that way the insurgents might take us for soldiers and fire upon us. My friends decided upon running no risk, and remained. I decided upon going, as my guide assured me he could take us by a road where there were no barricades. It was near one o'clock when we set out; the night was fine, and all was quiet save that now and then the silence was broken by a musketshot. My guide led me through several streets and at length to the house where he had his lodgings. . . .

I was up at 3½ o'clock. While I was dressing, a workman came in who had been sleeping in a neighboring room and asked for a bag of caps which he had left there. "Are you going to return to work again today?" asked my host of him. "Yes," was his laconic answer. We all went downstairs together. The man who asked for the caps was a quiet, intelligent-looking person, but there was a firmness and determination in his face which showed that the affair with him was a serious one. . . .

. . .The report of firearms was constant, the barricades began to be manned, and the troops and National Guards were preparing to move upon them. I obtained a handcart, got my baggage upon it, found a man to draw it, and started off with my guide again. . . . We passed near a number of barricades, turning up generally the first corner above them. These barricades were built of the paving stones, dug up by the insurgents and piled across the streets, forming a kind of stone wall, broad at the base and slanting toward the top. Those which I saw were not more than four or five feet high. . . .

I got safely into the city, and after changing my dress, I went to the office of the *Democratie Pacifique*. By this time it was ten o'clock. Orders had been issued to place sentinels in every street and let no one pass, so as to prevent men or supplies from going or being transported from any part of the city to the insurgents' quarters. I found myself completely blockaded in the house and could not stir out. . . .

Next morning after the battle was over, and the insurgents had surrendered or fled, I visited the upper portion of the boulevards toward the Place de la Bastille, the place itself, and the street of Faubourg Saint-Antoine. The entrance of the latter street was the center of the conflict. On the left a house was battered down and smoking in ruins. The other houses were pierced with cannon balls, window shutters torn off, the windows all broken, and the walls showing the marks of thousands of musket balls. . . .

† † †

Horace Greeley, of course, was quite a reporter himself. He also was a traveler and public speaker, heading out on numerous trips, leaving Charles A. Dana to run the *Tribune*. In 1859 Greeley went to the West, stopping to visit Lawrence, Kansas, which had been "sacked" in 1856 by Missourians, and the countryside where John Brown and his men summarily executed slave state sympathizers. Then he went on to the Rocky Mountains, where he interviewed the leader of the Church of Jesus Christ of Latter-day Saints—the Mormons—who had brought his people to the Salt Lake Valley in 1847. Greeley's recorded conversation with that leader, Brigham Young, is another of the famous news stories.

† † †

A VISIT WITH BRIGHAM YOUNG

New York Tribune, August 20, 1859.

H.G.: Am I to regard Mormonism (so-called) as a new religion, or as simply a new development of Christianity?

B.Y.: We hold that there can be no true Christian Church without a priesthood directly commissioned by and in immediate communication with the Son of God and Savior of Mankind. Such a church is that of the Latter-Day Saints, called by their enemies Mormons; we know no other that even pretends to have present and direct revelations of God's will.

H.G.: Then I am to understand that you regard all other churches professing to be Christian as the Church of Rome regards all churches not in communion with itself—as schismatic, heretical, and out of the way of salvation?

B.Y.: Yes, substantially.

H.G.: What is the position of your church with respect to slavery?

B.Y.: We consider it of divine institution and not to be abolished until the curse pronounced on Ham shall have been removed from his descendants.

H.G.: Are any slaves now held in this territory?

B.Y.: There are.

H.G.: Do your territorial laws uphold slavery?

B.Y.: Those laws are printed—you can read for yourself. If slaves are brought here by those who owned them in the States, we do not favor their escape from the service of those owners.

H.G. Am I to infer that Utah, if admitted as a member of the Federal Union, will be a slave state?

B.Y.: No, she will be a free state. Slavery here would prove useless and unprofitable. I regard it generally as a curse to the master. I myself hire many laborers and pay them fair wages; *I could not afford to own them.* I can do better than subject myself to an obligation to feed and clothe their families, to provide and care for them in sickness and health. Utah is not adapted to slave labor.

H.G.: Let me now be enlightened with regard more especially to your church policy: I understand that you require each member to pay over one tenth of all he produces or earns to the Church.

B.Y.: That is the requirement of our faith.

H.G. What is done with the proceeds of this tithing?

B.Y.: Part of it is devoted to building temples and other places of worship; part to helping the poor and needy converts on their way to this country; and the largest portion to the support of the poor among the Saints.

H.G.: Is none of it paid to bishops and other dignitaries of the Church?

B.Y.: Not one penny.

H.G.: How, then, do your ministers live?

B.Y.: By the labor of their own hands, like the first Apostles. *I am the only person in the Church who has not a regular calling apart from the Church's service.*

H.G.: Can you give any rational explanation of the aversion and hatred with which your people are generally regarded by those among whom they have lived and with whom they have been brought directly into contact?

B.Y.: No other explanation than is afforded by the crucifixion of Christ and the kindred treatment of God's ministers, prophets, and saints in all ages.

H.G.: How general is polygamy among you?

B.Y.: I could not say. Some of those present [heads of the Church] have each but one wife; others have more; each determines what is his individual duty.

H.G.: What is the largest number of wives belonging to any one man?

B.Y.: I have fifteen; I know no one who has more; but some of those sealed to me are old ladies whom I regard rather as mothers than wives, but whom I have taken home to cherish and support.

H.G.: Does not Christ say that he who puts away his wife, or marries one whom another has put away, commits adultery?

B.Y.: Yes; and I hold that no man should ever put away a wife except for adultery—not always even for that. Such is my individual view of the matter. I do not say that wives have never been put away in our church, but that I do not approve of that practice. . . .

† † †

The careers of Horace Greeley and Charles A. Dana suggest that the news function was as important to the personal editors as was the editorial function. To George W. Kendall of the *New Orleans Picayune,* a paper he founded in 1836, the news function seemed primary. Kendall was a reporter and adventurer who had made himself and his newspaper well known because of the bright and audacious writing it carried. He had gone into Mexico on trading expeditions; on one of these trips he was captured, and he began to agitate for war with Mexico. When General Zachary Taylor went into the storied land of Montezuma the reporter Kendall was with him, serving as the first American war correspondent and sending back colorful dispatches, some of them on special expresses he himself chartered. He was in Mexico City for the fall of that capital.

† † †

MEXICO CITY FALLS, AND A REPORTER IS PRESENT

New Orleans Picayune, September 14, 1847.

CITY OF MEXICO, SEPTEMBER 14, 1847—Another victory, glorious in its results and which has thrown additional luster upon the American arms, has been achieved today by the army under General Scott—the proud capital of Mexico has fallen into the power of a mere handful of men compared with the immense odds arrayed against them, and Santa Anna, instead of shedding his blood as he had promised, is wandering with the remnant of his army no one knows whither.

The apparently impregnable works on Chapultepec, after a desperate struggle, were triumphantly carried; Generals Bravo and Mouterde, besides a host of officers of different grades, taken prisoners; over 1000 noncommissioned officers and privates, all their cannon and ammunition, are in our hands; the fugitives were soon in full flight towards the different works which command the entrances to the city, and our men at once were in hot pursuit.

General Quitman, supported by General Smith's brigade, took the road by the Chapultepec aqueduct toward the Belén gate and the Ciudadela; General Worth, supported by General Cadwalader's brigade, advanced by the San Cosme aqueduct toward the garita of that name. Both routes were cut up by ditches and defended by breastworks, barricades, and strong works of every description known to military science. Yet the daring and impetuosity of our men overcame one defense after another, and by nightfall every work to the city's edge was carried. . . .

† † †

In 1841-1843, Henry J. Raymond was the associate editor on Greeley's *New York Tribune.* For Raymond it was not a happy relationship, nor for Greeley, though the two probably respected each other. Raymond came out of a background quite different from that of his employer; he was a New Yorker, born in 1820, a man with a University of Vermont education and degree—a contrast to the Horatio Alger background of Greeley. Raymond went from the *Tribune* to Webb's *Courier and Enquirer,* but a conversation with George Jones, who had worked in Greeley's business office, persuaded him that perhaps he, too, should have his newspaper. So he founded one with Jones in 1851 called the *New York Daily Times,* the fourth of the big penny papers in the city, and one that had almost none of the uncomfortable growing pains of its rivals. Besides being an editor Raymond was an active politician, first for the Whigs, then for the Republicans, and in 1864 he even served as chairman of the Republican National Committee in the second Lincoln campaign. (It is a bit mystifying, as a matter of fact, as one considers Raymond's career in politics: who was home putting out the paper?) Raymond's prospectus suggests the moderate tone the paper would take, not only in his time but in the twentieth century too.

† † †

A NEW PENNY PAPER IN NEW YORK CITY

New York Times, September 18, 1851.

We publish to-day the first number of the NEW-YORK DAILY TIMES, and we intend to issue it every morning, (Sundays excepted) for an indefinite number of years to come.

We have not entered upon the task of establishing a new daily paper in this city, without due consideration of its difficulties as well as its encouragements. We understand perfectly, that great capital, great industry, great patience are indispensable to its success, and that even with all these, failure is not impossible. But we know also, that within the last five years the reading population of this city has nearly doubled, while the number of daily newspapers is no greater now than it was then;—that many of those now published are really *class* journals, made up for particular classes of readers;—that others are objectionable upon grounds of morality;—and that no newspaper, which was really *fit* to live, ever yet expired for lack of readers.

As a *Newspaper,* presenting all the news of the day from all parts of the world, we intend to make THE TIMES as good as the best of those now issued in the City of New-York;—and in all the higher utilities of the Press —as a public instructor in all departments of action and of thought, we hope to make it decidedly superior to existing journals of the same class. . . .

Upon all topics,—Political, Social, Moral and Religious,—we intend that the paper shall speak for itself;—and we only ask that it may be judged accordingly. We shall be *Conservative,* in all cases where we think Conservatism essential to the public good;—and we shall be *Radical,* in everything which may seem to us to require radical treatment and radical reform. We do not believe that *everything* in Society is either exactly right, or exactly wrong;—what is good we desire to preserve and improve;—what is evil, to exterminate, or reform. . . .

† † †

Though Raymond, like his competitors, was one of the important personal journalists, and though his editorial influence was considerable, it is as a *news*paper that the early-day *New York Times* merits our main consideration. Raymond saw the *Times* as a journal of record from the beginning. In its New Year's Day issues it summarized the events of the preceding year.

† † †

NEW YORK'S CRIMINAL RECORD FOR 1852

New York Times, January 3, 1853.

We present our readers below with a chronological record of the most prominent cases of crime within this City and vicinity, taken from our files for the past year:

JAN. 8. Three colored women named Hannah Jones, Ellen Johnson and Annie Jones were convicted of highway robbery; they pursued a countryman named James Wade, knocked him down in the street and took from him $23 in money. They were sent to the State Prison for ten years.

15. The Grand Jury found a bill of indictment against the Commissioners of Emigration for allowing a nuisance to exist in a building under their supervision, Viz.: the emigrant lodging houses in Canal street.

22. The Chief of Police reports to the Common Council that within the last six years 180,646 arrests have been made by the officers of the department. . . .

23. The body of a German named Charles Greel was found on the ice near the Battery. He had evidently been murdered on the Battery, dragged to the parapet wall and thrown over. . . .

† † †

The news of the day was treated in the dignified fashion we have always associated—until recently, at least—with the *New York Times*. Raymond, quite predictably, offered news of politics, but these excerpts from the early *Times* suggest other news interests as well: the reception at the Pennsylvania capital of the Hungarian patriot, Louis Kossuth; debate on the Clayton-Bulwer treaty; and the monumental opening of Japan to the West by Commodore Perry.

† † †

A EUROPEAN PATRIOT ARRIVES IN PENNSYLVANIA

New York Times, January 15, 1852.

HARRISBURG, WEDNESDAY, JAN. 14.

GOV. KOSSUTH and suite accompanied by the Reception Committee, arrived here about 3 o'clock, per special train, having been detained on the route in consequence of the breaking of a carwheel. He was received by the Legislature and a large crowd of citizens. The party were conducted to sleighs drawn by four horses each, and the procession was formed entirely of individuals in sleighs. . . .

The House met at four o'clock. At about noon ladies began to fill the hall of the House, and long before the time of meeting, had completely filled the seats of members and the floor, . . .The rotunda and entrance to the Hall presented a scene of dire confusion—an immense crowd struggling for admittance. All kinds of curses were hurled at the Sergeant-at-arms and the officers on duty, and it was certainly the most rowdy demonstration we ever witnessed. . . .

† † †

DEBATE IN THE SENATE OVER A TREATY

New York Times, January 11, 1853.

The CLAYTON and BULWER Treaty occupied the attention of the Senate today, and, as you will see from the report of its proceedings, a highly interesting debate was held upon it. Senator MASON tried to get the floor, in order to make the explanation of Mr. KING's position, which I sent you last night, [published exclusively in the *Times* of yesterday morning,] but failed to do so. The turn which Mr. SEWARD gave the debate may change his purpose; but the explanation sent may be relied on as that which was at first agreed on for the defence. . . .

† † †

JAPAN OPENED TO THE WEST

New York Times, June 13, 1854.

The *Susquehanna* arrived at Hong Kong from Japan on the 2d (April), bringing the gratifying intelligence that Commodore PERRY had succeeded in the objects of his mission in a manner that will confer honor on his country and enduring fame on himself. The precise terms of a Commercial Treaty had not been definitely arranged when the *Susquehanna* left the Yedo on the 24th of March; but enough had been done to establish a friendly feeling between the two countries. *The opening of Three or more ports to the Commerce of America, and the furnishing of Coals for its Steamers, may be considered as matters settled,* and Captain ADAMS held himself in readiness to proceed in the *Saratoga* to bear the intelligence to the Government at Washington.

† † †

Henry J. Raymond, as much as his rival Greeley, was a man of manifest destiny, of the gospel of progress. Scientific developments especially interested him; when the Atlantic Cable was joined in 1858 the *Times* was exultant in a series of headlines.

† † †

HOW A PAPER GREETED THE ATLANTIC CABLE

New York Times, August 17, 1858.

THE OCEAN TELEGRAPH.

VICTORY AT LAST!

THE FIRST MESSAGE.

ENGLAND GREETS AMERICA.

QUEEN VICTORIA
TO
PRESIDENT BUCHANAN.

THE PRESIDENT'S REPLY.

TRIUMPHANT COMPLETION
OF THE
GREAT WORK OF THE CENTURY.

THE OLD WORLD AND THE NEW UNITED.

GLORIA IN EXCELSIS!

† † †

And a lesser-known editorial by Raymond suggests how much the *Times* editor admired technological progress. England had had its great Crystal Palace exposition; now New York could have its own exposition, and one of the fascinated visitors, who stood in awe before a mighty engine, was the editor of the *New York Times.*

† † †

A FASCINATED VIEW OF MACHINERY

New York Times, September 5, 1853.

The Crystal Palace Gas-Light Opening was effected on Friday evening, in presence of a delighted crowd. The machinery in the arcade was in full operation, and the picture-gallery was crowded with visitors. The general impression was one of high gratification with the sights seen there, if not with the sounds heard from the laboring engines and whirring wheels. The Palace from without was a glorious spectacle;—we have studied the word some minutes, and are satisfied it does not color too sunnily the beautiful building. The fences, and the uncurtained ends of the new building, were crowded with the unticketed, who yet were bound to have one glimpse of the interior and its treasures. Now let the outside world be assured that the thing is open. The shells of the big bivalve are fairly separated, and the juicy oyster lies exposed. The man who can visit it now, and come away dissatisfied and growling, should be caught and put on exhibition, as a greater wonder than any within its crystal boundaries.

The effect of illumination on the interior of the building was highly successful. The light coming from within, instead of from without, gave it an aerial lightness, and giving distance to the roof and dome, added to its apparent size. . . .

† † †

Some of the "personal" editors deserve this designation mainly for their editorials. One such was Samuel Bowles III, of the *Springfield Republican,* established in 1844 in an inland city in Massachusetts. Bowles shortly made it known that editors could have national influence and not be located in a major city. Part of his fame came, perhaps, from his crusty attitude. There is a story that the *Republican* once published news of a local man's death, that the man—who was very much alive— came to the newspaper to protest the story and demand a retraction, and that Bowles told him the retraction would have to come in the form of a birth announcement. Bowles, like Greeley, published a weekly paper, and like Greeley he was a Whig and a Republican and had a national audience. A *Springfield Republican* editorial defines what the election of 1856 was all about—in the opinion of Samuel Bowles, at least.

† † †

THE REAL ISSUE OF 1856

Springfield Republican, November 4, 1856.

The real abstract question between the two parties is, whether Congress shall control the destinies of the territories, and dedicate them as of old to freedom, or whether they shall be left for bitter and bloody struggles between the settlers, like those which in Kansas now shock the moral sense of civilization everywhere. Practically the question is whether the influence of the national government shall be used to extend slavery, and aggregate its political power, or to limit its bounds and weaken its hold over the politics, the business, and the religion of the nation. Were the issue thus plainly known of all men, there would be no dispute of the result. The American party stepped in at an inopportune moment, overwhelmed the true issue before the country, and turned aside the minds of many men by the glittering success which it momentarily won. And if the Republican party fails today to inaugurate that revolution in the national government which must come ere this generation passes away, or the government itself perishes, the responsibility cannot be escaped by the American organization. To its door must the defeat of John C. Fremont and the election of James Buchanan be laid. By implanting in many minds a weak substitution for the strongest issue, and by keeping temporarily in the Democratic ranks many who but for their opposition to Americanism would have rallied around the Republican standard, it has given fresh strength to the Democracy, and enabled them to contest this election with a fair prospect of success. . . .

The result of the struggle is in grave doubt, and the eagles of victory are as likely, perhaps, to perch on the one side as on the other, tomorrow morning. Of the two contestants, the Republicans can alone afford to be beaten. With the Democracy, defeat is destruction. The party is only held together by its alliance with the national treasury and the slaveholder. Separated from one, it becomes useless to the other, and its power is gone. But a reverse cannot break the Republican column. It has an enduring vitality in its principles, and a glorious destiny, as sure as the Republic has an existence. Whether it enters upon the affirmative exercise of its mission now, or four years hence, is to all seeming the only question of today. Time will only vindicate its truthfulness, its necessity, and its strength. It can afford to wait, if the country and the world can afford to have it. But the country cannot afford to wait for its healing, peaceful mission, and though we look not upon the day's struggle with confidence of victory, we await its result with a buoyant hope that the day and the hour of redemption have come.

† † †

Many of the great editors of the nineteenth century were able to articulate what the meaning of the press was in their time. Bennett and Greeley had written on the subject, and Samuel Bowles, too, gave voice to his profession and what it meant to him.

† † †

THE MISSION OF THE NEWSPAPER

Springfield Republican, January 4, 1851.

The increase of facilities for the transmission of news brought in a new era. The railroad car, the steamboat, and the magnetic telegraph, have made neighborhood among widely dissevered States, and the Eastern Continent is but a few days' journey away.

—These active and almost miraculous agencies have brought the whole civilized world in contact. . .

The appetite for news is one of those appetites that grows by what it feeds on. . . .The mind accustomed to the gossip of nations, cannot content itself with the gossip of families.

The tendency of this new state of things has, as yet, hardly claimed a moment's consideration from the moralist and the philosopher. Nations and individuals now stand immediately responsible to the world's opinion; and the world, interesting itself in the grand events transpiring in its various parts, and among its various parties, has become, and is still becoming, liberalized in feeling, and, being called away from its exclusive home-field, has forgotten, in its universal interests, the petty interests, feuds, gossips and strifes of families and neighborhoods. The wonderful extension of the field of vision; this compression of the human race into one great family, must tend to identify its interests, sympathies and motives.

The brilliant mission of the newspaper is not yet, and perhaps may never be, perfectly understood. It is, and is to be, the high priest of History, the vitalizer of Society, the world's great informer, the earth's high censor, the medium of public thought and opinion, and the circulating life blood of the whole human mind. It is the great enemy of tyrants, and the right arm of liberty, and is destined, more than any other agency, to melt and mould the jarring and contending nations of the world into that one great brotherhood which, through long centuries, has been the ideal of the Christian and the philanthropist. Its mission has just commenced. A few years more, and a great thought uttered within sight of the Atlantic, will rise with the morrow's sun and shine upon millions of minds by the side of the Pacific. The murmur of Asia's multitudes will be heard at our doors; and laden with the fruit of all human thought and action, the newspaper will be in every abode, the daily nourishment of every mind.

† † †

6

THE PRESS AND THE SLAVERY CRISIS

Historians are still offering interpretations of the causes of the Civil War. These have ranged from the belief that the war was based entirely on emotional sectionalism to the belief that only an analysis of the Karl Marx-Friedrich Engels letters can tell us the true meaning of the war. One historian, James G. Randall, blames the war on a "blundering generation." Another, Avery Craven, a follower of Frederick Jackson Turner, blames it on emotionalism, cultivated hostilities, and "ultimate hatred." Frank E. Owsley speaks of what he calls "egocentric sectionalism," especially in that old devil North. Arthur M. Schlesinger, Jr., sees the war as a moral issue. Richard Enmale, a Marxist, sees it as the second stage of the Marxian dialectic. Allan Nevins blames the war on a succession of weak presidents and weak national leaders. Charles and Mary Beard see it as the second American revolution. J. G. de Roulhac Hamilton blames it all on Lincoln. Edward A. Pollard sees it as a conflict between the Puritan North of materialism and the Cavalier South of refinement. Arnold Whittridge calls his analysis *No Compromise!* to present his beliefs concerning the leaders and their attitudes in the age of the great war.

There are some historians who seem quite able to write and teach about the war and view slavery as entirely incidental. Revisionism has greatly affected histories of the Civil War, but there are some unchallenged premises about the role played by the *press:* the newspaper came into its own, and the personal editors reached the zenith of influence.

War broke out with the bombing of Fort Sumter in Charleston harbor in the spring of 1861. There had been many warnings: the Missouri Compromise; the Tariff of Abominations of 1828; the nullification doctrine of certain southern leaders; the rise of

112

abolitionism in the 1830s; the annexation of Texas in 1845; the Compromise of 1850, with its stiffening of the Fugitive Slave Law; the publication of *Uncle Tom's Cabin* in 1852; Stephen A. Douglas and the Kansas-Nebraska Act of 1854; the events of "Bleeding Kansas"; the Dred Scott decision of 1857; the Lincoln-Douglas debates in 1858; William H. Seward's "irrepressible conflict" speech; John Brown's raid on Harpers Ferry in 1859, and the election of 1860.

Our documents of slavery and the Civil War begin with the prospectus of the first Negro newspaper in America, *Freedom's Journal,* started by John B. Russwurm and Samuel Cornish on March 6, 1827. Their newspaper came in response to the bigotry of some white papers, including the *New York Enquirer* of Mordecai Noah, which became part of Webb's *Courier and Enquirer.* Cornish was a minister; Russwurm was the first black to graduate from a college in the United States—Bowdoin, in 1826. The two eventually split over the issue of African colonization, but black journalism meanwhile had been launched, and there was a procession of papers bearing names like *Spirit of the Times, Weekly Advocate, Elevator, National Reformer, Freeman's Advocate, Ram's Horn,* and *North Star.* Here is the Russwurm-Cornish statement:

† † †

A NEGRO NEWSPAPER ISSUES ITS PROSPECTUS

Freedom's Journal, March 6, 1827.

In presenting our first number to our Patrons, we feel all the diffidence of persons entering upon a new and untried line of business. But a moment's reflection upon the noble objects, which we have in view by the publication of this Journal; the expediency of its appearance at this time, when so many schemes are in action concerning our people—encourage us to come boldly before an enlightened publick. For we believe, that a paper devoted to the dissemination of useful knowledge among our brethren, and to their moral and religious improvement, must meet with the cordial approbation of every friend to humanity.

The peculiarities of this Journal, render it important that we should advertise to the world the motives by which we are actuated, and the objects which we contemplate.

We wish to plead our own cause. Too long have others spoken for us. Too long has the publick been deceived by misrepresentations, in things which concern us dearly, though in the estimation of some mere trifles; for though there are many in society who exercise towards us benevolent feelings; still (with sorrow we confess it) there are others who make it their business to enlarge upon the least trifle, which tends to the discredit of any person of colour; and pronounce anathemas and denounce our whole body for the misconduct of this guilty one. We are aware that there [are] many instances of vices among us, but we avow that it is because no one has taught its subjects to be virtuous; many instances of poverty, because no sufficient efforts accommodated to minds contracted by slavery, and deprived of early education have been made, to teach them how to husband their hard earnings, and to secure to themselves comforts.

Education being an object of the highest importance to the welfare of society, we shall endeavour to present just and adequate views of it, and to urge upon our brethren the necessity and expediency of training their children, while young, to habits of industry, and thus forming them for becoming useful members of society. . . .

Though not desirous of dictating, we shall feel it our incumbent duty to dwell occasionally upon the general principles and rules of economy. The world has grown too enlightened, to estimate any man's character by his personal appearance. . . .

The civil rights of a people being of the greatest value, it shall ever be our duty to vindicate our brethren, when oppressed, and to lay the case before the publick. We shall also urge upon our brethren, (who are qualified by the laws of the different states) the expediency of using their elective franchise; and of making an independent use of the same. . . .

It is our earnest wish to make our Journal a medium of intercourse between our brethren in the different states of this great confederacy; that through its columns an expression of our sentiments, on many interesting subjects which concern us, may be offered to the publick; . . .

Useful knowledge of every kind, and every thing that relates to Africa, shall find a ready admission into our columns; and as that vast continent becomes daily more known, we trust that many things will come to light, proving that the natives of it are neither so ignorant nor stupid as they have generally been supposed to be.

And while these important subjects shall occupy the columns of the FREEDOM'S JOURNAL, we should not be unmindful of our brethren who are still in the iron fetters of bondage. They are our kindred by all the ties of nature; and though but little can be effected by us, still let our sympathies be poured forth, and our prayers in their behalf, ascend to Him who is able to succour them. . . .

In conclusion, whatever concerns us as a people, will ever find a ready admission into the FREEDOM'S JOURNAL, interwoven with all the principal news of the day.

THE EDITORS.

† † †

Greatest of all the black editors, dedicated to removing the evil of slavery from his people, was Frederick Douglass, a journalist and an educator, an orator and a writer of impassioned language. He was born Frederick Augustus Washington Bailey in 1817 in Maryland, and he, a slave, escaped to the North, choosing the name of Douglass from a character in Sir Walter Scott. In New Bedford,

Massachusetts, he became convinced that a wage slavery existed that was comparable to the Negro slavery in the South. In 1845 he published his *Autobiography,* and in those days of the Fugitive Slave Law he then felt it necessary to flee to England. He returned and began publishing the *North Star* in Rochester, New York, in 1847, changing its name to *Frederick Douglass's Paper* in 1851. As the leader of his race he wrote the story of his youth many years later.

† † †

A SLAVE ESCAPES FROM BONDAGE

By Frederick Douglass, *The Century,* I (XXIII, new series, Vol. 1, November, 1881), pp. 126-127.

It was the custom in the State of Maryland to require the free colored people to have what were called free papers. These instruments they were required to renew very often, and by charging a fee for this writing, considerable sums from time to time were collected by the State. In these papers the name, age, color, height, and form of the freeman were described, together with any scars or other marks upon his person which could assist in his identification. This device in some measure defeated itself—since more than one man could be found to answer the same general description. Hence many slaves could escape by personating the owner of one set of papers; and this was often done as follows: a slave, nearly or sufficiently answering the description set forth in the papers, would borrow or hire them till by means of them he could escape to a free State, and then, by mail or otherwise, would return them to the owner. . . . I had one friend—a sailor—who owned a sailor's protection, which answered somewhat the purpose of free papers—describing his person and certifying to the fact that he was a free American sailor. The instrument had at its head the American eagle, which gave it the appearance at once of an authorized document. This protection, when in my hands, did not describe its bearer very accurately. Indeed, it called for a man much darker than myself, and close examination of it would have caused my arrest at the start.

In order to avoid this fatal scrutiny on the part of railroad officials, I arranged with Isaac Rolls, a Baltimore hackman, to bring my baggage to the Philadelphia train just on the moment of starting, and jumped upon the car myself when the train was in motion. Had I gone into the station and offered to purchase a ticket, I should have been instantly and carefully examined, and undoubtedly arrested. . . . One element in my favor was the kind feeling which prevailed in Baltimore and other sea-ports at the time, toward "those who go down to the sea in ships." "Free trade and sailors' rights" just then expressed the sentiment of the country. . . . I was well on the way to Havre de Grace before the conductor came into the Negro car to collect tickets and examine the papers of his black passengers. . . .

Seeing that I did not readily produce my free papers, as the other colored persons in the car had done, he said to me, in friendly contrast with his bearing toward the others:

"I suppose you have your free papers?"

To which I answered:

"No sir; I never carry my free papers to sea with me."

"But you have something to show that you are a freeman, haven't you?"

"Yes, sir," I answered; "I have a paper with the American eagle on it, and that will carry me around the world."

With this I drew from my deep sailor's pocket my seaman's protection, as before described. The merest glance at the paper satisfied him, and he took my fare and went on about his business. . . .

The last point of imminent danger, and the one I dreaded most, was Wilmington. Here we left the train and took the steam-boat for Philadelphia. In making the change here I again apprehended arrest, but no one disturbed me, and I was soon on the broad and beautiful Delaware, speeding away to the Quaker City. . . .

My free life began on the third of September, 1838. On the morning of the fourth of that month, after an anxious and most perilous but safe journey, I found myself in the big city of New York, a *free man*— one more added to the mighty throng which, like the confused waves of the troubled sea, surged to and fro between the lofty walls of Broadway. . .

† † †

Russwurm, Cornish, and Douglass, especially the latter, were *black* abolitionists; their *white* counterparts were considerable, the most famous being James G. Birney, who published the *Philanthropist* in Cincinnati; Elijah Lovejoy, who published the *Observer* in St. Louis and then in Alton, Illinois, and William Lloyd Garrison, who published the *Liberator* in Boston from 1831 to 1865. Lovejoy was the chief white martyr to the cause of abolition, a single-minded individual who was driven out of St. Louis and then murdered in the nearby river town in Illinois. This was published in his newspaper, in Alton.

† † †

A CALL FOR ANTI-SLAVERY ACTION

Alton Observer, July 6, 1837.

ILLINOIS STATE ANTI-SLAVERY SOCIETY.—Is it not time that such a society should be formed? There are many, very many friends of the cause in this state, and their number is daily increasing. Ought not measures to be taken to embody their influence so as to make it tell with the greatest possible effect upon the holy cause of emancipation?

We would do nothing rashly, but it does seem to us that the time to form such a society has fully come. There are a number of local societies already existing in the state, and it would be every way better that their influence should be concentrated.

If it be decided that such a society ought to be formed, when and where shall the convention meet to form it? Shall it be in this place, or at Jacksonville, or Springfield, or elsewhere? . . .

We shall hope to have a response from the friends of the slave without delay. Every day do we feel more and more the necessity of action, decided and effective action, on this subject. With many we are already a "fanatic" and an "incendiary," as it regards this matter, and we feel that we must become more and more vile in their eyes. We have never felt enough, nor prayed enough, nor done enough in behalf of the perishing slave.

This day (the 4th) reproaches our sloth and inactivity. It is the day of our nation's birth. Even as we write, crowds are hurrying past our window, in eager anticipation, to the appointed bower, to listen to the declaration that "all men are born free and equal"—to hear the eloquent orator denounce, in strains of manly indignation, the attempt of England to lay a yoke upon the shoulders of our fathers, which neither they nor their children could bear. Alas! what bitter mockery is this. We assemble to thank God for our own freedom, and to eat and drink with joy and gladness of head, while our feet are upon the necks of nearly THREE MILLIONS of our fellow men! Not all our shouts of self-congratulation can drown their groans—even that very flag of freedom that waves over our heads is formed from materials cultivated by slaves, on a soil moistened with their blood drawn from them by the whip of a republican task-master!

Brethren and friends, this must not be—it can not be—for God will not endure it much longer. Come, then, to the rescue. The voice of three millions of slaves calls upon you to come and "unloose the heavy burdens, and LET THE OPPRESSED GO FREE!" And on this day when every freeman's heart is glad, let us remember that—

"Wearily every bosom pineth,
Wearily oh! wearily oh!
Where the chain of slavery twineth,
Wearily oh! wearily oh!"
There the warrior's dart
Hath no fleetness,
There the maiden's heart
Hath no sweetness.
Every flower of life declineth,
Wearily oh! wearily oh!
Wearily—wearily— wearily—
Wearily—wearily—wearily oh!
Wearily oh! wearily oh!"

† † †

In Alton, Elijah Lovejoy was murdered, and there he rests, on a hillside where a marker carries, in Latin, the inscription:

Here lies
LOVEJOY
Now spare his grave.

Lovejoy's even better-known contemporary was William Lloyd Garrison, a humorless fanatic whose paper, the *Liberator,* was the Bible of the antislavery movement. Garrison carried in his newspaper these words: "The existing Constitution of the United States is a convenant with death and an agreement with hell." He once burned a copy of our revered Constitution in public; he was once dragged through the streets of Boston by an angry mob. He continued forceful in his utterances through the war, absolutely unyielding in his positions. One of his famous editorials was about the most famous book of the day.

† † †

GARRISON COMMENTS ON *UNCLE TOM'S CABIN*

The *Liberator,* March 26, 1852.

In the execution of her very difficult task, Mrs. Stowe has displayed rare descriptive powers, a familiar acquaintance with slavery under its best and its worst phases, uncommon moral and philosophical acumen, great facility of thought and expression, and feelings and emotions of the strongest character. Intimate as we have been, for a score of years, with the features and operations of the slave system, and often as we have listened to the recitals of its horrors, from the lips of the poor hunted fugitives, we confess to the frequent moistening of our eyes, the making of our heart grow liquid as water, and the trembling of every nerve within us, in the perusal of the incidents and scenes so vividly depicted in her pages. The effect of such a work upon all intelligent and humane minds coming in contact with it, and especially upon the rising generation in its plastic condition, to awaken the strongest compassion for the oppressed and the utmost abhorrence of the system which grinds them to dust, cannot be estimated; it must be prodigious, and therefore eminently serviceable in the tremendous conflict now waged for the immediate and entire suppression of slavery upon American soil. . . .

† † †

As Garrison wrote, the western territories of Nebraska and Kansas were still not settled, but soon a dress rehearsal for war would be taking place in the eastern part of Kansas, where free state and slave state sympathizers were engaged in warfare over whether the territory should be free or slave. The problem was occasioned by Senator Stephen A. Douglas's bill, which virtually nullified the Missouri Compromise and established "squatter sovereignty," permitting the settlers of Kansas to decide for themselves whether they should be slavery supporters or free. Settlement began in Kansas in 1854, and soon the editors were bringing presses into the territory, at the same time that Beecher's Bibles—Sharp's rifles—were coming into the prairie settlements in huge packing boxes. Such newspapers debated the slavery question: the *Kansas Weekly Herald* in Leavenworth, first newspaper in the territory, and the *Squatter Sovereign* in Atchison, the *Herald of Freedom* and the *Free State* in Lawrence. Lawrence was the headquarters of the free state forces, and by 1856 the town had come under temporary control of officials installed by Missourians—sympathizers with slavery. On May 21, 1856, a band of men rode into the town from the heights where the University of Kansas is now located, and they shot up the town in what became known as the "Sack of Lawrence." In the territory to view the proceedings was William Phillips, a reporter for Horace Greeley's *New York Tribune.*

† † †

THE SACKING OF LAWRENCE

By William Phillips, in *The Conquest of Kansas by Missouri and Her Allies* (Boston: Phillips, Sampson & Co., 1856), pp. 296-300.

. . .The army of invasion formed into line and marched into Lawrence. A motley-looking crew they were; many of them had red flannel shirts, with curious border ruffian devices on them, so that they could be recognized by their friends in traveling. This scarlet uniform gave them some little the appearance of the "red coats;" and certainly never did such "tories" march to desecrate American soil, or trample under foot the rights of American freemen. As motley an assortment of banners floated over them. The flag of South Carolina, with a crimson star in the centre, [bore] the motto "Southern rights." Another flag resembled the American flag, in being striped like it; but there were no stars, and in their stead a rampant tiger,—fit emblem of the men it floated over, and the cause it vindicated. Another had white and black alternate stripes, which truly represented the cursed amalgamation of races which is ruining the slave states, and which these nullifying filibusters meant to introduce into Kansas, and to nationalize. One banner bore the inscription, "South Carolina;" another, "Supremacy of the white race," on the one side, and "Kansas the outpost," on the other. One bore an inscription in the shape of a sorry distich:

<blockquote>
"You Yankees tremble,
And abolitionists fall;
Our motto is
'Southern rights to all.' ". . .
</blockquote>

. . .The first place attacked was the printing office of the *"Free State."* It was in the second story of a concrete building. There was a store below. One of the ruffian officers entered the store and demanded of the proprietor if there was a mine under the building to blow it up. The merchant assured him there was not, when the interrogator told him that they were going up into the printing office, and that if anything happened he would hold him responsible. The "posse" or ruffians, either or both, entered the office of the *Free State,* and the work of demolition commenced. The press and other articles were first broken, so as to be rendered perfectly useless, and then thrown into the Kansas river. As this was some distance to carry the articles, they got tired of it, and began throwing the remainder in the street. Books and papers were thrown in the street. Many of these men got books they fancied, and kept them. Some of the officers ordered them to take nothing, saying "These Yankees will tell stories enough about us for this, without our stealing from them." Colonel Zadoc Jackson, of Georgia, exerted himself to prevent the plunder, as did several others; they were prepared for the most desperate war against Freedom and American rights, but they had too much honor, or too much pride, to wish to occupy the position of highwaymen. Unfortunately, these officers were unable to prevent these outrages, or restrain the villains they had gathered up to do their lawless work.

The office of the other paper in Lawrence, the *Herald of Freedom,* was entered by the Carolinians, shortly after their compatriots had commenced the work of demolition in the *Free State* office. The *Herald of Freedom* office is a tall, narrow, concrete building. Into this the gallant "chivalry" were afraid to venture. The dread of mines and infernal machines was a sort of nightmare with them. In order to *be safe* in entering the office in question, they drove some young men, residents of the town, up the stairs and into the building, at the point of the bayonet. How this stupid policy was to demonstrate anything, or afford security, it would be difficult to discover. In the *Herald of Freedom* office the same reckless work of destruction went on. The presses were broken in a thorough and *enlightened* manner, which showed the hand or the direction of a practical printer, the fragments being perfectly useless. Books and papers were thrown out in the street, or stolen. Several members of the posse were marching about the streets with books stuck on the points of their bayonets. Others were tearing books to shreds, but the more prudent carried them off.

The next step in the process was the destruction of the hotel. The enemy planted their artillery in front of the hotel, one hundred and fifty feet distant from it, across Massachusetts-street. The hotel was a very large building, three full stories high besides the basement; it seemed almost impossible that they could miss it. The proprietor of the establishment, Mr. Eldridge, was notified by Jones to remove his furniture in a certain time. This Mr. Eldridge said he could not do. Some of the posse went to work and began to carry articles of furniture out into the street; but they very soon got weary of this, and found a task more congenial. They discovered the wines and liquors, a good stock of which was on hand, and, helping themselves freely to these and to eatables and cigars, the heroes of this gallant campaign were soon in an interesting condition.

The hotel was cleared of people, and [Senator David] Atchison aimed the first gun fired at it. The worthy ex-vice-president was rather too tipsy to win many laurels as a gunner. He stooped over the gun. "A little higher, boys, a little lower—a little higher. That's it, boys; let her rip!" Bang went the gun, the ball missing the hotel altogether, going clear over it. The next gunner was rather more successful, putting a ball through the top corner of the right. Some fifty rounds were fired, when, finding it slow business, the hotel looking, externally, little the worse for it, they undertook to blow it up. Four kegs of gunpowder were placed in it, but only two of them exploded, and they made little report, and still less impression on the walls; but fire was communicated to the building in several places, and it was soon a magnificent sea of flame.

As the flames hissed and crackled, Jones leaned upon his horse and contemplated the spectacle. His eyes glistened with a wild delight, and he said, "This is the happiest moment of my life." . . .

The closing act was the burning of Governor Robinson's dwelling, which stood upon the brow of Mount Oread. This had been plundered through the day, and at night it was set on fire; and the pyramid of flame from the mount lighted up the pathway of the retreating army.

Besides the plundering in town, these men, both before and after the 21st, went about the country, and plundered many houses. It is supposed that not less than two hundred horses were taken, in and around Lawrence. There were also frightful stories of outrages, and of women being ravished. Such cases there may have been, but rare. There were villains in that posse who were certainly none too good for it.

Such was the sack of Lawrence. . . .

† † †

Kansas was of course only one of the stages on which the theater of war was being acted out in the 1850s. In New Orleans there was an important magazine called *DeBow's Review,* and it presented one southern position, in arguments marked by history, literature, and economics.

† † †

THE SOUTH AND THE COMPROMISE

DeBow's Review, July, 1850.

The Union is the source of our greatness and strength; its dismemberment will probably be of our impotence and ruin, whilst all the world will look on, with amazement, upon the dissolution of a fabric so fair and beautiful in its proportions.

Thus we should feel and think. Yet there must be an end, somewhere, of concessions. If not a *voluntary* end, a *necessary* one, when everything to be conceded is gone. It becomes the South to determine how far its safety will admit of concession. The stand should be made there. None can mistake the *anti-slavery* growth—it has no resting place. The cry is onward! When was there ever a step backward in its history? It will sweep over Mr. Webster as the whirlwind sweeps over the reed. Every concession made to it will induce a more imperious tone—every success will embolden and pave the way for a new and higher triumph. "Will you interpose the Constitution?" There is a voice higher than the Constitution! Will you make a compromise and hold up its sacred assurances? Majorities rule—numbers have assumed the sway—the edict of Congress goes out upon the land, backed by its fleets and its armies, potent as the nod of the autocrat of Russia, and unalterable as the law of the Medes and the Persians. The path is clear, the end undisputed. The protection of the national flag will be withheld from the slave, in his passage from one port to another in the Union. His arrest in a free State [will be] impossible. Slavery will go by the board in the District of Columbia—in the forts and navy yards. The trade between the States will be prohibited. The final act is not yet, but soon. There is a precedent in the British Parliament and the West Indies. *They will use the precedent.* We know the rest.

† † †

The writer for *DeBow's* addressed himself to the question of the Compromise of 1850. William Lloyd Garrison, in the *Liberator,* wrote about the strife in Kansas, but he looked at the affairs in that bleeding land and saw something that some distant commentators did not see: the Kansas settlers, their hearts bleeding for slavery, apparently preferred to have members of the black race as far away as possible.

† † †

ON ARMS FOR THE FREE-SOILERS IN KANSAS

The *Liberator,* April 4, 1856.

. . . We burn with indignation at the insults and outrages to which the settlers have thus been subjected, and acknowledge their position to be a most trying and perilous one. But we deny, in the first place, that they are acting upon principle, or contending for equal rights. They resent as a foul slander the charge of being abolitionists; they are pro-slavery in spirit and position, with regard to the millions who are now grinding in the Southern house of bondage; they have meanly and wickedly proscribed every man of color, and made it illegal for him to be a resident in the Territory; they do not object to slave-hunting on their soil, but recognize it as a constitutional obligation which they have no disposition to annul; they go for *all* the pro-slavery compromises of the American Constitution; they are contending for their own rights *as white men,* not for the rights of all, without distinction of caste or color; they have pursued a shuffling and compromising policy throughout; they have consented to make the existence of liberty or slavery in the Territory dependent upon the will of the majority, fairly expressed, and *to abide by the result.* The retribution now meted out to them is divinely ordered: having sown the wind, they are reaping the whirlwind. . . .

† † †

In stormy 1856, when the Missourians with their "border ruffian" flags and shirts invaded Lawrence, a man named John Brown came into the territory of Kansas and briefly stamped his name upon the history of the place, and of the nation, too. With his sons, and some others, he summarily executed, with sabers he had brought into Kansas in a covered wagon, slave state sympathizers. Three years later he was performing elsewhere, in an attempt to seize the arsenal at Harpers Ferry, Virginia, to obtain arms for a slave insurrection. He failed, and the *Herald of Freedom* of Lawrence, edited by George Washington Brown—*not* the most ardent of abolitionists— editorialized on the failure.

† † †

A KANSAS EDITOR WRITES OF JOHN BROWN

Herald of Freedom, December 17, 1859.

The ultra men of the North say of John Brown: "He has fallen a martyr to Freedom."

Freedom has had her martyrs, of whom ELIJAH P. LOVEJOY, who fell at Alton, defending the freedom of the press, is a worthy example. He fell in maintenance of his right to speak the truth on free soil.

Whatever John Brown may have been engaged in previously as a means of achieving the triumph of free principles, that cannot be construed as casting any luster on his last enterprise, unless it is proven a legitimate sequence of the defence of free principles. His avowed object, and that of his associates, was to set on foot a slave insurrection. Is that a legitimate sequence of the advocacy of free principles? If so, then insurrection is one of the noble and Heaven-ordained means of advancing the freedom of the African race—one which abolitionists can advocate, good citizens commend, and Christians laud its active promoters as men worthy of being enshrined as better than Washington, and equal to Jesus Christ; and the gallows of John Brown as honored as the cross of Jesus!

No sane man pretends that insurrection is the legitimate fruit of the anti-slavery gospel. Had John Brown taken his life in his hand, and gone into the slave States, preaching to slave holders and pro-slavery men anti-slavery truth as Rev. JOHN G. FEE and CASSIUS M. CLAY have done, and then had fallen a victim to violence for that cause, he would have been worthy of enrollment in the martyr-roll of today. Professedly believing in the ultimate triumph of truth, he showed his disbelief, in eschewing peaceful measures, and proclaiming "War to the knife—and the knife to the hilt." Apparently a very saint—doing lip service as a "follower of the meek and lowly Jesus," he preferred his own cunning and the strength of his right arm to the power either of God or his truth. In his case Christ's words were fulfilled—"He that taketh the sword shall perish by the sword"—a fate which Christ evidently considered neither very martyrlike nor exemplary—a course which met his emphatic condemnation. . . .

† † †

The war came, and great national leaders emerged within the ranks of the press. One of them had been well known since the mid-1850s—Joseph Medill, editor of the *Chicago Tribune,* a journal that had begun in the penny era. Medill had been exultant over the nomination of Abraham Lincoln in 1860, and a *Tribune* editorial offered a profile of the Rail Splitter.

† † †

LINCOLN, AS MEDILL SAW HIM

Chicago Tribune, May 23, 1860.

Ten thousand inquiries will be made as to the looks, the habits, tastes and other characteristics of Honest Old Abe. We anticipate a few of them.

Mr. Lincoln stands six feet and four inches high in his stockings. His frame is not muscular, but gaunt and wiry; his arms are long, but not unreasonably so for a person of his height; his lower limbs are not disproportioned to his body. In walking, his gait though firm is never brisk. He steps slowly and deliberately, almost always with his head inclined forward and his hands clasped behind his back.

In matters of dress he is by no means precise. Always clean, he is never fashionable; he is careless but not slovenly. In manner he is remarkably cordial, and, at the same time, simple. His politeness is always sincere but never elaborate and oppressive. A warm shake of the hand and a warmer smile of recognition are his methods of greeting his friends.

At rest, his features, though those of a man of mark, are not such as belong to a handsome man; but when his fine dark gray eyes are lighted up by any emotion, and his features begin their play, he would be chosen from among a crowd as one who had in him not only the kindly sentiments which women love, but the heavier metal of which full grown men and Presidents are made. His hair is black, and though thin is wiry. His head sits well on his shoulders, but beyond that it defies description. It nearer resembles that of Clay than that of Webster; but is unlike either. It is very large, and, phrenologically, well proportioned, betokening power in all its developments. A slightly Roman nose, a widecut mouth and a dark complexion, with the appearance of having been weather-beaten, completes the description.

In his personal habits, Mr. Lincoln is as simple as a child. He loves a good dinner and eats with the appetite which goes with a great brain; but his food is plain and nutritious. He never drinks intoxicating liquors of any sort, not even a glass of wine. He is not addicted to tobacco, in any of its shapes. He never was accused of a licentious act in all his life. He never uses profane language. A friend says that once, when in a towering rage in consequence of the efforts of certain parties to perpetrate a fraud on the State, he was heard to say "They shan't do it, d-n'em!" but beyond an expression of that kind, his bitterest feelings never carry him. He never gambles; we doubt if he ever indulges in any games of chance.

He is particularly cautious about incurring pecuniary obligations for any purpose whatever, and in debt, he is never content until the score is discharged. We presume he owes no man a dollar. He never speculates. The rage for the sudden acquisition of wealth never took hold of him. His gains from his profession have been moderate, but sufficient for his purposes. While others have dreamed of gold, he has been in pursuit of knowledge. In all his dealings he has the reputation of being generous but exact, and, above all, religiously honest. He would be a bold man who would say that Abraham Lincoln ever wronged any one out of a cent, or ever spent a dollar that he had not honestly earned. His struggles in early life have made him careful of money; but his generosity with his own is proverbial.

He is a regular attendant upon religious worship, and though not a communicant, is a pew-holder and liberal supporter of the Presbyterian Church, in Springfield, to which Mrs. Lincoln belongs. He is a scrupulous teller of the truth—too exact in his notions to suit the atmosphere of Washington as it is now. His enemies may say that he tells Black Republican lies; but no man ever charged that, in a professional capacity, or as a citizen dealing with his neighbors, he would depart from the Scriptural command.

At home he lives like a gentleman of modest means and simple tastes. A good sized house of wood, simply but tastefully furnished; surrounded by trees and flowers, is his own, and there he lives, at peace with himself, the idol of his family, and for his honesty, ability and patriotism, the admiration of his countrymen.

If Mr. Lincoln is elected President, he will carry but little that is ornamental to the White House. The country must accept his sincerity, his ability and his honesty, in the mould in which they are cast. He will not be able to make as polite a bow as Frank Pierce, but he will not commence anew the agitation of the Slavery question by recommending to Congress any Kansas-Nebraska bills. He may not preside at the Presidential dinners with the ease and grace which distinguish the "venerable public functionary," Mr. Buchanan; but he will not create the necessity for a Covode Committee and the disgraceful revelations of Cornelius Wendell. He will take to the Presidential chair just the qualities which the country now demands to save it from impending destruction—ability that no man can question, firmness that nothing can overbear, honesty that never has been impeached, and patriotism that never despairs.

† † †

Joseph Medill was one of several editors, most of them originating in the age of the penny press, who attained prominence. Where *propaganda* had been the word to describe the role of the press in the American Revolution, *news* was the one to describe the press in the Civil War, even though many reporters were not especially scrupulous in their telling of the news, some of them even fabricating on occasion. The newspapers of the penny editors were especially vigorous. James Gordon Bennett had thirty to forty reporters, alone, in the northern theaters; Greeley, Raymond, Bryant, and Bowles covered the war and served as armchair generals, not always well, though Bryant apparently had made an effort to learn something about military strategy. Most of the major newspapers, except for Bennett's, were Republican. In 1861 a Democratic publication was born, the *World,* edited by Manton Marble, and it was the *World* that published the account of the beginning of the war that finds its way, with good reason, into most anthologies. B. S. Osbon was the reporter.

† † †

HOW A GREAT WAR WAS INAUGURATED

New York World, April 13, 1861.

CHARLESTON, APRIL 12—The ball is opened. War is inaugurated.
The batteries of Sullivan's Island, Morris Island, and other points were opened on Fort Sumter at four o'clock this morning. Fort Sumter has returned the fire, and a brisk cannonading has been kept up.
The military are under arms, and the whole of our population are on the streets. Every available space facing the harbor is filled with anxious spectators.
The firing has continued all day without intermission.

Two of Fort Sumter's guns have been silenced, and it is reported that a breach has been made in the southeast wall.

The answer to General Beauregard's demand by Major Anderson was that he would surrender when his supplies were exhausted; that is, if he was not reinforced.

CHARLESTON, APRIL 12, 3 p.m.— Civil war has at last begun. A terrible fight is at this moment going on between Fort Sumter and the fortifications by which it is surrounded. The issue was submitted to Major Anderson of surrendering as soon as his supplies were exhausted, or of having fire opened on him within a certain time. He refused to surrender, and accordingly at twenty-seven minutes past four o'clock this morning Fort Moultrie began the bombardment by firing two guns.

Major Anderson has the greater part of the day been directing his fire principally against Fort Moultrie, the Stevens and floating battery, these and Fort Johnson being the only ones operating against him. The remainder of the batteries are held in reserve.

The Stevens battery is eminently successful and does terrible execution on Fort Sumter. Breaches, to all appearances, are being made in the several sides exposed to fire. Portions of the parapet have been destroyed, and several of the guns there mounted have been shot away.

The excitement in the community is indescribable. With the first boom of the gun, thousands rushed from their beds to the harbor front, and all day every available place has been thronged by ladies and gentlemen, viewing the solemn spectacle through their glasses. Most of these have relatives in the several fortifications, and many a tearful eye attested the anxious affection of the mother, wife, and sister, but *not a murmur came from a single individual.*

Business is entirely suspended. Only those stores are open necessary to supply articles required by the army.

Troops are pouring into the town by hundreds, but are held in reserve for the present, the force already on the islands being ample. The thunder of the artillery can be heard for fifty miles around, and the scene is magnificently terrible.

†   †   †

If it had not been for the overpowering element of tragedy, the Battle of Bull Run could have been regarded as a kind of comic opera event. For there were many in the North who were confident of victory, and on a pleasant summer day the ladies and gentlemen of Washington went out into the countryside to see the war come to an end at a little stream called Bull Run, near Manassas Junction. One of the penny editors, Henry J. Raymond, went back into town and wired news of the Union "victory" to the *Times,* and he returned in time to see the rout of the northern forces. Reporting for the *New York Herald* was an immigrant named Henry Villard, whose name would become important in journalism, railroading, and finance in later years.

† † †

A CLASSIC ACCOUNT OF BULL RUN

New York Herald, July 20 and 23, 1861.

CENTERVILLE, SIX AND A HALF MILES FROM MANASSAS JUNCTION, THURSDAY, JULY 18, 5 P.M.—I have just returned from the thickest of an action of considerable moment, between a portion of the rebel forces and the Fourth Brigade of General Tyler's division, composed of the Second and Third Michigan, the First Massachusetts, and Twelfth New York Volunteer regiments, under command of Colonel Richardson; and as the aide of General McDowell, who will carry the official report of the affair to General Scott, and who offers the only means of communication with Washington this evening, is about starting, I have only time to send you the following brief particular of today's operation.

At eleven o'clock General Tyler proceeded to make a reconnaissance in force, with Captain Ayres' (late Sherman's) battery, four companies of cavalry, and Colonel Richardson's brigade, composed as above stated. Advancing up the road to Bull's Run for about two miles, the column came to an opening, after passing through a long stretch of timber, when sight was caught of a strong body of the enemy. General Tyler immediately ordered Captain Ayres' battery to advance and open on them, which they did from a commanding elevation. Eight shells had been thrown, when suddenly a volley was fired upon us from a hidden battery, about a mile down the road.

Our howitzers then threw some grapeshot into the timber, when at once a terrific series of volleys of musketry was poured out from the woods upon the troops outside. At the same time a battery commenced playing upon us from an elevation in the rear. Shot of every description flew about us like hail; but it being, fortunately, nearly all aimed too high, hardly anyone was struck outside the woods.

A retreat was now ordered, when infantry, cavalry, and artillery fell back behind our battery on the hill. The Twelfth New York and a portion of the First Massachusetts broke ranks and scattered in different directions, in their hasty retreat, for some distance through the woods, in the rear of the battery.

Our troops fought under great disadvantage. Not one rebel ventured out of the woods during the action. *The affair was not an attack, but merely a reconnaissance* to discover the position and strength of the enemy.

HEADQUARTERS OF THE GRAND ARMY, CENTERVILLE, JULY 19, 8 A.M.—*Much of the haste and confusion of the retreat*

was due to the inefficiency and cowardice of some of the officers.
I can personally testify to the more than ordinary coolness and gallantry shown by Colonel Richardson during the action. A shower of rifle balls was constantly aimed at him, but they did not for a moment deter him from doing his whole duty. General Tyler also showed great courage on the occasion. He was exposed to the enemy's fire for nearly four hours.

The representatives of the press stood their ground as well as any, in spite of the shot, shell, and rifle balls that kept whizzing past them for hours.

FAIRFAX COURTHOUSE July 21—I am en route to Washington with details of a great battle.
We have carried the day.
The rebels accepted battle in their strength, but are totally routed.
Losses on both sides considerable.

* * * * *

The New York Herald, July 23, 1861
THE DISASTER AT BULL'S RUN
WASHINGTON, JULY 22, 1861—Our troops, after taking three batteries and gaining a great victory at Bull's Run, were eventually repulsed and commenced a retreat on Washington.

After the latest information was received from Centerville, at half-past seven o'clock last night, a series of unfortunate events took place which have proved disastrous to our army. Many confused accounts are prevalent, but facts enough are known to warrant the statement that we have suffered severely on account of a most unfortunate occurrence, which has cast a gloom over the retreating army and excited the deepest melancholy throughout Washington.

Our Union forces were advancing upon the enemy and taking his masked batteries gradually but surely, by driving the rebels towards Manassas Junction, when they seem to have been reinforced by twenty thousand men under General Johnston, who, it is understood, then took command and immediately commenced driving us back. We were retreating in good order, the rear well covered with a solid column, *when a panic among our troops suddenly occurred, and a regular stampede took place.*

† † †

Horace Greeley, the dominant personal editor, had perhaps the greatest influence of all editors during the Civil War. Though he had been launched into politics and journalism by Thurlow Weed and William H. Seward back in 1840, he had broken with those leaders, and in 1860 he promoted not Seward but Lincoln for the presidency. Greeley was a jealous man, though, and perhaps shrewish, and he must have been a constant pain for the beleaguered President.

Greeley was erratic—favoring, then opposing, secession; after Fort Sumter he made "Forward to Richmond!" the editorial page battle cry of the *Tribune*. But he was consistent on one matter; he favored emancipation of the slaves, and his most famous editorial came in the form of a letter to Lincoln.

† † †

THE PRAYER OF TWENTY MILLIONS

New York Tribune, August 20, 1862.

To Abraham Lincoln, President of the United States:
Dear Sir: I do not intrude to tell you—for you must know already—that a great proportion of those who triumphed in your election, and of all who desire the unqualified suppression of the Rebellion now desolating our country, are sorely disappointed and deeply pained by the policy you seem to be pursuing with regard to the slaves of Rebels. I write only to set succinctly and unmistakably before you what we require, what we think we have a right to expect, and of what we complain.

I. We require of you, as the first servant of the Republic, charged especially and preeminently with this duty, that you EXECUTE THE LAWS. Most emphatically do we demand that such laws as have been recently enacted, which therefore may fairly be presumed to embody the *present* will and to be dictated by the *present* needs of the Republic, and which after due consideration have received your personal sanction, shall by you be carried into full effect, and that you publicly and decisively instruct your subordinates that such laws exist, that they are binding on all functionaries and citizens, and that they are to be obeyed to the letter.

II. We think you are strangely and disastrously remiss in the discharge of your official and imperative duty with regard to the emancipating provisions of the new Confiscation Act. These provisions were designed to fight Slavery with Liberty. They prescribe that men loyal to the Union, and willing to shed their blood in her behalf, shall no longer be held, with the Nation's consent, to persistent, malignant traitors, who for twenty years have been plotting and for sixteen months have been fighting to divide and destroy our country. Why these traitors should be treated with tenderness by you, to the prejudice of the dearest rights of loyal men, we cannot conceive.

III. We think you are unduly influenced by the counsels, the representations, the menaces, of certain fossil politicians hailing from the Border Slave States. Knowing well that the heartily, unconditionally loyal portion of the white citizens of these States do not expect nor desire that slavery shall be upheld to the prejudice of the Union—(for the truth of which we appeal not only to every Republican residing in those States, but to such eminent loyalists as

H. Winter Davis, Parson Brownlow, the Union Central Committee of Baltimore, and the Nashville *Union*)—we ask you to consider that slavery is everywhere the inciting cause and sustaining base of treason: the most slaveholding sections of Maryland and Delaware being this day, though under the Union flag, in full sympathy with the Rebellion, while the Free-Labor portions of Tennessee and of Texas, though writhing under the bloody heel of Treason, are unconquerably loyal to the Union. . . .

IV. We think timid counsels in such a crisis calculated to prove perilous, and probably disastrous. It is the duty of a government so wantonly, wickedly assailed by Rebellion as ours has been to oppose force in a defiant, dauntless spirit. It cannot afford to compromise with traitors nor with semi-traitors. It must not bribe them to behave themselves, nor make them fair promises in the hope of disarming their causeless hostility. . . .

V. We complain that the Union cause has suffered, and is now suffering immensely, from mistaken deference to Rebel slavery. Had you, sir, in your inaugural address, unmistakably given notice that, in case the Rebellion already commenced were persisted in, and your efforts to preserve the Union and enforce the laws were resisted by armed force, *you would recognize no loyal person as rightfully held in slavery by a Traitor*, we believe the Rebellion would therein have received a staggering if not fatal blow. . . . Had you then proclaimed that Rebellion would strike the shackles from the slaves of every traitor, the wealthy and the cautious would have been supplied with a powerful inducement to remain loyal. . . .

VI. We complain that the Confiscation Act which you approved is habitually disregarded by your generals, and that no word of rebuke for them from you has yet reached the public ear. Fremont's proclamation and Hunter's Order favoring emancipation were promptly annulled by you; while Halleck's No. 3, forbidding fugitives from slavery to Rebels to come within his lines—an order as unmilitary as inhuman, and which received the hearty approbation of every traitor in America—with scores of like tendency, have never provoked even your remonstrance. We complain that the officers of your armies have habitually repelled rather than invited the approach of slaves who would have gladly taken the risk of escaping from their Rebel masters to our camps, bringing intelligence often of inestimable value to the Union cause. . .

VII. Let me call your attention to the recent tragedy in New Orleans, whereof the facts are obtained entirely through pro-slavery channels. A considerable body of resolute, able-bodied men, held in slavery by two Rebel sugar-planters in defiance of the Confiscation Act which you have approved, left plantations thirty miles distant and made their way to the great mart of the Southwest, which they knew to be in the undisputed possession of the Union forces. They made their way safely and quietly through thirty miles of Rebel territory, expecting to find freedom under the protection of our flag. . . . They came to us for liberty and protection, for which they were willing to render their best services; they met with hostility, captivity, and murder. . . .

VIII. On the face of this wide earth, Mr. President, there is not one disinterested, determined, intelligent champion of the Union cause who does not feel that all attempts to put down the Rebellion and at the same time uphold its inciting cause are preposterous and futile— that the rebellion, if crushed out tomorrow, would be renewed within a year if slavery were left in full vigor. . . .

IX. I close as I began with the statement that what an immense majority of the Loyal Millions of your countrymen require of you is a frank, declared, unqualified, ungrudging execution of the laws of the land, more especially of the Confiscation Act. That Act gives freedom to the slaves of Rebels coming within our lines, or whom those lines may at any time enclose—we ask you to render it due obedience by publicly requiring all your subordinates to recognize and obey it. The Rebels are everywhere using the late anti-negro riots in the North, as they have long used your officers' treatment of negroes in the South, to convince the slaves that they have nothing to hope from a Union success—that we mean in that case to sell them into a bitterer bondage to defray the cost of the war. Let them impress this as a truth upon the great mass of the ignorant and credulous bondmen, and the Union will never be restored—never. We cannot conquer Ten Millions of people united in solid phalanx against us, powerfully aided by Northern sympathizers and European allies. We must have scouts, guides, spies, cooks, teamsters, diggers and choppers, from the Blacks of the South, whether we allow them to fight for us or not, or we shall be baffled and repelled. As one of the millions who would gladly have avoided this struggle at any sacrifice but that of Principle and Honor, but who now feel that the triumph of the Union is indispensable not only to the existence of our country but to the well-being of mankind, I entreat you to render a hearty and unequivocal obedience to the law of the land.

HORACE GREELEY.

† † †

In the years after Greeley's death Whitelaw Reid of Ohio became editor of Greeley's *New York Tribune;* during the war years Reid was one of the best reporters, part of a gallery that included Murat Halstead of the *Cincinnati Commercial,* Henry M. Stanley of the *New York Herald,* and Albert D. Richardson and George W. Smalley of the *New York Tribune.* While working for the *Cincinnati Gazette,* Reid covered the battle of Shiloh, serving as the only reporter there (though others fabricated accounts), and then the even more famous battle of Gettysburg, with its now historic charge by the Confederate forces under General George Pickett.

† † †

GETTYSBURG, LANDMARK BATTLE OF THE WAR

Cincinnati Gazette, July 5, 1863.

. . . Ascending the high hill to the rear of Slocum's headquarters, I saw such a sight as few men may ever hope to see twice in a lifetime. Around our center and left, the rebel line must have been from four to five miles long, and over that whole length there rolled up the smoke from their two hundred and fifty guns. The roar, the bursting bombs, the impression of magnificent power, "all the glory visible, all the horror of the fearful field concealed," a nation's existence trembling as the clangor of those iron monsters swayed the balance—it was a sensation for a century!

About two the fire slackened a little, then broke out deadlier than ever, till, beaten out against our impenetrable sides, it ebbed and closed in broken, spasmodic dashes.

The great, desperate, final charge came at four. The rebels seemed to have gathered up all their strength and desperation for one fierce, convulsive effort, that should sweep over and wash out our obstinate resistance. They swept up as before, the flower of their army to the front, victory staked upon the issue. In some places they literally lifted up and pushed back our lines, but that terrible "position" of ours!—wherever they entered it, enfilading fires from half a score of crests swept away their columns like merest chaff. Broken and hurled back, they easily fell into our hands, and on the center and left the last half-hour brought more prisoners than all the rest.

So it was along the whole line; but it was on the Second Corps that the flower of the rebel army was concentrated; it was there that the heaviest shock beat upon and shook and even sometimes crumbled our line.

We had some shallow rifle pits, with barricades of rails from the fences. The rebel line, stretching away miles to the left, in magnificent array, but strongest here—Pickett's splendid division of Longstreet's corps in front, the best of A. P. Hill's veterans in support—came steadily and, as it seemed, resistlessly sweeping up. Our skirmishers retired slowly from the Emmetsburg road, holding their ground tenaciously to the last. The rebels reserved their fire till they reached this same Emmetsburg road, then opened with a terrific crash. From a hundred iron throats, meantime, their artillery had been thundering on our barricades.

Hancock was wounded; Gibbon succeeded to the command—approved soldiers, and ready for the crisis. As the tempest of fire approached its height, he walked along the line, and renewed his orders to the men to reserve their fire. The rebels—three lines deep—came steadily up. They were in point-blank range.

At last the order came! From thrice six thousand guns there came a sheet of smoky flame, a crash of leaden death. The line literally melted away; but there came the second, resistless still. It had been our supreme effort—on the instant we were not equal to another.

Up to the rifle pits, across them, over the barricades—the momentum of their charge, the mere machine strength of their combined action swept them on. Our thin line could fight, but it had not weight enough to oppose to this momentum. It was pushed behind the guns. Right on came the rebels. They were upon the guns, were bayoneting the gunners, were waving their flags above our pieces.

But they had penetrated to the fatal point. A storm of grape and canister tore its way from man to man and marked its track with corpses straight down their line! They had exposed themselves to the enfilading fire of the guns on the western slope of Cemetery Hill; that exposure sealed their fate.

The line reeled back—disjointed already—in an instant in fragments. Our men were just behind the guns. They leaped forward upon the disordered mass; but there was little need for fighting now. A regiment threw down its arms, and, with colors at its head, rushed over and surrendered. All along the field smaller detachments did the same. Webb's brigade brought in eight hundred taken in as little time as it requires to write the simple sentence that tells it. Gibbon's old division took fifteen stands of colors.

Over the fields the escaped fragments of the charging line fell back—the battle there was over. A single brigade, Harrow's (of which the Seventh Michigan is part), came out with fifty-four less officers, 793 less men than it took in! So the whole corps fought—so, too, they fought further down the line.

It was fruitless sacrifice. They gathered up their broken fragments, formed their lines, and slowly marched away. It was not a rout, it *was* a bitter, crushing defeat. For once the Army of the Potomac had won a clean, honest, acknowledged victory.

† † †

Gettysburg was one of two victories in 1863 that brought hope to the North, the other being the end of the long siege at Vicksburg, on the Mississippi. The famous battle in Pennsylvania, now perhaps the best known of the Civil War, had been preceded by many defeats and half-victories: the unsuccessful Peninsular Campaign of George McClellan, the inconclusive victory at Antietam, the disasters at Fredericksburg and Chancellorsville that had brought Burnside and Hooker down with them. In the western theater generals named Grant, Sherman, and Thomas were winning key battles, but not for the reporters of the big penny papers to report; those reporters were mainly following the Army of the Potomac. The battle of Gettysburg was followed by the most famous address in our history, and the illustrated magazine, *Harper's Weekly,* editorialized on the matter.

† † †

ON A BATTLEFIELD CEREMONY AT GETTYSBURG

Harper's Weekly, December 5, 1863.

The solemn ceremony at Gettysburg is one of the most striking events of the war. There are graveyards enough in the land—what is Virginia but a cemetery?—and the brave who have died for us in this fierce war consecrate the soil from the ocean to the Mississippi. But there is peculiar significance in the field of Gettysburg, for there "thus far" was thundered to the rebellion. This it is which separates it from all the other battlefields of this war. Elsewhere the men in the ranks have fought as nobly, and their officers have directed as bravely; but here their valor stayed the flood of barbarism, and like the precious shells that the highest storm tides strew upon the beach, showing how far the waters came, so the dead heroes of Gettysburg marked the highest tide of the war. Therefore shall their graves be peculiarly honored, and their memory especially sacred; and all that living men can bring of pomp and solemnity and significance to hallow their restingplace shall not be wanting.

The President and the Cabinet were there, with famous soldiers and civilians. The oration by Mr. Everett was smooth and cold. Delivered, doubtless, with his accustomed graces, it yet wanted one stirring thought, one vivid picture, one thrilling appeal.

The few words of the President were from the heart to the heart. They cannot be read, even, without kindling emotion. "The world will little note nor long remember what we say here, but it can never forget what they did here." It was as simple and felicitous and earnest a word as was ever spoken.

Among the Governors present was Horatio Seymour. He came to honor the dead of Gettysburg. But when they were dying he stood in New York sneeringly asking where was the victory promised for the Fourth of July? These men were winning their victory and dying for us all; and now he mourns, ex officio, over their graves.

When the war is over and verdict of history is rendered, it is not those who have steadily perplexed the government in every way— those who first incited and then palliated massacre and riot—who will be known as the friends of the soldiers, but those whose faith was firmest in the darkest hours, and who did not falter though the foe were at the door.

† † †

American histories are loaded in favor of the North; journalism histories say relatively little about the press in the South during the war years. There is a good reason; few papers had the national prominence of the giants in New York and Chicago, and economically and industrially the South was in much worse condition. But an editor named Robert Barnwell Rhett was active in Charleston with his *Mercury;* there was of course the vital *Picayune* in New Orleans; and each capital had an influential newspaper. One of the eloquent stories by a southern reporter was that written after Gettysburg by a reporter for the *Richmond Enquirer*. He told a story to his readers that probably seemed more horrifying to them than the stories filed after the ignominious defeat of the Union at Bull Run seemed to northern readers.

† † †

A SOUTHERNER TELLS OF PICKETT'S CHARGE

Richmond Enquirer, July 12, 1863.

The sun rises, clouds obscure its brightness as if loath to look upon the scene to witness such inhumanity, but from which no people are exempt who ever left a history or benefited the human race. The conflict began ere Tubal Cain first worked in brass, and will continue till a higher virtue than man has ever reached shall govern events.

The morning is now wearing away—at times a cannon shot breaks the quiet, and a shell comes screaming through the air—now and then the skirmishers break forth, varying from the sharp, quick crack of a single rifle to perfect volleys. Hour after hour thus passes; and the battle is not yet begun. Our troops are taking position— Ewell is on the left. Hill holds the center, and Longstreet is on the right. Long lines of men are moving across yonder fields, or marching through that piece of woods.

But where is that division which is to play so conspicuous a part in this day's tragedy? They are in line of battle, just fronting that frowning hill, from which heavy batteries are belching forth shell and shrapnel with fatal accuracy. The men are lying close to the ground. Hours pass, and the deadly missiles come thick and fast on their mission to death. See that shattered arm; that leg shot off; that headless body, and here the mangled form of a young and gallant lieutenant. That hill must be carried to rout the enemy; a terrible chastisement has been inflicted upon him; with immense loss he had been driven from his position two days previous—this is his stronghold. This captured, rout is inevitable. It is a moment of great emergency; if unshrinking valor or human courage can carry those heights, it will be done.

General Pickett receives the order to charge those batteries at the opportune moment. The cannonade still goes on with intense fury; our batteries are handled with great skill. This battery and that limber up, advance to the front, wheel into action, and again the roar of cannon becomes almost deafening. Our shells seem to burst with terrible accuracy. Now a caisson of the enemy's is blown up— quickly another follows—their fire slackens—the order comes to advance. That flag which waved amid the wild tempest of battle at Gaines' Mill, Frazier's Farm, and Manassas never rose more proudly. Kemper, with as gallant men as ever trod beneath that flag, leads the right; Garnett, with his heroes, brings up the left; and the veteran Armistead, with his brave troops, moves forward in support. The distance is more than half a mile. As they advance the enemy fire with great rapidity. Shell and solid shot give place to grape and canister. The very earth quivers beneath the heavy roar. Wide gaps are made in this regiment and that brigade. Yet they close up and move steadily onward.

That flag goes down. See how quickly it again mounts upward, borne by some gallant man who feels keenly the honor of his old commonwealth in this hour which is to test her manhood. The line moves onward, straight onward—cannons roaring, grape and canister plunging and plowing through the ranks—bullets whizzing as thick as hailstones in winter, and men falling as leaves fall when shaken by the blasts of autumn.

In a double-quick, and with a shout which rises above the roar of battle, they charge. Now they pour in volleys of musketry. They reach the works. The contest rages with intense fury. Men fight almost hand to hand. The red cross and gridiron wave defiantly in close proximity. The enemy are slowly yielding—a Federal officer dashing forward in front of his shrinking columns, and, with flashing sword, urges them to stand. General Pickett, seeing the splendid valor of his troops, moves among them as if courting death by his own daring intrepidity. The noble Garnett is dead, Armistead wounded, and the brave Kemper, with hat in hand, still cheering on his men, falls from his horse into the ranks of the enemy. His men rush forward, rescue their general, and he is borne mortally wounded from the field.

Where is the gallant Williams? The First is there, but his clear voice is no longer heard. He has fallen lifeless, and there goes his horse now riderless. There stand the decimated ranks of the Third; and Mayo, though struck, stands firm with his faithful men, animating them to yet more daring deeds; but Callcott, the Christian soldier, who stood unmoved amid this carnival of death, has fought his last battle.

The fight goes on—but few are left; and the shrinking columns of the enemy gain confidence from the heavy reinforcements advanced to their support. They, too, are moving in large force on the right flank. This division, small at first, with ranks now torn and shattered, most of its officers killed or wounded, no valor able to rescue victory from such a grasp, annihilation or capture inevitable, slowly, reluctantly, fell back. It was not given to these few remaining brave men to accomplish human impossibilities. The enemy dared not follow them beyond their works.

Night now approaches. The wounded are being borne off to their respective hospitals; many with slight wounds plodded along, leaving the ambulances to their less fortunate comrades. With night the battle closed, our army holding the same position from which it had driven the enemy two days previous. One by one the stars came out in the quiet sky, and over that field of carnage hung the sweet influences of the Pleiades. In the series of engagements a few pieces of artillery and eight thousand prisoners were captured by our army. Our loss in killed, wounded, and missing, supposed about ten thousand, whilst the enemy, we understand, acknowledges a loss of thirty thousand. The army of northern Virginia—with zeal unabated, courage, intrepid, devotion unchilled, with unbounded confidence in the wisdom of that great chieftain who has so often led them to victory—stands ready to advance their standards farther into the enemy's country, or repel any new invasion of the Confederacy. Though many a Virginia home will mourn the loss of some noble spirit, yet, at the name of Pickett's division and the battle of Gettysburg, how the eye will glisten and the blood course quicker, and the heart beat warm, as among its noble dead is recalled the name of some cherished one. They bore themselves worthy of their lineage and their state. Who would recall them from their bed of glory? Each sleeps in a hero's grave!

†   †   †

1864 brought a new general to command the Union armies, one who may not have won many battles but who never admitted that he had lost. Ulysses S. Grant was in command during the last furious fighting around the capital of the Confederacy, Richmond—the Wilderness, Cold Harbor, Petersburg—and on April 9, 1865, Robert E. Lee surrendered to Grant at Appomattox Courthouse. Five days later, on Good Friday, the President went to Ford's Theater to see *Our American Cousin.* Many newspapers, of course, told this epochal story; the example here is a series of dispatches, excerpted, as printed in Greeley's newspaper.

†   †   †

A PRESIDENT IS ASSASSINATED

New York Tribune, April 14, 1865.

First Dispatch

To the Associated Press
WASHINGTON, FRIDAY, APRIL 14, 1865—The President was shot in a theater tonight, and perhaps mortally wounded.

Second Dispatch

To Editors: Our Washington agent orders the dispatch about the President "stopped." Nothing is said about the truth or falsity of the dispatch.

Third Dispatch

Special Dispatch to the *New York Tribune*
The President was just shot at Ford's Theater. The ball entered his neck. It is not known whether the wound is mortal. Intense excitement.

Fourth Dispatch

Special Dispatch to the *New York Tribune*
The President expired at a quarter to twelve.

Fifth Dispatch

To the Associated Press
WASHINGTON, APRIL 15, 12:30 A.M.—The President was shot in a theater tonight, and is perhaps mortally wounded.

The President is not expected to live through the night.
Secretary Seward was also assassinated.
No arteries were cut.
Particulars soon.

Sixth Dispatch

Special Dispatch to the *New York Tribune*
WASHINGTON, FRIDAY, APRIL 14, 1865—Like a clap of thunder out of a clear sky spread the announcement that President Lincoln was shot while sitting in a box at Ford's Theater. The city is wild with excitement. A gentleman who was present thus describes the event:

At about 10½ o'clock, in the midst of one of the acts, a pistol shot was heard, and at the same instant a man leaped upon the stage from the same box occupied by the President, brandished a long knife, and shouted, *"Sic semper tyrannis!"* then rushed to the rear of the scenes and out of the back door of the theater. So sudden was the whole thing that most persons in the theater supposed it a part of the play, and it was some minutes before the fearful tragedy was comprehended. The man was pursued, however, by someone connected with the theater to the outer door and seen to mount a horse and ride rapidly away. A regiment of cavalry have started in all directions, *with orders to arrest every man found on horseback. . . .*

Seventh Dispatch

Special Dispatch to the *New York Tribune*
WASHINGTON, FRIDAY, APRIL 14, 1865—The President attended Ford's Theater tonight, and about ten o'clock an assassin entered his private box and shot him in the back of the head. The ball lodged

in his head, and he is now lying insensible in a house opposite the theater. No hopes are entertained of his recovery. *Laura Keene claims to have recognized the assassin as the actor, J. Wilkes Booth.* A feeling of gloom like a pall has settled on the city. . . .

Eleventh Dispatch

Special Dispatch
WASHINGTON, FRIDAY, APRIL 14, 1865, 1¼ A.M.—The President is slowly dying. The brain is slowly oozing through the ball hole in his forehead. He is of course insensible. There is an occasional lifting of his hand, and heavy stertorous breathing; that's all.

Mrs. Lincoln and her two sons are in a room of the house opposite the Ford Theater, where the President was taken, and adjoining that where he is lying. Mr. Sumner is seated at the head of the bed. Secretary Stanton, Welles, Dennison, Usher, and McCullock, and Mr. Speed are in the room. A large number of surgeons, generals, and personal family friends of Mr. Lincoln fill the house. All are in tears. Andy Johnson is here. He was in bed in his room at the Kirkwood when the assassination was committed. He was immediately apprised of the event, and got up. . . .

Later—The accounts are confused and contradictory. One dispatch announces the President died at 12½ P.M. Another, an hour later, states that he is still living, but dying slowly. We go to press without knowing the exact truth, but presume there is not the slightest ground for hope.

† † †

7

NEWSMEN IN THE WILD, WILD WEST

Of all the time periods in the history of American journalism one that exerts a special fascination for many readers is that of the nineteenth century western frontier. American histories sometimes make one wonder whether some historians thought the only important things taking place were in the East and in our big cities. Some historians, of course, became so attached to the frontier thesis of Frederick Jackson Turner that they overdid historical inter-pretations in *that* direction. In looking at the press of the frontier one must consider the role played by newspapers, by literature and by subliterature, the role played by motion pictures, radio, and television—films like *The Man Who Shot Liberty Valance,* with its heroic newspaper editor; television shows like *Tombstone Territory,* also with an editor on hand. Separating the legend of the frontier from the truth of the frontier is not only difficult but perhaps fruitless as well.

As for the frontier newspapers, there were journalists in such places as Texas even before that huge land became a state, long before, in fact: the *Gaceta de Texas* in Nacogdoches in 1813; the *Texas Republican* in the same town in 1819; the *Telegraph and Texas Register* of Gail Borden in San Felipe, the paper that reported the disaster of the Alamo in 1836. There were feuding newspapers in Oregon after that territory was settled, the first paper there being the *Oregon Spectator* in 1851. The Mormon pioneers went to Utah and started the *Deseret News* in 1850; a Mormon named Sam Brannan went on to the town of Yerba Buena—later San Francisco—and started the *California Star.* Out of the *Star* and a sheet called the *Californian* came the fabled *Alta California* in 1848. There were newspapers in Nevada and Arizona and in Nebraska and Kansas in the pre-Civil War and railroad boom days. In Colorado there were the *Rocky Mountain News* of William N. Byers in 1859 and the

Greeley Tribune, whose nameplate resembled the nearly illegible handwriting of the famous founder of the *New York Tribune.*

We begin with the best-known and best-loved frontier reporter-editor-printer of them all, Samuel L. Clemens, and some of his writings. One of them is a long joke, which we look at only briefly. The trouble with Clemens—Mark Twain, of course—is that we do not always know, even with his "true" stories, what is true and what is imagination. His *Autobiography* belongs comfortably upon a shelf with his fiction. Mark Twain published a sketch in 1871 called "Journalism in Tennessee," and, true or not, it can serve as an introduction to this section of documents of western—frontier—journalism.

† † †

JOURNALISM IN TENNESSEE

By Mark Twain, 1871, in *Sketches New and Old* (New York: Harper, 1875), pp. 35-43.

. . . I was told by the physician that a Southern climate would improve my health, and so I went down to Tennessee, and got a berth on the *Morning Glory and Johnson County War-Whoop* as associate editor. When I went on duty I found the chief editor sitting tilted back in a three-legged chair with his feet on a pine table. There was another pine table in the room and another afflicted chair, and both were half buried under newspapers and scraps and sheets of manuscript. There was a wooden box of sand, sprinkled with cigar stubs and "old soldiers," and a stove with a door hanging by its upper hinge. The chief editor had a long-tailed black cloth frock coat on, and white linen pants. His boots were small and neatly blacked. He wore a ruffled shirt, a large seal ring, a standing collar of obsolete pattern, and a checkered neckerchief with the ends hanging down. Date of costume about 1848. He was smoking a cigar, and trying to think of a word, and in pawing his hair he had rumpled his locks a good deal. He was scowling fearfully, and I judged that he was concocting a particularly knotty editorial. He told me to take the exchanges and skim through them and write up the "Spirit of the Tennessee Press," condensing into the article all of their contents that seemed of interest. . . .

I passed my manuscript over to the chief editor for acceptance, alteration, or destruction. He glanced at it and his face clouded. He ran his eye down the pages, and his countenance grew portentous. It was easy to see that something was wrong. Presently he sprang up and said:

"Thunder and lightning! Do you suppose I am going to speak of those cattle that way? Do you suppose my subscribers are going to stand such gruel as that? Give me the pen!"

I never saw a pen scrape and scratch its way so viciously, or plow through another man's verbs and adjectives so relentlessly. While he was in the midst of his work, somebody shot at him through the open window, and marred the symmetry of my ear.

"Ah," said he, "that is that scoundrel Smith, of the *Moral Volcano*—he was due yesterday." And he snatched a navy revolver from his belt and fired. Smith dropped, shot in the thigh. The shot spoiled Smith's aim, who was just taking a second chance, and he crippled a stranger. It was me. Merely a finger shot off.

Then the chief editor went on with his erasures and interlineations. Just as he finished them a hand-grenade came down the stove pipe, and the explosion shivered the stove into a thousand fragments. However, it did no further damage, except that a vagrant piece knocked a couple of my teeth out.

"That stove is utterly ruined," said the chief editor. . . .

About this time a brick came through the window with a splintering crash, and gave me a considerable of a jolt in the back. I moved out of range—I began to feel in the way.

The chief said, "That was the Colonel, likely. I've been expecting him for two days. He will be up now right away."

He was correct. The Colonel appeared in the door a moment afterward with a dragoon revolver in his hand.

He said, "Sir, have I the honor of addressing the poltroon who edits this mangy sheet?"

"You have. Be seated, sir. Be careful of the chair, one of its legs is gone. I believe I have the honor of addressing the putrid liar, Colonel Blatherskite Tecumseh?"

"Right, sir. I have a little account to settle with you. If you are at leisure we will begin. . . ."

Both pistols rang out their fierce clamor at the same instant. The chief lost a lock of his hair, and the Colonel's bullet ended its career in the fleshy part of my thigh. . . .

At the end of the next three hours I had been through perils so awful that all peace of mind and all cheerfulness were gone from me. Gillespie had called and thrown *me* out of the window. Jones arrived promptly, and when I got ready to do the cowhiding he took the job off my hands. In an encounter with a stranger, not in the bill of fare, I had lost my scalp. Another stranger, by the name of Thompson, left me a mere wreck and ruin of chaotic rags. And at last, at bay in the corner, and beset by an infuriated mob of editors, blacklegs, politicians, and desperadoes, who raved and swore and flourished their weapons about my head till the air shimmered with glancing flashes of steel, I was in the act of resigning my berth on the paper when the chief arrived, and with him a rabble of charmed and enthusiastic friends. Then ensued a scene of riot and carnage such as no human pen, or steel one either, could describe. People were shot, probed, dismembered, blown up, thrown out of the window. There was a brief tornado of murky blasphemy, with a confused and frantic war-dance glimmering through it, and then all was over. . . .

[The chief editor] said, "You'll like this place when you get used to it."

I said, "I'll have to get you to excuse me; I think maybe I might write to suit you after a while; as soon as I had had some practice and learned the language I am confident I could. . . . I like this berth well enough, but I don't like to be left here to wait on the customers. . . . The Southern heart is too impulsive; Southern hospitality is too lavish with the stranger. The paragraphs which I have written to-day, and into whose cold sentences your masterly hand has infused the fervent spirit of Tennesseean journalism, will wake up another nest of hornets. All that mob of editors will come—and they will come hungry, too, and want somebody for breakfast. I shall have to bid you adieu. I decline to be present at these festivities. I came South for my health, I will go back on the same errand, suddenly. Tennesseean journalism is too stirring for me."

After which we parted with mutual regret, and I took apartments at the hospital.

† † †

One of the newspapers for which Mark Twain worked was the *Territorial Enterprise,* in Virginia City, Carson Valley, Nevada, a paper founded in late 1858. Virginia City is now mainly a tourist town, but there is a kind of charm there, especially in the office of the *Enterprise,* a place that trades very much on the memory of Mark Twain. There is even a toilet in a corner with a sign above it, "MARK TWAIN SAT HERE." Though the following were not by Mark Twain (he was not yet on the scene), they are excerpts from an early issue of this historic newspaper.

† † †

FROM A FRONTIER PAPER IN NEVADA

Territorial Enterprise, January 1, 1859.

Nothing more completely baffles one who is full of trick and duplicity, than straightforward and simple integrity in another. . . .

Our thanks are due A. BADLAM, JR., of Sacramento, for full files of California and Atlantic papers. Keep sending them.

*****

FIVE passengers, who left here in the stage on Tuesday morning last, crossed the mountains in a sleigh.

*****

The President's message arrived just as we were going to press.

*****

THAT LOAD.—Yesterday, about 12 o'clock, we were startled from our meditations by the rattling of the stage coach through the streets, and delighted with the Eolian tones of female voices; we rushed furiously to the door, and, lo! such a sight—the stage was filled with fairies, on their way to Eagle Valley to attend the New Year's party. On the "first blush of the moment" we determined to get aboard; we looked again, saw the Stars and Stripes floating over the galaxy of beauty beneath; we became patriotic, lost sight of our responsibilities, and in the frenzy of the moment were about to leap inside the coach, when with thundering tones, the everlasting and unwelcome cry of copy was trumpeted in our ears, which brought us down again to our unceasing toil.

† † †

Mark Twain went to Nevada to work for his brother, Orion, who had been appointed secretary to the territorial governor. In *Roughing It* he chronicled his adventures in the West, including enough imaginary stuff to becloud the whole wonderful tale. From the mining country of Nevada he went out to San Francisco, and spent some time in the gold fields there, too, picking up the yarn that became his first famous published writing, "The Celebrated Jumping Frog of Calaveras County," in 1865. He then spent a few months on the *San Francisco Call* in the mid-sixties; his stories about the Chinese in the San Francisco of Barbary Coast days are of some interest, though it would be difficult to describe Mark Twain, from these stories, as a great stylist.

† † †

THE CHINESE OF SAN FRANCISCO

By Mark Twain, *San Francisco Call*, July 9 and 12, 1864, in Edgar M. Branch, ed., *Clemens of the Call: Mark Twain in San Francisco* (Berkeley: University of California Press, 1969), pp. 70-72.

The ingenuity of the Chinese is beyond calculation. It is asserted that they have no words or expressions signifying abstract right or wrong. They appreciate "good" and "bad," but it is only in reference to business, to finance, to trade, etc. Whatever is successful is good; whatever fails is bad. So they are not conscience-bound in planning and perfecting ingenious contrivances for avoiding the tariff on opium, which is pretty heavy. The attempted swindles appear to have been mostly, or altogether, attempted by the Coolie passengers—the Chinese merchants, either from honorable motives or from policy, having dealt honestly with the Government. But the passengers have reached the brains of rascality itself, to find means for importing their delicious drug without paying the duties. To do this has called into action the inventive genius of brains equal in this respect to any that ever lodged on the top end of humanity.

They have, doubtless, for years smuggled opium into this port continuously. The officers of Customs at length got on their track, and the traffic has become unprofitable to the Coolies, however well it has been paying the officials through the seizures made. The opium has been found concealed in double jars and brass eggs, as heretofore described, brought ashore in bands around the body, and by various other modes. The latest dodge detected was sausages, Bolognas, as it were, filled with opium; and yesterday we saw a tin can, with a false bottom about one third the distance from the base, the lower third of the can filled with opium, the rest with oil. John himself will have to be opened next—he is undoubtedly full of it.

Captain Douglass and Watchman Hager boarded the ship Clara Morse, on Sunday morning, the moment she arrived, and captured nineteen Chinese girls, who had been stolen and brought from Hongkong to San Francisco to be sold. They were a choice lot, and estimated to be worth from one hundred and fifty to four hundred dollars apiece in this market. They are shut up for safe-keeping for the present, and we went and took a look at them yesterday; some of them are almost good-looking, and none of them are pitted with smallpox—a circumstance which we have observed is very rare among China women. . . .

† † †

The most important journalistic writings of Mark Twain were a series of dispatches he composed for the *Alta California*—plus a few for the *New York Herald* and the *New York Tribune*—in the course of a voyage to the Holy Land beginning in late 1867 on the steamship *Quaker City*. He contracted with the *Alta* to send back letters, and they were published. When he returned from the journey he edited the letters and added a few to create his first published volume, *The Innocents Abroad*. Almost any chapter from that book is a joy to read, even though, as with other writings of Mark Twain, we do not know how much of the story is a fabrication. Here is Mark in the land of Jesus and Moses.

† † †

A REPORTER IN THE HOLY LAND

By Mark Twain, *The Innocents Abroad* (New York: Bantam, 1964 ed.), pp. 342-343.

We entered the great Latin convent which is built over the traditional dwelling place of the Holy Family. We went down a flight of fifteen steps below the ground level and stood in a small chapel tricked out with tapestry hangings, silver lamps, and oil paintings. A spot marked by a cross in the marble floor, under the altar, was exhibited as the place made forever holy by the feet of the Virgin when she stood up to receive the message of the angel. So simple, so unpretending a locality to be the scene of so mighty an event! The very scene of the Annunciation—an event which has been commemorated by splendid shrines and august temples all over the civilized world, and one which the princes of art have made it their loftiest ambition to picture worthily on their canvas; a spot whose history is familiar to the very children of every house and city and obscure hamlet of the furthest lands of Christendom; a spot which myriads of men would toil across the breadth of a world to see, would consider it a priceless privilege to look upon. It was easy to think these thoughts. But it was not easy to bring myself up to the magnitude of the situation. I could sit off several thousand miles and imagine the angel appearing, with shadowy wings and lustrous countenance, and not the glory that streamed downward upon the Virgin's head while the message from the Throne of God fell upon her ears—anyone can do that beyond the ocean, but few can do it here. I saw the little recess from which the angel stepped, but could not fill its void. The angels that I know are creatures of unstable fancy—they will not fit in niches of substantial stone. Imagination labors best in distant fields. I doubt if any man can stand in the grotto of the Annunciation and people with the phantom images of his mind its too tangible walls of stone.

They showed us a broken granite pillar, depending from the roof, which they said was hacked in two by the Muslim conquerors of Nazareth in the vain hope of pulling down the sanctuary. But the pillar remained miraculously suspended in the air and, unsupported itself, supported then and still supports the roof. By dividing this statement up among eight, it was found not difficult to believe it.

These gifted Latin monks never do anything by halves. If they were to show you the Brazen Serpent that was elevated in the wilderness, you could depend upon it that they had on hand the pole it was elevated on also, and even the hole it stood in. They have got the "grotto" of the Annunciation here; and just as convenient to it as one's throat is to his mouth, they have also the Virgin's kitchen, and even her sitting room, where she and Joseph watched the infant Saviour play with Hebrew toys eighteen hundred years ago. All under one roof, and all clean, spacious, comfortable "grottoes." It seems curious that personages intimately connected with the Holy Family always lived in grottoes—in Nazareth, in Bethlehem, in imperial Ephesus—and yet nobody else in their day and generation thought of doing anything of the kind. If they ever did, their grottoes are all gone, and I suppose we ought to wonder at the peculiar marvel of the preservation of these I speak of. . . .

† † †

One of the famous sagas in the history of western settlement is that of the "Mormons," driven out of Illinois after the murder of their leader and after similar expulsions from Ohio and Missouri. Under the inspired leadership of a hard-driving man named Brigham Young the Mormons went across the plains and reached

Utah territory on July 24, 1847. They named their new home Deseret, and they founded their own newspaper in 1850.

† † †

PROSPECTUS OF THE MORMON NEWSPAPER

The *Deseret News,* June 15, 1850.

We propose to publish a small weekly sheet, as large as our local circumstances will permit, to be called *"Deseret News,"* designed originally to record the passing events of our State, and in connexion, refer to the arts and sciences, embracing general education, medicine, law, divinity, domestic and political economy, and every thing that may fall under our observation, which may tend to promote the best interest, welfare, pleasure and amusement of our fellow citizens.

We hold ourselves responsible to the highest Court of truth for our intentions, and the highest Court of equity for our execution. When we speak, we shall speak freely, without regard to men or party, and when, like other men, we err, let him who has his eyes open, correct us in meekness, and he shall receive a disciple's reward. . . .

† † †

It was the newspaper press that contributed so importantly to the process of making legends and myths and heroes in the Old West— though popular magazines and dime novels played their parts, too. One of the greatly loved of these heroes was General George Armstrong Custer, who led his Seventh Cavalry against the Indians on June 26, 1876. He became, for a time at least, a martyr, for his troops were wiped out, and he died on a hillside in the valley of the Little Big Horn in southeastern Montana. Among the dead was a reporter for the *New York Herald,* Mark Kellogg, who had ridden with Custer. One of the first accounts of the battle was the reconstruction and description published in a newspaper in Minnesota.

† † †

THE BATTLE AT LITTLE BIG HORN

St. Paul-Minneapolis Pioneer-Press and Tribune, July 1-6, 1876.

SIOUX EXPEDITION

Mouth of the Big Horn, July 1,
Via Bismarck, D.T., July 6.

Long before the arrival of this dispatch you will have heard of the tragedy which has been enacted here. The ghastly details would seem to court oblivion if it were in the nature of things possible to forget or cloak them.

At noon on the 22nd day of June, General Custer, at the head of his fine regiment of twelve veteran companies, left camp at the mouth of the Rosebud, to follow the trail of a very large band of hostile Sioux, leading up the river, and westward in the direction of the Big Horn. The signs indicated that the Indians were making for the eastern branch of the last named river, marked on the map as the Little Big Horn.

At the same time General Terry, with Gibbon's command of five companies of infantry, four of cavalry, and the Gatling battery, started to ascend the Big Horn, aiming to assail the enemy in the rear. The march of the two columns was so planned as to bring Gibbon's command within co-operating distance of the anticipated scene of action by the evening of the twenty-sixth. In this way only could the infantry be made available, as it would not do to encumber Custer's march with foot troops. . . .

The march of the next morning revealed at every step some evidence of the conflict which had taken place two days before. At an early hour the head of the column entered a plain half a mile wide, bordering the left bank of the Little Big Horn, where had recently been an immense Indian village, extending three miles along the stream, and where were still standing two funeral lodges, with horses slaughtered around them, and containing the bodies of nine chiefs. The ground was strewn everywhere with carcasses of horses, and cavalry equipments, besides buffalo robes, packages of dried meat, and weapons and utensils belonging to the Indians. . . .

Just then a breathless scout arrived, with the intelligence that Colonel Reno, with a remnant of the Seventh Cavalry, was entrenched on a bluff near by, waiting for relief. The command pushed rapidly on, and soon came in sight of a group surrounding a cavalry guidon, upon a lofty eminence on the right bank of the river. . . .

In the center of the enclosure was a depression in the surface, in which the wounded were sheltered, covered with canvas. Reno's command had been fighting from Sunday noon of the 25th until the night of the 26th, when General Terry arrived, which caused the Indians to retire. Up to this time Reno and those with him were in complete ignorance of the fate of the other five companies, which had been separated from them early on the 25th, to make an attack under Custer on the village at another point. While preparations were being made for the removal of the wounded, a party was sent on Custer's trail to look for traces of his command. They found awaiting them a sight fit to appall the stoutest heart. At a point about three miles down the right bank of the stream, Custer had evidently attempted to ford and attack the village from the ford. The trail was found to lead back up the bluff and to the northward, as if the troops had been repulsed and compelled to retreat, and at the same time had been cut off from regaining the forces under Reno. The bluffs along the right bank come sharply down to the water, and are interspersed by numerous ravines. All along the slopes and ridges, and in the ravines, lay the dead, arranged in order of battle, lying as they had fought, line behind line, showing where the defensive positions had been successfully taken up, and held till none were left to fight. There, huddled in a narrow compass, horses and men were piled promiscuously. At the highest point of the ridge lay Custer, surrounded by a chosen band. . . . Not a man had escaped to tell the tale, but it was inscribed on the surface of these barren hills in a language more eloquent than words.

† † †

When news of the Battle of Little Big Horn reached the East there was sadness and there were expressions of editorial horror, all of this placing a damper upon the country's celebration of its centennial. The already ancient poet-editor William Cullen Bryant was stricken, and Walt Whitman wrote a poem in honor of Custer and the other fallen. The *New York Herald* of James Gordon Bennett Jr. had been a strong journalistic backer of Custer; Bennett had met Custer on the plains, and of course his reporter, Kellogg, was among the dead. The *Herald* published an editorial about the battle.

† † †

THE GALLANT CUSTERS
New York Herald, July 7, 1876.

There is a terrible pithiness in the curt dispatch, "The whole Custer family died at the head of their column;" and again, "General Custer, his two brothers, his nephew and brother-in-law were killed." Never, perhaps, in American history, did a family ever offer up so many lives for the flag in a single engagement. We recall the Curiatii from Roman history and the Macabees from the Hebrew. Beside them in heroic remembrance must stand the name of Custer. In that mad charge up the narrow ravine, with rocks above raining down lead upon the fated three hundred, with fire spouting from every bush ahead, with the wild, swarming horsemen circling along the heights like shrieking vultures waiting for the moment to swoop down and finish the bloody tale, every form, from private to general, raises to heroic size, and the scene fixes itself indelibly upon the mind. "The Seventh fought like tigers," says the dispatch; yea, they died as grandly as Homer's demigods. In the supreme moment of carnage, as death's relentless sweep gathered in the entire command, all distinctions of name and rank were blended, but the family that "died at the head of their column" will lead the throng when history recalls their deed. It was mad, it was rash, but, though "some one has blundered," it was

Theirs not to reason why
Theirs but to do or die.

Success was beyond their grasp, so they died—to a man.

† † †

Frontier legend-making was taking place elsewhere, too, though the state in which the following story appeared—Missouri—was not quite *frontier* then. That state was the stamping grounds of the beloved Jesse James, who "robbed from the rich, and he gave to the poor, [who]had a hand, a heart, and a brain." The press undoubtedly helped build the name and fame of Jesse James, and when Jesse was shot in the back by Robert Ford, "that dirty little coward" of song and story, the story was a big one.

† † †

JESSE JAMES IS SHOT IN THE BACK

St. Joseph, Mo., Tribune, April 3, 1882.

St. Joseph, Mo., April 3—A great sensation was created in this city this morning by the announcement that Jesse James, the notorious bandit and trainrobber, had been shot and killed here in St. Joseph. The news spread with great rapidity, but most people received it with doubts until an investigation established the fact beyond question. Then the excitement became more and more intense, and crowds of people rushed to that quarter of the city where the shooting took place, anxious to view the body of the dead outlaw and to learn the particulars.

The body is that of a man of magnificent physique, who in the pride of health and strength must have been a commanding figure, six feet tall, and weighing 175 pounds, with every muscle developed and hardened by active life. It is a body that would fill with delight the surgeon seeking material for demonstrating anatomy. The features, but little disturbed in death are not unpleasing, and bear the imprint of self-reliance, firmness and dauntless courage. To look upon that face is to believe that the wonderful deeds of daring ascribed to Jesse James have not been exaggerated. . . .

A superficial examination of the body would alone afford strong proof that the dead body is that of Jesse James. He has been literally shot to pieces in his daring exploits, and his old wounds would have killed any one cast in a less rugged mold. Two bullets have pierced the abdomen, and are still in the body. There is a bullet-hole in the right wrist, and another in the right ankle. Two more disfigure the left thigh and knee. . . .

† † †

Much further west, too, legend-making was taking place, in Tombstone, Arizona, which had a paper with the delightful name of the *Epitaph*. This paper was friend and protector of a sometime marshal, sometime hoodlum named Wyatt Earp, who fought the Clantons at the O. K. Corral, a story as couched in legend as any we have. The *Tombstone Epitaph* had a standing head, "Death's Doings," to cover brief reports of homicides and other violent matters, and the town in truth did have so much violence that one more murder was almost a dog-bites-man incident. This story is about a character named John O'Rourke, alias "Johnny-Behind-the-Deuce," and though it mentions Earp's brother Virgil there is no mention of the more famous Wyatt.

† † †

MURDER IN A FAMOUS ARIZONA TOWN

Tombstone Epitaph, January 17, 1881.

Again, the bloody hand of a murderer has been raised against a peaceable citizen; again the law is scoffed at and Justice derided. Yesterday's sun rose bright and cheerful over our neighboring village of Charleston, mellowing the crisp night air with its rays. Once more her toilers began their daily avocations with renewed energy, little dreaming of the damnable deed that, in the glowing light of noonday, was to await one of their number.

Sometime since the cabin of Mr. W. P. Schneider, chief engineer of the Corbin Mill, was entered and robbed of several articles including some clothing. Circumstances pointed very strongly to two parties, one of whom is so well known by the cognomen of "Johnny-Behind-the-Deuce" that we were unable last night to obtain his real name, but direct proof not being sufficient, no arrest was made. Yesterday at noon Mr. Schneider left his duties and went to a restaurant where he was accustomed to take his meals, and on entering approached the stove and, noticing a friend standing by, entered into conversation. Having just left the heated engine room the air without felt cool which brought from Mr. S. a remark to that effect. "Johnny-Behind-the-Deuce" who was also in the room, then said, "I thought you never got cold." Not desiring to have anything to do with one of his character, Mr. Schneider turned and said, "I was not talking to you, sir." This raised the lurking devil in the diminutive heart of "J-B-the-D.," who blurted out, "G-d d-n you I'll shoot you when you come out," and left the room. After eating his dinner Mr. Schneider passed out the door, and was proceeding to the mill, when, true to his promise, the lurking fiend, who had secreted himself with hell in his heart and death in his mind, drew deadly aim and dropped his victim dead in his tracks. . . .

. . . Marshal Sippy, realizing the situation at once, in the light of the repeated murders that have been committed and the ultimate liberty of the offenders, had secured a well armed posse of over a score of men to prevent any attempt on the part of the crowd to lynch the prisoner; but feeling that no guard would be strong enough to resist a justly enraged public long, procured a light wagon in which the prisoner was placed, guarded by himself, Virgil Earp and Deputy Sheriff Behan, assisted by a strong posse well armed. . . .

† † †

In the tales of the West the one that can truly capture the imagination is that of the joining of the railroads at Promontory Point, Utah, in 1869, the historic event that Horace Greeley had dreamed of for so long. Two accounts offer flavor and facts, the first an excerpt from a major eastern newspaper.

† † †

JOINING OF EAST AND WEST

New York Times, May 11, 1869.

PROMONTORY, Utah, Monday, May 10.
   The long-looked-for moment has arrived. The construction of the Pacific Railroad is *un fait accompli.* The inhabitants of the Atlantic seaboard and the dwellers on the Pacific slopes are henceforth emphatically one people. Your correspondent is writing on Promontory Summit amid the deafening shouts of the multitude, with the tick, tick, of the telegraph close to his ear. . . .

WASHINGTON, Monday, May 10.
   The completion of the Pacific Railroad has monopolized public attention here to-day to the exclusion of everything else. The feeling is one of hearty rejoicing at the completion of this great work. . . .

† † †

The second is, of all things, a poem—more or less. It too was published when the railroads came together, and though it is not quite the caliber of a verse by Whitman (more like that of Joaquin Miller, maybe), it helps to tell the story of the Golden Spike.

† † †

DRIVING THE LAST SPIKE

San Francisco Bulletin, May 10, 1869.

I.

Hark! the sound
Comes through the air, and o'er the ground
Clang of bells and cannon's roar.
From Eastern strand and Western shore
        Peals ring out,
        Millions shout
        The work is done.

II.

Work is done!
And echoing sound returns—is one
East and West, which once were twain
And echoing answer speaks again
        The marriage vow,
        Uttered now
        Binds bride and groom.

III.

From gloomy gorge and beetling brow
While rocking engines, whirling wheel,
And rattling car, the tremor feel,
        Spans the land,
        Iron band
        And thews of brass.

IV.

Over land
And mountain peak and golden sand,
Across Sierra's glittering snows
Where lightning music comes and goes
        Joy to tell,
        Gun and bell
        Proclaim abroad.

V.

North and South,
Hand to hand and heart to mouth
Infant lisp and manhood's voice:
Let every listening heart rejoice,
        Hail and tell
        All is well
        The Nation's one.

VI.

Lightning's play
On cable's span, proclaim the day
To Europe and to Asia far
The rising of the western star
        Across the sea
        They and we
        Together joined.

VII.

O'er the world
With lightning speed the news is hurled:
"The East and West are bound with bands
The occident with father-lands."
      Iron rail
      Never fail
      In peace or war.

VIII.

Hail! and praise!
That our eyes have seen the days
When thews of iron span the land
From East and West—join hand in hand
      Hosannas sing,
      Voices ring:
      Glory to God—Amen!

✝   ✝   ✝

8

THE AGE OF THE GREAT BARBECUE

Few historical eras are as absorbing, as romantic, as the one that followed the Civil War, the one called, from the book by Mark Twain and Charles Dudley Warner, *The Gilded Age*. In that book a confidence man named Colonel Sellers moves in on Washington, in the age of Jay Gould and Jim Fisk, and carries out his nefarious operations. Twain and Warner have an opportunity to comment on the cheapness, the coarseness, the ugliness, and ultimately, too, the excitement of the time. The period is known not only as the Gilded Age; it was also, to historian Lewis Mumford, *The Brown Decades;* to Claude G. Bowers, *The Tragic Era*. Edwin L. Godkin, of the *Nation* and the *New York Evening Post,* viewed America in that time as a "chromo civilization," and in one of the most apt figures of speech, Vernon L. Parrington in *Main Currents in American Thought* styled it "the great barbecue." For it *was* like a great feast, but a feast to which not all were invited. Walt McDougall of the *New York World,* one of the most able cartoonists of the time, caught the spirit well in his 1884 cartoon called "Belshazzar's Feast": diamond-studded robber barons surrounding presidential candidate James G. Blaine at a sagging banquet table, where the guests dine on "lobby pie," "monopoly pudding," and "Gould soup," with a hungry man, woman and child standing off to the side, waiting for crumbs to fall from the table.

News accounts and editorials of the time commented, of course, on the disparities of wealth and poverty, on the rising plutocracy, on the lax public morality, on the sometimes horrendous public and private taste, on corruption. It was the period of Reconstruction, of the successful accommodation between North and South after the election of 1876. It was the time when those men ruled whom Richard Hofstadter labeled the "spoilsmen": the Tweed ring, the Credit Mobilier gang, Blaine and "burn this letter, kind regards to Mrs.

Fisher." America was also in a period of internationalism, when Secretary Seward was purchasing Alaska, when eyes were looking covetously at the Hawaiian Islands, when we were intervening in the Venezuela boundary dispute, enunciating a policy called the Open Door, and finally going to war with Spain. Labor and agriculture were in revolt; the Molly Maguires were spreading terror in the coal fields of Pennsylvania; later a bomb was thrown into a crowd in the Haymarket area of Chicago; Coxey and his army marched on the national capital; a railway strike seared the country in 1877, and the Pullman strike was a major event of 1894. Gould and Fisk cornered the gold market; "Nothing is lost save honor!" said Fisk. Big combinations were created in oil, in cotton, in whiskey, in sugar, in steel; social Darwinism justified the existence of these mergers as a "survival of the fittest."

Scientists announced new ideas in mathematics, geology, paleontology. New inventions came out of the busy factories: Hoe's rotary press, Mergenthaler's typesetting machine, which Whitelaw Reid christened the Linotype; Westinghouse's air brake; the automobile, what historians call an "anonymous invention"; Edison's phonograph, incandescent lamp, and motion pictures; Bell's telephone. Great new skyscrapers changed the skyline. And despite some outwardly shoddy manifestations of the age, there were such major writers as Mark Twain, Henry James, and William Dean Howells; such novelists of naturalism as Theodore Dreiser, Stephen Crane, and Jack London; such historians as Henry Adams; such social commentators as Edward Bellamy, Henry George, and Thorstein Veblen; such architects as Louis Sullivan and H. H. Richardson; such painters as Winslow Homer and Thomas Eakins.

A new generation of editors was coming into being, personal editors quite in a class with the ones who had gone before. Ben Day had long passed from the scene, and his successor, Moses Beach, had sold off the *Sun* in 1867. Bennett died in 1872, with his son, Bennett, Jr., already running the *Herald*. Greeley, too, died in 1872, after a quixotic run for the presidency as candidate of both Liberal Republicans and Democrats. Henry J. Raymond died of an apoplectic stroke in 1869; Medill survived to the 1890s; Bryant died in 1878, after several years of semi-retirement.

The first of the new crop was Edwin L. Godkin, the most influential figure in magazine-newspaper journalism for more than a generation. He was an "orange Irishman," a resident of this country since 1857, founder of a magazine called the *Nation* in 1865, and editor of the *New York Evening Post* from 1881 to 1899. Like Walter Lippmann in a later time he exerted such influence that some readers said they did not know what to think about issues of the day until they had read the latest copy of the *Nation*. Godkin here criticizes President Andrew Johnson.

† † †

PRELUDE TO AN IMPEACHMENT

The *Nation*, April 5, 1866.

There has been such a glamour thrown round the Presidential office by the war that a great many people seem totally to have forgotten the precise nature of the President's relations to Congress and the country. And it is because they have forgotten it that the present conflict between the legislature and the executive possesses much political importance. We are, in reality, witnessing at this moment, in the difference which convulses the country, the legitimate result of the departures from constitutional usage into which we were driven in the excitement and confusion of 1861. Nobody can, perhaps, be fairly blamed for the irregularities into which the Government then fell. They were the natural result of the alarm and anxiety and distrust of everybody and everything by which the nation was pervaded. But there is no denying the fact that our political machine received a severe jar on the day when Mr. Lincoln was allowed, of his own mere motion, the power of suspending the *habeas corpus*. Congress ought not to have lost a moment after its meeting in asserting its sole exclusive authority to meddle for any purpose whatever with the safeguards placed by the common law and the Constitution round individual liberty. . . .

At the close of the war Mr. Johnson appointed provisional governors. So far all was well; executive officers of some sort there had to be to prevent anarchy. He went further, and called conventions to reorganize the governments. This, too, was not open to objection. He was still acting within his sphere as commander-in-chief. The various States needed to have some means of expressing their wishes. But this is as far as we can go with him. He had no business to make discriminations between classes of the citizens. He, as commander-in-chief, had nothing to do with State policy or State laws. . . . once the conventions had met, he was as a holder of the war power *functus officio*. He should then have called Congress together and said: "The rebellion is over; the South is at your mercy. I have re-established order; I have provided the people of the revolted States with the means of addressing you. . . ."

He, however, did nothing of the kind. He did not call Congress together. He did not wait for its coming together. He set to work to make laws with great assiduity. He issued edicts with a rapidity equal to that of Louis Napoleon in December, 1851. He first of all arbitrarily excluded all colored men from voting. He next arbitrarily excluded all persons from voting who had taken part in the rebellion, . . . He then—we beg the reader's attention to this point— began to exact certain qualifications from revolted States as conditions of their readmission to the Union. . . .

We confess that for our part we think the public acquiescence in the unwarrantable assumptions of power on which the President's whole interference with the Reconstruction process is based, has gone far enough. Whatever excuse there might have been for it three years or even one year ago, there is none now. It is too late to undo the irregularities committed during the war; but it is not too late to force every branch of the government to betake itself once more to its own business, and confine itself to the sphere traced out for it by the Constitution. . . .

† † †

Godkin's magazine and newspaper were not part of the movement called "mass journalism"; the *Evening Post* remained even more stodgy than it had been under Bryant, but its intellectual content was surpassing. A popular quip of the day went: "The *Sun* makes vice attractive in the morning, and the *Post* makes virtue unattractive in the evening." That newspaper where vice was being made attractive was, of course, the first one in the age of the penny press—the creation of Ben Day. It survived and prospered, but the Beach family tired of it and sold it in 1867. The next year Charles A. Dana became the editor. This was the Dana who had been Greeley's associate editor, and he became the leading personal editor of his time, publishing a newspaper with a much larger readership than the *Post* of Edwin Godkin. His was the paper whose city editor, John B. Bogart, defined news in man-bites-dog terms. His was the paper that carried a column called "Sunbeams," that said "No king, no clown, to rule this town," that described presidential candidate Winfield Scott Hancock as "a good man, weighing two hundred fifty pounds." A concentration on news, an emphasis on good writing—these marked the *Sun* in the days of Dana.

† † †

ON NEWS AND REPORTING

By Charles A. Dana, lecture, Wisconsin Editorial Association, 1888, in Frank Luther Mott and Ralph D. Casey, eds., *Interpretations of Journalism* (New York: Crofts, 1937), pp. 159-160.

. . . The newspaper must be founded upon human nature. It must correspond to the wants of the people. It must furnish that sort of information which the people demand, or else it never can be successful. The first thing which an editor must look for is news. If the newspaper has not the news, it may have everything else, yet it will be comparatively unsuccessful; and by news I mean everything that occurs, everything which is of human interest, and which is of sufficient importance to arrest and absorb the attention of the public or of any considerable part of it. There is a great disposition in some quarters to say that the newspapers ought to limit the amount of news that they print; that certain kinds of news ought not to be published. I do not know how that is. I am not prepared to maintain any abstract proposition in that line; but I have always felt that whatever the Divine Providence permitted to occur I was not too proud to report. . . .

News is undoubtedly a great thing in a newspaper. A newspaper without news is no newspaper. The main function of a newspaper is to give the news, and tell you what has happened in the world, what events have occurred of all sorts, political, scientific, and nonsensical. By the way, one person that I have not mentioned is the scientific man. That is also a place that has to be filled by special cultivation. A scientific man, one who knows electricity and chemistry; one who can really understand the inventions of Edison, and who can tell what is going on in the scientific world where so many men of genius are incessantly at work bringing out and developing new things—there must be a man of that sort on a newspaper. That is a department of news of supreme consequence...

† † †

Dana was *the* cynic of the Gilded Age; a youthful admirer of Fourierism and Transcendentalism, he had become an apologist for wealth and position and was even able to mix his cynicism with human interest. In the 1880s a message sent by President Grover Cleveland to Congress blew off the desk of the telegraph editor into the street, and to explain this disaster—and omission—Dana blamed it on the office cat. Readers of the *Sun* came to greatly admire this nonexistent animal, which they pictured as sitting on old Dana's lap as he knocked out his famous editorials.

† † †

OUR OFFICE CAT

New York Sun, January 12, 1885.

The universal interest which this accomplished animal has excited throughout the country is a refutation that genius is not honored in its own day and generation. Perhaps no other living critic has attained the popularity and the vogue now enjoyed by our cat. For years he worked in silence, unknown, perhaps, beyond the limits of the office. He is a sort of Rosicrucian cat, and his motto has been "to know all and to keep himself unknown." But he could not escape the glory his efforts deserved, and a few mornings ago he woke up, like Byron, to find himself famous.

We are glad to announce that he hasn't been puffed up by the enthusiastic praise which comes to him from all sources. He is the same industrious, conscientious, sharp-eyed, and sharp-toothed censor of copy that he has always been, nor should we have known that he is conscious of the admiration he excites had we not observed him in the act of dilacerating a copy of the Graphic containing an alleged portrait of him. It was impossible not to sympathize with his evident indignation. The Graphic's portrait did foul injustice to his majestic and intellectual features. Besides, it represented him as having a bandage over one eye, as if he had been involved in a controversy and had had his eye mashed. Now, aside from the fact that he needs both eyes to discharge his literary duties properly, he is able to whip his weight in office cats, and his fine large eyes have never been shrouded in black, and we don't believe they ever will be. He is a soldier as well as a scholar.

We have received many requests to give a detailed account of the personal habits and peculiarities of this feline Aristarchus. Indeed, we have been requested to prepare a full biographical sketch to appear in the next edition of "Homes of American Authors." At some future day we may satisfy public curiosity with the details of his literary methods. But genius such as his defies analysis, and the privacy of a celebrity ought not to be rudely invaded.

It is not out of place, however, to indicate a few traits which illustrate his extraordinary faculty of literary decomposition, so to speak. His favorite food is a tariff discussion. When a big speech, full of wind and statistics, comes within his reach, he pounces upon it immediately, and digests the figures at his leisure. During the discussion over the Morrison bill he used to feed steadily on tariff speeches for eight hours a day, and yet his appetite remained unimpaired.

When a piece of stale news or a long-winded, prosy article comes into the office, his remarkable sense of smell instantly detects it, and it is impossible to keep it from him. He always assists with great interest at the opening of the office mail, and he files several hundred letters a day in his interior department. The favorite diversion of the office boys is to make him jump for twelve-column articles on the restoration of the American merchant marine.

He takes a keen delight in hunting for essays on civil service reform, and will play with them, if he has time, for hours. They are so pretty that he hates to kill them, but duty is duty. Clumsy and awkward English he springs at with indescribable quickness and ferocity; but he won't eat it. He simply tears it up. He can't stand everything.

We don't pretend that he is perfect. We admit he has an uncontrollable appetite for the Congressional Record. We have to keep this particular publication out of his reach. He will sit for hours and watch with burning eyes the iron safe in which we are obliged to shut up the Record for safe-keeping. Once in a while we let him have a number or two. He becomes uneasy without it. It is his catnip. With the exception of this pardonable excess he is a blameless beast. He mouses out all the stupid stuff and nonsense that finds its way into the office, and goes for it, tooth and claw. He is the biggest copyholder in the world. And he never gets tired, his health is good, and we have not deemed it necessary to take out a policy on any one of his numerous lives.

Many of our esteemed contemporaries are furnishing their offices with cats, but they can never hope to have the equal to the *Sun's* venerable polyphage. He is a cat of genius.

† † †

In that heyday of the *Sun,* even when some papers were amassing much greater circulations, newspapermen came to look to the *Sun* as a model for their own writing. Perhaps the coverage of the event was not always the best, but the way the *Sun* said things provided a constant and valuable example. In 1889 the terrible flood struck Johnstown, Pennsylvania, and thousands perished. On the scene was a reporter for the *Sun,* of course. But an even more routine disaster merited special treatment in the newspaper, though the blizzard of '88, not as spectacular as the Johnstown flood, was scarcely routine. Whoever wrote the following story did not feel compelled to say, in each sentence, "according to the weather bureau." The style is fresh, the treatment is exciting.

† † †

BLIZZARD WAS KING

New York Sun, March 13, 1888.

It was as if New York had been a burning candle upon which nature had clapped a snuffer, leaving nothing of the city's activity but a struggling ember.

At a little after 12 o'clock on Sunday night, or Monday morning, the severe rain that had been pelting down since the moment of the opening of the church doors suddenly changed to a sleet storm that plated the sidewalks with ice. Then began the great storm that is to become for years a household word, a symbol of the worst of weathers and the limit of nature's possibilities under normal conditions. . . .

The streets were blocked with snowdrifts. The car tracks were hid, horse cars were not in the range of possibilities, a wind of wild velocity howled between the rows of houses, the air was burdened with soft, wet, clinging snow, only here and there was a wagon to be seen, only here and there a feebly moving man.

The wind howled, whistled, banged, roared and moaned as it rushed along. It fell upon the house sides in fearful gusts, it strained great plate glass windows, rocked the frame houses, pressed against doors so that it was almost dangerous to open them. . . .

† † †

It was not Charles A. Dana but editorial writer Francis P. Church who wrote the most famous editorial ever published in the *Sun,* and probably the most famous ever published in the United States. Little background is necessary to acquaint most readers with what we call today "Dear Virginia"; many of us have not *read* the editorial, but almost everyone has *heard* of it. It has a universality that has kept it ever-fresh, and one need not be a believer in a jolly old gentleman who leaves toys on Christmas night to appreciate the sentiment and the meaning.

† † †

IS THERE A SANTA CLAUS?

New York Sun, September 21, 1897.

We take pleasure in answering at once and thus prominently the communication below, expressing at the same time our great gratification that its faithful author is numbered among the friends of The Sun.

> Dear Editor: I am eight years old. Some of my little friends say there is no Santa Claus. Papa says "if you see it in The Sun it's so." Please tell me the truth, is there a Santa Claus?
>
> Virginia O'Hanlon.
> 115 West 95th Street.

Virginia, your little friends are wrong. They have been affected by the skepticism of a skeptical age. They do not believe except they see. They think that nothing can be which is not comprehended by their little minds. All minds, Virginia, whether they be men's or children's are little. In this great universe of ours man is a mere insect, an ant, in his intellect, as compared with the boundless world about him, as measured by the intelligence capable of grasping the whole of truth and knowledge.

Yes, Virginia, there is a Santa Claus. He exists as certainly as love and generosity and devotion exist, and you know that they abound and give to our life its highest beauty and joy. Alas! how dreary would be the world if there were no Virginias. There would be no childish faith then, no poetry, no romance, to make tolerable this existence. We should have no enjoyment, except in sense and sight. The eternal light with which childhood fills the world would be extinguished.

Not believe in Santa Claus! You might as well not believe in fairies! You might get your papa to hire men to watch in all the chimneys on Christmas Eve to catch Santa Claus, but even if they did not see Santa Claus coming down, what would that prove? Nobody sees Santa Claus, but that is no sign that there is no Santa Claus. The most real things in the world are those that neither children nor men can see. Did you ever see fairies dancing on the lawn? Of course not, but that's no proof that they are not there. Nobody can conceive or imagine all the wonders there are unseen and unseeable in the world.

You may tear apart the baby's rattle and see what makes the noise inside, but there is a veil covering the unseen world which not the strongest men, nor even the united strength of all the strongest men that ever lived, could tear apart. Only fancy, poetry, love, romance can push aside that curtain and view and picture the supernal beauty and glory behind. Is it all real? Ah, Virginia, in all this world there is nothing else real and abiding.

No Santa Claus! Thank God! he lives and he lives forever. A thousand years from now, Virginia, nay, ten times ten thousand years from now, he will continue to make glad the heart of childhood.

† † †

Rivaling the *Sun* in its writing, and surpassing it in circulation, was the *Herald*, the creature of James Gordon Bennett. Now it was in the hands of Bennett, Jr., an imperious, arrogant, unprincipled—and rather fascinating—man, born amidst the troubles of his father's "moral war" and educated in Europe. His great accomplishment was the founding of the *Paris Herald* in 1887; of lesser note were the reports that he drove his coach while stark naked out in the moonlit countryside, that he loved to crash down onto an afternoon procession of young ladies from a boarding house and sweep them into maidenly confusion, that his engagement came to an end when he urinated in the fireplace at a New Year's party at his fiancee's home. Though such matters are not especially crucial to journalism they do help to explain the decline of the *Herald* and to make us see the nature of Bennett journalism. Where his father had mainly covered the news, Bennett chose to make it. The making of it could range from sending an expedition to find the legendary northwest passage to sending a Welsh-born reporter named Henry M. Stanley to find a Scottish Presbyterian missionary in darkest Africa. It is hard to deny the power of the latter story, or its epochal quality. Stanley was born illegitimate, came to America as a cabin-boy, found a protector in the port of New Orleans who brought him up and gave him the name of Stanley, fought briefly in the Civil War (on both sides), covered the war and the Indian battles in the West. He was summoned to Bennett's bedside in Paris, told to draw enough money and then draw more and then draw more, but "find Living-stone!" He found Livingstone.

† † †

A REPORTER FINDS DAVID LIVINGSTONE

New York Herald, August 10, 1872.

...At half-past two A.M. the men were ready, and, stealing silently past the huts, the guide opened the gates, and we filed out one by one as quickly as possible. The moon was bright, and by it we perceived that we were striking across a burned plain in a southerly direction, and then turned westward, parallel with the highroad, at a distance of four miles, sometimes lessening or increasing that distance as circumstances compelled us. At eight A.M. we halted for breakfast, having marched nearly six hours within the jungle which stretched for miles around us.

We were only once on the point of being discovered, through the mad freak of a weakbrained woman who was the wife of one of the black soldiers. We were crossing the knee-deep Rusizi when this woman, suddenly and without cause, took it into her head to shriek and shout as if a crocodile had bitten her. The guide implored me to stop her shrieking, or she would alarm the whole country, and we would have hundreds of angry Wahha about us. The men were already preparing to bolt—several being on the run with their loads. At my order to stop her noise she launched into another fit of hysterical shrieking, and I was compelled to stop her cries with three or four sharp cuts across her shoulders, though I felt rather ashamed of myself; but our lives and the success of the expedition were worth more, in my opinion, than a hundred of such women. As a further precaution she was gagged and her arms tied behind her, and a cord led from her waist to that of her liege lord's, who gladly took upon himself the task of looking after her, and who threatened to cut her head off if she made another outcry. . . .

We strode from the frontier at the rate of four miles an hour, and, after six hours' march, the tired caravan entered the woods which separated the residence of the Chief of Ukaranga from the villages on the Mkuti River. As we drew near the village we went slower, unfurled the American and Zanzibar flags, presenting quite an imposing array. . . .

A couple of hours brought us to the base of a hill, from the top of which the Kiraogozi said we could obtain a view of the great Tanganyika Lake. Heedless of the rough path or of the toilsome steep, spurred onward by the cheery promise, the ascent was performed in a short time. I was pleased at the sight; and, as we descended, it opened more and more into view until it was revealed at last into a grand inland sea, bounded westward by an appalling and black-blue range of mountains, and, stretching north and south without bounds, a gray expanse of water.

From the western base of the hill was a three hours' march, though no march ever passed off so quickly. The hours seemed to have been quarters, we had seen so much that was novel and rare to us who had been traveling so long on the highlands. The mountains bounding the lake on the eastward receded and the lake advanced. We had crossed the Ruche, or Linche, and its thick belt of tall matted grass. We had plunged into a perfect forest of them and had entered into the cultivated fields which supply the port of Ujiji with vegetables, etc., and we stood at least on the summit of the last hill of the myriads we had crossed, and the port of Ujiji, embowered in palms, with the tiny waves of the silver waters of the Tanganyika rolling at its feet, was directly below us.

We are now about descending—in a few minutes we shall have reached the spot where we imagine the object of our search—our fate will soon be decided. No one in that town knows we are coming; least of all do they know we are so close to them. If any of them ever heard of the white man at Unyanyembe they must believe we are there yet. We shall take them all by surprise, for no other but a white man would dare leave Unyanyembe for Ujiji with the country in such a distracted state—no other but a crazy white man, whom Sheik, the son of Nasib, is going to report to Syed or Prince Burghas for not taking his advice.

Well, we are but a mile from Ujiji now, and it is high time we should let them know a caravan is coming; so "Commence firing" is the word passed along the length of the column, and gladly do they begin. They have loaded their muskets half full, and they roar like the broadside of a line-of-battle ship. Down go the ramrods, sending huge charges home to the breech, and volley after volley is fired. The flags are fluttered; the banner of America is in front, waving joyfully; the guide is in the zenith of his glory. The former residents of Zanzita will know it directly and will wonder—as well they may— as to what it means. Never were the Stars and Stripes so beautiful to my mind—the breeze of the Tanganyika has such an effect on them. The guide blows his horn, and the shrill, wild clangor of it is far and near; and still the cannon muskets tell the noisy seconds. By this time the Arabs are fully alarmed; the natives of Ujiji, Waguha, Warundi, Wanguana, and I know not whom hurry up by the hundreds to ask what it all means—this fusillading, shouting, and blowing of horns and flag flying. There are Yambos shouted out to me by the dozen, and delighted Arabs have run up breathlessly to shake my hand and ask anxiously where I come from. But I have no patience with them. The expedition goes far too slow. I should like to settle the vexed question by one personal view. Where is he? Has he fled?

Suddenly a man—a black man—at my elbow shouts in English, "How do you do, sir?"

"Hello, who the deuce are you?"

"I am the servant of Dr. Livingstone," he says; and before I can ask any more questions he is running like a madman towards the town.

We have at last entered the town. There are hundreds of people around me— I might say thousands without exaggeration, it seems to me. It is a grand triumphal procession. As we move, they move. All eyes are drawn towards us. The expedition at last comes to a halt; the journey is ended for a time; but I alone have a few more steps to make.

There is a group of the most respectable Arabs, and as I come nearer I see the white face of an old man among them. He has a cap with a gold band around it, his dress is a short jacket of red blanket cloth, and his pants—well, I didn't observe. I am shaking hands with him. We raise our hats, and I say:

"Dr. Livingstone, I presume?"

And he says, "Yes."

Finis coronat opus.

†   †   †

It was in the days of Bennett, Jr., on the *Herald,* too, that someone—not Bennett himself, however—returned journalism briefly to the college boy days of seeing bison grazing on the moon and Monck Mason crossing the Atlantic in a balloon in three days. Our scene is New York City, in the mid-1870s.

† † †

THE WILD ANIMAL HOAX

New York Herald, November 9, 1874.

Another Sunday of horror has been added to those already memorable in our city annals. The sad and appalling catastrophe of yesterday is a further illustration of the unforeseen perils to which large communities are exposed. Writing even at a late hour, without full details of the terrors of the evening and night, and with a necessarily incomplete list of the killed and mutilated, we may pause for a moment in the widespread sorrow of the hours to cast a hasty glance over what will be felt to be a great calamity for many years. Few of the millions who have visited Central Park, and who, passing through the entrance at East Sixty-fourth Street, have stopped to examine the collection of birds and animals grouped around the old Arsenal building, could by any possibility have foreseen the source of such terrible danger to a whole city in the caged beasts around him as the trivial incidents of yesterday afternoon developed. The unfortunate man to whose fatal imprudence all accounts attribute the outbreak of the wild animals in the menagerie has answered with his life for his temerity, but we have a list of calamities traceable from his act which one life seems inadequate to expiate. We have a list of forty-nine killed, of which only twenty-seven bodies have been identified, and it is much to be feared that the large total of fatalities will be much increased with the return of daylight.

The list of mutilated, trampled and injured in various ways must reach nearly two hundred persons of all ages, of which, so far as known, about sixty are very serious, and of these latter, three can hardly outlast the night. Many of the slightly injured were taken to their homes, so that at least for another day the full extent of the calamity cannot be measured. We have only to hope that no further fatalities will occur. Twelve of the wild carnivorous beasts are still at large, their lurking places not being known for a certainty, but the citizens may rest assured that if they will only exercise ordinary prudence and leave the task of hunting down the animals to the authorities, who have somewhat tardily taken the matter in hand, there will be no further casualties to register as the outcome of the unauthorized act of a reckless keeper in Central Park. . . .

Of course the entire story given above is a pure fabrication. Not one word of it is true. Not a single act or incident described has taken place. It is a huge hoax, a wild romance, or whatever other epithet of utter untrustworthiness our readers may choose to apply to it. It is simply a fancy picture which crowded upon the mind of the writer a few days ago while he was gazing through the iron bars of the cages of the wild animals in the menagerie at Central Park. . . .

† † †

The Gilded Age was not always a good time for Whitelaw Reid and the *Tribune,* nor was it a good time for the *New York Times.* For Raymond was dead, and the new editor, after a time, was George Jones, the business office associate who had helped to found the paper in 1851. Of all *Times* stories in the nineteenth century few are as memorable as the coverage of—the exposure of—the William Tweed ring in 1870 and 1871. The *Times,* and *Harper's Weekly,* with the incisive cartoons of Thomas Nast, exposed Tweed, and the *Times* had a brief period as a reform journal. Tweed was, of course, the boss of Tammany Hall, and he and his gang were among the most famous boodlers in American political history. We offer a *Times* editorial.

† † †

EXPOSING BOSS TWEED

New York Times, July 8, 1871.

Reliable and incontrovertible evidence of numerous gigantic frauds on the part of the rulers of the city has been given to the public from time to time. Few, if any, of the frauds, however, which have been thus exposed will be found to be of greater magnitude or of a more shameful character than those which are presented in this article. The facts which are narrated are obtained from what we consider a good and trustworthy source, and the figures which help to explain them are transcribed literally from the books in the Controller's office. If Controller Connolly can prove them to be inaccurate he is heartily welcome to do so.

[A wealth of evidence is presented to show that amazing frauds were perpetrated in the rental of armories. Long-unoccupied buildings were selected by the "Ring" and rented for armory purposes, although entirely unsuitable. When Tweed's partner, James H. Ingersoll, rented a building for an armory, he proceeded to look it up to make sure it remained unused.]

During the year 1869, with the exception of the Eighty-fourth, there were no changes made in the location of the different regiments, and but little repairs were attempted, and yet, within thirty days, commencing March 12, 1870, more than HALF A MILLION DOLLARS were paid out of the City Treasury for "repairs on armories and drill rooms." The checks representing this amount were drawn in favor of Ingersoll and Watson, A. Garvey, Keyser and Co., but they were all returned from the bank bearing the indorsement of James H. Ingersoll. [Among the outstanding cases of fraudulent rentals was that in the amount of $16,500 paid for stable lofts that would not bring $2500 in the real-estate market.]

In addition to this, Ingersoll and Watson have been drawing Five Thousand Dollars a year for an indefinite period for an armory that never had any existence. It is described as being at No. 53 Chrystie Street, but the most diligent inquiry through the building and the neighborhood has failed to elicit the fact that any part of the premises has ever been used for military purposes. The building is in a wretched neighborhood, in the rear of Ingersoll and Watson's store, at No. 71 Bowery. The upper floors are let to different parties and are all occupied; the store and basement have been unoccupied since the first of May, up to which time they were occupied by a tobacco manufactory—so that the pretext that any part of the building has ever been used as an armory is glaringly false and fraudulent.

The following is a recapitulation of the amounts paid as rent for the armories now occupied, compared with what *should* be paid:

Yearly Rent   *Worth*
Total: $190,600 $46,600

Unoccupied Armories for which Rent is Paid ... [Total] Yearly Rent, $85,500.

Who are responsible for these frauds? First, Mayor Hall and Controller Connolly, who pass upon these claims and sign checks for their payment—knowing them to be fraudulent. Second, William M. Tweed and Peter B. Sweeny, who pocket their share of the proceeds—knowing it to have been fraudulently obtained. Third, James H. Ingersoll, Joseph B. Young, Clerk to the Board of Supervisors, and Stephen C. Lynes, Jr., the present City Auditor, whose agency in these matters is as palpable as it is shameful.

†   †   †

On July 22, a week or so later, the *Times* really broke with established practice, for it published its first multi-column headline over a detailed description of Tammany corruption called "THE SECRET ACCOUNTS." It followed with the secret accounts published in German, for the benefit of the city's growing immigrant population. Soon, with the help of the Nast cartoons—"them damn pictures," Tweed called them—the boss fled, was captured in Europe, and left reform-minded editors and readers exultant.

Gilded Age journalism boomed in other cities. Melville Stone founded the *Chicago Daily News* in 1876; Harvey W. Scott became editor of the *Oregonian* in Portland in 1865; Lucius Nieman purchased the *Milwaukee Journal* in 1882. Even more vital than it had been in an earlier time was the *Chicago Tribune* of Joseph Medill. The paper had one of its major stories to cover in 1871, for that was the year when Chicago burned—a fire that *may* have been started by Mrs. O'Leary's cow, though this is one more of those legends with which we will never be able to come to grips.

† † †

A COW AND A GREAT FIRE IN CHICAGO

Chicago Tribune, October 11, 1871.

During Sunday night, Monday and Tuesday, this city has been swept by a conflagration which has no parallel in the annals of history for the quantity of property destroyed, and the utter and almost irremediable ruin which it wrought. A fire in a barn on the West Side was the insignificant case of a conflagration which has swept out of existence hundreds of millions in property, has reduced to poverty thousands who, the day before, were in a state of opulence, has covered the prairies, now swept by the cold southwest wind, with thousands of homeless unfortunates, which has stripped 2,600 acres of buildings, which has destroyed public improvements that it has taken years of patient labor to build up, and which has set back for years the progress of the city, diminished her population and crushed her resources. But to a blow, no matter how terrible, Chicago will not succumb. Late as it is in the season, general as the ruin is, the spirit of her citizens has not given way, and before the smoke has cleared away, and the ruins are cold, they are beginning to plan for the future. Though so many have been deprived of homes and sustenances, aid in money and provisions is flowing in from all quarters and much of the present distress will be alleviated before another day has gone by.

It is at this moment impossible to give a full account of the losses by the fire, or to state the number of total accidents which have occurred. So much confusion prevails, and people are so widely scattered that we are unable for a day to give absolutely accurate information concerning them. We have, however, given a full account of the fire, from the time of its beginning. . . . .

† † †

At 9:30 a small cow barn attached to a house on the corner of DeKoven and Jefferson streets, one block north of Twelfth street, emitted a light, followed by a blaze, and in a moment the building was hopelessly on fire. Before any aid could be extended the fire had communicated to a number of adjoining sheds, barns and dwellings and was rapidly carried north and east, despite the efforts of the firemen. The fire seemed to leap over the engines and commenced far beyond them, and, working to the east and west, either surrounded the apparatus or compelled it to move away; in less than ten minutes the fire embraced the area between Jefferson and Clinton for two blocks north, and rapidly pushed eastward to Canal street.

When the fire first engulfed these blocks and the efforts of the undaunted engineers became palpably abortive to quench a single building, an effort was made to head it off from the north, but so great was the area that it already covered at 10:30 o'clock and so rapidly did it march forward that by the time the engines were at work the flames were ahead of them, and again they moved on north. From the west side of Jefferson street as far as the eye could reach in an easterly direction—and that space was bounded by the river—a perfect sea of leaping flames covered the ground. The wind increased in fierceness as the flames rose, and the flames wailed more hungrily for their prey as the angry gusts impelled them onward. . . . . It was now about 1:15 o'clock.

But, while it seemed as if the demon of flame had reached a desert and needs must die, a new danger appeared to threaten the city. From the South Side, in the neighborhood of Adams street, whereabouts no one on the West Side could guess with any degree of certainty, rose a column of fire, not large, but horribly suggestive. Such engines as could be moved were called off from the West to protect the South Side's property, and the flames left to die of inanition.

The fire of Saturday burned the region in the West Division from Van Buren street northward to Adams, and all east of Clinton street to the river, Murry Nelson's elevator alone standing. The light from the burning remnants of these eighteen acres of ruins illumined the heavens on Sunday evening. Precisely at half-past 9 o'clock, the fire bells sounded an alarm, and a fresh light, distinct from the other only to those living west of the fire, sprung up. . . . The wind carried this fire straight before it, through the next block, and so on northward until it reached Van Buren street, where it struck the south line of the district burnt the night before. Here this fire ought to have stopped, and here, under ordinary circumstances, it would have stopped. But the wind, fierce and direct, carried the flames before it, cutting as clean and as well defined a swath as does the reaper in the field, and the fire gradually but rapidly extended laterally. . . .

† † †

Another of the important American newspapers came into being in those years, the *Kansas City Star*. The year was 1880, and the founder was an outsized entrepreneur from Indiana named William Rockhill Nelson, who became one of the new business barons but who also had one of the sharper instincts for news and for staff members yet known to journalism. The *Star* was a penny paper and thrived because it covered its still-frontier community in good style and because it fought the good fights against monopolies, for civic progress, against slums, for a beautiful city, and a beautiful Missouri Valley. Nelson's great monument was his campaign for city parks and boulevards, a campaign begun with an editorial.

† † †

A CAMPAIGN FOR A BEAUTIFUL CITY

Kansas City Star, May 19, 1881.

With a population of over 65,000 Kansas City has no public parks, no place of resort where the people can congregate with their families and spend a pleasant hour or so, away from the hot and dusty streets. The need of a public park is forcibly illustrated every Sunday afternoon by the large number of people who gather at the fairgrounds and promenade over its green acres. People will go somewhere and in lieu of a park, they assemble at these grounds and wander aimlessly about, the only attractions there being the green grass and shade trees. The time, too, is rapidly approaching when even this boon will be denied the people, as in a year or so at least, the fairgrounds will be laid off into lots and sold. A few years ago this valuable property was available and could have been purchased very cheap by the city for a public park. As the years have rolled by, however, it has become more valuable, until now the price is beyond the reach of the city, thus preventing the possibility of a purchase. Five years ago a gentleman who owns a piece of property very suitable for a public park, offered it to the city at a reasonable price per acre and on twenty years time. This was the last opportunity the city ever had, or probably ever will have, to secure an eligible location for a park, on such terms as were offered. The opportunity was not approved, and Kansas City today, with all its enterprise and vim, is without a park.

In the meantime property is advancing all the time, and will in a year or so command fabulous prices. In view of this fact is it not about time that the young metropolis of the border should be taking some steps to provide a public park? The officials may dodge the issue, and seek to excuse themselves by saying the new city charter prohibits the expenditure of money for any such purpose. This, however, will not strictly satisfy the people, nor condone official negligence in this matter, as special legislation to secure a park could easily be had, provided there was an earnest movement for the purpose. If Kansas City ever expects to have a public park there will never be a more favorable opportunity than now. It would be a crowning act in the history of Mayor Frink's administration if he would take measures that would result in securing to the city a public park. Will he do it?"

† † †

In Louisville, Kentucky, the famous figure of the age was Henry Watterson, "Marse Henry," a long-haired, mustachioed gentleman known as the goodwill ambassador from Kentucky to the rest of the nation from 1868 until his retirement in 1919 as editor of the *Courier-Journal.* Watterson was colorful, his language was florid, extravagant; he invited fellow editors, like Dana, to "Come and see us, and bring your knitting and stay most all the day." He was a good Democrat, and he defended his Democratic attitudes in a famous editorial.

† † †

A DEMOCRAT IN KENTUCKY

Louisville Courier-Journal, December 25, 1868.

. . . We are, for the most part, Democrats; we vote the Democratic ticket; we decline to vote for Republican candidates and measures; we are perfectly honest and think we have a right, as free citizens of a free republic, to decide for ourselves.

For so doing and so thinking we are denounced as traitors to our country and a despotism is sought to be placed over us by those who claim that we ought to be forced to vote for Republican candidates and Republican measures, and who declare that if we do not, we are guilty of rebellion and should be punished therefor.

This was not the spirit of Boone and his companions, who prayed God to bless Massachusetts on Christmas day, 1778. It was not the spirit of the Kentuckians who fought the battles of the country from King's mountain to the City of Mexico. It is a new-born spirit; the spirit of rapine and war, not of liberty and peace. . . .

† † †

In Atlanta the great figure in journalism was Henry W. Grady, whose years in journalism were brief, but whose influence was mighty. Grady bought a one-quarter interest in the *Atlanta Constitution* in 1880, after a notable beginning as a reporter in Georgia. He became a marked man, advancing the idea of bringing the South back into the union in a time when many southerners were still sulking in their tents. Grady advanced this cause in an oration at a banquet of the New England Society in New York City. It became known to generations of Georgia schoolboys, who especially venerated it after the editor's untimely death in 1889, when he was only 39.

† † †

THE NEW SOUTH

By Henry W. Grady, December 21, 1886, in Edwin Du Bois Shurter, ed., *The Complete Orations and Speeches of Henry W. Grady* (Norwood, Mass.: South-West Publishing Co., 1910), pp. 7-19.

"There was a South of slavery and secession—that South is dead. There is a South of union and freedom—that South, thank God, is living, breathing, growing every hour." These words, delivered from the immortal lips of Benjamin H. Hill, at Tammany Hall, in 1886, true then and truer now, I shall make my text tonight. . . .

Will you bear with me while I tell you of [an] army that sought its home at the close of the late war?—an army that marched home in defeat and not in victory, in pathos and not in splendor, but in glory that equaled yours, and to hearts as loving as ever welcomed heroes home? Let me picture to you the footsore Confederate soldier, as, buttoning up in his faded gray jacket the parole which was to bear testimony to his children of his fidelity and faith, he turned his face southward from Appomattox in April, 1865. . . .

What does he do—this hero in gray with a heart of gold? Does he sit down in sullenness and despair? Not for a day. Surely God, who had stripped him of his prosperity, inspired him in his adversity. As ruin was never before so overwhelming, never was restoration swifter. The soldier stepped from the trenches into the furrow; horses that had charged federal guns marched before the plow, and fields that ran red with human blood in April were green with the harvest in June; women reared in luxury cut up their dresses and made breeches for their husbands, and, with a patience and heroism that fit women always as a garment, gave their hands to work. . . .

The old South rested everything on slavery and agriculture, unconscious that these could neither give nor maintain healthy growth. The new South presents a perfect democracy, the oligarchs leading in the popular movement; a social system compact and closely knitted, less splendid on the surface, but stronger at the core; a hundred farms for every plantation, fifty-homes for every palace; and a diversified industry that meets the complex needs of this complex age.

The new South is enamored of her new work. Her soul is stirred with the breath of a new life. The light of a grander day is falling fair on her face. She is thrilling with the consciousness of growing power and prosperity. As she stands upright, full-statured and equal among the people of the earth, breathing the keen air and looking out upon the expanded horizon, she understands that her emancipation came because, through the inscrutable wisdom of God, her honest purpose was crossed and her brave armies were beaten.

† † †

9

CULMINATION OF
THE MASS PRESS

The idea of a press for the masses goes back at least to the ballad journalism of old England. It was certainly a mass press that American newspaper readers came to know in the penny journalism of the 1830s and 1840s. Penny practitioners had recognized that people have a basic interest in human behavior; they knew that stories of crime, sex, and conflict—with human interest—are likely to have a larger audience than stories of government and finance. But, as with the penny press, the producers of mass journalism from the 1880s on did not consciously initiate a revolution. The leader in the new movement, Joseph Pulitzer, mainly pulled together the various threads of nineteenth century journalism—the news function, human interest and sensation, public service, and editorial leadership.

Pulitzer was a man of his time, and it is symbolic that this editor who produced a newspaper so dear to the emerging masses, people new to our shores in many cases, should have been an immigrant himself. He was born in 1847 near Budapest, and he came to America as a soldier who had been recruited to fight in a New York cavalry regiment in the Civil War. He saw little action, and when the war was over the footloose young man—"Joey" to his derisive acquaintances—went to St. Louis, probably because that city had a large German-speaking population. He became associated with Carl Schurz of the *Westliche Post,* entered Republican politics and became a Democrat after the defeat of Greeley in 1872. He rose to such a position in St. Louis politics and journalism that he was able to buy two dying newspapers, the *Post* and the *Dispatch,* and merge them in 1878 as the *St. Louis Post-Dispatch.* On that newspaper, ably assisted by the brilliant editor John Cockerill, Pulitzer carried out the campaigns and covered the stories of the "new journalism," working to improve the streets of St. Louis, fighting wealthy tax-dodgers, fighting gambling and corruption. His *Post-Dispatch* became and remained one of the best of American newspapers, a fighting journal that stayed in the Pulitzer family and worked for the betterment of city, state, region, and nation. Two *Post-Dispatch* editorials of the Pulitzer years illustrate the theme of public service.

† † †

A FIGHTING NEWSPAPER IN THE MIDWEST

St. Louis Post-Dispatch, November 9, 1881, and
February 18, 1882.

This sort of thing must be stopped. Murdering must be made odious in St. Louis. The corrupt Four Courts must be purified. The thievish shysters who cluster there... must be driven out. The first great duty of society is self-protection. Order and security are necessary at whatever cost. We kill mad-dogs for the protection of the community and we must kill human mad-dogs for the same reason. A Committee of Safety must be organized at once to employ able attorneys to assist in the prosecution of murderers, to collect testimony, to war upon the shysters and generally uphold the courts in the administration of justice. There is no need of mob violence— certainly not as yet. A stern, unyielding determination upon the part of our citizens to have the law enforced.. will put a stop to this reign of bloodshed. There must be an end to the supineness and indif- ference... of our citizens.

*   *   *   *   *

A few thoroughfares in the center of the city are in a passable condition; the balance of the town has been neglected, until the alleged streets are simply so many miles of torn-out and washed-out soft roadbed covered with limestone mud to a depth varying from two to ten inches. At places where the heavy traffic is frequent, about the railroad depots, the elevators and the great mills and factories, the streets have been worn into holes two and three feet deep, where wagons are mired and carrying brought to a stop... The tribute which the bad streets exact from the industries of this city... can be estimated only in millions... Why are the streets of St. Louis worse than those of any other city in America?

† † †

Joseph Pulitzer was an ambitious man, and he was restless; unlike some of his contemporaries he could not be confined to a smaller regional capital. In 1879 the financier Jay Gould had bought that New York paper, the *World,* which had been edited by the Democratic party leader, Manton Marble. It was a losing venture for both men and Gould offered it for sale. Joseph Pulitzer was the purchaser, beginning his era on the *World* on May 11, 1883. Though the paper was not radically different in appearance from what it had been, it was quite different in content, the lead stories on the first day dealing with a devastating storm in New Jersey, an interview with a condemned slayer, a dynamiting in Haiti. The paper sold every copy printed—and it had been *losing* circulation. In the prospectus Joseph Pulitzer defined what he saw as the mission of the *World,* and in 1886 he redefined what he thought a newspaper should be.

† † †

PULITZER AND THE MISSION OF THE PRESS

New York World, May 11, 1883, and October 3, 1886.

The entire WORLD newspaper property has been purchased by the undersigned, and will, from this day on, be under different management—different in men, measures and methods—different in purpose, policy and principle—different in objects and interests—different in sympathies and convictions—different in head and heart. . . .

There is room in this great and growing city for a journal that is not only cheap but bright, not only bright but large, not only large but truly Democratic—dedicated to the cause of the people rather than that of purse-potentates—devoted more to the news of the New than the Old World—that will expose all fraud and sham, fight all public evils and abuses—that will serve and battle for the people with earnest sincerity. . . .

JOSEPH PULITZER.

* * * * *

HENRY WATTERSON's ideal of a newspaper is that "it should, to begin with, be a history, and a complete history, of YESTERDAY, neatly and justly told," and that "it should, to end with, be a chronicle of the life and thought and, as far as may be, a reflection of the temper and tone of the people done with absolute fidelity." At the bottom of this scheme he places as the foundation three cardinal principles—"disinteredness, cleanliness, capacity."

This ideal is a worthy one, as far as it goes, but it does not go far enough. The time has come in the history of this country, and in the growth of the press in power and opportunity, when a great paper can do more, and must do more if it is to occupy the place open to it, than to give a "History of YESTERDAY" or even a picture of TO-DAY, and to make honest and able comment upon it. These, though essentials of the new journalism, are not all of it. That is a short-range view and a narrow ambition which take in only the affairs of yesterday and to-day. The newspaper that is true to its highest mission will concern itself with the things that *ought to happen tomorrow,* or next month, or next year, and will seek to make what ought to be come to pass. It is not enough to chronicle the life and thought of the people and to reflect their tone and temper. This is a most important service. But a paper which has the moral sense, the intellectual perception and the political independence to speak to the heart, the mind and the conscience of the people and tell them what they will feel that it is for their good to hear and to heed, can do more to benefit the country than can a hundred pulpits or a score of Governors—more than any one session of Congress, or any four-year President, or any party.

The highest mission of the press is to *render public service.* It does this by publishing the news and by speaking the truth fearlessly in regard to current events. . . . There are dangers to confront, evils to combat, inequalities to correct and abuses to cure which did not exist in this country a few years ago. . . . An aristocracy of mere wealth, the growing tyranny of corporations, an ominous unrest among the working people, corruptions in politics and incapacity in government complicate the problems before the nation. In helping to solve these rightly the press may make itself a power for promoting the public good which shall be greater than that of any other single influence in the land. To lead in this work is the ambition of THE WORLD. It seeks the highest possible circulation, but, more than that, it seeks the highest attainable point in character, educative force and actual public service rendered.

† † †

The *World* was, on occasion, a mad paper, with its reporters racing off after stories, on snowshoes in the great storm of '88, as an example; wildly campaigning and crusading against the crooks; pushing for dimes from the school children of America to complete the base for the Statue of Liberty. Pulitzer and Cockerill (he had joined his St. Louis employer) in the big city had many major stories, and one of their reporters was a woman named Elizabeth Cochrane, who called herself "Nellie Bly." It was Nellie who raced Father Time, attempting to surpass the fictional record of Jules Verne's Phileas Fogg, who had gone *Around the World in Eighty Days.* Here is the *World's* story.

† † †

NELLIE BLY GOES AROUND THE WORLD

New York World, January 26, 1890.

A Monsieur Jules Verne, Amiens, France:
Mademoiselle Nellie Bly est arrivée a New York aujourd'hui. Elle a fini son tour du monde en soixante-douze jours, six heures et quelques minutes. Le New York WORLD présente ses compliments et

désire votre opinion sur le voyage accompli. Réponse est payée a
votre discrétion.
                                    —DIRECTEUR DU WORLD

Amiens, Jan. 25.—Jamais doute du succes de Nellie Bly. Son
intrépidité le laissait prevoir. Hurrah pour elle et pour directeur
du "World"! Hurrah! Hurrah!
                                    —JULES VERNE

It is finished.

Sullen echoes of cannon across the gray waters of the bay and over
the roofs and spires of three cities.

People look at their watches. It is only 4 o'clock. Those cannot be
the sunset guns.

Is some one dead?

Only an era. And the booming yonder at the Battery and Fort
Greene tolls its passing away. The stage-coach days are ended and
the new age of lightning travel begun.

A little woman is stepping from the platform of a railroad train in
Jersey City. Ten thousand eyes are on her. A mad crowd surges to
and fro about her as if it would sweep her against the great grim
wheels of the locomotive which whirled her thither. Men push and
strain against each other in a struggle fierce as if it were for life and
death. Hats are knocked off, eyeglasses vanish. Big policemen wave
their locusts wildly, and are brushed about in that clutch of the
eager, irresistible throng.

And amid all the tumult walks the little lady, with just a foot of
space between her and the madly joyous mob. She is carrying a little
walking stick in one hand and with the other waves her checkered
little fore-and-aft traveling cap, and laughs merrily as her name is
hoarsely shouted from innumerable throats. Tense faces stare from
the long galleries that bend ominously beneath their awful load of
humanity. The tops of passenger coaches lying on side tracks are
black with men and boys.

Grimy railroad men, their smutty and bewhiskered faces wreath-
ed in smiles, swing their dirty caps and cry hurrah to the little
traveler. Policemen are almost at fisticuffs with the crowd there.
From the balconies bunches of flowers are thrown into the struggling crowd.

But the little girl trips gayly along. The circuit of the globe is
behind her. Time is put to blush. She has brushed away distance as if
it were down. Oceans and continents she has traversed. She has
tripped through war-trodden Europe, where the armies of centuries
have tramped up and down in ceaseless and unavailing bloodshed.
London has squinted sleepily at her from the fog. Paris has cried
"Voilà!" Old Rome has breathed her its benediction. Naples has
smiled out at her own Capri, and the blue Mediterranean which
tossed the pious Aeneas has kissed the prow of her bark and lulled

her to sleep o'nights. The Pyramids with their hoary centuries have lifted up sleepy heads to wink at her. The Indian Ocean, China and Japan have ushered her ever eastward, and the great fatherly Pacific took her in strong, peaceful arms to hand her back to her native land.

Faster, ever faster. Her latest journey was her swiftest. She has turned the wildest dream of a French fiction-master into sober truth, and Nellie Bly's fact of today has made the fancy of a quarter of a century ago seem like a twice-told tale. And now she is home, a happy little heroine, with a sunburnt nose and a proud, glad heart. There are smiles and plaudits and love and fame for a welcome. . . .

One day last November the people knew that Nellie Bly, with all her former honors thick upon her, was going to undertake a new and gigantic task.

M. Jules Verne was credited wifth the most limitless of imaginations. It reached out to infinity, and took in the moon and all the planets. It plunged into the depths of the sea which no McGinty could hope to fathom. Nellie Bly, THE WORLD said, was going to show M. Verne that he had not imagined half wildly enough; that this Puck of his, this globe-girdler, this Phineas Fogg, was a slow old poke.

So with an outfit made up to avoid the cumbersome delays of baggage travel, the young woman made a neat apology to Jules Verne, invoked the auspices of her stars and started.

On a bright November morning—it was the 14th—in 1889 she set sail on the steamship *Augusta Victoria*. Fond hands waved her goodbye, she steamed down the Narrows with all the world before her, and the great race against time and fable was begun. . . .

And now she is home. The ghost of Phileas Fogg may sit and sip ghostly hot-Scotches somewhere in the realm of fancy, and sign over his old age and his glory now outdone.

When Nellie Bly's honest little feet plumped down on the grimy planking of the Jersey City Station yesterday, she had made the tour of the globe in 72 days, 6 hours, 10 minutes and some seconds.

✝   ✝   ✝

The *World* was sensational, and a bit artificial, a combination of Stanley finding Livingstone and Monck Mason in his balloon. But it was at the heart of the new journalism. There were scoffers, and there were critics, one of them astutely capturing the split personality of not only the newspaper but of its editor-publisher. This was the old humor magazine, *Life,* in "New York Newspaper Directory, Revised," and here is the stanza on the *World.*

✝   ✝   ✝

A COMMENTARY ON THE WORLD, IN VERSE

Life Magazine, quoted in Alleyne Ireland,
An Adventure with a Genius (New York: Dutton, 1914), p. 106.

> A dual personality is this,
> Part yellow dog, part patriot and sage;
> When 't comes to facts the rule is hit or miss,
> While none can beat its editorial page.
> Wise counsel here, wild yarns the other side,
> Page six its Jekyll and page one its Hyde;
> At the same time conservative and rash,
> The *World* supplies us good advice and trash.

† † †

Joseph Pulitzer continued the theme of working for municipal progress that had marked his five years on the *St. Louis Post-Dispatch.* He did so in a time when far too many people believed reform was foolish, that there should be no interference with the laws of nature.

† † †

WORKING FOR A BETTER NEW YORK

New York World, January 1, 1884.

New York City is marching on.

The last census gave us probably 100,000 less population than we were honestly entitled to at the time it was taken. . . . In ten or fifteen years the city proper will be climbing up to the neighborhood of that total. (2 million). . .

Within the past ten years we have added to our advantage the Elevated Railroads and the Brooklyn Bridge. The great work of the Hell Gate explosions has benefited the shipping of the port and is only the beginning of important improvements. . . . Handsomer buildings, both in stores, offices and private residences, have been erected within the last decade than ever before. . . .

What we need now is a continuance of a liberal spirit of public improvement which will stimulate and warrant private improvements, and increased watchfulness over the sanitary regulations of the city. . . .

New York City has a great future. Our population will eventually exceed that of London. If our legislators, our city authorities and our wealthy residents have the intelligence to understand and the enterprise to encourage and help forward our manifest destiny, it will not be many years before New York will take position as the leading metropolis of the civilized world in population, commerce, healthfulness, grandeur and beauty.

† † †

A "purse potentate" himself, Pulitzer was a friend of the rich and mighty, playing cards and dining with them at the clubs of New York, and it puzzled him that his attacks on wealth and privilege should bother the very people he was attacking. Much of the *World's* notable campaigning against such privilege came in election years, as in 1884, when the cartoonist did "Belshazzar's Feast," and editorials pinned James G. Blaine and the Republicans to the wall. One *World* editorial showed the newspaper's disdain for those who belonged to a mere "plutocracy."

† † †

AMERICANS AND THE WORSHIP OF WEALTH

New York World, February 5, 1884.

... the fact remains that the material causes of national prosperity here have brought about in a perfectly natural way a regard for money as such which was long ago fitly characterized by WASHINGTON IRVING as the worship of the Almighty Dollar.

It is easy to see why a country which offers such unlimited chances to all classes to acquire wealth, and where the struggling millions have opportunities to develop tastes, desires and appetites that wealth alone will gratify, should, especially in its great centres of activity, come to look upon money as the one desideratum of human existence. It is not so easy to show that this condition is a temporary vice that will disappear, or at least become modified, as we accrete a large conservative and influential class of intelligent and independent citizens. One of the most disagreeable aspects of the case is presented in the constant elevation of mere money-holders to positions of great social honor. There is not at present, we regret to say, that honor shown to talent, skill, bravery, learning and honesty that is freely accorded in older countries. . . .

† † †

Up until the 1890s the word was "sensationalism," a development in journalism not very different from the journalism of the James Gordon Bennetts. "Sensationalism" became "yellow journalism," and perhaps the shift to that new development was caused by increased competition; perhaps it was the availability of new technology—faster presses, automatic typesetting machines, color printing, photoengraving. An issue of the *World* might have

headlines such as these, from early 1884: GARROTED BY
DAYLIGHT, A SALESMAN MISSING, THE COAL-PIT
TRAGEDY, A MOTHER'S SEARCH FOR HER CHILD, AN
UNGRATEFUL GUEST, FACE TO FACE WITH DEATH.
News of government often was sensationalized. Yellow journalism was sensationalism gone mad—scareheads, large type,
screaming type, many pictures, picture-faking, frauds and
impostures, pseudo-science, colored comics, trashy features, a
demagogic sympathy with the underdog. Thus Frank Luther Mott
defines the term. Sunday magazines were especially florid, and each
of the competing newspapers was likely to have such a magazine.
But it was the entrance of William Randolph Hearst onto the New
York stage that brought the now-famous circulation war of the
1890s, and that brought, at least in part, the war with Spain as well.
The story of Hearst we shall treat later, but it is important to note
that this editor bought the *New York Journal* in 1895, that he had
long admired what Pulitzer was doing and had imitated him in San
Francisco, that he was more audacious and perhaps more irresponsible than Pulitzer, and that he had more money. He bought
away part of the Pulitzer staff, obtaining such features as the
popular comic of R. F. Outcault that featured "The Yellow Kid," and
such people as Morrill Goddard and Arthur Brisbane. Then came the
war with Spain.

Some people tend to overgeneralize about the role of Pulitzer and
Hearst; by themselves they did not start a war, but they and some
others, including some in government, did help to create an
emotional climate for war. America was a world power by 1898, and
some of our leaders had read with enthusiasm that work by Alfred T.
Mahan called *The Influence of Sea Power upon History*. Here was
justification for engaging in enterprises that would put America in a
class with England, which had defeated the Spanish Armada and
become mighty. Certain leaders in the 1890s were propagandizing
for a stronger American role in world affairs, and social Darwinism
was giving racists a rationale for moving into lands inhabited by
"little brown brothers." Cuba had been in revolt against the imperial
power of Spain for decades, and that revolt was used by William
Randolph Hearst and Joseph Pulitzer as a basis for stories,
editorials, and crusades. From March, 1895, when the Cuban
insurrection began in earnest, until April, 1898, when war began,
stories about Cuba were a commonplace in the New York papers,
stories that were inflammatory, shouting at the tops of their voices
in many cases. Hearst seized especially upon the indignities to
which a Cuban girl, Evangelina Cisneros, had supposedly been
exposed; and the arrival of a Spanish general named Valerian
Weyler, rapidly labeled "The Butcher," helped the cause of big
circulations. A familiar story is that Hearst told his artist-reporter,
Frederic Remington, "You furnish the pictures. I'll furnish the war."

Somebody furnished a war. President William McKinley was
reluctant, but he finally saw the light. And the sinking of the
battleship *Maine* in Havana harbor, wildly reported by *World* and

Journal on February 16, 1898, was the episode that launched America into war and drove the newspapers to even greater frenzies. That swashbuckling journalist of fortune, Richard Harding Davis, went to Cuba. Remington, artist of the Old West, reported in print as well as in illustrations. Frank Norris, Sylvester Scovel, and Stephen Crane were there, the latter reporting for the *World,* and learning, to his great pleasure, that war was quite the way he had described it in *The Red Badge of Courage.*

† † †

AN INCIDENT IN THE SPANISH-AMERICAN WAR

By Stephen Crane, *New York World,* June 13, 1898.

On board The World Dispatch Boat Triton, off Guantanamo, Via Porto Antonio, Jamaica, June 12—

For thirteen hours, the marines, under Lieutenant Colonel Huntington, who landed from the *Panther* and raised Old Glory over the battered fortifications of the Spanish at the mouth of Guantanamo Harbor, sustained an attack made by the Spaniards.

Four of our men are killed and one wounded. The killed are:

Assistant Surgeon John Blair Gibbs of Richmond, Va.

Sergeant Charles H. Smith, of Smallwood.

Private William Dunphy, of Goucester, Mass.

Private James McColgan, of Stoneham, Mass.

Corporal Glass was slightly wounded on the head.

The advance pickets under Lieutenants Neville and Shaw are thought to be prisoners.

The attack began at three o'clock Saturday afternoon. It lasted with almost continuous skirmishing until this morning.

It is not known how great was the Spanish loss. Their dead and wounded were carried off. It is thought from blood splashes found after the fighting that their loss was heavy.

The Spaniards advanced upon our outposts through thick tropical underbrush and began firing.

Sergeant Smith, who was at the extreme picket post relieving the guard, fell at the first fire.

The firing at first was desultory. The Spaniards drove in the outposts, a part of Captain Spicer's company.

They fell back upon the camp, where the fighting was continued until five o'clock, when the Spaniards were repulsed.

Captain McCalla landed reinforcements from the marines of the *Marblehead* in the launch. Ensign Sullivan afterward went close to the shore in the launch, trying to draw the enemy's fire, but failed to accomplish this.

The bodies of Privates McColgan and Dunphy were found in the brush. Each was shot in the head. The large cavities caused by the bullets, which inside a range of five hundred yards have a rotary motion, indicate that they were killed at close range. Their bodies were stripped of shoes, hats, and cartridges and horribly mutilated.

The marines received the attack upon the camp formed into three sides of a hollow square. The country about was craggy, cut with ravines, and covered with a tropical thicket. The Spaniards up to midnight attacked from the cover of this undergrowth.

The afternoon was cloudy and the night windy. After sunset it grew very dark. At night the enemy was discoverable only by the flashes of their arms, save when occasionally the searchlights of the ships sweeping along the deep foliage discovered a party of the Spaniards.

Whenever this happened the guns of the marines lined along the camp and the machine gun of the launch of the *Marblehead* volleyed at the assailants.

The launch pushed up the bay along the shore, firing upon the Spaniards with her gun. It is believed that her fire was deadly.

About midnight the Spaniards charged up the hill from the southwest upon the camp. Upon repeated volleys of bullets they broke and retreated. So close did they come that revolvers were used.

Three Spaniards got to the edge of the camp, where Colonel Jose Campina, the Cuban guide, fired upon them. They turned and ran helter-skelter down the hills.

It was during this assault that Assistant Surgeon Gibbs was killed. He was shot in the head in front of his own tent. He fell into the arms of Private Sullivan, and both dropped. A second bullet threw dust in their faces. Surgeon Gibbs lived ten minutes, but did not regain consciousness.

Firing was kept up by small squads of Spaniards. The marines had lain upon their arms, and some of them, worn out with the fatigue of two days' labor and fighting almost without rest, had fallen asleep. At dawn all were aroused in anticipation of a second assault, but one was not made.

When daylight made it possible to use field guns, three twelve-pounders opened upon the few Spaniards then visible, who fled.

Our men behaved well and are praised by their officers. The great majority of them had never before been under fire, and though a night attack is especially trying, not one of them flinched.

They themselves give credit for courage to the Spaniards, whom they express a desire to meet again.

† † †

William Randolph Hearst himself was on the war scene on occasion—Hearst, a hero-villain of our journalism, the Hearst of *Citizen Hearst* and of *Citizen Kane,* too. His story is one of the famous ones and bears some retelling. He was born in 1863 in San Francisco, and his father was Senator George Hearst, who had made his money in the mines of the West and obtained himself a seat in the Senate. The elder Hearst had a newspaper in San Francisco, the *Examiner,* and after the son was ousted from Harvard for various minor infractions he persuaded his father to give him the paper.

So Hearst was a publisher at 24; he had watched the methods of Pulitzer, and he wanted to try them out on the west coast, with such staff members as Ambrose Bierce, cartoonist Homer Davenport, and Winifred Black, who called herself "Annie Laurie" as Pulitzer's sob sister called herself "Nellie Bly." Hearst entered the New York newspaper field, then, in 1895, and he engaged in his celebrated duel with Pulitzer. Everything seemed to be sensationalized in the *Journal*—in pictures, type, innuendo. The *Journal* even achieved the feat of reviewing a Henry James novel in a sensational way. Hearst was on the side of justice, as was Pulitzer, and whether his demagoguery was greater we do not know, but it did seem greater to some observers. Hearst's *Journal* was the most jingoistic of American papers and continued its imperialistic ways after Pulitzer had recovered his sanity at the end of the war with Spain. One of the *Journal's* notable dispatches was by the boss himself, the story of the capture of the village of Caney in 1898.

† † †

AN EDITOR HIMSELF COVERS THE WAR

By William Randolph Hearst, *New York Journal,* July 4, 1898.

Special Cable Dispatch to the *New York Journal*—WITH THE ARMY IN FRONT OF SANTIAGO, JULY 1, MIDNIGHT, VIA KINGSTON, JAMAICA, JULY 3—
Tonight, as I write, the ambulance trains are bringing in the wounded soldiers from the fierce battle around the little inland village of Caney.
Siboney, the base of the army, is a hospital and nothing more. There is no saying when the slaughter will cease. The tents are crowded with wounded, and the hard-worked surgeons are busy with their mechanical work. There is an odor of anesthetics and the clatter of ambulances in the one narrow street.
Under the fierce firing of far-heavier artillery forces than it was supposed the Spaniards had, the American infantry and dismounted cavalry have done their work, and done it nobly.
I have been at the artillery positions all day to see what our guns could or could not do. There is no question of skill or courage of American gunners. Their work was as near perfect as gunnery gets to be, but there was no artillery to speak of.
The War Department has furnished the necessary heavy guns, but they remain in the rear because of the difficulty of transportation from the coast.
I set out before daybreak this morning on horseback with Honore Laine, who is a colonel in the Cuban Army, and has served for months as the Journal's correspondent in Cuba. We rode over eight miles of difficult country which intervenes between the army based on the coast and the fighting line which is being driven forward toward Santiago. . . .
With a rush they swept up the slope, and the stone fort was ours.

Then you should have heard the yell that went up from the knoll on which our battery stood. Gunners, drivers, Cubans, correspondents, swung their hats and gave a mighty cheer. Immediately our battery stopped firing for fear we would hurt our own men, and dashing down into the valley hurried across to take up a position near the infantry, who were now firing on Caney from its new position before the musketry firing ceased and the Spaniards, broken into small bunches, fled from Caney in the direction of Santiago. . . .

† † †

Hearst and his reporters proved that journalism could be memorable at the same time that it was sensational. One of his reporters was James Creelman, who covered the war between China and Japan in 1894 before he went to work for Hearst, and was there to cover the battle that the boss himself described. Another of the reporters was Winifred Black—Annie Laurie, one of a long line of distinguished women who worked for the Hearst newspapers. She exposed the horrors of life in a big city hospital. She wrote about a leper colony on Molokai in Hawaii. She covered the San Francisco fire on orders from Hearst, and she was there for the story of Harry Thaw, Stanford White, and "the girl in the red velvet swing." One of Winifred Black's best stories was a description of the devastation in Galveston, Texas, which was struck by a hurricane and tidal wave in 1900, killing seven thousand people.

† † †

THE AFTERMATH OF THE GREAT GALVESTON STORM

New York Journal, September 14, 1900.

GALVESTON, Sept. 14—I begged, cajoled and cried my way through the line of soldiers with drawn swords who guard the wharf at Texas City and sailed across the bay on a little boat which is making irregular trips to meet the relief trains from Houston.

The engineer who brought our train down from Houston spent the night before groping around in the wrecks on the beach looking for his wife and three children. He found them, dug a rude grave in the sand and set up a little board marked with his name. Then he went to the railroad company and begged them to let him go to work.

The man in front of me on the car had floated all Monday night with his wife and mother on a part of the roof of his little home. He told me that he kissed his wife good-by at midnight and told her that he could not hold on any longer; but he did hold on, dazed and half conscious, until the day broke and showed him that he was alone on his piece of dried wood. He did not even know when the women that he loved had died. . . .

We sat on the deck of the little steamer. The four men from out-of-town cities and I listened to the little boat's wheel ploughing its way through the calm waters of the bay. The stars shone down like a benediction, but along the line of the shore there rose a great leaping column of blood-red flame.

"What a terrible fire!" I said. "Some of the large buildings must be burning." A man who was passing the deck behind my chair heard me. He stopped, put his hand on the bulwark and turned down and looked into my face, his face like the face of a dead man, but he laughed.

"Buildings?" he said. "Don't you know what is burning over there? It is my wife and children, such little children; why, the tallest was not as high as this"—he laid his hand on the bulwark—"and the little one was just learning to talk.

"She called my name the other day, and now they are burning over there, they and the mother who bore them. She was such a little, tender, delicate thing, always so easily frightened, and now she's out there all alone with the two babies, and they're burning them. If you're looking for sensations, there's plenty of them to be found over there where that smoke is drifting."

"That's right," said the U.S. Marshal of Southern Texas, taking off his broad hat and letting the starlight shine on his strong face. "That's right. We've had to do it. We've burned over 1,000 people to-day, and to-morrow we shall burn as many more.

"Yesterday we stopped burying the bodies at sea; we had to give the men on the barges whiskey to give them courage to do their work. They carried out hundreds of the dead at one time, men and women, negroes and white people, all piled up as high as the barge could stand it, and the men did not go out far enough to sea, and the bodies have begun drifting back again."

"Look!" said the man who was walking the deck, touching my shoulder with his shaking hand. "Look there!"

Before I had time to think I did look, and I saw floating in the water the body of an old, old woman, whose hair was shining in the starlight. A little further on we saw a group of strange driftwood. We looked closer and found it to be a mass of wooden slabs with names and dates cut upon them, and floating on top of them were marble stones, two of them.

The graveyard, which has held the sleeping citizens of Galveston for many, many years, was giving up its dead. . . .

I went toward the heart of the city. I did not know what the names of the streets were or where I was going. I simply picked my way through the masses of slime and rubbish which scar the beautiful wide streets of this once beautiful city. They won't bear looking at, those piles of rubbish. There are things there that gripe the heart to see—a baby's shoe, for instance, a little red shoe, with a jaunty tasseled lace; a bit of a woman's dress and letters. . . .

† † †

William Randolph Hearst went on to build a huge and powerful chain of newspapers, many magazines, a small empire in motion pictures, and a castle complex on the California coastal highway known as San Simeon. His reputation declined, as he finagled to become a leader in politics and then settled for king-making, as his populist attitudes slowly shifted to the far right. When critics spoke of yellow journalism—and many were doing so in the Pulitzer-Hearst years and the decades that followed—they usually had Hearst in mind, like an editorial writer for a newspaper in 1901.

† † †

YELLOW JOURNALISM AND ANARCHY

Brooklyn Eagle, September 11, 1901.

The journalism of anarchy shares responsibility for the attack on President McKinley. It did not mean that he should be shot. It only wished to sell more papers by commenting on and cartooning him as "a tyrant reddening his hands in the blood of the poor and filling his pockets and those of others with dollars coined out of the sweat and tears and hunger of helpless strikers, their wan wives, and their starving children." Today the journalism or the oratory which may have inspired Leon Czolgosz to his deed is the most tearful, sympathetic, and grief-stricken journalism or oratory in America. It editorializes, interviews, and moralizes on the lovableness of the man whom it lately and long and habitually portrayed as a monster, a despot, and a coward. It is very scared, very sorry—or very politic, or would like to seem to be so. Let us hope it is really sorry. Then let us hope that its sorrow will last long enough to persuade it that the selling of more papers or the getting of more votes is not the chief end of journalism or of oratory, when it leads one to defamation as a delight, to vilification as an industry, and to printed, pictorial, or platform blackguardism as a trade.

† † †

The yellow press moved inland in the 1890s and early twentieth century. Denver, Colorado, became a setting for it on October 28, 1895, when two adventurers named Frederick G. Bonfils and Harry H. Tammen—a gambler and a bartender—bought the *Denver Evening Post.* They made the *Post* one of the wildest—and most entertaining—papers in the land—lurid red type on the frontpage, crusades headed "So the People May Know," campaigns to kill plague-carrying rabbits. For a time back in the nineties the Post even sold coal to fight the trusts.

† † †

A NEWSPAPER ENTERS THE COAL BUSINESS

Denver Post, January 21, 1897.

So the People May Know.
To Day The Post Will Begin Selling Northern Coal
at $3.50 a Ton
And continue to sell coal to all that may desire it—until the Coal
Trust sees fit to quit robbing the people. It is not the purpose of The
Post to go into the coal business, yet at the same time if there is a
necessity for it, in order that the people may be able to buy coal at a
fair price, it will do so.

In being able to sell coal at $3.50 The Post makes no profit; that, of
course, can easily be understood when one stops to think—that the
Coal Trust, banded as they are with railroads and coal mine owners,
put such obstacles in the way—that it's next to impossible to buy
coal without a conditional contract that $4.00 shall be the selling
price. . . .

In the meantime, we have opened a coal department and hope all
Post subscribers and others will favor us with their orders.

Bring $3.50 to The Post to-day and buy a ton of The Post's coal.

It is all well enough for newspapers to kick and expose trusts. The
Post believes that the practical way is to actually perform a service.
Talk is cheap, but to positively accomplish something is The Post's
way.

† † †

The *Post* had a special train that went to Frontier Days in
Cheyenne, Wyoming. It conducted campaigns to clean up the state
penitentiary at Canon City. It sponsored a girls' wrestling match,
and an Eve, who went into the Rocky Mountain National Park area
and was joined by an uninvited Adam from Omaha. Harry Houdini
did stunts for the *Post*. The paper had a circus, with an American-
born elephant, which died and was stuffed and kept in the *Post*
building, which had, by the way, a business office painted a fire
engine red. One of its earliest campaigns was in behalf of parole for a
man-eater named Alfred Packer, a story by another Denver
newsman.

† † †

CANNIBALISM IN THE COLORADO ROCKIES

Rocky Mountain Herald, June 13, 1942, and *Rocky Mountain News,*
April 14, 1883, quoted in Robert L. Perkin, *The First Hundred Years*
(Garden City, N.Y.: Doubleday, 1959), pp. 345-346.

. . . Alfred Packer had engaged to lead a party of prospectors from
Provo, Utah to a new strike in the Colorado mountains. Sometime

between February 9 and April 16 of 1874 the six men became trapped
in a snowstorm and lost their way high in the rugged San Juans. On
the latter date Packer walked into the Los Pinos Indian Agency
carrying live coals in a coffeepot. He had run out of matches, he
explained, and had to carry his campfire with him.

Packer appeared to be very sleek and well fed for a man lost sixty
days in wild, unnourishing country. Under questioning he broke
down and confessed that his five companions had died or killed each
other, or he had killed them, and he had been living off portions of
their bodies. The man-eater escaped jail in Saguache but was
recaptured in 1883 in Wyoming and brought to trial at Lake City.
Folklore insists that Judge Melville B. Gerry, an old-school Southern
gentleman from Georgia, meted out the death sentence in this
fashion:

"Stan' up, yah voracious man eating son of a bitch, stand up!
"They was sivin Dimmicrats in Hinsdale County, and ye eat five
of thim, God damn ye!

"I sintins ye t'be hanged by the neck until ye're dead, dead, DEAD,
as a warnin' ag'in reducin' the Dimmycratic population of th' state."

Another version of the sentencing has Judge Gerry saying:
"Alfred Packer, you voracious Republican cannibal, I would
sentence you to hell but the statutes forbid it."

Actually Gerry lectured Packer with "awful solemnity" and
reviewed his crime with a good deal of compassion, ending with . . .
"on said 19th day of May, A.D., 1883. . . you, then and there,
by said Sheriff, be hung by the neck until you are dead, dead,
dead, and may God have mercy upon your soul."

† † †

Alfred Packer was paroled in 1901, and became a beloved elder
citizen in the suburb of Littleton, Colorado. In October 1909, the Post
editors invaded Kansas City, Missouri, where the staid Star was
clearly in charge of journalism in the midlands. Their stay in
Kansas City was brief, for Rocky Mountain-style journalism would
not work in competition with that of William Rockhill Nelson. And
in the 1920s the Post was still engaged in crusading, as it would be in
a later time as well. One big story was about the system of granting
pardons in Colorado.

† † †

A NEWSPAPER INDICTS A PARDONING
GOVERNOR

Denver Post, January 5, 1927.

Suspension of Warden Tynan of the state penitentiary by
Governor Morley, Tuesday, brought in its wake the most shocking
pardon scandal in the state's history, a scandal that will rock the

state from end to end and undoubtedly will result in an investigation of Morley's activities with respect to pardons and paroles, either by the twenty-sixth general assembly or a grand jury.

As his answer to Morley's attempt to oust him from office and turn the management of the big state prison over to the Ku Klux Klan, Tynan, Wednesday morning, made public the list of pardons and paroles issued by Morley since he became the state's executive in January, 1925.

The list surpasses anything in the state's history. Twenty-three life terms, nineteen murderers, several rapists and two highwaymen were turned loose upon society by the governor during the two years he was in office. Included in the list of murderers are three men who were sentenced to hang by the juries who tried them, but whose sentences were commuted to life imprisonment by two of Morley's predecessors.

All told, the list made public by Tynan includes the names of 149 prisoners. In addition there are eighty-five prisoners who had their sentences shortened when the governor cut five days for every month they had been employed upon highway construction. . . .

† † †

Pulitzer and Hearst were newspaper barons of a special stripe; their lesser-known rival—and contemporary—was Edward Wyllis Scripps, who was building a chain about the time Pulitzer was buying the *St. Louis Post-Dispatch* and before Hearst had even gotten out of Harvard. Scripps came from a newspaper family that already had made itself well known in the upper Midwest. He persuaded his half-brothers, James and George, to back him, and he started the *Cleveland Press* in 1878. From there he moved to cities of medium size, amassing a chain of thirty-four papers in fifteen states by the 1892-1914 period. He later added to his chain the United Press, the Newspaper Enterprise Association, and Science Service. But his papers were more than links in a chain; they were inexpensive to buy, working to help the poor, fighting for labor unions and laboring causes, favoring such things as a federal income tax. Scripps himself was scarcely in the poor-boy pattern of a Horace Greeley. He was a self-admitted "damned old crank"—a heavy drinker, a man with a low opinion of women, an opponent of college men, and quite interestingly the author of some "disquisitions" that are among the best common sense philosophies in our journalism.

† † †

IS HONEST JOURNALISM POSSIBLE?

By E. W. Scripps, November 29, 1908, in Oliver Knight, ed., *I Protest: Selected Disquisitons by E. W. Scripps* (Madison: University of Wisconsin Press, 1966), pp. 239-243.

. . . There are tricks in all trades, especially in our trade. I am a newspaper owner. Newspaper owners do not like competition. They want as few newspapers in existence as possible. It is but natural—even if to be natural is to be dishonest—for newspaper owners to desire to create the impression that it requires tremendous sums of money to found a newspaper, and that even when founded a newspaper is not a very profitable property.

Yet, as a matter of fact, although I do not know the full history of all of the great newspapers in the United States, and only know in a general way the history of a large majority of them, I can say that I am not personally acquainted with the history of a single great and successful and influential American newspaper, the first cost of the founding of which has been equal to the cost of founding any third- or fourth-grade business in the locality where the newspaper was founded, at the time of the founding of that paper.

As a matter of fact, no great newspaper has been founded by the aid of large capital. As a matter of fact, no more substantial obstacle to success can be presented to the founder of any newspaper, than the possession of abundant capital. . . .

In journalism, money does not make money. In journalism, money makes for failure. . . .

The possessor of great wealth may be, and frequently is, corrupted. No matter how good or moral a man may be, the possession of great wealth must have a certain amount of corrupting influence upon him. The possession of wealth isolates a man to a great extent from his fellows. This isolation results in a constantly diminishing sympathy for human kind. The duties connected with the administration of a large property are so absorbing and so strenuous as to permit a man, who is the possessor of wealth, no time to think of even his own misfortunes, and much less of the misfortunes of others. Perhaps only the very rich men are those who fully appreciate the fact that the most unhappy men are those who are farthest from the center of the general average. The very rich and the very poor are, if not equally unhappily situated, at least far more unhappily situated than the great mass of men who occupy the intermediate space between wealth and poverty.

10

REFORM AND CONFLICT IN A NEW CENTURY

The student of journalism cannot study the press and its distinctive documents of the progressive era—the age of the muckrakers—without considering first what the American scene was like at the turn of the century, as these reforming reporters were emerging. To start with, the ideas and the morality of the Gilded Age—of Parrington's "Great Barbecue"—appeared to have triumphed. Agrarian discontent had brought little more than two defeats at the polls for the presidential candidate of the populists, William Jennings Bryan, and another defeat lay ahead. The forces of hard money were victorious. The great fortunes had been built up—the Astors in fur, the Vanderbilts and the Harrimans in railroading, the Rockefellers in oil, the Carnegies in steel, the Swifts and Armours in meat. When Thorstein Veblen offered that weighty (stylistically, at least) tract called *The Theory of the Leisure Class,* he offered a portrait of his times along with a commentary on the human experience. Others, like Veblen, believed that the times had been weighed in the balances and found wanting—Henry Adams, even though he cronied with some of the scoundrels; William Dean Howells, whose *Traveller from Altruria* was amazed by what he saw in America; Edward Bellamy, whose hero awakened in the year 2000 and looked backward with horror on the 1880s; Henry George, whose panacea was a single tax, one upon the land.

Corruption in civic and private life had continued. Great trusts had been created—mighty combinations like Standard Oil and Vanderbilt put the point of view of the barons well, "The public be damned." Though the Sherman Antitrust Act had been passed, its greatest effectiveness had been in breaking the back of labor in the Pullman strike of 1894. Little effort was made to curb, or even to understand, economic distress, the "panics," as they were labeled; the law of supply and demand would always take care of such problems. Vast areas of the public land no longer belonged to the public, though in the early years of the twentieth century the national park system would be realized more than in previous years, and the Forest Reserve and Carey Act, to treat the problems of irrigation and reclamation, would come into being.

Out of all this—the American scene—came a protest, journalistic and literary. Theodore Dreiser, who had known privation himself and had reported in Chicago, St. Louis, and Pittsburgh, wrote such naturalistic novels as *Sister Carrie* and those portrayals of a traction magnate, *The Financier* and *The Titan.* Jack London, mixing Darwin, Marx, and Nietzsche, wrote such books as *The Iron Heel.* Frank Norris described the Southern Pacific railroad in his story of wheat, *The Octopus.*

Reform emerged in the journalism of newspapers and magazines. The major figures of the newspaper press at the turn of the century were Joseph Pulitzer, William Randolph Hearst, and E. W. Scripps, corporate leaders who altered the patterns of American journalism, and Adolph S. Ochs, of the *New York Times.* In this age of progressivism, personal journalism survived in Watterson and Harvey Scott, with Jonathan Daniels in North Carolina, with Edgar Watson Howe and William Allen White in Kansas. Howe was a misanthropic iconoclast who ran the *Atchison Globe* from 1877 to 1910 and who in his time was the most-quoted small-town editor in America. He was an exceptional reporter, one who cruised up and down the streets of Atchison, paper and pencil in hand, jotting down all the little bits and pieces of town and country life, attacking religion and at least superficially criticizing women, making himself a national figure with his novel, *The Story of a Country Town.* Howe had a column called "Globe Sights," but the "sights" actually were scattered throughout his little four-page sheet.

† † †

A COLUMN OF "GLOBE SIGHTS"

Atchison Globe, April 25, 1903.

No man ever loved a woman he was afraid of.

William Randolph Hearst and God still reign.

Remember this: a man doesn't have to look the part.

The weather is pretty fair, but the Octopus is as bad as ever.

A young woman seems to get as much comfort out of a love letter as an older woman finds in a cup of tea.

An Atchison girl has such a good time single, that no one can explain why she intends to get married.

Today, for the first time in the history of THE GLOBE, rooms for rent are advertised with ladies preferred as tenants.

If there is anything in this "blot upon the escutcheon," and you have one, don't you suppose it looks like a boy's copy book?

An Atchison girl who has never been fifty miles from home, tries to create the impression that she has been to England by calling an elevator a "lift."

Five minutes after a man started for his room to retire, the noise is heard all over the house of his shoes dropping, and that means that he is all in for twelve hours.

"I wouldn't mind getting a new job," said a man today. "I believe that I would light on my feet, but I am afraid the flight through the air might be painful."

This Freedom you hear so much about; there's mighty little of it in this country. Think it over: how much Freedom have you? Isn't there some one standing over you with a club night and day?

It is related that when an Atchison woman found a hair on her husband's coat, he became indignant because she cared, stating that if she were as bald as he, she couldn't care where the hairs came from, so that she had them.

A description of the ideal modern wife in a woman's magazine says that "when the children get sick, she must pack them off to the hospital, and not worry over them, and lose her good looks." There seems to be a domestic anarchist who has received so much encouragement that she is expounding dangerous theories.

Lillian DeTalente, the girl who married Olin Castle, is described as follows in the telegraph: "A slim girl of medium height, with gold hued hair worn pompadour, light blue eyes, and big, frank freckles." We suppose by "frank freckles" is meant that she used no face powder to conceal them. Are your freckles "frank" ones?

† † †

Ed Howe had a field day—or a field week—in 1900 when the Reverend Charles M. Sheldon of Topeka, a minister of the Congregational Church who had written an enormously popular book called *In His Steps,* persuaded the *Topeka Daily Capital* to let him publish the paper for a week "as Christ would have done it." *Much* of the Kansas press had a field day, as a matter of fact, but one of the most pointed of the commentaries was Howe's prediction of how news would be covered by Sheldon during his editorial tenure.

† † †

A PREDICTION OF THE NEWS—ACCORDING TO JESUS

Atchison Globe, February 12, 1900.

Editorial paragraphs in course of preparation by Rev. Charles M. Sheldon:

Behold, it came to pass that Corbett and Jeffries did even meet in the ring yesterday.

And lo, Jeffries girded up his loins, and encompassed Corbett around about, and smote him with great potency.

And Corbett lifted up his voice and cried: "Why sluggest thou me?"

And behold, Jeffries grew exceedingly wrath, and smote his antagonist hip and thigh, that it might be fulfilled which was spoken of by the prophet: "Ye the boiler maker shall even give the pompadour some dizzy pokes."

And it came to pass that the centurion rang the bell, and the sluggers returned to their corners, and were refreshed with locusts and wild honey.

And behold, there was much uproar in the galleries, caused by the scribes, Pharisees and hypocrites, who had put up their sheckels on Jeffries.

And it was even so.

† † †

The country editor who unseated Edgar Watson Howe from his position as the best-known small-town editor in America was another Kansan, William Allen White of the *Emporia Gazette,* who bought his newspaper in 1895—the very year Bonfils and Tammen were invading Denver and Hearst was invading New York. The *Emporia Gazette* was no *Denver Post,* no *New York Journal,* but it was quite possibly the best small-town paper ever published in America. White was a member of the Kansas establishment, a young smartaleck who had attended but failed to graduate from the state university, a former employee of William Rockhill Nelson on the *Kansas City Star,* a conservative who deplored the pushy Populists who were trying to thrust themselves into power in White's state in the year of the McKinley-Bryan election. It took White only a year to become nationally known. An editorial written in anger by this admittedly pompous young snob was picked up by the Republican National Committee and used in the campaign against Bryan. White later said he was ashamed of the editorial, for its logic was not always sound and its name-calling content was overwhelming. The editorial, despite its defects, is one of the best-known editorials in our journalistic history.

† † †

WHAT'S THE MATTER WITH KANSAS?

Emporia Gazette, August 15, 1896.

To-day the Kansas department of agriculture sent out a statement which indicates that Kansas has gained less than two thousand people in the last year. There are about two hundred and twenty-five thousand families in the state, and there were about ten thousand babies born in Kansas, and yet so many people have left the state that the natural increase is cut down to less than two thousand net. This has been going on for eight years.

If there had been a high brick wall around the state eight years ago, and not a soul had been admitted or permitted to leave, Kansas would be a half million souls better off than she is today. And yet the nation has increased in population. In five years ten million people have been added to the national population, yet instead of gaining a share of this—say, half a million—Kansas has apparently been a plague spot, and in the very garden of the world, has lost population by ten thousands every year.

Not only has she lost population, but she has lost money. Every moneyed man in the state who could get out without loss has gone. Every month in every community sees some one who has a little money pack up and leave the state. This has been going on for eight years. Money has been drained out all the time. In towns where ten years ago there were three or four or half a dozen money-lending concerns stimulating industry by furnishing capital, there is now none, or one or two that are looking after the interests and principle already outstanding.

No one brings any money into Kansas any more. What community knows over one or two men who have moved in with more than $5,000 in the past three years? And what community cannot count half a score of men in that time who have left, taking all the money they could scrape together?

Yet the nation has grown rich, other states have increased in population and wealth—other neighboring states. Missouri has gained over two million, while Kansas has been losing half a million. Nebraska has gained in wealth and population while Kansas has gone down hill. Colorado has gained every way, while Kansas has lost every way since 1888.

What's the matter with Kansas?

There is no substantial city in the state. Every big town save one has lost in population. Yet Kansas City, Omaha, Lincoln, St. Louis, Denver, Colorado Springs, Sedalia, the cities of the Dakotas, St. Paul and Minneapolis and Des Moines—all cities and towns in the West have steadily grown.

Take up the government blue book and you will see that Kansas is virtually off the map. Two or three little scrubby consular places in yellow-fever-stricken communities that do not aggregate ten thousand dollars a year is all the recognition that Kansas has. Nebraska draws about one hundred thousand dollars; little old North Dakota draws about fifty thousand dollars; Oklahoma doubles Kansas; Missouri leaves her a thousand miles behind; Colorado is almost seven times greater than Kansas—the whole West is ahead of Kansas.

Take it by any standard you please, Kansas is not in it.

Go east and you hear them laugh at Kansas, go west and they sneer at her, go south and they "cuss" her, go north and they have forgotten her. Go into any crowd of intelligent people gathered anywhere on the globe, and you will find the Kansas man on the defensive. The newspaper columns and magazines once devoted to praise of her, to boastful facts and startling figures concerning her resources, are now filled with cartoons, jibes and Pefferian speeches. Kansas just naturally isn't in it. She has traded places with Arkansas and Timbuctoo.

What's the matter with Kansas?

We all know; yet here we are at it again. We have an old mossback Jacksonian who snorts and howls because there is a bathtub in the statehouse; we are running that old jay for governor. We have another shabby, wild-eyed, rattle-brained fanatic who has said openly in a dozen speeches that "the rights of the user are paramount to the rights of the owner"; we are running him for chief justice, so that capital will come tumbling over itself to get into the state. We have raked the old ash heap of failure in the state and found an old human hoop skirt who has failed as a business man, who has failed as an editor, who has failed as a preacher, and we are going to run him for congressman-at-large. He will help the looks of the Kansas delegation in Washington. Then we have discovered a kid without a law practice and have decided to run him for attorney-general. Then for fear some hint that the state had become respectable might percolate through the civilized portions of the nation, we have decided to send three or four harpies out lecturing, telling the people that Kansas is raising hell and letting the corn go to weeds.

Oh, this is a state to be proud of! We are a people who can hold up our heads! What we need is not more money, but less capital, fewer white shirts and brains, fewer men with business judgment, and more of those fellows who boast that they are "just ordinary clodhoppers, but they know more in a minute about finance than John Sherman"; we need more men who are "posted," who can bellow about the crime of '73, who hate prosperity, and who think because a man believes in national honor, he is a tool of Wall Street. We have had a few of them—some hundred fifty thousand, but we need more.

We need several thousand gibbering idiots to scream about the "Great Red Dragon" of Lombard Street. We don't need population, we don't need wealth, we don't need well-dressed men on the streets, we don't need cities on the fertile prairies; you bet we don't! What we are after is the money power. Because we have become poorer and ornrier and meaner than a spavined, distempered mule, we, the people of Kansas, propose to kick; we don't care to build up, we wish to tear down.

"There are two ideas of government," said our noble Bryan at Chicago. "There are those who believe that if you just legislate to make the well-to-do prosperous, this prosperity will leak through on those below. The Democratic idea has been that if you legislate to make the masses prosperous their prosperity will find its way up and through every class and rest upon us."

That's the stuff! Give the prosperous man the dickens! Legislate the thriftless man into ease, whack the stuffing out of the creditors and tell the debtors who borrowed the money five years ago when money "per capita" was greater than it is now that the contraction of the currency gives him a right to repudiate.

Whoop it up for the ragged trousers; put the lazy, greasy fizzle who can't pay his debts on the altar, and bow down and worship him. Let the state ideal be high. What we need is not the respect of our fellow men, but the chance to get something for nothing.

Oh, yes, Kansas is a great state. Here are people fleeing from it by the score every day, capital going out of the state by the hundreds of dollars; and every industry but farming paralyzed, and that crippled, because its products have to go across the ocean before they can find a laboring man at work who can afford to buy them. Let's don't stop this year. Let's drive all the decent, self-respecting men out of the state. Let's keep the old clodhoppers who know it all. Let's encourage the man who is "posted." He can talk, and what we need is not mill hands to eat our meat, nor factory hands to eat our wheat, nor cities to oppress the farmer by consuming his butter and eggs and chickens and produce. What Kansas needs is men who can talk, who have large leisure to argue the currency question while their wives wait at home for that nickel's worth of bluing.

What's the matter with Kansas?

Nothing under the shining sun. She is losing wealth, population, and standing. She has got her statesmen, and the money power is afraid of her. Kansas is all right. She has started in to raise hell, as Mrs. Lease advised, and she seems to have an over-production. But that doesn't matter. Kansas never did believe in diversified crops. Kansas is all right. There is absolutely nothing wrong with Kansas. "Every prospect pleases and only man is vile."

† † †

White became a marked man with that editorial, a friend and adviser to presidents, notably Theodore Roosevelt, a Bull Mooser in 1912, a novelist of some repute, a friendly commentator on the American scene. He wrote a loving tribute when his daughter was killed in a fall from a horse. In 1922 he wrote an editorial that won him a Pulitzer prize and demonstrated how the young conservative had turned into a civil libertarian, a position that he took even more in 1924 when he made a quixotic third party attempt—this good Kansas Republican—for the governorship in a year when the Ku Klux Klan was riding high. The prize-winning editorial was a response to a letter from Fred J. Atwood of Concordia, Kansas, who could not understand why White was backing the right of the strikers in a railroad dispute in Kansas.

† † †

TO AN ANXIOUS FRIEND

Emporia Gazette, July 27, 1922.

You tell me that law is above freedom of utterance. And I reply that you can have no wise laws nor free enforcement of wise laws unless there is free expression of the wisdom of the people—and, alas, their folly with it. But if there is freedom, folly will die of its own poison, and the wisdom will survive. That is the history of the race. It is the proof of man's kinship with God. You say that freedom of utterance is not for time of stress, and I reply with the sad truth that only in time of stress is freedom of utterance in danger. No one questions it in calm days, because it is not needed. And the reverse is true also; only when free utterance is suppressed is it needed, and when it is needed, it is most vital to justice. Peace is good. But if you are interested in peace through force and without free discussion—that is to say, free utterance decently and in order—your interest in justice is slight. And peace without justice is tyranny, no matter how you may sugar-coat it with expediency. This state today is in more danger from suppression than from violence, because, in the end, suppression leads to violence. Violence, indeed, is the child of suppression. Whoever pleads for justice helps to keep the peace; and whoever tramples upon the plea for justice temperately made in the name of peace only outrages peace and kills something fine in the heart of man which God put there when we got our manhood. When that is killed, brute meets brute on each side of the line.

So, dear friend, put fear out of your heart. This nation will survive, this state will prosper, the orderly business of life will go forward if only men can speak in whatever way given them to utter what their hearts hold—by voice, by posted card, by letter or by press. Reason never has failed men. Only force and repression have made the wrecks in the world.

† † †

At least one other Kansan of national prominence lived in the progressive era, the days of Howe and White. She was pretty tangentially a journalist, even though she did publish a paper she called *The Smasher's Mail.* "The Smasher" was Mrs. Carry Nation, who went in for "hatchetation." She smashed saloons, made war on Demon Rum, and even grabbed cigars from the mouths of innocent men on the streets. The *Topeka Daily Capital* described her raid in Wichita during the Christmas holidays of 1900.

† † †

WHAT HAPPENED WHEN "THE SMASHER" CAME TO TOWN

Topeka Daily Capital, December 28, 1900.

Special to the Capital, Dec. 27—Mrs. Carrie Nation, president of Barber County Woman's Christian Temperance Union, began today a raid on the saloons in Wichita. As a result of her work she is now under arrest and placed behind the bars at the county jail.

At 9:45 this morning she entered the saloon in the basement of the Carey hotel and without a word of warning pulled from a bundle of papers which she carried in her hands two large stones. Before the clerks and bartenders could realize what was going on, Mrs. Nation sent one of the stones whizzing through a large oil painting of Cleopatra nude at the Roman bath. The painting was valued at $100. As a result of the stone hitting the painting the picture is completely spoiled.

After damaging this picture, the woman suddenly turned herself about and with much force sent another large stone through a valuable $1,500 mirror which is situated directly back of the bar. She then left the saloon.

While in the saloon she also broke about $25 worth of bottled goods and also a window. As soon as she left the saloon she was arrested. . . .

Mrs. Nation, when seen by a reporter for the Capital, said:

"I am a law abiding citizen and I have not gone out of the bounds of the law. I have a husband who is a lawyer and he says they cannot prosecute me. . . ."

† † †

In the crusading journals of Pulitzer, Hearst, and Scripps the newspaper press had been making its force felt. In the Pulitzer newspapers, especially, crusading was basic to the very formula of journalism. Pulitzer's editor in the first decade of this century was Frank I. Cobb, a man out of Detroit, an editor with a solid background in history, government, and economics. In Pulitzer's *World,* Cobb wrote about the Northern Securities decision of the Supreme Court, perhaps the biggest story affecting business in the decade—with the exception of the stories in the movement known as muckraking.

† † †

ON A HISTORIC SUPREME COURT DECISION

New York World, March 15, 1904.

The decision of the Supreme Court against the Northern Securities Merger is an event of vital and far-reaching importance. . . So clear, so obvious, so important are the issues involved that wonder grows that a final decision in a case of the first magnitude was not reached until almost fourteen years after the passage of the Sherman Act.

What is the decision; what the circumstances that led up to it; what its probable effects?

I.—THE CASE

The first railway across the continent was necessarily a monopoly. As each additional line was opened an effort was made to prevent competition. This effort was particularly active in the Northwest, where the Northern Pacific and the Great Northern railroads were natural rivals.

The Burlington and the Union Pacific were other parallel lines. The Northern Pacific secured control of the Burlington by a stock-conversion deal. To protect their interests the masters of the Union Pacific set out to capture the Northern Pacific, and this led to the great Northern Pacific war and the panic of May 9, 1901.

The financiers of Wall Street met to restore peace and apportion the spoils, and out of their efforts grew the Northern Securities Merger, organized in November, 1901, under the laws of New Jersey, for the purpose of holding the stock of the Northern Pacific and Great Northern companies, including the control of the Burlington. . . .

II.—THE LAW

On March 3, 1902, Attorney-General Knox, urged thereto by President Roosevelt, filed a petition against the combination and its two constituent companies in the United States Circuit Court of Minnesota, under the Sherman Anti-Trust Act of 1890. . . .

III.—THE DECREE

The case was vigorously pushed. One week later the Attorney-General alleged in a bill in equity filed at St. Paul that the Northern Pacific and Great Northern were "the only transcontinental lines of railway extending across the northern tier of States west of the Great Lakes. . . to the Pacific Ocean, and were (previously) engaged in active competition for freight and passenger traffic;" that by the merger the defendants were monopolizing interstate and foreign commerce in violation of the Sherman Act and that the Securities Company "was not organized in good faith to purchase and pay for" the roads it acquired, but "solely to incorporate the pooling of the stocks of said companies.". . .

IV.—THE SUPREME COURT

By a majority of five to four in the Supreme Court itself the decree of the Circuit Court is now confirmed. This is final. There is no appeal.

The decision, written by Justice Harlan, states that, "no scheme or device could certainly more effectively come within the prohibition of the Anti-Trust law." The law is not an interference with the right of the States to charter companies. The authority of Congress is supreme. Sweeping away by broad principles a maze of technicalities, Justice Harlan finds that the merger is "a combination in restraint of interstate and international commerce, and that is enough to bring it under the condemnation of the Act.". . .

V.—THE EFFECT

Of business interests the decision is conservative, not destructive, not obstructive. Because of it no wheel need cease to turn, no property is destroyed, no right of wealth invaded, no legitimate ambition assailed. The sun will rise and set as before, the rain will fall, the grain will grow as bravely in all that vast region which the merger sought to make subject in the important matter of transportation to one corporate will.

Mr. Morgan himself once pointed out that the real value in the railroads could not be destroyed by the courts. The very securities of the "holding company" which is forbidden have value as denoting ownership in the original railroad. More, or other, or greater value they could never have had save at the people's cost by "killing competition, and capitalizing the corpse.". . . .

No man of sense desires the destruction of all forms of capitalistic combination which the larger scale of modern industrial development demands. But the limit of safety is passed when the rights of the people are encroached upon. If there were no limit, the great railway systems, already consisting in some cases of 20,000 miles of track, could be combined in "holding companies," and these holding companies combined in still larger ones until the universal "merger" was reached; and a single man might thus control many times the amount of its capital and sway the transportation of the entire country.

The will of the people, as embodied in the law, is that this shall not be made possible. A "campaign of education," by all means; but let the school be opened in Wall Street, not on the farm!

† † †

Public service remained the chief cause for Pulitzer's *World* and for its sister paper in St. Louis, the *Post-Dispatch*. It was the latter that became the standard-bearer for the ideals of Pulitzer, especially after the *World* came to an end in 1931. And it was the *Post-Dispatch* that daily published the creed of Joseph Pulitzer, the platform he enunciated early in the century.

† † †

THE PLATFORM OF THE POST-DISPATCH

By Joseph Pulitzer, April 10, 1907, in *The Story of the St. Louis Post-Dispatch* (St. Louis: Post-Dispatch booklet, 1968, 9th ed.)

I know that my retirement will make no difference in its cardinal principles, that it will always fight for progress and reform, never tolerate injustice or corruption, always fight demagogues of all parties, never belong to any party, always oppose privileged classes and public plunderers, never lack sympathy with the poor, always remain devoted to the public welfare, never be satisfied with merely printing news, always be drastically independent, never be afraid to attack wrong, whether by predatory plutocracy or predatory poverty.

† † †

In the January 1903 issue of *McClure's Magazine* the readers were told, in an editorial by the publisher, S. S. McClure, that a singular thing was taking place in magazine journalism. McClure was the genius behind that thing—something now known as muckraking. He did not actually send out his editors and reporters to "rake muck." The writers went out, instead, on stories of current interest, and such stories became muckraking. McClure was one of the familiar American success stories: born in Ireland, a man who had known poverty and near-starvation, a printer's devil in the Midwest, a student at Knox College in Galesburg, Illinois, and the editor of a house organ called *The Wheelman,* started when the sharp young man observed that a good many people were riding things called bicycles. McClure also started a syndicate, employing the services of scores of famous writers, and himself writing recipes under the name of Patience Winthrop. McClure founded his magazine in 1893, and it was one of the most successful mass publications of its time, though one should not think of the word "mass" in later twentieth century connotations. His editors included Lincoln Steffens, Ida M. Tarbell, and Ray Stannard Baker, and it was this journalistic triumvirate about whom he wrote that famous editorial.

† † †

ABOUT THREE ARTICLES IN ONE ISSUE OF *McCLURE'S*

By S. S. McClure, *McClure's Magazine,* XX (January, 1903), p. 336.

How many of those who have read through this number of the magazine noticed that it contains three articles on one subject? We did not plan it so; it is a coincidence that the January *McClure's* is such an arraignment of American character as should make every one of us stop and think. How many noticed that?

The leading article, "The Shame of Minneapolis," might have been called "The American Contempt of Law." That title could well have served for the current chapter of Miss Tarbell's History of Standard Oil. And it would have fitted perfectly Mr. Baker's "The Right to Work." All together, these articles come pretty near showing how universal is this dangerous trait of ours.

Miss Tarbell has our capitalists conspiring among themselves, deliberately, shrewdly, upon legal advice, to break the law so far as it restrained them, and to misuse it to restrain others who were in their way. Mr. Baker shows labor, the ancient enemy of capital, and the chief complainant of the trusts' unlawful acts, itself committing and excusing crimes. And in "The Shame of Minneapolis" we see the administration of a city employing criminals to commit crimes for the profit of the elected officials, while the citizens—Americans of good stock and more than average culture, and honest, healthy Scandinavians—stood by complacent and not alarmed.

Capitalists, workingmen, politicians, citizens—all breaking the law, or letting it be broken. Who is left to uphold it? The lawyers? Some of the best lawyers in this country are hired, not to go into court to defend cases, but to advise corporations and business firms how they can get around the law without too great a risk of punishment. The judges? Too many of them so respect the laws that for some "error" or quibble they restore to office and liberty men convicted on evidence overwhelmingly convincing to common sense. The churches? We know of one, an ancient and wealthy establishment, which had to be compelled by a Tammany hold-over health officer to put its tenements in sanitary condition. The colleges? They do not understand.

There is no one left; none but all of us. Capital is learning (with indignation at labor's unlawful acts) that its rival's contempt of law is a menace to property. Labor has shrieked the belief that the illegal power of capital is a menace to the worker. These two are drawing together. Last November when a strike was threatened by the yardmen on all the railroads centering in Chicago, the men got together and settled by raising wages, and raising freight rates too. They made the public pay. We all are doing our worst and making the public pay. The public is the people. We forget that we all are the people; that while each of us in his group can shove off on the rest the bill of today, the debt is only postponed; the rest are passing it on back to us. We have to pay in the end, every one of us. And in the end the sum total of the debt will be our liberty.

† † †

Of the three major figures writing for *McClure's,* a reporter named Lincoln Steffens is perhaps best representative of the muckrakers. Steffens was a Californian, born in 1866, a college man (University of California), a reporter well trained in covering the big city. His series in *McClure's* was called *The Shame of the Cities*, exposés of such places as New York, Chicago, Pittsburgh, Minneapolis, St. Louis. He was a careful investigator, a student of government, and few questioned the veracity of his findings.

† † †

PHILADELPHIA: CORRUPT AND CONTENTED

By Lincoln Steffens, *McClure's,* July, 1903, in *The Shame of the Cities* (New York: Hill & Wang, 1957 ed.), pp. 134-139.

... Other American cities, no matter how bad their own condition may be, all point with scorn to Philadelphia as worse— "the worst-governed city in the country." St. Louis, Minneapolis, Pittsburg submit with some patience to the jibes of any other community; the most friendly suggestion from Philadelphia is rejected with contempt. The Philadelphians are "supine," "asleep"; hopelessly ring-ruled, they are "complacent." "Politically benighted," Philadelphia is supposed to have no light to throw upon a state of things that is almost universal.

This is not fair. Philadelphia is, indeed, corrupt; but it is not without significance. Every city and town in the country can learn something from the typical political experience of this great representative city. New York is excused for many of its ills because it is the metropolis, Chicago because of its forced development; Philadelphia is our "third largest" city and its growth has been gradual and natural. Immigration has been blamed for our municipal conditions; Philadelphia, with 47 percent. of its population native-born of native-born parents, is the most American of our greater cities. It is "good," too, and intelligent. I don't know just how to measure the intelligence of a community, but a Pennsylvania college professor who declared to me his belief in education for the masses as a way out of political corruption, himself justified the "rake-off" of preferred contractors on public works on the ground of a "fair business profit." Another plea we have made is that we are too busy to attend to public business, and we have promised, when we come to wealth and leisure, to do better. Philadelphia has long enjoyed great and widely distributed prosperity; it is the city of homes; there is a dwelling house for every five persons,—men, women, and children,—of the population; and the people give one a sense of more leisure and repose than any community I ever dwelt in. Some Philadelphians account for their political state on the ground of their ease and comfort. There is another class of optimists whose hope is in an "aristocracy" that is to come by and by; Philadelphia is surer that it has a "real aristocracy" than any other place in the world, but its aristocrats, with few exceptions, are in the ring, with it, or of no political use. Then we hear that we are a young people and that when we are older and "have traditions," like some of the old countries, we also will be honest. Philadelphia is one of the oldest of our cities and treasures for us scenes and relics of some of the noblest traditions of "our fair land." Yet I was told how once, "for a joke," a party of boodlers counted out the "divvy" of their graft in unison with the ancient chime of Independence Hall. ...

Disgraceful? Other cities say so, But I say that if Philadelphia is a disgrace, it is a disgrace not to itself alone, nor to Pennsylvania, but to the United States and to American character. For this great city, so highly representative in other respects, is not behind in political experience, but ahead, with New York. . . .

The machine controls the whole process of voting, and practices fraud at every stage. The assessor's list is the voting list, and the assessor is the machine's man. . . . The assessor pads the list with the names of dead dogs, children, and non-existent persons. One newspaper printed the picture of a dog, another that of a little four-year-old negro boy, down on such a list. A ring orator in a speech resenting sneers at his ward as "low down" reminded his hearers that that was the ward of Independence Hall, and naming over signers of the Declaration of Independence, he closed his highest flight of eloquence with the statement that "these men, the fathers of American liberty, voted down here once. And," he added, with a catching grin, "they vote here yet.". . .

† † †

Ida M. Tarbell was already well known for her magazine writing, including a biography of Abraham Lincoln, and the reporting she did for *McClure's* stands today as an important piece of history, where some of the muckraking has tended to become hoary with age. Her work was called *The History of the Standard Oil Company,* and it has been suggested that she wrote the work in part because her father was one of those who got in the way of John D. Rockefeller's ambitions—and his power. Miss Tarbell's series was not rancorous, but its effect was acute, and the name and reputation of Rockefeller never again, even after Rockefeller had been aided by a public relations genius named Ivy Lee, had the standing they had had prior to the *McClure's* series.

† † †

ROCKEFELLER AND THE OIL WAR OF 1872

By Ida M. Tarbell, *McClure's,* January, 1903, in Arthur and Lila Weinberg, eds., *The Muckrakers* (New York: Capricorn, 1964), pp. 35-39.

. . . no number of resolutions could wipe out the memory of the forty days of terrible excitement and loss which the region had suffered. No triumph could stifle the suspicion and the bitterness which had been sown broadcast through the region. Every particle of independent action had been outraged. Their sense of fair play, the saving force of the region in the days before law and order had been established, had been violated. These were things which could not be forgotten. There henceforth could be no trust in those who had devised a scheme which, the producers believed, was intended to rob them of their business.

It was inevitable that under the pressure of their indignation and resentment some person or persons should be fixed upon as responsible, and should be hated accordingly. Before the lifting of the embargo this responsibility had been fixed. It was the Standard Oil Company of Cleveland, so the Oil Regions decided, which was at the bottom of the business, and the "Mephistopheles of the Cleveland Company," as they put it, was John D. Rockefeller. Even the Cleveland *Herald* acknowledged this popular judgment. "Whether justly or unjustly," the editor wrote, "Cleveland has the odium of having originated the scheme." This opinion gained ground as the days passed. The activity of the president of the Standard in New York, in trying to save the contracts with the railroads, and his constant appearance with Mr. Watson, and the fact brought out by the Congressional investigation that a larger block of the South Improvement Company's stock was owned in the Standard than in any other firm, strengthened the belief. But what did more than anything else to fix the conviction was what they had learned of the career of the Standard Oil Company in Cleveland. Before the oil war the company had been known simply as one of several successful firms in that city. It drove close bargains, but it paid promptly, and was considered a desirable customer. Now the Oil Regions learned for the first time of the sudden and phenomenal expansion of the company. Where there had been at the beginning of 1872 twenty-six refining firms in Cleveland, there were but six left. In three months before and during the oil war the Standard had absorbed twenty plants. It was generally charged by the Cleveland refiners that Mr. Rockefeller had used the South Improvement scheme to persuade or compel his rivals to sell to him. "Why," cried the oil men, "the Standard Oil Company has done already in Cleveland what the South Improvement Company set out to do for the whole country, and it has done it by the same means.". . .

Those theories which the body of oil men held as vital and fundamental Mr. Rockefeller and his associates either did not comprehend or were deaf to. This lack of comprehension by many men of what seems to other men to be the most obvious principles of justice is not rare. Many men who are widely known as good, share it. Mr. Rockefeller was "good." There was no more faithful Baptist in Cleveland than he. Every enterprise of that church he had supported liberally from his youth. He gave to its poor. He visited its sick. He wept with its suffering. . . . He was simple and frugal in his habits. He never went to the theater, never drank wine. He was a devoted husband, and he gave much time to the training of his children, seeking to develop in them his own habits of economy and of charity. Yet he was willing to strain every nerve to obtain for himself special and illegal privileges from the railroads which were bound to ruin every man in the oil business not sharing them with him. Religious emotion and sentiments of charity, propriety and self-denial seem to have taken the place in him of notions of justice and regard for the rights of others. . . .

† † †

And of course, there was Ray Stannard Baker. He was engaged in muckraking for many years, and he later achieved a new reputation as a historian and biographer. Baker wrote about labor and conflicts between the races.

† † †

RACIAL TROUBLES IN A SOUTHERN CITY

By Ray Stannard Baker, *American Magazine,* May, 1907, in Arthur and Lila Weinberg, *The Muckrakers,* pp. 219-220.

. . . One of the points in which I was especially interested was the "Jim Crow" regulations, that is, the system of separation of the races in street cars and railroad trains. Next to the question of Negro suffrage, I think the people of the North have heard more of the Jim Crow legislation than of anything else connected with the Negro problem. I have seen, so far, no better place than the street car for observing the points of human contact between the races, betraying as it does every shade of feeling upon the part of both. In almost no other relationship do the races come together, physically, on anything like a common footing. In their homes and in ordinary employment, they meet as master and servant; but in the street cars they touch as free citizens each paying for the right to ride, the white not in a place of command, the Negro without an obligation of servitude. Street-car relationships are, therefore, symbolic of the new conditions. A few years ago, the Negro came and went in the street cars in most cities and sat where he pleased, but gradually Jim Crow laws or local regulations were passed forcing him into certain seats at the back of the car. . . .

I was curious to see how the system worked out in Atlanta. Over the door of each car, I found this sign:

WHITE PEOPLE WILL SEAT FROM
FRONT OF CAR TOWARD THE BACK,
AND COLORED PEOPLE FROM REAR
TOWARD FRONT

Sure enough, I found the white people in front and the Negroes behind. As the sign indicates, there is no definite line of division between the white seats and the black seats, as in many other Southern cities. This very absence of a clear demarcation is significant of many relationships in the South. *The color line is drawn, but neither race knows just where it is.* Indeed, it can hardly be definitely drawn in many relationships, because it is constantly changing. This uncertainty is a fertile source of friction and bitterness. . . .

† † †

Many writers besides these three joined the movement. William Allen White wrote for *McClure's*. Burton J. Hendrick described scandals in insurance companies. Charles Edward Russell covered state governments. A former financier named Thomas Lawson wrote *Frenzied Finance*. Samuel Hopkins Adams wrote about patent medicines, and Edward W. Bok about the Lydia E. Pinkham compounds that had been consumed by so many women for so long. Kibbe Turner and Will Irwin were among the writers, but the reporter who set off the explosion was David Graham Phillips, whose *The Treason of the Senate* seemed the most sensational of all the articles. The one who exploded was President Theodore Roosevelt, a mild sort of reformer himself, and he exploded in a speech; he had accepted some of the others, but Phillips was too much. The occasion of the speech was the laying of the cornerstone of the House of Representatives office building in Washington.

† † †

A PRESIDENT DENOUNCES SOME REFORMERS

By Theodore Roosevelt, April 14, 1906, in Arthur and Lila Weinberg, *The Muckrakers*, pp. 58-59.

Over a century ago Washington laid the cornerstone of the Capitol in what was then little more than a tract of wooded wilderness here beside the Potomac. We now find it necessary to provide by great additional buildings for the business of the government. This growth in the need for the housing of the government is but a proof and example of the way in which the nation has grown and the sphere of action of the national government has grown. We now administer the affairs of a nation in which the extraordinary growth of population has been outstripped by the growth of wealth and the growth in complex interests. The material problems that face us today are not such as they were in Washington's time, but the underlying facts of human nature are the same now as they were then. Under altered external form we war with the same tendencies toward evil that were evident in Washington's time, and are helped by the same tendencies for good. It is about some of these that I wish to say a word today.

In Bunyan's *Pilgrim's Progress* you may recall the description of the Man with the Muckrake, the man who could look no way but downward, with a muckrake in his hands; who was offered a celestial crown for his muckrake, but who would neither look up nor regard the crown he was offered, but continued to rake to himself the filth of the floor.

In *Pilgrim's Progress* the Man with the Muckrake is set forth as the example of him whose vision is fixed on carnal instead of on spiritual things. Yet he also typifies the man who in this life consistently refused to see aught that is lofty, and fixes his eyes with solemn intentness only on that which is vile and debasing. Now, it is very necessary that we should not flinch from seeing what is vile and debasing. There is filth on the floor, and it must be scraped up with the muckrake; and there are times and places where this service is the most needed of all the services that can be performed. But the man who never does anything else, who never thinks or speaks or writes save of his feats with the muckrake, speedily becomes, not a help to society, not an incitement to good, but one of the most potent forces of evil. . . .

I hail as a benefactor every writer or speaker, every man who, on the platform or in book, magazine or newspaper, with merciless severity makes such attack, provided always that he in his turn remembers that the attack is of use only if it is absolutely truthful. . . .

† † †

Theodore Roosevelt's words did not end muckraking. The muckrakers wore the new appellation with pride, and the magazine editors were finding that muckraking helped circulation, though not as much as some commentators on the movement have suggested. First *McClure's,* and then *Collier's,* the *American, Cosmopolitan, Everybody's,* the *Ladies' Home Journal*—all published muckraking articles. Upton Sinclair, who was still bent on reform in the 1960s, published his muckraking in a fictional work. He wrote a book called *The Jungle,* about Chicago, the packing-house district, the factories, and the canneries. It was horrifying to many; some were scandalized, and could not believe that the sausage they had eaten could have gone through such a nasty process.

† † †

MUCKRAKING: THE MEAT AMERICANS ATE

By Upton Sinclair, *The Jungle* (New York: Signet, 1960 ed.), pp. 135-136.

With one member trimming beef in a cannery, and another working in a sausage factory, the family had a first-hand knowledge of the great majority of Packingtown swindles. For it was the custom, as they found, whenever meat was spoiled that it could not be used for anything else, either to can it or else to chop it up into sausage. With what had been told them by Jonas, who had worked in the pickle rooms, they could now study the whole of the spoiled-meat industry on the inside, and read a new and grim meaning into that old Packingtown jest—that they use everything of the pig except the squeal.

Jonas had told them how the meat that was taken out of pickle would often be found sour, and how they would rub it up with soda to take away the smell, and sell it to be eaten on free-lunch counters; also of all the miracles of chemistry which they performed, giving to any sort of meat, fresh or salted, whole or chopped, any color and any flavor and any odor they chose. In the pickling of hams they had an ingenious apparatus, by which they saved time and increased the capacity of the plant—a machine consisting of a hollow needle attached to a pump; by plunging this needle into the meat and working with his foot a man could fill a ham with pickle in a few seconds. And yet, in spite of this, there would be hams found spoiled, some of them with an odor so bad that a man could hardly bear to be in the room with them. To pump into these the packers had a second and much stronger pickle which destroyed the odor—a process known to the workers as "giving them thirty percent." Also, after the hams had been smoked, there would be found some that had gone to the bad. Formerly these had been sold as "Number Three Grade," but later on some ingenious person had hit upon a new device, and now they would extract the bone, about which the bad part generally lay, and insert in the hole a white-hot iron. After this invention there was no longer Number One, Two, and Three Grade—there was only Number One Grade. . . .

It was only when the whole ham was spoiled that it came into the department of Elzbieta. Cut up by the two-thousand-revolutions-a-minute flyers, and mixed with half a ton of other meat, no odor that ever was in a ham could make any difference. There was never the least attention paid to what was cut up for sausage; there would come all the way back from old Europe old sausage that had been rejected, and that was mouldy and white—it would be dosed with borax and glycerine, and dumped into the hoppers, and made over again for home consumption. There would be meat that had tumbled out on the floor, in the dirt and sawdust, where the workers had tramped and spit uncounted billions of consumption germs. There would be meat stored in great piles in rooms; and the water from leaky roofs would drip over it, and thousands of rats would race about on it. It was too dark in these storage places to see well, but a man could run his hand over these piles of meat and sweep off handfuls of the dried dung of rats. . . .

† † †

Sinclair got results he had not expected; this compassionate reporter had aimed at our hearts, he said, but hit us in our stomachs instead. He did help to bring about reform, in the Pure Food and Drug and the Meat Inspection Acts, just as the other muckrakers, in association with progressives in government, brought about numerous other changes, notably the income tax and Senate amenddments, as well as changes initiated originally in such forward-looking states as Wisconsin. Upton Sinclair continued to rake muck: the schools, in *The Goose-Step;* Henry Ford, in *The Flivver King;* the oil industry, in *Oil!;* the Sacco-Vanzetti case, in *Boston.* He became, too, a pioneering critic of the press, telling in a book of 1920 called *The Brass Check* of his battles for justice and freedom of the press. One of the contemporaries of the muckrakers was a columnist named Finley Peter Dunne, and no account of the times in which he lived would be complete without a sample of his work. Dunne created an Irish bartender character named Mr. Dooley, who commented in thick brogue on the foibles of his time. Mr. Dooley took off after Theodore Roosevelt himself, and Roosevelt read the column and said, "How he does get at any joint in the harness?" and then wrote to Dunne, "I regret to state that my family and intimate friends are delighted with your review of my book."

† † †

MR. DOOLEY REVIEWS A BOOK

By Finley Peter Dunne, *Mr. Dooley at His Best* (New York: Scribner, 1938), pp. 99-103.

"Well sir," said Mr. Dooley, "I jus' got hold iv a book, Hinnissy, that suits me up to th' handle, a gran' book, th' grandest iver seen. Ye know I'm not much throubled be lithrachoor, havin' manny worries iv me own, but I'm not prejudiced agin books. I am not. Whin a rale good book comes along I'm as quick as anny wan to say it isn't so bad, an' this here book is fine. I tell ye 'tis fine."

"What is it?" Mr. Hennessy asked languidly.

"'Tis 'Th' Biography iv a Hero be Wan Who Knows.' 'Tis 'Th' Darin' Exploits iv a Brave Man be an Actual Eye Witness.' 'Tis 'Th' Account iv th' Desthruction iv Spanish Power in th' Ant Hills,' as it fell fr'm th' lips iv Tiddy Rosenfelt an' was took down be his own hands. Ye see 'twas this way, Hinnissy, as I r-read th' book. Whin Tiddy was blowed up in th' harbor iv Havana he instantly concluded they must be war. He debated th' question long an' earnestly an' fin'lly passed a jint resolution declarin' war. So far so good. But there was no wan to carry it on. What shud he do? I will lave th' janial author tell th' story in his own wurruds.

"'Th' sicrety iv war had offered me,' he says, 'th' command of a rig'mint,' he says, 'but I cud not consint to remain in Tampa while perhaps less audacious heroes was at th' front,' he says. 'Besides,' he says, 'I felt I was incompetent f'r to command a rig'mint raised be another,' he says. 'I determined to raise wan iv me own,' he says. 'I selected fr'm me acquaintances in th' West,' he says, 'men that had thravelled with me acrost th' desert an' th' storm-wreathed mountain,' he says, 'sharin' me burdens an' at times confrontin' perils almost as gr-reat as anny that beset me path,' he says. 'Together we had faced th' turrors iv th' large but vilent West,' he says, 'an' these brave men had seen me with me trusty rifle shootin' down th' buffalo, th' elk, th' moose, th' grizzly bear, th' mountain goat,' he says, 'th' silver man, an' other ferocious beasts iv thim parts,' he says. 'An they niver flinched,' he says. 'In a few days I had thim perfectly tamed,' he says, 'an' ready to go annywhere I led,' he says. 'On th' thransport goin' to Cubia,' he says, 'I wud stand beside wan iv these r-rough men threatin' him as an akel, which he was in ivrything but birth, education, rank, an' courage, an' together we wud look up at th' admirable stars iv that tolerable southern sky an' quote th' Bible fr'm Walt Whitman,' he says. 'Honest, loyal, thrue-hearted la-ads, how kind I was to thim,' he says.

"'We had no sooner landed in Cubia than it become nicissry f'r me to take command iv th' ar-rmy which I did at wanst. A number of days was spint be me in reconnoitring, attinded on'y be me brave an' fluent body guard, Richard Harding Davis. I discovered that th' inimy was heavily inthrenched on th' top iv San Joon hill immej-iately in front iv me. At this time it become apparent that I was handicapped by th' prisence iv th' ar-rmy,' he says. 'Wan day whin I was about to charge a block house sturdily definded by an ar-rmy corps undher Gin'ral Tamale, th' brave Castile that I aftherwards killed with a small ink-eraser that I always carry, I r-ran into th' entire military force iv th' United States lying on its stomach. 'If ye won't fight,' says I, 'let me go through,' I says. 'Who ar-re ye?' says they. 'Colonel Rosenfelt,' says I. 'Oh, excuse me,' says the gin'ral in command (if me mimry serves me thrue it was Miles) r-risin' to his knees an' salutin'. This showed me 'twud be impossible f'r to carry th' war to a successful con-clusion unless I was free, so I sint th' arm-rmy home an' attackted San Joon hill. Ar-rmed on'y with a small thirty-two which I used in th' West to shoot th' fleet prairie dog, I climbed that precipitous ascent in th' face iv th' most gallin' fire I iver knew or heerd iv. But I had a few r-rounds iv gall mesilf an' what cared I? I dashed madly on cheerin' as I wint. Th' Spanish throops was dhrawn up in a long line in th' formation known among military men as a long line. I fired at th' man nearest to me an' I knew be th' expression iv his face that th' trusty bullet wint home. It passed through his frame, he fell, an' wan little home in far-off Catalonia was made happy be th' thought that their riprisintative had been kilt be th' future governor iv New York. Th' bullet sped on its mad flight an' passed through th' intire line fin'lly imbeddin' itself in th' abdomen iv th' Arc-rch-bishop iv Santago eight miles away. This ended th' war.'

"'They has been some discussion as to who was th' first man to r-reach th' summit iv San Joon hill. I will not attempt to dispute th' merits iv th' manny gallant sojers, statesmen, corryspondints, an' kinetoscope men who claim th' distinction. They ar-re all brave men an' if they wish to wear me laurels they may. I have so manny annyhow that it keeps me broke havin' thim blocked an' irned. But I will say f'r th' binifit iv posterity that I was th' on'y man I see. An' I had a tillyscope.'

"I have thried, Hinnissy," Mr. Dooley continued, "to give you a fair idee iv th' contints iv this remarkable book, but what I've tol' ye is on'y what Hogan calls an outline iv th' principal pints. Ye'll have to r-read th' book ye'ersilf to get a thrue conciption. I haven't time f'r to tell ye th' wurruk Tiddy did in ar-armin' an' equippin' himsilf, how he fed himsilf, how he steadied himsilf in battle an' encouraged himsilf with a few well-chosen wurruds whin th' sky was darkest. Ye'll have to take a squint into th' book ye'ersilf to larn thim things."

"I won't do it," said Mr. Hennessy. "I think Tiddy Rosenfelt is all r-right an' if he wants to blow his hor-rn lave him do it."

"Thrue f'r ye," said Mr. Dooley, "an' if his valliant deeds didn't get into this book 'twud be a long time befure they appeared in Shafter's histhry iv th' war. No man that bears a gredge again himsilf iver be governor iv a state. An' if Tiddy done it all he ought to say so an relieve th' suspinse. But if I was him I'd call th' book 'Alone in Cubia.'"

† † †

Muckraking was not the only kind of reporting to occupy the energies of American journalists in the early part of the century; along with the crusading exposes and the fiery editorials there were those famous news stories that come ringing down through time either because of the way they were written or because of the subject matter itself. Several major events marked the period before World War I, beginning with a story published in the first year of muck-raking. Few news stories have captured our imaginations in quite the way this report captured them.

† † †

THE FIRST FLIGHT OF MAN

Norfolk Virginian-Pilot, December 18, 1903.

The problem of aerial navigation without the use of a balloon has been solved at last.

Over the sand hills of the North Carolina coast yesterday, near Kittyhawk, two Ohio men proved that they could soar through the air in a flying machine of their own construction, with the power to steer and speed it at will.

This, too, in the face of a wind blowing at the registered velocity of twenty-one miles an hour.

Like a monster bird, the invention hovered above the breakers and circled over the rolling sand hills at the command of its navigator and, after soaring for three miles, it gracefully descended to earth again, and rested lightly upon the spot selected by the man in the car as a suitable landing place.

While the United States government has been spending thou-sands of dollars in an effort to make practicable the ideas of Professor Langley, of the Smithsonian Institute, Wilbur and Orville Wright, two brothers, natives of Dayton, Ohio, have, quietly, even secretly, perfected their invention and put it to a successful test.

They are not yet ready that the world should know the methods they have adopted in conquering the air, but the Virginian-Pilot is able to state authentically the nature of their invention, its principles and its chief dimensions.

The idea of the box kite has been adhered to strictly in the basic formation of the flying machine.

A huge framework of light timbers, thirty-three feet wide, five feet deep, and five feet across the top, forms the machine proper.

This is covered with a tough, but light, canvas.

In the center, and suspended just below the bottom plane, is the small gasoline engine which furnished the motive power for the propelling and elevating wheels.

These are two six-bladed propellers, one arranged just below the center of the frame, so gauged as to exert an upward force when in motion, and the other extends horizontally to the rear from the center of the car, furnishing the forward impetus.

Protruding from the center of the car is a huge, fan-shaped rudder of canvas, stretched upon a frame of wood. This rudder is controlled by the navigator and may be moved to each side, raised, or lowered.

Wilbur Wright, the chief inventor of the machine, sat in the operator's car, and when all was ready his brother unfastened the catch which held the invention at the top of the slope.

The big box began to move slowly at first, acquiring velocity as it went, and when halfway down the hundred feet the engine was started.

The propeller in the rear immediately began to revolve at a high rate of speed, and when the end of the incline was reached the machine shot out into space without a perceptible fall.

By this time the elevating propeller was also in motion, and keeping its altitude, the machine slowly began to go higher and higher until it finally soared sixty feet above the ground.

Maintaining this height by the action of the under wheel, the navigator increased the revolutions of the rear propeller, and the forward speed of the huge affair increased until a velocity of eight miles was attained.

All this time the machine headed into a twenty-one-mile wind.

The little crowd of fisherfolk and coast guards, who have been watching the construction of the machine with unconcealed curiosity since September, were amazed.

They endeavored to race over the sand and keep up with the thing in the air, but it soon distanced them and continued its flight alone, save the man in the car.

Steadily it pursued its way, first tacking to port, then to starboard, and then driving straight ahead.

"It is a success," declared Orville Wright to the crowd on the beach after the first mile had been covered.

But the inventor waited. Not until he had accomplished three miles, putting the machine through all sorts of maneuvers en route, was he satisfied.

Then he selected a suitable place to land and, gracefully circling, drew his invention slowly to the earth, where it settled, like some big bird, in the chosen spot.

"Eureka!" he cried, as did the alchemists of old.

The success of the Wright brothers in their invention is the result of three years of hard work. Experiment after experiment has been made and failure resulted, but each experiment had its lesson, and finally, when the two reappeared at Kittyhawk last fall, they felt more confident than ever.

The spot selected for the building and perfecting of the machine is one of the most desolate upon the Atlantic seaboard. Just on the southern extremity of that coast stretch known as the graveyard of American shipping, cut off from civilization by a wide expanse of sound water and seldom in touch with the outer world save when a steamer once or twice a week touches at the little wharf to take and leave government mail, no better place could scarcely have been selected to maintain secrecy.

And this is where the failures have grown into success.

The machine which made yesterday's flight easily carried the weight of a man of 150 pounds, and is nothing like so large as the ill-fated *Buzzard* of Potomac River fame.

It is said the Wright brothers intend constructing a much larger machine, but before this they will go back to their homes for the holidays.

Wilbur Wright, the inventor, is a well-groomed man of prepossessing appearance. He is about five feet, six inches tall, weighs about 150 pounds, and is of swarthy complexion. His hair is raven-hued and straight, but a piercing pair of deep-blue eyes peer at you over a nose of extreme length and sharpness.

His brother, Orville, on the other hand, is a blond, with sandy hair and fair complexion, even features, and sparkling black eyes. He is not quite as large as Wilbur, but is of magnificent physique.

The pair have spent almost the entire fall and winter and early spring months of the past three years at Kittyhawk, working upon their invention, leaving when the weather began to grow warm and returning in the early fall to work.

Their last appearance was on September 1, and since then they have been actively engaged upon the construction of the machine which made yesterday's successful flight.

† † †

Three years later came another epochal event of those times that social historian Walter Lord calls *The Good Years*. San Francisco, that city by the bay, was struck by earthquake and fire, and such celebrities as Enrico Caruso and John Barrymore were there to tell their stories. Many wrote about the great earthquake. The account considered a masterpiece was by a Californian, one who was able to provide a vivid account of the disaster. This was Jack London, who was asked by a magazine to tell what had happened.

† † †

THE SAN FRANCISCO FIRE AND EARTHQUAKE

By Jack London, *Collier's Weekly*, May 5, 1906.

The earthquake shook down in San Francisco hundreds of thousands of dollars' worth of walls and chimneys. But the conflagration that followed burned up hundreds of millions of dollars' worth of property. There is no estimating within hundreds of millions the actual damage wrought. Not in history has a modern imperial city been so completely destroyed. San Francisco is gone! Nothing remains of it but memories and a fringe of dwelling houses on its outskirts. Its industrial section is wiped out. Its social and residential section is wiped out. The factories and warehouses, the great stores and newspaper buildings, the hotels and the palaces of the nabobs, are all gone. Remains only the fringe of dwelling houses on the outskirts of what was once San Francisco.

Within an hour after the earthquake shock the smoke of San Francisco's burning was a lurid tower visible a hundred miles away. And for three days and nights this lurid tower swayed in the sky, reddening the sun, darkening the day, and filling the land with smoke.

On Wednesday morning at a quarter past five came the earthquake. A minute later the flames were leaping upward. In a dozen different quarters south of Market Street, in the working-class ghetto, and in the factories, fires started. There was no opposing the flames. There was no organization, no communication. All the cunning adjustments of a twentieth-century city had been smashed by the earthquake. The streets were humped into ridges and depressions and piled with debris of fallen walls. The steel rails were twisted into perpendicular and horizontal angles. The telephone and telegraph systems were disrupted. And the great water mains had burst. All the shrewd contrivances and safeguards of man had been thrown out of gear by thirty seconds' twitching of the earth crust.

By Wednesday afternoon, inside of twelve hours, half the heart of the city was gone. At that time I watched the vast conflagration from out on the bay. It was dead calm. Not a flicker of wind stirred. Yet from every side wind was pouring in upon the city. East, west, north, and south, strong winds were blowing upon the doomed city. The heated air rising made an enormous suck. Thus did the fire of itself build its own colossal chimney through the atmosphere. Day and night this dead calm continued, and yet, near to the flames, the wind was often half a gale, so mighty was the suck. . . .

Wednesday night saw the destruction of the very heart of the city. Dynamite was lavishly used, and many of San Francisco's proudest structures were crumbled by man himself into ruins, but there was no withstanding the onrush of the flames. . . .

An enumeration of the buildings destroyed would be a directory of San Francisco. An enumeration of the buildings undestroyed would be a line and several addresses. An enumeration of the deeds of heroism would stock a library and bankrupt the Carnegie medal fund. An enumeration of the dead—will never be made. . . .

San Francisco, at the present time, is like the crater of a volcano, around which are camped tens of thousands of refugees. At the Presidio alone are at least twenty thousand. All the surrounding cities and towns are jammed with the homeless ones, where they are being cared for by the relief committees. . . .

† † †

In 1844 the newspapers had published brief accounts in which the writers commented on the "magnetic telegraph" and the "annihilation of space." Now, in 1907, there was a great new feat, one that, though it was not realized at the time, heralded the coming of radio. The chief journalistic sponsor of a man named Guglielmo Marconi in his development of the wireless was the *New York Times,* and it is therefore fitting that the *Times* should have carried the story of the first wireless press message across the Atlantic, of the wireless joining two worlds, as the *Times* phrased it in its headline.

† † †

WIRELESS CROSSES THE ATLANTIC

New York Times, October 18, 1907.

LONDON, Oct. 17.—This message marks the opening of the transatlantic wireless service. It is handed to the Marconi Company here for transmission to Ireland, and thence to Cape Breton, Nova Scotia, and New York. As it is limited to fifty words, I can send at present only one of the many messages received for transmission to The New York Times to signalize the event. This message, from Privy Councillor Lord Avebury, formerly Sir John Lubbock, follows:

"I trust that the introduction of the wireless will more closely unite the people of the United States and Great Britain, who seem to form one nation, though under two Governments, and whose interests are really identical. AVEBURY."

- - - - -

MARCONI'S CONGRATULATIONS!

The above message, received early yesterday morning, was quickly followed by one from The Times's correspondent at Glace Bay, as follows:

"Glace Bay, N.S., Oct. 17.
"Mr. Marconi says: 'Congratulate New York Times on having received first westward press message."'. . .

† † †

Wireless was part of two other major stories in the *New York Times* in the same period. Always interested in scientific advancement, in exploration, especially, the *Times* followed the efforts of Commander Robert E. Peary to reach the North Pole. So this too became an important event.

† † †

PEARY DISCOVERS THE NORTH POLE

New York Times, September 7, 1909.

Commander Robert E. Peary, U.S.N., has discovered the north pole. Following the report of Dr. F. A. Cook that he had reached the top of the world comes the certain announcement from Mr. Peary, the hero of eight polar expeditions, covering a period of twenty-three years, that at last his ambition has been realized, and from all over the world comes full acknowledgment of Peary's feat and congratulations on his success.

The first announcement of Peary's exploit was received in the following message to *The New York Times:*

Indian Harbor, Labrador, via Cape Ray, N. F., Sept. 6.
The *New York Times,* New York:
I have the pole, April sixth. Expect arrive Chateau Bay, September seventh. Secure control wire for me there and arrange expedite transmission big story. PEARY.

Following the receipt of Commander Peary's message to the *New York Times* several other messages were received in this city from the explorer to the same effect. . . .

† † †

The other major story was memorialized not only in print but in song: "It was sad when the great ship went down." The *Titanic.* The credit belongs in great part to an editor named Carr V. Van Anda, as brilliant for the *Times* as Frank Cobb was for the *World,* a man hired by that "honorable titan," Adolph S. Ochs, who had purchased the dying *Times* in 1896 and offered solid, responsible, conservative competition to Hearst and Pulitzer in the days of yellow journalism. Van Anda pulled together the staff of the *Times* to gather information about the sinking of the *Titanic,* which sank four hours after hitting an iceberg. The *Times* banner line said that 886 had been rescued by the *Carpathia,* that probably 1,250 had perished, that famous people were among the missing.

†   †   †

THE SINKING OF THE *TITANIC*

New York Times, April 16, 1912.
Special to the New York Times.

CAPE RACE, N. F., April 15.—The White Star liner Olympic reports by wireless this evening that the Cunarder Carpathia reached, at daybreak this morning, the position from which wireless calls for help were sent out last night by the Titanic after her collison with an iceberg. The Carpathia found only the lifeboats and the wreckage of what had been the biggest steamship afloat.

The Titanic had foundered at about 2:20 A. M. in latitude 41:16 north and longitude 50:14 west. This is about 30 minutes of latitude, or about 34 miles, due south of the position at which she struck the iceberg. All her boats are accounted for and about 655 souls have been saved of the crew and passengers, most of the latter presumably women and children.

There were about 2,100 persons aboard the Titanic.

The Leyland liner California is remaining and searching the position of the disaster, while the Carpathia is returning to New York with the survivors.

It can be positively stated that up to 11 o'clock tonight nothing whatever had been received at or heard by the Marconi station here to the effect that the Parisian, Virginian or any other ships had picked up any survivors, other than those picked up by the Carpathia.

The first news of the disaster to the Titanic was received by the Marconi wireless station here at 10:25 o'clock last night [as told in yesterday's *New York Times.*] The Titanic was first heard giving the distress signal "C. Q. D.," which was answered by a number of ships, including the Carpathia, the Baltic and the Olympic. The Titanic said she had struck an iceberg and was in immediate need of assistance, giving her position as latitude 41:46 north and longitude 50:14 west.

At 10:55 o'clock the Titanic reported she was sinking by the head, and at 11:25 o'clock the station here established communication with the Allan liner Virginian, from Halifax for Liverpool, and notified her of the Titanic's urgent need of assistance and gave her the Titanic's position.

The Virginian advised the Marconi station almost immediately that she was proceeding toward the scene of the disaster.

At 11:36 o'clock the Titanic informed the Olympic that they were putting the women off in boats and instructed the Olympic to have her boats ready to transfer the passengers.

The Titanic, during all this time, continued to give distress signals and to announce her position.

The wireless operator seemed absolutely cool and clear-headed, his sending throughout being steady and perfectly formed, and the judgment used by him was of the best.

The last signals heard from the Titanic were received at 12:27 a.m., when the Virginian reported having heard a few blurred signals which ended abruptly.

11

COVERING THE WAR IN EUROPE

I didn't raise my boy to be a soldier... there's a long, long trail a-winding, into the land of my dreams... pack up your troubles in your old kit bag and smile, smile, smile... it's a long way to Tipperary, it's a long way to go... K-K-K-Katy, beautiful Katy, you're the only g-g-g-girl that I adore... mademoiselle from Armentieres, parlez-vous... keep the home fires burning, while your hearts are yearning... how you gonna keep 'em down on the farm, after they've seen Paree? The reporters of World War I, as well as the doughboys, saw Paree, and that war, the great war of 1914-1918, gave to the American people some memorable pieces of journalism.

It was not a romantic war, though it was viewed romantically by some observers, even *after* the fact. Some went off with banners waving, perhaps dreaming of French mademoiselles, like the one in the 1925 movie, *The Big Parade:* Renée Adoree running after John Gilbert down a long line of marching men. American men did not enter the war until 1917, but Americans had been covering it since its beginning. June 28, 1914, it began, really, in Sarajevo, Serbia, when a youth named Gavrilo Princip assassinated the Archduke Ferdinand of Austria and his wife. The Central Powers and the Allies, in a series of complex secret treaties, found themselves at war, which was declared on April 6, 1917. Woodrow Wilson, our president, "kept us out of war" through 1916, at least, or so the Democratic slogan of the 1916 election put it, and then the American Expeditionary Force was assembled, though there was no sizeable American force in France until 1918. But the reporters who were "over there," as George M. Cohan called it in the most famous war song of them all, had to endure the same dirty, ugly, treacherous trench warfare that was the lot of the troops.

It is not surprising that Richard Harding Davis was there, the handsome, flamboyant reporter who had been almost a matinee idol since the 1880s, the man who had reported many wars and had been a man about town rather like the Cortland Van Bibber about whom he had once written. Davis was near the end of his life, and what a life it had been. It is singular, in a way, that Davis's most famous dispatch, the one that follows, should have been written not for an American newspaper but for the *News Chronicle* of London.

† † †

DAVIS DESCRIBES A "RIVER OF STEEL"

London News Chronicle, August 23, 1914.

BRUSSELS, FRIDAY, AUGUST 21, 2 P.M.—The entrance of the German army into Brussels has lost the human quality. It was lost as soon as the three soldiers who led the army bicycled into the Boulevard du Regent and asked the way to the Gare du Nord. When they passed the human note passed with them.

What came after them, and twenty-four hours later is still coming, is not men marching, but a force of nature like a tidal wave, an avalanche or a river flooding its banks. At this minute it is rolling through Brussels as the swollen waters of the Conemaugh Valley swept through Johnstown.

At the sight of the first few regiments of the enemy we were thrilled with interest. After for three hours they had passed in one unbroken steel-gray column we were bored. But when hour after hour passed and there was no halt, no breathing time, no open spaces in the ranks, the thing became uncanny, inhuman. You returned to watch it, fascinated. It held the mystery and menace of fog rolling toward you across the sea.

The gray of the uniforms worn by both officers and men helped this air of mystery. Only the sharpest eye could detect among the thousands that passed the slightest difference. All moved under a cloak of invisibility. Only after the most numerous and severe tests at all distances, with all materials and combinations of colors that give forth no color, could this gray have been discovered. That it was selected to clothe and disguise the German when he fights is typical of the German staff in striving for efficiency to leave nothing to chance, to neglect no detail.

After you have seen this service uniform under conditions entirely opposite you are convinced that for the German soldier it is his strongest weapon. Even the most expert marksman cannot hit a target he cannot see. It is a gray green, not the blue gray of our Confederates. It is the gray of the hour just before daybreak, the gray of unpolished steel, of mist among green trees.

I saw it first in the Grand Palace in front of the Hôtel de Ville. It was impossible to tell if in that noble square there was a regiment or a brigade. You saw only a fog that melted into the stones, blended with the ancient house fronts, that shifted and drifted, but left you nothing at which you could point.

Later, as the army passed below my window, under the trees of the Botanical Park, it merged and was lost against the green leaves. It is no exaggeration to say that at a hundred yards you can see the horses on which the uhlans ride, but you cannot see the men who ride them.

If I appear to overemphasize this disguising uniform it is because of all the details of the German outfit it appealed to me as one of the most remarkable. The other day when I was with the rear guard of the French Dragoons and Cuirassiers and they threw out pickets, we could distinguish them against the yellow wheat or green gorse at half a mile, while these men passing in the street, when they have reached the next crossing, become merged into the gray of the paving stones and the earth swallows them. In comparison the yellow khaki of our own American army is about as invisible as the flag of Spain.

Yesterday Major General von Jarotsky, the German Military Governor of Brussels, assured Burgomaster Max that the German army would not occupy the city, but would pass through it. It is still passing. I have followed in campaigns six armies, but excepting not even our own, the Japanese, or the British, I have not seen one so thoroughly equipped. I am not speaking of the fighting qualities of any army, only of the equipment and organization. The German army moved into this city as smoothly and as compactly as an Empire State Express. There were no halts, no open places, no stragglers.

This army has been on active service three weeks, and so far there is not apparently a chin strap or a horseshoe missing. It came in with the smoke pouring from cookstoves on wheels, and in an hour had set up post-office wagons, from which mounted messengers galloped along the line of columns, distributing letters, and at which soldiers posted picture postcards.

The infantry came in in files of five, two hundred men to each company; the Lancers in columns of four, with not a pennant missing. The quick-firing guns and fieldpieces were one hour at a time in passing, each gun with its caisson and ammunition wagon taking twenty seconds in which to pass.

The men of the infantry sang *Fatherland, My Fatherland.* Between each line of song they took three steps. At times two thousand men were singing together in absolute rhythm and beat. When the melody gave way the silence was broken only by the stamp of iron-shod boots, and then again the song rose. When the singing ceased, the bands played marches. They were followed by the rumble of siege guns, the creaking of wheels, and of chains clanking against the cobblestones and the sharp bell-like voices of the bugles.

For seven hours the army passed in such solid columns that not once might a taxicab or trolley car pass through the city. Like a river of steel it flowed, gray and ghostlike. Then, as dusk came and thousands of horses' hoofs and thousands of iron boots continued to tramp forward, they struck tiny sparks from the stones, but the horses and the men who beat out the sparks were invisible.

At midnight pack wagons and siege guns were still passing. At seven this morning I was awakened by the tramp of men and bands playing jauntily. Whether they marched all night or not I do not know; but now for twenty-six hours the gray army has rumbled by with the mystery of fog and the pertinacity of a steam roller.

† † †

Another dispatch from Richard Harding Davis, published a short time later, appeared in the *New York Tribune*, a paper that though in decline was still publishing some of its most notable stories, written by such reporters as Davis, Will Irwin, and Floyd Gibbons. There is burning indignation in Davis' story, and it is an account that suggests why the mood of the American people should have been shifting as the years went by from "I Didn't Raise My Boy to Be a Soldier" to "Over There," a mood that made possible the 1917 declaration of war.

† † †

THE DESTRUCTION OF LOUVAIN

New York Tribune, August 31, 1914.

LONDON, AUGUST 30—I left Brussels on Thursday afternoon and have just arrived in London. For two hours on Thursday night I was in what for six hundred years has been the city of Louvain. The Germans were burning it, and to hide their work kept us locked in the railroad carriages. But the story was written against the sky, was told to us by German soldiers incoherent with excesses; and we could read it in the faces of women and children being led to concentration camps and of citizens on their way to be shot.

The Germans sentenced Louvain on Wednesday to become a wilderness, and with the German system and love of thoroughness they left Louvain an empty blackened shell. The reason for this appeal to the torch and the execution of noncombatants, as given to me on Thursday morning by General von Lutwitz, military governor of Brussels, was this: on Wednesday while the German military commander of the troops of Louvain was at the Hôtel de Ville talking to the Burgomaster, a son of the Burgomaster with an automatic pistol shot the chief of staff and German staff surgeons.

Lutwitz claims this was the signal for the civil guard, in civilian clothes on roofs, to fire upon the German soldiers in the open square below. He said also the Belgians had quick-firing guns, brought from Antwerp. As for a week the Germans had occupied Louvain and closely guarded all approaches, the story that there was any gunrunning is absurd.

Fifty Germans were killed and wounded. For that, said Lutwitz, Louvain must be wiped out. So in pantomime with his fist he swept the papers across his table.

"The Hôtel de Ville," he added, "was a beautiful building; it is a pity it must be destroyed."

Ten days ago I was in Louvain when it was occupied by Belgian troops and King Albert and his staff. The city dates from the eleventh century, and the population was 42,000. The citizens were brewers, lacemakers, and manufacturers of ornaments for churches. The university once was the most celebrated in European cities, and still is, or was, headquarters of the Jesuits.

In the Louvain college many priests now in America have been educated, and ten days ago over the green walls of the college, I saw hanging two American flags. I found the city clean, sleepy, and pretty, with narrow twisting streets and smart shops and cafes set in flower gardens of the houses, with red roofs, green shutters, and white walls.

Over those that faced south had been trained pear trees, their branches heavy with fruit spread out against the walls like branches of candelabra. The Town Hall was very old and very beautiful, an example of Gothic architecture, in detail and design more celebrated even then the Town Hall of Bruges or Brussels. It was five hundred years old, and lately had been repaired with great taste and at great cost.

Opposite was the Church of St. Pierre, dating from the fifteenth century, a very noble building, with many chapels filled with carvings of the time of the Renaissance in wood, stone, and iron. In the university were 150,000 volumes.

Near it was the bronze statue of Father Damien, priest of the leper colony in the South Pacific, of which Robert Louis Stevenson wrote. All these buildings now are empty, exploded cartridges. Statues, pictures, carvings, parchments, archives—all are gone.

No one defends the sniper. But because ignorant Mexicans when their city was invaded fired upon our sailors, we did not destroy Vera Cruz. Even had we bombarded Vera Cruz, money could have restored it. Money can never restore Louvain. Great architects, dead these six hundred years, made it beautiful, and their handiwork belonged to the world. With torch and dynamite the Germans have turned these masterpieces into ashes, and all the Kaiser's horses and all his men cannot bring them back again.

When by troop train we reached Louvain, the entire heart of the city was destroyed and fire had reached the Boulevard Tirlemont, which faces the railroad station. The night was windless, and the sparks rose in steady, leisurely pillars, falling back into the furnace from which they sprang. In their work the soldiers were moving from the heart of the city to the outskirts, street by street, from house to house.

In each building, so German soldiers told me, they began at the first floor, and when that was burning steadily passed on to the one next. There were no exceptions—whether it was a store, chapel, or private residence it was destroyed. The occupants had been warned to go, and in each deserted shop or house the furniture was piled, the torch was stuck under it, and into the air went the savings of years, the souvenirs of children, of parents, heirlooms that had passed from generation to generation.

The people had time only to fill a pillowcase and fly. Some were not so fortunate, and by thousands, like flocks of sheep, they were rounded up and marched through the night to concentration camps. We were not allowed to speak to any citizen of Louvain, but the Germans crowded the windows, boastful, gloating, eager to interpret.

We were free to move from one end of the train to the other, and in the two hours during which it circled the burning city war was before us in its most hateful aspect.

In other wars I have watched men on one hilltop, without haste, without heat, fire at men on another hill, and in consequence on both sides good men were wasted. But in those fights there were no women and children, and the shells struck only vacant stretches of veldt or uninhabited mountainsides.

At Louvain it was war upon the defenseless, war upon churches, colleges, shops of milliners and lacemakers; war brought to the bedside and fireside; against women harvesting in the fields, against children in wooden shoes at play in the streets.

At Louvain that night the Germans were like men after an orgy. . . .

† † †

That account, remember, was written in 1914, three years before the United States was in the war. Another story that became a standard appeared in 1915 by the veteran Will Irwin, who had been through the Pulitzer-Hearst age and the years of muckraking. His story revealed the terrible fact that a new kind of warfare—by gas—had been introduced by the Germans. It was a story that had considerable psychological impact in America.

† † †

POISON GAS ENTERS MODERN WARFARE

New York Tribune, April 27, 1915.

BOULOGNE, APRIL 25—The gaseous vapor which the Germans used against the French divisions near Ypres last Thursday, contrary to the rules of the Hague Convention, introduces a new element into warfare. The attack of last Thursday evening was preceded by the rising of a cloud of vapor, greenish gray and iridescent. That vapor settled to the ground like a swamp mist and drifted toward the French trenches on a brisk wind. Its effect on the French was a violent nausea and faintness, followed by an utter collapse. It is believed that the Germans, who charged in behind the vapor, met no resistance at all, the French at their front being virtually paralyzed.

Everything indicates long and thorough preparation for this attack. The work of sending out the vapor was done from the advanced

German trenches. Men garbed in a dress resembling the harness of a diver and armed with retorts or generators about three feet high and connected with ordinary hose pipe turned the vapor loose towards the French lines. Some witnesses maintain the Germans sprayed the earth before the trenches with a fluid which, being ignited, sent up the fumes. The German troops, who followed up this advantage with a direct attack, held inspirators in their mouths, thus preventing them from being overcome by the fumes.

In addition to this, the Germans appear to have fired ordinary explosive shells loaded with some chemical which had a paralyzing effect on all the men in the region of the explosion. Some chemical in the composition of these shells produced violent watering of the eyes, so that the men overcome by them were practically blinded for some hours.

The effect of the noxious trench gas seems to be slow in wearing away. The men come out of their nausea in a state of utter collapse. Some of the rescued have already died from the aftereffects. How many of the men, left unconscious in the trenches when the French broke, died from the fumes it is impossible to say, since those trenches were at once occupied by the Germans.

This new form of attack needs for success a favorable wind. Twice in the day that followed the Germans tried trench vapor on the Canadians who made on the right of the French position a stand which will probably be remembered as one of the heroic episodes of this war. In both cases the wind was not favorable, and the Canadians managed to stick through it. The noxious, explosive bombs were, however, used continually against the Canadian forces and caused some losses.

† † †

As war continued in Europe, the United States was still involved in the Mexican intervention, an action that for a time had drawn in such correspondents as Richard Harding Davis, Jack London, and the cartoonist John T. McCutcheon. Americans were beginning their long love affair with the automobile, were dancing to Irving Berlin's songs, and were seeing more and more "liberated women," and some of those liberated women were agitating more and more for the right to vote. That, a peacetime issue in the years before we entered the European affair, was the subject matter of an editorial.

† † †

ON THE RIGHT OF WOMEN TO VOTE

New York World, March 14, 1915.

Woman suffrage will not reform government in the conventional moral sense, although in the long run it will produce a more representative and responsible government. If we may judge the future by the past, the immediate effect of woman suffrage will be to disorganize government and add to its confusion. That is what has always happened when the franchise was extended. Each new influx of voters submerged the old order, and the former standards of public service deteriorated for the time being, much to the anguish of the Brahmin classes, but not to the permanent injury of society. Enlarging the suffrage does not purify government, but enlarging the suffrage stabilizes and strengthens democracy, and hence the ultimate influence is invariably for the general good. In a democracy the people do not exist for the government, but the government exists for the people, and every adult person subject to government may reasonably ask for a voice in ordering the policies of that government.

For women to demand suffrage on the ground that they are purer and nobler and holier than men is to argue against their own cause. An obligarchy of virtue would be only one degree less oppressive than an oligarchy of vice. Nobody has ever obtained the franchise on the mere pretext that he was pure in heart, and nobody ever will. The franchise is not granted in order that politics may be purified, but in order that the holder of the franchise may the better protect his life, liberty, property and welfare under the government to which he is responsible as a citizen.

Votes for women will not improve the quality of government, but it will make women more intelligent and more responsible, and hence society as a whole must inevitably benefit. The ballot box is a mighty university. It has proved so in the case of men, and it must prove so in the case of women, or the experience of history is false.

Moreover, the political influence already exerted by a few women makes it highly desirable that all women be enfranchised in order to reestablish the balance. Under republican institutions power without responsibility is a grave evil. Women today have great power in government, but no responsibility. Various organizations of women, which probably do not represent ten per cent of the sex, maintain at times a veritable reign of terror in legislative bodies by pretending to speak in the name of all women. In consequence, half the country is now bedevilled by some form or other of harem government which in no respect is a true expression of public opinion. . . .

We know what would probably happen if government were in the hands of women, and Anthony Comstock, Charles Edward Russell, and the Anti-Saloon League were accepted as the spokesmen for all the disfranchised males. Yet something of that sort is going on all the time in State capitals in the name of women. The only antidote to the influence of some women upon government is the influence of all women upon government. When all sex limitations upon suffrage have been removed the political power of those women who are obsessed with the idea that government must assume the spiritual characteristics of a communistic prayer meeting will be restricted to their own votes, and the votes of those who are actually in sympathy with them. . . .

Eliminating from the suffrage controversy all of its cant and twaddle, the question is a straight issue of whether all the adult citizens of the State shall be entitled to a vote in making the laws to which all of them are subject, or whether this privilege shall be the exclusive property of half of these citizens who gain their political power by the accident of sex.

Lincoln once said that this republic was founded upon the rule of "root, hog, or die," and women are no less amenable to that principle than are men. The amiable theory that it is man's function to provide and woman's function to be sheltered is a living lie, as millions of women wage-earners can testify. Sometimes man provides, and sometimes he doesn't. The woman who is sheltered today may be working in a factory tomorrow to support herself and her children. Hunger knows no sex. Want knows no sex. Necessity knows no sex. Law knows no sex. Property knows no sex. Only the ballot box knows sex.

But the ballot box once knew rank. It once knew land and primogeniture. It once knew income and money and family. All those paraphernalia of privilege have been swept away, and the disability of sex will follow. In the steady sweep of democracy the time will come when the present opposition to woman suffrage will seem as short-sighted and senseless as the former opposition to manhood suffrage now seems.

Democracies always move forward. That is their law of self-preservation. If they stand still or retrograde they are lost.

† † †

He kept us out of war, and he was reelected in 1916, again as a minority president, as in 1912. Woodrow Wilson's opponent was Charles Evans Hughes, and the election was close. One of the publications supporting the president was the *New Republic,* founded as recently as 1914, by Herbert Croly, author of *The Promise of American Life,* assisted by Walter Lippmann and Walter Weyl, and with the financial aid of Willard Straight. It was a magazine of liberalism, though like Wilson the editor seems today more a *nineteenth century* than a *twentieth century* liberal.

† † †

THE REELECTION OF WOODROW WILSON

New Republic, IX, No. 117 (November 11, 1916), pp. 31-32.

The re-election of Mr. Wilson even by such a narrow margin is one of the most extraordinary achievements in the political annals of the United States. In 1912 his huge majority in the electoral college was earned for him by an actual minority of the vote. His supporters amounted to only about forty per cent of the American electorate.

His four years of office have been among the most troubled in the country's history. He has had to deal with a number of novel and critical problems which, no matter how he handled them, obliged him to alienate certain of his former supporters. Many thousands of Democrats among the professional and business men of the country withdrew their allegiance because of the infirmities of his foreign policy. Many thousands of the Irish and German-Americans became his bitter and unscrupulous enemies because of his benevolent neutrality toward the Allies. One can only guess how much the default has amounted to, but taking all the people with grievances together it could hardly have been less than 500,000 votes. In order to win reelection he was obliged to convert into Democrats between 1,000,000 and 1,500,000 new voters; and the job was the more difficult because he could not count upon the assistance of an expansive personality which the ordinary American voter would understand and like. Yet he succeeded somehow in getting the necessary support. His gains were chiefly among the farmers and women voters in those parts of the country where Mr. Roosevelt's popularity had formerly been most emphatic. Without the women voters, for the increase of whom he has done so little, Mr. Wilson might have failed of election.

One outstanding fact about the election is the novel and significant distribution of the strength of the two major political parties. Mr. Hughes carried the East and the Middle West, Mr. Wilson the South and the Far West. In the case of every important industrial community except Ohio Mr. Hughes was victorious, although by widely different margins. Broadly speaking the lineup was between town and country, between industry and agriculture. The Democrats had expected to obtain a large measure of support from the wage-earners in the big industries of the country. It looks now as if they had received less than usual. The Republicans were apparently successful in the last two weeks of the campaign in holding a sufficient proportion of the votes of the laborers in the protected manufactures. But they lost much of their grip on the agrarian communities of the Mississippi Valley and the mountain States. The Democrats were saved from a severe defeat only by their success in making inroads on the normal support received by the Republicans from the farmers in the newer parts of the country. More than any election which has taken place since the Civil War, the old American territorial democracy, the democracy of Jackson and Douglas, has reasserted itself. Mr. Wilson has done what Mr. Bryan failed to do. He has recovered for the Democratic party the support of a great majority of the predominantly agricultural States. This support has not the same economic meaning as it had during the pioneer period, when the farmers in the newer parts of the country were in debt and thought themselves oppressed by the money power. The Far West is not aggrieved and rebellious as it was at the time of the "greenback" and "Populist" movements. But it still has a mind of its own, sharply defined from that of the rest of the country. In a combination with the solid South and with one or two other industrial States of the Middle West it is strong enough barely to swing a national victory.

† † †

When Germany moved to a policy of unrestricted submarine warfare it lost much of its support in the United States. By early 1917 the newspapers of America were swinging more and more to the Allies, in part because of the historic associations with England and France, in part because of anti-German propaganda and inept German propaganda. The sinking of the *Lusitania* in 1915 caused many papers to shift to the Allied side, or to become neutral; an early poll of the *Literary Digest* had shown 240 editorials neutral, 105 pro-ally, and 20 pro-German. In the *New York World,* editor Frank Cobb was arguing that isolationism was a policy of the eighteenth century, that the world had changed since the time Washington had given his farewell address.

† † †

1796 OR 1917?

New York World, January 30, 1917.

The policy of isolation that was urged upon the American people in Washington's Farewell Address was constructed upon this hypothesis:

> Europe has a set of primary interests which to us have none, or a very remote connection. Hence she must be engaged in frequent controversies the causes of which are essentially foreign to our concerns.

This was true in 1796 when the United States was a great experiment in self-government, when there was no steamship, no railroad, no cable, no wireless, when the republic was geographically as well as politically isolated from the rest of the world; but is it true today?

Will anybody affirm that the primary interests of British democracy differ essentially from our own primary interests? Or French democracy? Or Italian democracy? Or even the mass of Germans for whom Maximilian Harden alone has the courage and vision to be spokesman? Various European governments may have interests which are foreign to our interests, but even there can we say that those interests do not concern us?

June 28, 1914, a double murder was committed in a street of Sarajevo, a town in Bosnia. Although the victims were an Austrian Archduke and Archduchess, nothing in 1796 would have been less concern to the United States than a crime perpetrated in a Balkan province of Austria-Hungary.

Yet this murder in Sarajevo brought the United States to the verge of another civil war. It will cost the American people thousands of millions of dollars in taxation. It has set back for half a century the work of assimilating the immigrant population of this country. It has diverted the mind of the nation from its most vital domestic problems. It has all but embroiled us in the most ghastly war of human history. It has complicated our affairs with the whole world, disorganized all internal affairs, and in a way left us denationalized, divided into hostile camps of European tribesmen.

If the fundamental principle of Washington's farewell address still has vital force, what happened in Sarajevo was "essentially foreign to our vital concerns." Nevertheless, we all know what has befallen us, and the question is whether we are to sit by and permit it to happen again without having anything to say about it.

Had there been almost any kind of council of the nations, this war could never have taken place. Conference and discussion alone would have averted it. The war was possible only because a secret and tortuous diplomacy made it possible. But had Vienna, dealing at first with Belgrade and then with Petrograd, known that it would have to reckon in the end with all the civilized nations, there would have been no ultimatum to Serbia.

This war marked the collapse of the system of entangling alliances intriguing for the balance of power. Civilization, in its own interest, is now compelled to take a step forward. Is American democracy to hold aloof? Have we no obligations whatever to the rest of mankind which would impel us to throw our influence into the balance to prevent a repetition of this war? Because George Washington in 1796 wisely decided that a policy of isolation was then for the best interest of the United States, must we refuse to admit that there has been any change in the world since 1796 and that our interests and obligations now are precisely what they were then?

The men who are against participation by the United States in a League to Enforce Peace on the ground that it conflicts with Washington's Farewell Address are spiritual brothers of the man who ardently defended the institution of slavery on the ground that George Washington was a slaveowner. What was moral in 1796 was still moral in 1860 to the Southern slaveholder. What was a wise foreign policy in 1796 is still a wise foreign policy to the mandarins of the United States Senate who can never believe that the world moves forward.

Before many months have elapsed the American people must decide for themselves whether the United States in relation to the other nations is living in the year 1796 or the year 1917. Are they ready to cooperate with the other great countries in the common interest, or are they by the policy of isolation to invite the other great countries to cooperate against them? It will inevitably be one or the other.

† † †

As submarine warfare was changing attitudes in America, it provided for one reporter a first-hand account that is one of the most famous stories of war. The reporter was Floyd Gibbons, who later would lose an eye by German machinegun fire, causing him to wear an eyepatch that would be his trademark for a generation. Gibbons was aboard the Cunard liner *Laconia* in February, 1917. He lived the story he wrote.

† † †

THE SINKING OF THE *LACONIA*

Chicago Tribune, February 26, 1917.

QUEENSTOWN, FEBRUARY 26 (VIA LONDON)—I have serious doubts whether this is a real story. I am not entirely certain that it is not all a dream and that in a few minutes I will wake up back in stateroom B 19 on the promenade deck of the Cunarder *Laconia* and hear my cockney steward informing me with an abundance of "and sirs" that it is a fine morning.

It is now a little over thirty hours since I stood on the slanting decks of the big liner, listened to the lowering of the lifeboats, heard the hiss of escaping steam and the roar of ascending rockets as they tore lurid rents in the black sky and cast their red glare over the roaring sea.

I am writing this within thirty minutes after stepping on the dock here in Queenstown from the British mine sweeper which picked up our open lifeboat after an eventful six hours of drifting and darkness and baling and pulling on the oars and of straining aching eyes toward the empty, meaningless horizon in search of help. But, dream or fact, here it is:

The Cunard liner *Laconia,* 18,000 tons' burden, carrying seventy-three passengers—men, women, and children—of whom six were American citizens—manned by a mixed crew of 216, bound from New York to Liverpool, and loaded with foodstuffs, cotton, and raw material, was torpedoed without warning by a German submarine last night off the Irish coast. The vessel sank in about forty minutes.

Two American citizens, mother and daughter, listed from Chicago and former residents there, are among the dead. . . .

The first cabin passengers were gathered in the lounge Sunday evening, with the exception of the bridge fiends in the smoke room.

Poor Butterfly was dying wearily on the talking machine, and several couples were dancing.

About the tables in the smoke room the conversation was limited to the announcement of bids and orders to the stewards. Before the fireplace was a little gathering which had been dubbed the Hyde Park corner—an allusion I don't quite fully understand. This group had about exhausted available discussion when I projected a new bone of contention.

"What do you say are our chances of being torpedoed?" I asked.

"Well," drawled the deliberative Mr. Henry Chetham, a London solicitor, "I should say four thousand to one."

Lucien J. Jerome, of the British diplomatic service, returning with an Ecuadorian valet from South America, interjected: "Considering the zone and the class of this ship, I should put it down at two hundred and fifty to one that we don't meet a sub."

At this moment the ship gave a sudden lurch sideways and forward. There was a muffled noise like the slamming of some large door at a good distance away. The slightness of the shock and the meekness of the report compared with my imagination were disappointing. Every man in the room was on his feet in an instant.

"We're hit!" shouted Mr. Chetham.

"That's what we've been waiting for," said Mr. Jerome.

"What a lousy torpedo!" said Mr. Kirby in typical New Yorkese. "It must have been a fizzer."

I looked at my watch. It was 10:30 PM.

Then came the five blasts on the whistle. We rushed down the corridor leading from the smoke room at the stern to the lounge, which was amidship. We were running, but there was no panic. The occupants of the lounge were just leaving by the forward doors as we entered. . . .

The torpedo had hit us well astern on the starboard side and had missed the engines and the dynamos. I had not noticed the deck lights before. Throughout the voyage our decks had remained dark at night and all cabin portholes were clamped down and all windows covered with opaque paint. . . .

Steam began to hiss somewhere from the giant gray funnels that towered above. Suddenly there was a roaring swish as a rocket soared upward from the captain's bridge, leaving a comet's tail of fire. I watched it as it described a graceful arc in the black void overhead, and then, with an audible pop, it burst in a flare of brilliant colors.

There was a tilt to the deck. It was listing to starboard at just the angle that would make it necessary to reach for support to enable one to stand upright. In the meantime electric floodlights—large white enameled funnels containing clusters of bulbs—had been suspended from the promenade deck and illuminated the dark water that rose and fell on the slanting side of the ship. . . .

A hatchet was thrust into my hand and I forwarded it to the bow. There was a flash of sparks as it crashed down on the holding pulley. One strand of the rope parted and down plunged the bow, too quick for the stern man. We came to a jerky stop with the stern in the air and the bow down, but the stern managed to lower away until the dangerous angle was eliminated.

Then both tried to lower together. The list of the ship's side became greater, but, instead of our boat sliding down it like a toboggan, the taffrail caught and was held. As the lowering continued, the other side dropped down and we found ourselves clinging on at a new angle and looking straight down on the water.

Many feet and hands pushed the boat from the side of the ship, and we sagged down again, this time smacking squarely on the pillowy top of a rising swell. It felt more solid than mid-air, at least. But we were far from being off. The pulleys stuck twice in their fastenings, bow and stern, and the one ax passed forward and back, and with it my flashlight, as the entangling ropes that held us to the sinking *Laconia* were cut away.

Some shout from that confusion of sound caused me to look up, and I really did so with the fear that one of the nearby boats was being lowered upon us. . . .

As we pulled away from the side of the ship, its receding terrace of lights stretched upward. The ship was slowly turning over. We were opposite that part occupied by the engine rooms. There was a tangle of ears, spars, and rigging on the seat and considerable confusion before four of the big sweeps could be manned on either side of the boat. . . .

We rested on our oars, with all eyes on the still lighted *Laconia*. The torpedo had struck at 10:30 P.M., according to our ship's time. It was thirty minutes afterward that another dull thud, which was accompanied by a noticeable drop in the hulk, told its story of the second torpedo that the submarine had dispatched through the engine room and the boat's vitals from a distance of two hundred yards.

We watched silently during the next minute, as the tiers of lights dimmed slowly from white to yellow, then to red, and nothing was left but the murky mourning of the night, which hung over all like a pall.

A mean, cheese-colored crescent of a moon revealed one horn above a rag bundle of clouds in the distance. A rim of blackness settled around our little world, relieved only by general leering stars in the zenith, and where the *Laconia's* lights had shone there remained only the dim outline of a blacker hulk standing out above the water like a jagged headland, silhouetted against overcast sky.

The ship sank rapidly at the stern until at last its nose stood straight up in the air. Then it slid silently down and out of sight like a piece of disappearing scenery in a panorama spectacle. . . .

† † †

Since 1868 Henry Watterson had been writing editorials for the *Louisville Courier-Journal*. It was now 1917, almost the end of the old man's days in journalism. He had long believed that America would have to enter the war, and he wrote an editorial that he introduced with the old backwoods song, "The Hunters of Kentucky," from the days of Andrew Jackson. In style it stood in harsh contrast to the cold logic of a Frank Cobb.

† † †

"MARSE HENRY" ON THE WAR

Louisville Courier-Journal, April 7, 1917.

"Rally round the flag, boys"—Uncle Sam's Battle song;
"Sound the gold anthem! War dogs are howling;
Proud bird of Liberty screams through the air!"
—The Hunters of Kentucky

It is with solemnity, and a touch of sadness, that we write the familiar words of the old refrain beneath the invocation to the starry banner, the breezy call of hero-breeding bombast quite gone out of them; the glad shout of battle; the clarion note of defiance; because to us, not as to Nick of the Woods and his homely co-mates of the forest, [but] rather as to the men of '61, comes this present call to arms.

We may feel with the woman's heart of Rankin, of Montana, yet repudiate with manly disdain the sentimental scruples of Kitchin, of North Carolina.

There are times when feeling must be sent to the rear; when duty must toe the line; when the aversion brave men have for fighting must yield to the adjuration, "Give me liberty, or give me death!" That time is now upon us.

Unless Patrick Henry was wrong—unless Washington and the men of the Revolution were wrong, that time is upon us. It is a lie to pretend that the world is better than it was; that men are truer, wiser; that war is escapable; that peace may be had for the planning and the asking. The situation which without any act of ours rises before us is as exigent as that which rose before the Colonists in America when a mad English King, claiming to rule without accountability, asserted the right divine of Kings and sent an army to enforce it. A mad German Emperor, claiming partnership with God, again elevates the standard of right divine and bids the world to worship, or die.

From the beginning the issue was not less ours than of the countries first engaged. Each may have had ends of its own to serve. Nor were these ends precisely alike. At least France—to whom we owe all that we have of sovereignty and freedom—and Belgium, the little David of Nations—fought to resist invasion; wanton, cruel invasion; to avert slavery, savage, pitiless slavery. Yet, whatever the animating purpose—whatever the selfish interests of England and Russia and Italy—the Kaiser scheme of world conquest justified it.

In us it sanctifies it. Why should any American split hairs over the European rights and wrongs involved when he sees before him grim and ghastly the mailed figure of Absolutism with hand uplifted to strike Columbia where these three years she has stood pleading for justice, peace and mercy? God of the free heart's hope and home forbid!

Each of these three years the German Kaiser was making war upon us. He was making war secretly, through his emissaries in destruction of our industries, secretly through his diplomats plotting not merely foreign but civil war against us, and, as we now know, seeking to foment servile and racial insurrection; then openly upon the high seas levying murder upon our people and visiting all our rights and claims with scorn and insult—with scorn and insult unspeakable—at this moment pretending to flout us with ignominy and contempt. Where would the honest pacifist draw the line?

Surely the time has arrived—many of us think it was long since overdue—for calling the braves to the colors. Nations must e'en take stock on occasion and manhood come to a showdown. It is but a truism to say so.

Fifty years the country has enjoyed surpassing prosperity. This has overcommercialized the character and habits of the people. Twenty-five years the gospel of passivism, with "business is business" for its text, has not only been preached—indiscriminately-oracularly—without let or hindrance, but has been richly financed and potentially organized. It has established a party. It has made a cult, justifying itself in a fad it has called Humanity—in many ways a most spurious humanity—and has set this above and against patriotic inclination and duty.

Like a bolt out of the blue flashed the war signal from the very heart of Europe. Across the Atlantic its reverberations rolled to find us divided, neutral, and unprepared. For fifteen years a body of German reservists disguised as citizens have been marching and counter-marching. They grew at length bold enough to rally to the support of a pan-German scheme of conquest and a pro-German propaganda of "kultur," basing its effrontery in the German-American vote, which began its agitation by threatening us with civil war if we dared to go to war with Germany. There followed the assassin sea monsters and the air-ship campaign of murder.

All the while we looked on with either simpering idiocy, or dazed apathy. Serbia? It was no affair of ours. Belgium? Why should we worry? Foodstuffs soaring—war stuffs roaring—everybody making money—the mercenary, the poor of heart, the mean of spirit, the bleak and barren of soul, could still plead the hypocrisy of Uplift and chortle: "I did not raise my boy to be a soldier." Even the Lusitania did not awaken us to a sense of danger and arouse us from the stupefaction of ignorant and ignorable self-complacency.

First of all on bended knee we should pray to God to forgive us. Then erect as men, Christian men, soldierly men, to the flag and the fray—whatever they lead us—over the ocean—through France to Flanders—across the Low Countries to Koln, Bonn and Koblens—tumbling the fortress of Ehrenbreitatein into the Rhine as we pass and damning the mouth of the Moselle with the debris of the ruin we make of it—then on, on to Berlin, the Black Horse Cavalry sweeping the Wilhelmstrasse like lava down the mountainside, the Junker and the saber rattler flying before us, the tunes being "Dixie" and "Yankee Doodle," the cry being, "Hail the French Republic—Hail the Republic of Russia—welcome the Commonwealth of the Vaterland—no peace with the Kaiser—no parley with autocracy, Absolutism and the divine right of Kings—to Hell with the Hapsburg and the Hohenzollern!"

† † †

So war came in the spring of 1917, and the American reporters began to write about a war in which their own country was involved. Among those reporters was a group associated with a paper called the *Stars and Stripes,* created in the headquarters of General John J. Pershing, published in Paris by a crew that included a boss named Guy T. Viskniskki; a former tramp reporter named Harold Ross; a portly critic named Alexander Woollcott; a sportswriter-to-be named Grantland Rice; a poet, later our own Samuel Pepys, named Franklin P. Adams. Here are writings from *Stars and Stripes:* an editorial written by Harold Ross for the fighting men; an ode to ice cream soda by Adams; an editorial praising the troops after Chateau-Thierry, one of the great battles of the war, fought in June, 1918; a poem contributed by one of the soldiers; and, of course, that famous story by the cynic Woollcott, about a young soldier and his dog.

† † †

HOW A SOLDIER SHOULD BEHAVE WHILE ON LEAVE

Stars and Stripes, February 22, 1918.

Nobody, of course, expects the American soldier on leave to go about with a prayer-book neatly folded between his hands and a millstone hung about his neck. Far from it. He will be a better fighting man after his leave if he gives his body and mind a holiday and seeks the things such as outdoor exercise, reading and sightseeing that interest him without imparing his efficiency. The things that are expected of the A.E.F. man on leave are: That he conduct himself as a gentleman. That, like the knights of King Arthur's Round Table—whose spiritual successor, from the nature of his task, he most certainly is—he consider himself bound to 'hold all women as sacred.' That he allow himself to indulge in no excesses that will impair his efficiency as a member of one of Uncle Sam's combative units. One can have a bully good time in France—or anywhere else, for that matter—and still live up to those three cardinal principles."

† † †

AN ODE TO ICE CREAM SODA

By Franklin P. Adams, *Stars and Stripes,* April 19, 1918.

You may talk of *vin* and *biere*
When you're quartered over there
In New York or Abilene or Sleepy Hollow,
But when belts are growing tauter,
It is ice-cream soda water
That you'd give a dollar-ninety just to swallow.
In the well-known U.S.A.,
Where we used to work and play,

Attending to our pleasure and our biz,
Of all the liquid crew
The finest drink I knew
Was our brimming glass of ice-cream soda fizz!
It was fizz! fizz! fizz!
You foamin' glass o' chocolate soda fizz!
Gimme strawberry, vanilla,
Coffee, peach or sarsaparilla—
Gimme any kind o' ice-cream soda fizz!

† † †

THE BATTLE OF CHATEAU-THIERRY

Stars and Stripes, June 21, 1918.

Infantry and Marines share alike the glory of Chateau-Thierry. Not all the fighting was in that little junction town on the Marne, or even near it; but, thanks to our Yankee passion for labelling things, the swift succession of attack on attack along that whole sector during the first vivid days of June is likely to go down in the history of France and America as the battle of Chateau-Thierry.

If the future historian of that fighting shall record that both Infantryman and Marine won their laurels which shall never fade, glory which shall never be dimmed, he will be stating the truth, but stating it in more words than he needs.

For instead of writing Infantryman and Marine, he can say simply, "The American Soldier."

† † †

A TRIBUTE TO "MY GIRL OVER THERE"

By Irwin Salem, Tank Center, *Stars and Stripes,* May 13, 1918.

I remember you, dear friend,
When homeward I did wend
My way, with you, through overhanging trees;
And I don't forget the talks
We had on those homeward walks,
Even though I am far off across the seas.
And on many of those nights,
As we passed beneath the lights,
I would glance at you, and I could plainly see—
But I couldn't quite get started,
Before at last we parted,
To speak more plainly, dear, of you and me.
This much I'll tell to you—

And believe me, it is true—
That life is not worth living out—unless
You have something, or someone,
To protect from sun to sun,
And to fight for ere you gain your happiness.
That is what I'm doing now,
And it makes me feel, somehow,
As if all I love is menaced by the Hun;
For it's just such girls as you
Who will make us stick it through,
And keep it up until the fight is won.

† † †

A FAMOUS STORY ABOUT A MARINE AND A DOG

By Alexander Woollcott, *Stars and Stripes*, June 14, 1918.

This is the story of Verdun Belle, a trench dog who adopted a young leatherneck, of how she followed him to the edge of the battle around Chateau-Thierry, and was waiting for him when they carried him out. It is a true story.

Belle is a setter bitch, shabby white, with great splotches of chocolate brown in her coat. Her ears are brown and silken. Her ancestry is dubious. She is undersize and would not stand a chance among the haughtier breeds they show in splendor at Madison Square Garden back home. But the marines think there never was a dog like her since the world began.

No one in the regiment knows whence she came, nor why. When she joined the outfit in a sector near Verdun, she singled out one of the privates as her very own and attached herself to him for the duration of the war. The young marine would talk long and earnestly to her, and everyone swore that Belle could "compree" English.

She used to curl up at his feet when he slept, or follow silently to keep him company at the listening post. She would sit hopefully in front of him whenever he settled down with his laden mess kit, which the cooks always heaped extra-high in honor of Belle.

Belle was as used to war as the most weather-beaten poilu. The tremble of the ground did not disturb her, and the whining whir of the shells overhead only made her twitch and wrinkle her nose in her sleep. She was trench-broken. You could have put a plate of savory pork chops on the parapet, and nothing would have induced her to go up after them.

She weathered many a gas attack. Her master contrived a protection for her by cutting down and twisting a French gas mask. At first this sack over her nose irritated her tremendously, but once, when she was trying to claw it off with her forepaws, she got a whiff of the poisoned air. Then a great light dawned on Belle, and after that, at the first *alerte,* she would race for her mask. You could not have taken it from her until her master's pat on her back told her everything was all right.

In the middle of May, Belle presented a proud but not particularly astonished regiment with nine confused and wriggling puppies, black and white or, like their mother, brown and white, and possessed of incredible appetites. Seven of these were alive and kicking when, not so very many days ago, the order came for the regiment to pull up stakes and speed across France to help stem the German tide north of the troubled Marne.

In the rush and hubbub of marching orders, Belle and her brood were forgotten by everyone but the young marine. It never once entered his head to leave her or her pups behind. Somewhere he found a market basket and tumbled the litter into that. He could carry the pups, he explained, and the mother dog would trot at his heels.

Now the amount of hardware a marine is expected to carry on the march is carefully calculated to the maximum strength of the average· soldier, yet this leatherneck found extra muscle somewhere for his precious basket. If it came to the worst, he thought, he could jettison his pack. It was not very clear in his mind what he would do with his charges during a battle, but he trusted to luck and Verdun Belle.

For forty kilometers he carried his burden along the parched French highway. No one wanted to kid him out of it, nor could they if they would. When there followed a long advance by camion, he yielded his place to the basket of wriggling pups, while he himself hung on the tailboard.

But then there was more hiking, and the basket proved too much. It seemed that the battle line was somewhere far off. Solemnly, the young marine killed four of the puppies, discarded the basket, and slipped the other three into his shirt.

Thus he trudged on his way, carrying those three, pouched in forest green, as a kangaroo carries its young, while the mother dog trotted trustingly behind.

One night he found that one of the black and white pups was dead. The road, by this time, was black with hurrying troops, lumbering lorries jostling the line of advancing ambulances, dust-gray columns of soldiers moving on as far ahead and as far behind as the eye could see. Passing silently in the other direction was the desolate procession of refugees from the invaded countryside. Now and then a herd of cows or a little cluster of fugitives from some desolated village, trundling their most cherished possession in wheelbarrows and babycarts, would cause an eddy in the traffic.

Somewhere in this congestion and confusion, Belle was lost. In the morning there was no sign of her, and the young marine did not know what to do. He begged a cup of milk from an old Frenchwoman, and with the eyedropper from his kit he tried to feed the two pups. It did not work very well. Faintly, the veering wind brought down the valley from far ahead the sound of the cannon. Soon he would be in the thick of it, and there was no Belle to care for the pups.

Two ambulances of a field hospital were passing in the unending caravan. A lieutenant who looked human was in the front seat of one of them, a sergeant beside him. The leatherneck ran up to them, blurted out his story, gazed at them imploringly, and thrust the puppies into their hands.

"Take good care of them," he said. "I don't suppose I'll ever see them again."

And he was gone. A little later in the day, that field hospital was pitching its tents and setting up its kitchens and tables in a deserted farm. Amid all the hurry of preparation for the big job ahead, they found time to worry about those pups. The problem was food. Corned willy was tried and found wanting.

Finally, the first sergeant hunted up a farm-bred private, and the two of them spent that evening chasing four nervous and distrustful cows around a pasture, trying vainly to capture enough milk to provide subsistence for the new additions to the personnel.

Next morning the problem was still unsolved. But it was solved that evening.

For that evening a fresh contingent of marines trooped by the farm, and in their wake—tired, anxious, but undiscouraged—was Verdun Belle. Ten kilometers back, two days before, she had lost her master and, until she should find him again, she evidently had thought that any marine was better than none.

The troops did not halt at the farm, but Belle did. At the gate she stopped dead in her tracks, drew in her lolling tongue, sniffed inquiringly the evening air, and like a flash—a white streak along the drive—she raced to the distant tree where, on a pile of discarded dressings in the shade, the pups were sleeping.

All the corps men stopped work and stood around and marveled. For the onlooker it was such a family reunion as warms the heart. For the worried mess sergeant it was a great relief. For the pups it was a mess call, clear and unmistakable.

So, with renewed faith in her heart and only one worry left in her mind, Verdun Belle and her puppies settled down on detached service with this field hospital. When, next day, the reach of the artillery made it advisable that it should move down the valley to the shelter of a fine hillside chateau, you may be sure that room was made in the first ambulance for the three casuals.

This was the Chateau of the Guardian Angel, which stands on the right of the Paris-Metz road, just north of La Ferte as you hike toward Chateau-Thierry.

In a grove of trees beside the house the tents of the personnel were pitched, and the cots of the expected patients ranged side by side. The wounded came—came hour after hour in steady streams, and the boys of the hospital worked on them night and day. They could not possibly keep track of all the cases, but there was one who did. Always a mistress of the art of keeping out from underfoot, very quietly Belle hung around and investigated each ambulance that turned in from the main road and backed up with its load of pain to the door of the receiving room.

Then one evening they lifted out a young marine, listless in the half stupor of shell shock. To the busy workers he was just Case Number Such-and-Such, but there was no need to tell anyone who saw the wild jubilance of the dog that Belle had found her own again at last.

The first consciousness he had of his new surroundings was the feel of her rough pink tongue licking the dust from his face. And those who passed that way on Sunday last found two cots shoved together in the kindly shade of a spreading tree. On one the mother dog lay contented with her puppies. Fast asleep on the other, his arm thrown out so that one grimy hand could clutch one silken ear, lay the young marine.

Before long they would have to ship him on to the evacuation hospital, on from there to the base hospital, on and on and on. It was not very clear to anyone how another separation could be prevented. It was a perplexing question, but they knew in their hearts they could safely leave the answer to someone else. They could leave it to Verdun Belle.

† † †

One of the most famous stories of the war does not appear in this anthology: the celebrated gaffe by the United Press, telling American readers that the war had come to an end—four days before it actually did. But then the war ended. It was at 11 o'clock in the morning, on the eleventh day of the eleventh month of the year, 1918; the trenches became silent, and the fighting was over in no man's land. The war to end wars was over and would become known in a generation as "World War I," and of course there never again would be a war involving American boys. Among the intellectuals, among the pacifists, among the socialists who had opposed the war all along, there was cynicism about the matter. In the conventional press, such as the veteran *New York Herald,* there was exultation, because the horror of war was ended for all time. A Pulitzer prize went to the Herald for its editorial, published three years after the war was over.

† † †

THE UNKNOWN SOLDIER

New York Herald, November 11, 1921.

That which takes place today at the National Cemetery in Arlington is a symbol, a mystery and a tribute. It is an entombment only in the physical sense. It is rather the enthronement of Duty and Honor. This man who died for his country is the symbol of these qualities; a far more perfect symbol than any man could be whose name and deeds we know. He represents more, really, than the unidentified dead, for we cannot separate them spiritually from the war heroes whose names are written on their gravestones. He—the spirit whom we honor—stands for the unselfishness of all.

This, of all monuments to the dead, is lasting and immutable. So long as men reverse the finer things of life the tomb of the nameless hero will remain a shrine. Nor, with the shifts of time and mind, can there be a changing of values. No historian shall rise to modify the virtues or the faults of the Soldier. He has an immunity for which kings might pray. The years may bring erosion to the granite but not to the memory of the Unknown.

It is a common weakness of humanity to ask the questions that can never be answered in this life. Probably none to whom the drama of the Unknown Soldier has appealed has not wondered who, in the sunshine of earth, was the protagonist of today's ceremony. A logger from the Penobscot? A well driller from Texas? A machinist from Connecticut? A lad who left his hoe to rust among the Missouri corn? A longshoreman from Hell's Kitchen? Perhaps some youth from the tobacco fields, resting again in his own Virginia. All that the army tells us of him is that he died in battle. All that the heart tells is that some woman loved him. More than that no man shall learn. In this mystery, as in the riddle of the universe, the wise wonder; but they would not know.

What were his dreams, his ambitions? Likely he shared those common to the millions: a life of peace and honest struggle, with such small success as comes to most who try; and at the end the place on the hillside among his fathers. Today to do honor at his last resting place comes the greatest soldier of the age, famous statesmen from other continents, the President, the high judges and the legislators of his own country, and many men who, like himself, fought for the flag. At his bier will gather the most remarkable group that America has seen. And the tomb which Fate reserved for his is, instead of the narrow cell on the village hillside, one as lasting as that of Rameses and as inspiring as Napoleon's.

It is a great religious ceremony, this burial today. The exaltation of the nameless bones would not be possible except for Belief. Where were Duty and Honor, the wellsprings of Victory, if mankind feared that death drew a black curtain behind which lay nothing but the dark? So all in whom the spark of hope has not died can well believe that we, to whom the Soldier is a mystery, are not a mystery to him. They can believe that the watchers at Arlington today are not merely a few thousands of the living but the countless battalions of the departed. "Though he were dead, yet shall he live"—there is the promise to which men hold when everything of this earth has slipped away.

All the impressive ritual of today would be a mockery if we did not believe that, out in an infinity which astronomers cannot chart or mathematicians bound, the Unknown Soldier and all the glorious dead whom we honor in his dust are looking down upon this little spinning ball, conscious of our reverence. And when noon strikes, signal for the moment of silent prayer, few of those who stand with bared head will lack conviction that the rites at Arlington are viewed by other than mortal eyes. Only in that spirit may we honor the Unknown Soldier and those who, like him, died for this Republic.

Unknown, but not unknowing.

† † †

12

LISTENING TO THE TWENTIES ROAR

All our parents did not dance the Charleston. Many of them probably never heard of bathtub gin. Somewhere out in the land there were people who could not have identified Rudolph Valentino, Dorothy Parker, Red Grange, F. Scott Fitzgerald, or Izzie and Moe.

The 1920s did not roar for everybody, though it would be difficult to reach such a conclusion from reading some historical accounts of the time, some of the fiction, or seeing some of the movies, especially those that continue to recall the good old days of "Yes, Sir, That's My Baby" and the "Black Bottom." Here is where history, legend, and myth become intertwined, and any view of the 1920s that did not present the "roaring" view of that decade would be laughed out of court. So the documents of this fascinating time in our history are a mixture of the sober—and of the intoxicated.

An ancient cover of *Newsweek* demonstrates what many see as the symbolism of the giddy age. In the center is a flat-chested flapper, looking very much like Clara Bow. Her right hand almost touches a copy of Fitzgerald's *The Beautiful and Damned.* Below the book we see the Lone Eagle—Charles A. Lindbergh—looking mystically into the future, and his tiny plane, the *Spirit of St. Louis.* To the right are Rudy Vallee, singing through a megaphone, and a huge saxophone, grasped by a black hand.

How might one describe the 1920s? It was a period of reaction, not unlike the periods following other wars, with a typical postwar shift away from worry and responsibility. A red scare, launched by Woodrow Wilson's attorney-general, A. Mitchell Palmer, began the decade, though it was started in 1919, on the eve of the silly time. The wartime president found it hard to sell the League of Nations and the Versailles Treaty to the American people, and impossible to sell to the leaders of the opposition in Congress. The business of America was business, Calvin Coolidge said, and some Americans, at least, wanted to play, not to concern themselves with such boring matters as disarmament conferences and economics. The American people made the election of Warren G. Harding the signal event of 1920, and set the mood for the years that followed. Even with the shocking disclosures of Teapot Dome (or perhaps they were not as shocking to the masses as some historians suggest), Harding remained a greatly loved figure after his sudden death in 1923, and the election of his vice president, Coolidge, was a sweep in 1924. That year was no time for LaFollette and the Progressives, let alone the more conservative John Davis, nominee of the Democrats.

"Super-trials" were the hot, page one stories. Two aliens, Sacco and Vanzetti, were the cause celebre of the decade. Two brilliant college boys, Loeb and Leopold, experimented with crime in Chicago. Two veterans of the courtroom and the stump, William Jennings Bryan and Clarence Darrow, performed for the nation in Dayton, Tennessee. In Kentucky, in a different kind of trial, Floyd Collins fought for his life, trapped in a cave.

Some commentators liked to use the word "jazz" to symbolize the time; after all, George Gershwin introduced his *Rhapsody in Blue,* Paul Whiteman, curiously labeled "the Jazz King," was leading a big band, and Negro groups were moving out of Storyville and St. Louis and Kansas City to the bigger capitals. The morals of some— jazz morals?—did appear to be on the loose side, but many Americans were quiet, staid, old-fashioned, living in their small towns, not terribly troubled that they could not buy liquor in this time of nationwide prohibition.

It seemed a time of heroes; were the newspapers and magazines, the movies and the newly introduced radio giving undue stress to these tinsel celebrities? The Four Horsemen and Red Grange on the football fields; Johnny Weissmuller in the Olympics; Gertrude Ederle in the English Channel; Jack Dempsey and Gene Tunney in the ring; Babe Ruth in Yankee Stadium; Bobby Jones on the links. Valentino, *The Sheik;* Greta Garbo, the mysterious new actress from Sweden, and John Gilbert, her Latin-appearing sweetheart; Ramon Novarro, of *Ben-Hur;* Lon Chaney, of the great horror movies; Clara Bow and Mae Murray and the "bee-sting" lips; Chaplin, Fairbanks, and Mary Pickford. Eugene O'Neill and Freud in the theater; Maxwell Anderson and Laurence Stallings introducing theatergoers to swear words; Philip Barry and his sophisticates; Mae West in the courtroom. Even the writers were celebrities: F. Scott Fitzgerald, of the lost generation; Ernest Hemingway, shadow boxing in the streets of Paris and sitting admiringly at the feet of Gertrude Stein; Sinclair Lewis, knocking down one idol after another and beginning to pursue the dynamic young foreign correspondent, then on the rise, Dorothy Thompson.

Capone and Dion O'Banion, showy funerals for slain vice lords, the St. Valentine's Day massacre in a Clark Street garage. And the big bull market, ending on an October day in 1929.

Was all of this America in the 1920s? In Frederick Lewis Allen's *Only Yesterday,* and in many other books to follow, yes, it was. In journalism, it was still the age of newspapers, of the printed word; though some voices were being heard coming out of radio sets, and though newspapers like the *New York Daily News* were publishing photographs that would endure long after the written accounts: the sinking of the *Vestris,* the Wild Bull of the Pampas knocking Dempsey out of the ring, the Prince of Wales astride a horse.

The columnists came into their own in the 1920s, taking the place of the editors themselves in many cases. Some of the columnists were writing about government and politics; these became preeminent. Others were better known for light humor, for the kind of thing that had marked the work of Finley Peter Dunne and Eugene Field in another age. One of these columnists was Don Marquis, who wrote about a cockroach named archy, who typed out his observations at night after the staff had left the office, and who did not have enough strength to press down the key for capital letters, and about the cat, mehitabel, about whom archy loved to write. In late 1919 the newsmen who covered City Hall in the big city were having their problems, and archy the cockroach wrote about them.

† † †

A LETTER FROM MEHITABEL

New York Sun, December 20, 1919.

well archy mehitabel says to
me as i cannot
work the typewriter would
you mind writing an open
letter for me in
the sun dial here goes i
said and she dictated
as follows to
the city government i
hear you are thinking
of employing a lot of
cats at six dollars and a
half a year
to keep the rats and mice
from eating the archives and
the tired employees
in the city offices i
can understand that
when an employee goes to sleep
he might be in great
danger of being eaten
what you want is cats with
some class to them
and you will not be able to

get them for the money
i have a large feline
acquaintance one or
two of them are cats
almost as big as a tiger
no reflection on tammany
is intended i could
get you the services of hundreds
of cats at a decent wage
but first it would take a
little propaganda to get the
right sort of cats
interested in the idea a
fund is necessary for the
propaganda i would be
willing to administer this
fund and get recruits and
organize them
for a good salary but lay off
the six dollar and a
half a year stuff
communicate any offer you have
to make through archy
my publicity agent and general
business representative
                    mehitabel the cat
                            per archy
dictated but not read
ps tell the
mayor if the price is
right i can get a cat
for the reporters room
at the city hall who
would be able to eat a
reporter in four or five
bites and who would be
willing to do so if
properly approached all
the mayor would need to do
would be to point out
which reporter and
this cat would do the
rest or we might agree on
a flat rate for all the
reporters or we could say
ten reporters a year for
ten dollars a reporter just
as soon as one reporter is
eaten another will of course
take his place they

are fearless creatures these
reporters always willing
to go to their death
without stopping to make a
will but for a thousand
dollars a year i will agree to
keep the city hall
clear of reporters for at least
three days a week but
the first thing is the
propaganda fund
      mehitabel
            purr archy

† † †

Franklin P. Adams was *the* model of the columnist for many aspiring writers, though few writers had such wit and perception. He had had a poetry column in the *Stars and Stripes* of the late war, and verse was frequently the medium he employed. Later he became best known to those Americans who heard him on the radio or saw him in the movies; for he was one of the panel on a program called "Information, Please." Going back to that most famous of diarists, Samuel Pepys—Franklin P. Adams, F.P.A. to his fans—affected a style that was used in his "colyuming" throughout the decade. And he still wrote poetry, too.

† † †

A SHORT NOTE FROM F.P.A. PEPYS

New York Sun, May 21, 1928.

Monday, May 21.
I noted how this day W. Winchell hath chidden H. Broun for spelling kibitzer khibitzer, and made game of him Tuesday, for not dropping his h, but Walter himself spoke of Oliver P. H. Garrett, and I vowed that I should ask him whether it was Oliver Perry Hazard that won the Battle of Lake Erie.

† † †

THE TOXIN OF GENIUS

By F.P.A., *New York World,* 1928.

Homer and Milton were blind;
   Johnson was somewhat sclerotic;
Thomas Carlyle had abundance of bile;
DeQuincey was supernarcotic.

Poe was addicted to drink;
   Burns was a bibulous guy;
Gibbon and Scott were too cold or too hot,
   And Luther had pressure too high.

Nietzsche had headaches a lot;
   Keats had a kidney attack;
So for my art there is hope in my heart;
   I've got a pain in the back.

† † †

Will Rogers was not a journalist, at least not by training, but he was one of a long line of people who were celebrated enough in their time to be able to become columnists—with training on neither beat nor desk. He was born in 1879 in Indian Territory; he was a cowboy, a trick roper, a performer in rodeos and then in vaudeville and in the Ziegfeld Follies. Rogers had a wry and gentle wit, and he sometimes commented on current affairs as he twirled his rope. In the 1920s, in the midst of a career on the stage and also in the movies, he began to do a column, meanwhile becoming well-known for his appearances at national political conventions and on the radio. Here—a sample of Rogersisms.

† † †

WILL ROGERS COMMENTS ON LIFE

A Sampling from His Newspaper Column.

I would like to stay in Europe long enough to find some country that don't blame America for everything in the World that's happened to 'em in the last 15 years: debts, depression, disarmament, disease, fog, famine, or frostbite.

* * * * *

My family didn't come over on the Mayflower. But they met the boat.

* * * * *

A debt is just as hard for a government to pay as an individual. No debt ever came due at a good time. Borrowing is the only thing that is handy all the time.

* * * * *

Argentina exports wheat, meat, and gigolos, and the United States puts a tariff on the wrong two.

* * * * *

I don't belong to a regular, organized political party. I'm a Democrat.

* * * * *

I was the last of 7 children. My folks looked me over and instead of the usual drowning procedure, they said: "This thing has gone far enough, if they are going to look like this, we will stop."

* * * * *

Give an American a one-piece bathing suit, a hamburger and five gallons of gas, and they are just as tickled as a movie star with a new divorce.

* * * * *

Pacifists say that if you are ready for a war, you will have one. I bet there has not been a man insulted Jack Dempsey since he has been champion.

* * * * *

There is one thing about a Democrat! He would rather make a Speech than a Dollar.

* * * * *

A sure certainty about our Memorial Days is as fast as the ranks from one war thin out the ranks from another take their place. Prominent men run out of Decoration Day speeches, but the world never runs out of wars. People talk peace, but men give their life's work to war. It won't stop till there is as much brains and scientific study put to aid peace as there is to promote war.

† † †

No one surpassed Walter Lippmann as a political columnist, in the 1920s or since, even though his major role in the roaring years was as editor of the New York *World*. Lippmann was a kind of Renaissance man: one of the storied group who studied at Harvard early in this century; an aide to the muckraking Lincoln Steffens; a co-founder of the *New Republic;* an adviser to Wilson. He took over on the *World* after the death of Frank Cobb, and he went to the *Herald Tribune* when the *World* succumbed (to all intents and purposes) in 1931. His list of books is imposing—*A Preface to Politics, The Public Philosophy,* and that original work of 1922 called *Public Opinion,* in which he enunciated the concept of stereotypes—the pictures in our heads. A representative piece of column writing by Lippmann was from the *New Republic* years.

† † †

SKETCHES IN THE SAND

By Walter Lippmann, *New Republic,* August 7, 1915, reprinted in *New Republic* 40th anniversary issue, 131, No. 21 (November 25, 1954), p. 14.

That is what kills political writing, this absurd pretence you are delivering a great utterance. You never do. You are just a puzzled man making notes about what you think. You are not building the Pantheon, then why act like a graven image? You are drawing sketches in the sand which the sea will wash away. What more is your book but your infinitesimal scratching, and who the devil are you to be grandiloquent and impersonal? The truth is you're afraid to be wrong. And so you put on these airs and use these established phrases, knowing that they will sound familiar and will be respected. But this fear of being wrong is a disease. You cover and qualify and elucidate, you speak vaguely, you mumble because you are afraid of the sound of your own voice. And then you apologize for your timidity by frowning learnedly on anyone who honestly regards thought as an adventure, who strikes ahead and takes his chances. You are like a man trying to be happy, like a man trying too hard to make a good mashie shot in golf. It can't be done by trying so hard to do it. Whatever truth you contribute to the world will be one lucky shot in a thousand misses. You cannot be right by holding your breath and taking precautions.

† † †

With such columnists as Walter Lippmann, Frank R. Kent of *The Great Game of Politics,* David Lawrence, Mark Sullivan, and Paul Mallon a new journalistic genre came into being. The concept of interpretation of current affairs accompanied this new development, and there is little question that certain magazines, notably one called *Time,* played major roles in the development of interpretation. *Time* was the creation of two bright young men not long out of Yale, Briton Hadden and Henry Luce, who wanted what they thought of as their "newspaper," and who brought out a new magazine in 1923 that bore some similarity to the *Literary Digest* but that was for the most part an original. Their idea was a weekly summing up of the news, an analysis, a pulling together of developments that would provide guidance for certain readers—especially those who did not have the "time" to do all the other reading they otherwise might do. Volume I, Number 1, of *Time* appeared March 3, 1923. Except for its black-and-white cover it was much like the *Time* of later years. Soon the founders were experimenting with inverted sentences, multiple modifiers, and a rather free interpretation of the news that later made their magazine as disliked by some as admired by others.

† † †

A SAMPLING FROM THE NEW "NEWS MAGAZINE"

Time, I, No. 1 (March 3, 1923), p. 1. Reprinted by permission from *Time,* The Weekly Newsmagazine: Copyright Time Inc.

MR. HARDING'S DEFEAT

Seeking only the nation's welfare, Mr. Harding has suffered defeat at the hands of Congress. Not only that, but the man who was elected President by the largest plurality in history has been reproved by a Congress controlled by his own party.

The Ship Subsidy Bill, never popular, and never made so by the President, was politely strangled to death. . . .

IN 1924

Who will be the Democratic Presidential nominee in 1924? Before Senator Oscar Underwood sailed for Egypt last week he wrote the following sentence in a letter to a fellow Alabaman: "When I return I shall give very careful and thorough consideration to the friendly suggestions that are being made in reference to the advisability of my entering the fight for the Presidential nomination of our party.". . .

A NEW WORLD COURT

Mr. Harding and Mr. Hughes proposed that the United States join The Hague Permanent Court of International Justice. The suggestion gained the support of two men as far apart politically as former President Wilson and Ambassador Harvey. . . .

† † †

An organization calling itself the American Society of Newspaper Editors was founded in 1922, and a major function performed in its early years was to enunciate a code of conduct and to deal with the behavior of some newspapers in an age whose news stories undoubtedly contributed to a laxness in press treatment. One of the problems was whether to expel Frederick Bonfils of the *Denver Post,* whose role in the Teapot Dome was said to have been the blackmailing of an oil boss named Harry Sinclair. At the first annual meeting of the ASNE, in 1923, a statement of principles was adopted.

† † †

CANONS OF JOURNALISM

American Society of Newspaper Editors, April, 1923, in Frank Luther Mott and Ralph D. Casey, eds., *Interpretations of Journalism* (New York: Crofts, 1937), pp. 457-459.

The primary function of newspapers is to communicate to the human race what its members do, feel, and think. Journalism, therefore, demands of its practitioners the widest range of intelligence, of knowledge, and of experience, as well as natural and trained powers of observation and reasoning. To its opportunities as a chronicle are indissolubly linked its obligations as teacher and interpreter.

To the end of finding some means of codifying sound practice and just aspirations of American journalism, these canons are set forth:

I

Responsibility.—The right of a newspaper to attract and hold readers is restricted by nothing but consideration of public welfare. The use a newspaper makes of the share of public attention it gains serves to determine its sense of responsibility, which it shares with every member of its staff. A journalist who uses his power for any selfish or otherwise unworthy purpose is faithless to a high trust.

II

Freedom of the Press.—Freedom of the press is to be guarded as a vital right of mankind. It is the unquestionable right to discuss whatever is not explicitly forbidden by law, including the wisdom of any restrictive statute.

III

Independence.—Freedom from all obligations except that of fidelity to the public interest is vital.

I. Promotion of any private interest contrary to the general welfare, for whatever reason, is not compatible with honest journalism. So-called news communications from private sources should not be published without public notice of their source or else substantiation of their claims to value as news, both in form and substance.

2. Partisanship in editorial comment which knowingly departs from the truth does violence to the best spirit of American journalism; in the news columns it is subversive of a fundamental principle of the profession.

IV

Sincerity, Truthfulness, Accuracy.—Good faith with the reader is the foundation of all journalism worthy of the name.

1. By every consideration of good faith a newspaper is constrained to be truthful. It is not to be excused for lack of thoroughness or accuracy within its control or failure to obtain command of these essential qualities.

2. Headlines should be fully warranted by the contents of the articles which they surmount.

V

Impartiality.—Sound practice makes clear distinction between news reports and expressions of opinion. News reports should be free from opinion or bias of any kind.

1. This rule does not apply to so-called special articles unmistakably devoted to advocacy or characterized by a signature authorizing the writer's own conclusions and interpretations.

VI

Fair Play.—A newspaper should not publish unofficial charges affecting reputation or moral character without opportunity given to the accused to be heard; right practice demands the giving of such opportunity in all cases of serious accusation outside judicial proceedings.

1. A newspaper should not invade private rights or feelings without sure warrant of public right as distinguished from public curiosity.

2. It is the privilege, as it is the duty, of a newspaper to make prompt and complete correction of its own serious mistakes of fact or opinion, whatever their origin.

VII

Decency.—A newspaper cannot escape conviction of insincerity if, while professing high moral purposes, it supplies incentives to base conduct, such as are to be found in details of crime and vice publication of which is not demonstrably for the public good. Lacking authority to enforce its canons, the journalism here represented can but express the hope that deliberate pandering to vicious instincts will encounter effective public disapproval or yield to the influence of a preponderant professional condemnation.

† † †

It was a decade of interpretation of the news, and of lofty codes of conduct. But it was still the roaring twenties, the time of the stories Americans still like to recall. For reasons that would seem obvious to anyone who closely follows sports, the 1920s were a golden age, to use a much overworked term. Celebrities abounded. Many of them were genuinely good, if not great, people who inevitably would be compared for fifty years with others who came along. It also was a golden age for sports writers. One of them was W. O. McGeehan, whose golden age story most remembered was the one about Jack Dempsey and Luis Angel Firpo.

† † †

THE MANASSA MATADOR AND THE WILD BULL OF THE PAMPAS

New York Herald, September 14, 1923.

The Manassa matador dropped the Wild Bull of the Pampas, but not until the matador was gored by the bull so that he will remember it for many a day. Fifty-seven seconds after the bell rang for the second round at the Polo Grounds last night, Luis Angel Firpo, the hope and pride of Latin America, rolled over near the ropes at the south side of the ring inert, unconscious—knocked out.

But what happened before this was as hard to follow as the shifting colors of a kaleidoscope. It was the most savage heavyweight bout that ever was staged, while it lasted. The first round was startlingly like that sanguinary affair at Toledo when Dempsey knocked out Jess Willard and won his championship.

Seven times Dempsey dropped the Argentine giant last night, and seven times the giant pulled himself up to his feet. He came up each time fighting, and lashing savagely but blindly at the champion. It was a right to the jaw that dropped Firpo the first time. The other six times the giant was felled by volleys of blows, on the head, on the body, all over his huge bulk. As he dropped for the fourth time it seemed that he could not rise.

Charles Schwegler, the old prize fighter, who was at the bell, rose in his chair and counted. Firpo turned his seemingly sightless eyes in the direction of the bell as the counter shouted "Nine!" He dragged himself upward painfully and slowly, only to be knocked down again and again. . . .

Near the ringside the pack sensed the fact that it would be over in the second round. They crowded closer to the ring. At the bell starting the bout Dempsey, with his teeth bared in that ring snarl and the face suggesting the wolf, rushed out of his corner. He battered Firpo against the ropes.

Then there was a gasp as though all the spectators had caught the same fear. Firpo swung that cave man's right of his and caught the champion under the chin. Dempsey reeled against the ropes, groggy. Then he slipped through them on the south side of the ring in among the typewriters and telegraph instruments.

The man at the bell bawled his count. He reached the count of three when Dempsey was pushed back into the ring. The champion looked a bit wobbly. His eyes seemed to be glazed for just a fraction of a second. His jaw was sunk, and he looked bewildered. But that was just for a fleeting instant. The scowl came back again, and Dempsey settled down to his killing of the Wild Bull. . . .

Dempsey stood a little back from the fallen giant as he fell for the last time. He listened for the final count just a little wobbly on his own clean-cut legs. As it went to eight he licked his lips in a wolfish fashion. At "ten" he rushed to his corner into the arms of his younger brother and Johnny Dempsey. Then he raised his gloves in acknowledgment of the cheering that finally came.

This was no boxing match. It was a fight, and a most primitive one at that. . . .

† † †

Heywood Broun was much more than sports writer, but he *was* of that group who wrote the famous sports tales. He was a correspondent in World War I, one of the pioneering newspaper columnists, a conscience of the press on the New York *World,* and later founded the American Newspaper Guild. Broun, like Walter Lippmann, was a Harvard man; he would have been of the class of 1910 had he graduated. He was a rumple-suited intellectual, looking to one of his cronies in the Thanatopsis Poker and Inside Straight Club, Dorothy Parker, like an unmade bed. Part of his brilliance as a columnist and even political commentator was that he wrote everything as clearly and entertainingly as though it were a sports story; he appeared to know that *good* sports writing is about the best journalistic writing there is.

† † †

BABE RUTH IN THE 1923 WORLD SERIES

By Heywood Broun, *New York World,* October 12, 1923.

The Ruth is mighty and shall prevail. He did yesterday. Babe made two home runs, and the Yankees won from the Giants at the Polo Grounds by a score of four to two. This evens up the World Series, with one game for each contender.

It was the first game the Yankees won from the Giants since October 10, 1921, and it ended a string of eight successive victories for the latter, with one tie thrown in.

Victory came to the American League champions through a change in tactics. Miller Huggins could hardly fail to have observed Wednesday that terrible things were almost certain to happen to his men if they paused anyplace along the line from first to home.

In order to prevent blunders in base running he wisely decided to eliminate it. The batter who hits a ball into the stands cannot possibly be caught napping off any base.

The Yankees prevented Kelly, Frisch, and the rest from performing tricks in black magic by consistently hammering the ball out of the park or into sections of the stand where only amateurs were seated. . . .

For the first time since coming to New York, Babe achieved his full brilliance in a World Series game. Before this he has varied between pretty good and simply awful, but yesterday he was magnificent.

Just before the game John McGraw remarked:

"Why shouldn't we pitch to Ruth? I've said before, and I'll say again, we pitch to better hitters than Ruth in the National League."

Ere the sun had set on McGraw's rash and presumptuous words, the Babe had flashed across the sky fiery portents which should have been sufficient to strike terror and conviction into the hearts of all infidels. But John McGraw clung to his heresy with a courage worthy of a better cause.

In the fourth inning Ruth drove the ball completely out of the premises. McQuillan was pitching at the time, and the count was two balls and one strike. The strike was a fast ball shoulder-high, at which Ruth had lunged with almost comic ferocity and ineptitude.

Snyder peeked at the bench to get a signal from McGraw. . . . McGraw scratched his nose, to indicate: "Try another of those shoulder-high fast ones on the Big Bam and let's see if we can't make him break his back again."

But Babe didn't break his back, for he had something solid to check his terrific swing. The ball started climbing from the moment it left the plate. It was a pop fly with a brand-new gland and, though it flew high, it also flew far.

When last seen the ball was crossing the roof of the stand in deep right field at an altitude of 315 feet. We wonder whether new baseballs conversing together in the original package ever remark: "Join Ruth and see the world."

In the fifth Ruth was up again, and by this time McQuillan had left the park utterly and Jack Bentley was pitching. . . .

Snyder called for the delivery as directed, and Ruth half topped a line drive over the wall of the lower stand in right field. With that drive the Babe tied a record. Benny Kauff and Duffy Lewis are the only other players who ever made two home runs in a single World Series game.

But was McGraw convinced and did he rush out of the dugout and kneel before Ruth with a cry of "Maestro" as the Babe crossed the plate? He did not. He nibbled at not a single word he has ever uttered in disparagement of the prowess of the Yankee slugger. In the ninth Ruth came to bat with two out and a runner on second base. By every consideration of prudent tactics an intentional pass seemed indicated.

Snyder jerked his head around and observed that McGraw was blowing his nose. The Giant catcher was puzzled, for that was a signal he had never learned. By a process of pure reasoning he attempted to figure out just what it was that his chief was trying to convey to him. . . .

McGraw was saying: "Pitch to the big bum if he hammers every ball in the park into the North River."

And so, at Snyder's request, Bentley did pitch to Ruth, and the Babe drove the ball deep into right center; so deep that Casey Stengel could feel the hot breath of the bleacherites on his back as the ball came down and he caught it. If that drive had been just a shade to the right it would have been a third home run for Ruth. As it was, the Babe had a great day, with two home runs, a terrific long fly, and two bases on balls. . . .

† † †

Grantland Rice was another of the legendary names, one of the crew who worked for Guy Viskniskki on *Stars and Stripes*. Rice has been quoted by countless followers over the years for his celebrated verse: "For when the One Great Scorer comes to mark against your name, /He writes—not that you won or lost—but how you played the game." And he was the one who looked out and saw Harry Stuhldreher, Jim Crowley, Elmer Layden, and Don Miller, and put them into sports history—the Four Horsemen, not of the Apocalypse, but of Notre Dame. Like Heywood Broun he wrote one of the deservedly famous stories of baseball, though his hero was not Babe Ruth but was Walter Johnson, who was known for throwing the fastest ball in history.

✝   ✝   ✝

A CLASSIC MOMENT FOR A CLASSIC PITCHER

By Grantland Rice, *New York Tribune,* October 10, 1924.

WASHINGTON, Oct. 10.—Destiny, waiting for the final curtain, stepped from the wings to-day and handed the king his crown.

In the most dramatic moment of baseball's sixty years of history the wall-eyed goddess known as Fate, after waiting eighteen years, led Walter Johnson to the pot of shining gold that waits at the rainbow's end.

For it was Johnson, the old Johnson, brought back from other years with his blazing fast ball singing across the plate for the last four rounds, that stopped the Giant attack, from the ninth inning through the twelfth and gave Washington's fighting ball club its world series victory by the score of 4 to 3, in the seventh game of a memorable struggle.

Washington won just at the edge of darkness, and it was Johnson's great right arm that turned the trick. As Earl McNeely singled and Muddy Ruel galloped over the plate with the winning run in the last of the twelfth, 38,000 people rushed on the field with a roar of triumph never heard before, and for more than thirty minutes, packed in one vast, serried mass around the bench, they paid Johnson and his mates a tribute that no one present will ever forget. It was something beyond all belief, beyond all imagining. Its crashing echoes are still singing out across the stands, across the city, on into the gathering twilight of early autumn shadows. There was never a ball game like this before, never a game with as many thrills and heart throbs strung together in the making of drama that came near tearing away the soul, to leave it limp and sagging, drawn and twisted out of shape.

Washington, facing the last of the eighth inning, was a beaten team, with the dream about closed out. And then like a heavy blast from hidden explosives, a rally started that tied the score, the two most important tallies of baseball lore sweeping over the plate as Bucky Harris's infield blow skirted the ground and suddenly leaped upward over Lindstrom's glove.

It was this single from the great young leader that gave Johnson his third and final chance. For, as the Giants came to bat in the ninth, with the score knotted at 3 and 3, there came once more the old familiar figure, slouching across the infield sod to his ancient home in the box. Here once more was the mighty moment, and as 38,000 stood and cheered, roared and raved, Johnson began to set the old-time fast one singing on its way. . . .

Johnson was on his way, and neither Destiny nor the Giants could head him off. He had suffered two annihilations, but his mighty moment had come and he was calling back stuff from a dozen years ago. To show that he was headed for another triumph and that young blood was coursing through his veins again, he came to the eleventh and struck out Frisch and Kelly. It was the first time in four years of world series play that any pitcher had struck out the keen-eyed Frisch. . . .

This was the spot which destiny picked as the place to hand "Old Barney" the long delayed crown, . . . Johnson was safe on Jackson's error at short, and with only one out McNeely decided to follow the Harris attack. He slashed one along the ground to third, and as Lindstrom came in for the ball for the second time in the game the ball suddenly bounded high over his head as Ruel crossed with the run that brought world series glory to Washington's game and crippled club. . . .

† † †

Both American literature and the movies have leaned on the next account, that of Floyd Collins, the young explorer who died in a cave in Kentucky. Robert Penn Warren wrote about the incident—or about something closely resembling it—in *The Cave,* and Billy Wilder depicted it in a shocking film called *Ace in the Hole.* It was without doubt one of the major stories of its time, and the reporter who won recognition for telling it was William Burke (Skeets) Miller of the *Louisville Courier-Journal.*

† † †

A YOUNG MAN DIES IN A CAVE

Louisville Courier-Journal, February 3, 1925.

SAND CAVE, CAVE CITY, KENTUCKY, FEBRUARY 3—Death holds no terror for Floyd Collins, he told me when I fed him tonight, more than 115 hours after he was trapped in Sand Cave, but he does not expect to die in the immediate future.

"I believe I would go to heaven," Collins said as I place a bottle of milk to his lips, "but I can feel that I am to be taken out alive and—with both of my feet."

I have been in the cave three times since 5:30 o'clock this afternoon at the head of as many rescue parties. I am small and able to get back to the prisoner with the least possible difficulty. I am confident we are working now on a plan that will save Collins' life, and Collins shares my views.

Our plan is simple. I lead the way into the small, narrow, and extremely cold passageway and squirm back more than one hundred feet.

Thirteen other men crawl in behind me and pass a small chip hammer along to me. With this I work as best I can, enlarging the cave, and, as soon as I have succeeded in getting loose a large piece, I pass it back to the men behind me and, in this way, it is relayed out to the entrance.

It is terrible inside. The cold, dirty water numbs us as soon as we start in. We have come to dread it, but each of us tells ourselves that our suffering is as nothing compared to Collins'.

His patience during long hours of agony, his constant hope when life seemed nearing an end, is enough to strengthen the heart of anyone.

Collins doesn't know it, but he is playing a very, very big part in his own rescue.

Late this afternoon it was decided that Collins might possibly be rescued by drilling through the side of a hill and tunneling through behind him. The work was started by seven drillers of the Kentucky Rock Asphalt Company, but it was halted after a short time. It was feared that vibrations would dislodge huge rocks above Collins and crush him to death.

It was then decided to send rescuers in to him. I went first, starting in at 5:30 o'clock. In the next hour we made more progress than had been made in any single attempt before, and our waning confidence came back.

Time after time large and small rocks were passed along the human chain and out of the cave, which trapped Collins at ten o'clock Friday morning after the first attempt to explore it.

A minute seems an hour in there, and the water-sharpened rocks cut like a knife. But the numbness has its compensations. It keeps one from feeling the cuts and bruises.

All of us were exhausted, finally, and the word was passed back to crawl out. The air outside revived us quickly.

† † †

That terrible and tragic story took place in Kentucky; just to the south, in Tennessee, and in the same year, more social and journalistic history was being made. In later years, the central figure in what we call the Monkey Trial could not even remember the circumstances of how he got himself involved; he was not even sure that he had ever actually taught Darwin's theory of evolution. But this man, John T. Scopes, who was a junior high school teacher in Dayton, Tennessee, did agree to stand trial in a test case for the American Civil Liberties Union. It was the stuff of high drama, but also of comedy, and it, like the Floyd Collins story, became drama in the theater and on film. The nation watched the Scopes trial in Dayton not because of John T. Scopes, or even because it was about man and his monkey ancestry, but because Clarence Darrow and

William Jennings Bryan were there. Darrow was nationally known for both his liberal leanings and his courtroom theatricality; he had defended Eugene Debs, the McNamara brothers, Big Bill Haywood, and Loeb and Leopold. Now he was defending Scopes, and Bryan, the Boy Orator of the Platte, the man who had run three times for the presidency, been secretary of state under Woodrow Wilson, and toured the land as a Chautauqua orator, was prosecuting him. And Bryan himself became a defense witness for Darrow.

† † †

BRYAN TAKES THE STAND IN DAYTON

By the Associated Press, July 21, 1925.

Dayton, Tenn., July 20 (A.P.)—Admitted agnosticism met fundamentalism here today as Clarence Darrow, counsel for the defense in the Scopes evolution case, drew out William Jennings Bryan, associate counsel for the prosecution, upon the witness stand.

Hundreds of men and women, drawn from the peaceful hills and valleys for miles around, pushed close to the rough wooden platform behind the courthouse as the verbal swords of the two clashed time and again, sending off flashes that drew volleys of handclapping and booming mountain fox calls.

A silence, broken only by the rustling of the maple trees, settled over the crowd as Arthur Garfield Hayes [sic] announced the intention of the defense to call Bryan to the witness stand.

The purpose was explained later by Mr. Darrow as an effort to "show the people what fundamentalism is." Bryan arose from the witness stand to tell Darrow, the judge and the assembled spectators that its purpose was to cast "slurs upon the Bible."

The nature of the examination brought Atty. Gen. A.T. Stewart and other members of counsel for the prosecution to their feet time after time to interpose objections. Frequently it even caused Darrow to arise with objections as the witness proceeded to direct the course himself. . . .

The questioning began with the usual qualifying questions for the expert witness, and after Bryan had announced his intention of calling to the stand Mr. Darrow, Dudley Field Malone and Mr. Hays.

The witness said that he had made considerable study of the Bible, including its interpretation, on the particular question involved.

"Do you claim that everything in the Bible should be literally interpreted?"

"I believe that everything in the Bible should be accepted as it is given there. Some of the Bible is given illustratively. For instance, ye are the salt of the earth. I would not insist that man was actually salt or that he had flesh of salt, but it is used in the sense of salt as saving God's people."

"But when you read that Jonah swallowed the whale—or that the whale swallowed Jonah— excuse me please, how do you literally interpret that?"

"When I read that a big fish swallowed Jonah it doesn't say whale."

"Doesn't it? Are you sure?"

"That is my recollection of it. A big fish, and I believe it, and I believe in a God who can make a whale and can make a man and can make both do what he pleases.". . . .

† † †

Darrow and Bryan were not the only celebrities at Dayton; many others came to see the fantastic show, and the best known of the reporters was Henry L. Mencken, who had edited *The Smart Set* with George Jean Nathan, was now editing the *American Mercury,* and was the darling of all those who admired a facile writer who could throw off terms like "booboisie" and the "Sahara of the Bozart," both of them to describe the slobs of the land who were not in a class with him. Mencken was a veteran of newspaper work, mainly in Baltimore, and he believed that anyone who did not live in that city was just "camping out." He camped out, presumably, in Dayton, where he served as a kind of Greek chorus, obviously loving the garish goings-on. When the trial was all over, he chortled his way back east, and then had a final comment to make, for the old fundamentalist orator, Bryan, was dead, with the trial just barely ended.

† † †

WILLIAM JENNINGS BRYAN

By H. L. Mencken, *American Mercury,* October, 1925, reprinted in Lawrence E. Spivak and Charles Angoff, eds., *The American Mercury Reader* (Philadelphia: Blakiston, 1944), pp. 34-36. Reprinted courtesy of the American Mercury, P.O. Box 1306, Torrance, Calif.

Has it been marked by historians that the late William Jennings Bryan's last secular act on this earth was to catch flies? A curious detail, and not without its sardonic overtones. He was the most sedulous flycatcher in American history, and by long odds the most successful. His quarry, of course, was not *Musca domestica* but *Homo neandertalensis.* For forty years he tracked it with snare and blunderbuss, up and down the backways of the Republic. Wherever the flambeaux of Chautauqua smoked and guttered, and the bilge of Idealism ran in the veins, and Baptist pastors dammed the brooks with the saved, and men gathered who were weary and heavy laden, and their wives who were unyieldingly multiparous and full of Peruna—there the indefatigable Jennings set up his traps and spread his bait.

He knew every forlorn country town in the South and West, and he could crowd the most remote of them to suffocation by simply winding his horn. The city proletariat, transiently flustered by him in 1896, quickly penetrated his buncombe and would have no more of him; the gallery jeered him at every Democratic national convention for twenty-five years. But out where the grass grows high, and the horned cattle dream away the lazy days, and men still fear the powers and principalities of the air—out there between the corn-rows he held his old puissance to the end. There was no need of beaters to drive in his game. The news that he was coming was enough. For miles the flivver dust would choke the roads. And when he rose at the end of the day to discharge his Message there would be such breathless attention, such a rapt and enchanted ecstasy, such a sweet rustle of amens as the world had not known since Johanan fell to Herod's headsman.

There was something peculiarly fitting in the fact that his last days were spent in a one-horse Tennessee village, and that death found him there. The man felt at home in such scenes. He liked people who sweated freely, and were not debauched by the refinements of the toilet. Making his progress up and down the Main street of little Dayton, surrounded by gaping primates from the upland valleys of the Cumberland Range, his coat laid aside, his bare arms and hairy chest shining damply, his bald head sprinkled with dust—so accoutred and on display he was obviously happy. He liked getting up early in the morning, to the tune of cocks crowing on the dunghill. He liked the heavy, greasy victuals of the farmhouse kitchen. He liked country lawyers, country pastors, all country people. I believe that this liking was sincere—perhaps the only sincere thing in the man.

His nose showed no uneasiness when a hillman in faded overalls and hickory shirt accosted him on the street, and besought him for light upon some mystery of Holy Writ. The simian gabble of a country town was not gabble to him, but wisdom of an occult and superior sort. In the presence of city folks he was palpably uneasy. Their clothes, I suspect, annoyed him, and he was suspicious of their too delicate manners. . . .

He was born with a roaring voice, and it had the trick of inflaming half-wits. His whole career was devoted to raising these half-wits against their betters, that he himself might shine. His last battle will be grossly misunderstood if it is thought of as a mere exercise in fanaticism—that is, if Bryan the Fundamentalist Pope is mistaken for one of the bucolic Fundamentalists. There was much more in it than that, as everyone knows who saw him on the field. What moved him, at bottom, was simply hatred of the city men who had laughed at him so long, and brought him at last to so tatterdemalion an estate. He yearned to lead the anthropoid rabble against them, to set *Homo neandertalensis* upon them, to punish them for the execution they had done upon him by attacking the very vitals of their civilization. He went far beyond the bounds of any merely religious frenzy, however inordinate. When he began denouncing the notion that man is a mammal even some of the hinds at Dayton were agape. And when, brought upon Darrow's cruel hook, he writhed and tossed in a very fury of malignancy, bawling against the baldest elements of sense and decency like a man frantic—when he came to that tragic climax there were snickers among the hinds as well as hosannas.

Upon that hook, in truth, Bryan committed suicide, as a legend as well as in the body. He staggered from the rustic court ready to die, and he staggered from it ready to be forgotten, save as a character in a third-rate farce, witless and in execrable taste. . . .

He lived long enough to make patriots thank the inscrutable gods for Harding, even for Coolidge. Dullness has got into the White House, and the smell of cabbage boiling, but there is at least nothing to compare to the intolerable buffoonery that went on in Tennessee. The President of the United States doesn't believe that the earth is square, and that witches should be put to death, and that Jonah swallowed the whale. . . .

† † †

The story of Nicola Sacco and Bartolomeo Vanzetti had begun much earlier in the decade, when they were arrested May 5, 1920, on a charge of committing a payroll robbery-murder in South Braintree, Massachusetts. Even in a time of so much excitement and so much controversy their story could not be ignored, especially when it followed the frenzy of the red scare set off by Attorney-General Palmer, when aliens and anarchists and Bolsheviks were scaring the daylights out of millions of Americans. By the time Sacco and Vanzetti went to the electric chair on August 23, 1927, after their case had been reviewed and a seal of approval placed upon the verdict by a blue ribbon commission, there had been worldwide protests, and few journalists were more stricken than Heywood Broun of the *World,* who was so upset that he broke with his editor, Ralph Pulitzer, and brought his notable career on that newspaper to a close.

† † †

A COMMENTARY ON SACCO AND VANZETTI

By Heywood Broun, *New York World,* August 5, 1927.

When at last Judge Thayer in a tiny voice passed sentence upon Sacco and Vanzetti, a woman in the court room said with terror: "It is death condemning life!"

The men in Charlestown Prison are shining spirits, and Vanzetti has spoken with an eloquence not known elsewhere within our time. They are too bright, we shield our eyes and kill them. We are the dead, and in us there is not feeling nor imagination nor the terrible torment of lust for justice. And in the city where we sleep smug gardeners walk to keep the grass above our little houses sleek and cut whatever blade thrusts up a head above its fellows.

"The decision is unbelievably brutal," said the Chairman of the Defense Committee, and he was wrong. The thing is worthy to be believed. It has happened. It will happen again, and the shame is wider than that which must rest upon Massachusetts. I have never believed that the trial of Sacco and Vanzetti was one set apart from many by reason of the passion and prejudice which encrusted all the benches. Scratch through the varnish of any judgment seat and what will you strike but hate thick-clotted from centuries of angry verdicts? Did any man ever find power within his hand except to use it as a whip? . . .

By now there has been a long and careful sifting of the evidence in the case. It is ridiculous to say that Sacco and Vanzetti are being railroaded to the chair. The situation is much worse than that. This is a thing done coldbloodedly and with deliberation. But care and deliberation do not guarantee justice. Even if every venerable college President in the country tottered forward to say "guilty" they could not alter facts. The tragedy of it all lies in the fact that though a Southern mountain man may move more quickly to a dirty deed of violence, his feet are set no more firmly in the path of prejudice than a Lowell ambling sedately to a hanging. . . .

I've said these men have slept, but from now on it is our business to make them toss and turn a little, for a cry should go up from many million voices before the day set for Sacco and Vanzetti to die. We have a right to beat against tight minds with our fists and shout a word into the ears of the old men: We want to know, we will know—"Why?"

† † †

And so the dizzy years roared along. The national imagination was stirred in the twenties, and many times in later years, by another of the courtroom dramas, this one involving Richard Loeb and Nathan Leopold, Jr., who had committed a thrill killing, their victim being a young boy named Bobby Franks. Clarence Darrow was the courtroom star here, too, and his defense saved the boys from death in the electric chair.

† † †

DARROW PLEADS FOR MERCY

By the Associated Press, August 1, 1924.

CHICAGO, July 31.—Mitigation, not of crime, but of punishment; mercy of judgment, founded not on the cold letter of the law, but on considerations of humanity—these were the points emphasized today by the defense in the hearing to determine the penalty Nathan

Leopold, jr., and Richard Loeb must pay for the murder of Robert Franks.

Clarence S. Darrow, 67-year-old veteran of court battles, fighting for the principles he has advocated in and out of court for many years, put squarely before Judge John R. Caverly the issue whether considerations of this character were to be written into the jurisprudence of Illinois.

"The state's attorney's office seems to feel the universe will crumble unless these boys hang," he said.

"We seek not mitigation of the crime, but only mitigation of the punishment, because of a diseased condition of the mind, constant in character but not amounting to legal insanity," was the keynote of the defense.

"I never have seen before the enthusiasm for the death penalty that has appeared in this case," Mr. Darrow said in his argument. He declared the prosecution had halted at nothing to gain its end, and added:

"That end is death.

"Youth itself is a mitigating circumstance," Mr. Darrow continued. "Until a person is 21 he may not enter into contracts or marry, legally, without consent of his parents or guardian. This is because of the minor's lack of discretion and mature judgment—in other words, his state of mind.

"These boys are minors and I cannot understand the glib attorneys who insist on hanging two young boys. I never have seen a more deliberate effort to turn human society into an organization of wolves.

"Human sympathy, common human kindness ought to count for something, also. Human judgments are uncertain at the best, but we have full faith this court will hear every proper piece of evidence and save these young lives."

Mr. Darrow's voice ranged from the quiet tone of a heart-to-heart talk to ringing vibrations that were audible in the corridors. At times he hooked his thumbs in his worn suspenders.

When discussing the youthfulness and mental conditions of his clients he crooned, but when denouncing "the blood-thirstiness" of the prosecution he raised a clenched fist above his head and brought it down with a vigorous swing.

Loeb and Leopold leaned forward to catch every word of their chief defender.

The boys found little opportunity to exchange their usual smiling confidences over the progress of the case. They greeted their relatives with the usual nod and in the recesses held brief conversations with them.

In one of these intervals Allen Loeb asked Dick whether he wished anything, and the youthful defendant leaned over and whispered a desire for some stick candy. It was promised him.

When the afternoon recess came a grimy-faced youngster slipped past the bailiffs at the door and accosted Jacob Franks, father of the victim of Leopold and Loeb.

"I am Carl Farmer and I used to know your boy," said the lad. "He did not belong to my gang, but we beat his gang at baseball once." Robert's father tried to slip a coin to the visitor but it was refused. "I don't want that," said Carl. "I just wanted you to know that all us kids are sorry.". . .

† † †

Did newspaper reporters in Chicago, or anywhere, ever behave the way they behaved in *The Front Page*? The argument goes on and on, an argument that began when Ben Hecht and Charles MacArthur, two reporters who had lived the Chicago experience, opened their play on Broadway in 1928. The play became a movie in 1931, again in 1940 (when the hero became a heroine), and again in 1974, all versions wild and funny and, maybe, improbable. For sure the 1920s were the years of jazz journalism, gutter journalism, tabloid journalism. History books treat the Sacco and Vanzetti case and the Scopes trial, but most of them give little space to Ruth Snyder, Hall-Mills, and the Brownings. These were the big stories of the new tabloids, the first of which was launched in 1919 by Joseph Medill Patterson, with help from his cousin, Robert R. McCormick, after the two had met while in Europe during the war and had plotted what was called, at first, the *Illustrated Daily News*. The newspaper made pictures an important part of the formula, along with sensation, and its name became the *New York Daily News*. The jazz age was made for such a paper, or perhaps such a paper was made for the jazz age. How proper it seems that the Snyder-Gray case should be told by that inhabitant of Manhattan, Damon Runyon, who would write all those glorious tales of guys and dolls and Apple Mary and the Lemon Drop Kid and Harry the Horse. The account by Runyon was written not for the *Daily News* but for the International News Service; the *News* made special history when a photographer named Tom Howard showed Ruth Snyder in the electric chair—as the jolts were going through her body. It was the most shocking photograph of a shocking era.

† † †

THE SNYDER-GRAY CASE

By Damon Runyon, International News Service, April 19-May 9, 1927.

A chilly-looking blonde with frosty eyes and one of those marble, you-bet-you-will chins, and an inert, scare-drunk fellow that you couldn't miss among any hundred men as a dead setup for a blonde, or the shell game, or maybe a gold brick.

Mrs. Ruth Snyder and Henry Judd Gray are on trial in the huge weatherbeaten old courthouse of Queens County in Long Island

City, just across the river from the roar of New York, for what might be called for want of a better name, The Dumbbell Murder. It was so dumb.

They are charged with the slaughter four weeks ago of Albert Snyder, art editor of the magazine, *Motor Boating,* the blonde's husband and father of her nine-year-old daughter, under circumstances that for sheer stupidity and brutality have seldom been equaled in the history of crime.

It was stupid beyond imagination, and so brutal that the thought of it probably makes many a peaceful, home-loving Long Islander of the Albert Snyder type shiver in his pajamas as he prepares for bed.

They killed Snyder as he slumbered, so they both admitted in confessions—Mrs. Snyder has since repudiated hers— first whacking him on the head with a sash weight, then giving him a few whiffs of chloroform, and finally tightening a strand of picture wire around his throat so he wouldn't revive.

This matter disposed of, they went into an adjoining room and had a few drinks of whisky used by some Long Islanders, which is very bad, and talked things over. They thought they had committed "the perfect crime," whatever that may be. It was probably the most imperfect crime on record. It was cruel, atrocious, and unspeakably dumb.

They were red-hot lovers then, these two, but they are strangers now.

Mrs. Snyder, the woman who has been called a Jezebel, a lineal descendant of the Borgia outfit, and a lot of other names, came in for the morning session of court stepping along briskly in her patent-leather pumps, with little short steps.

She is not bad-looking. I have seen much worse. She is thirty-three and looks just about that, though you cannot tell much about blondes. She has a good figure, slim and trim, with narrow shoulders. She is of medium height, and I thought she carried her clothes off rather smartly. She wore a black dress and a black silk coat with a collar of black fur. Some of the girl reporters said it was dyed ermine; others pronounced it rabbit. . . .

Gray, a spindly fellow in physical build, entered the courtroom with quick, jerky little steps behind an officer, and sat down between his attorneys, Samuel L. Miller and William L. Millard. His back was to Mrs. Snyder, who sat about ten feet distant. Her eyes were on a level with the back of his narrow head.

Gray was neatly dressed in a dark suit, with a white starched collar and subdued tie. He has always been a bit on the dressy side, it is said. He wears big, horn-rimmed spectacles, and his eyes have a startled expression. You couldn't find a meeker, milder-looking fellow in seven states, this man who is charged with one of the most horrible crimes in history. . . .

† † †

A special bit of gore was dished up for the readers of another of the tabloids, William Randolph Hearst's *Daily Mirror,* which followed the *Daily News* by five years. This was the Hall-Mills case: the gruesome murder of an Episcopal minister and a woman in his choir, their bodies being found under a tree in the countryside near New Brunswick, New Jersey, in 1922. Again, the classic account was published in a newspaper different from the one that pushed the story hardest, the writer being Dudley Nichols, who would go on to fame in Hollywood as a writer of notable screenplays, such as *The Informer.*

† † †

ABOUT A WITNESS CALLED "THE PIG WOMAN"

By Dudley Nichols, *New York World,* November 18, 1926. Copyright New York World Press Publishing Co., 1926.

COUNTY COURT HOUSE, SOMERVILLE, N.J., Nov. 18.—Like something brought in from the graveyard, Mrs. Jane Gibson, the "pig woman," lay flat on an iron hospital bed, between a doctor and a nurse, in court here to-day and croaked out how she had shuffled down De Russey's Lane one night more than four years ago when "the moon was shinin' bright and pretty" and run smack into the middle of New Jersey's most sensational murder, the Hall-Mills case.

With her face as white as death she told of her braying mule, the rickety wagon she followed, of the shadowy figures prowling, of a flashlight and a glittering thing, and then four shots in the dark.

And she pointed out Mrs. Frances Stevens Hall and her brothers, Henry and Willie Stevens, as the guilty people. . . .

Timing herself to the moment, when her mattress was lifted to a stretcher and four huskies took hold to remove her to the waiting ambulance, the "pig woman" rolled up her left elbow, turned a wild face at the three astonished defendants, and uttered loudly as she shook her right finger vindictively:

"I've told the truth, so help me God; and you know it; and you know it.". . .

Never had a more theatrical day in court been staged. For an hour and a quarter the pokey courtroom—built for three hundred but crammed with five—had been on pins and needles. Bulletins came by word of mouth and each mile of the ambulance's approach toward Somerville was ticked off.

Then came the nervous "She's here!" and the court atmosphere turned creepy as the aisles were cleared and four men came slowly, like pallbearers, with a stretcher on which something of flesh and blood lay hidden by sheets.

All the bailiffs in the country couldn't have kept that court room sitting then. All were standing, craning. There simply was something clammy about the whole thing, something begotten of nerves and the smell of iodoform and formaldehyde and excitement long pent and murder and impending death.

"Oh," said a woman weakly, "I do feel I'm going to faint." And another woman near on the left was trembling. . . .

Under [Prosecutor Alexander] Simpson's questioning she told her story. Her voice was papery and throaty at first, like the thin croaking of a frog in early spring. There was no noise but the rushing of pencils over paper as she croaked on in her queer way:

"My farm's on Hamilton Road near New Brunswick. That Thursday night between 8 and 9 I was sitting outside listening. I tied the dog out to a tree and sat right there ev'ry night... Somebody went and stole twenty rows of corn off my field... The dog stopped barkin' and I set on the swing and listened. . . .

"Jist then a wagon come, a rickety old wagon that rattled and rattled and rattled. . . . I put the saddle on Jenny and started out the road. . . . That wagon rattled down De Russey's Lane and I followed. When I got down the lane my mule brayed. I was afeard and stayed about fifty feet behind. . . .

"The wagon rattled right through the land onto Easton Avenue and jist as I turned round an automobile turned in with a white woman an' a colored man. An' she didn't have no hat on."

"Have you learned who she was?" asked Simpson, standing close by the bed.

"Yes. Mrs. Hall!"

"And the man?"

"Willie Stevens!". . .

"I went far back and tied Jenny to two little cedar trees in the field of the lane * * * When I got as fur as a big cedar tree I heered mumbling voices—men's voices and women's voices.* * * They was comin' closer, and I stood still. They was comin' from DeRussey's lane. * * *

"The men was saying, 'G.d. it,' and everything like that—all that kind of stuff, swearin' and carryin' on.

Somebody was hittin', hittin', hittin'. I could hear somebody's wind goin' out, and somebody said, 'ugh!' then somebody said, 'G.d.it, let go! a man hollered—he hollered, 'God damn it, let go!'. . .

Then somebody threw a flash toward where they was hollering. A flashlight. Yes, an' see something glitter an' I see a man, and I see another man like they were wrastlin' together, and wrastlin' together. One man was Henry Stevens.* * *

"Then the light went out and I heered a shot. Then I hear like somethin' fall heavy. Then I run for my mule.* * *

"I heard a woman's voice say, after the shot, 'Oh, Henry!'—easy, very easy. An' the other woman began to scream, scream, scream, oh, so loud: 'Oh my, oh my, oh my, oh my'— so terrible loud.". . .

"Yes, I run for the mule after that first shot, but that woman was screaming, screaming, screaming, try-to run away or somethin'— screaming, screaming, screaming, an' jist about got my foot in the stirrup when bang, bang, bang—three quick shots.* * *

"An' then I listened, and then I heered the voice of a man. It seemed kinda like a woman hollered along there or someone. An' then I heered the voice of a man, and the moon was shin' down very bright, an' so I heered it agin, an' I looked right at the cedar, an' crossed over the lane right at the cedar, an' I seen a big white-haired woman doin' something with her hands, crying or something.

"She was bendin' down, facin' something. She was kneelin' down, fixin' something, an' it was the woman I seen in the lane earlier in the evening—Mrs. Hall.". . .

† † †

Bernarr Macfadden was a physical culturist, a small but sturdy man who drank great quantities of carrot juice, liked to pose in the nude, had three wives, and published *Physical Culture, Liberty, True Story,* and the *New York Evening Graphic.* The latter was the third of the steamy tabloids of the 1920s, and the one least likely to be remembered by posterity. Macfadden was assisted in the venture by an editor named Emile Gauvreau, who developed a photographic technique called the "composograph"; Gauvreau recalled how he produced an illustration for the *Graphic* showing Rudolph Valentino entering the spirit world and meeting celebrities who had preceded him into that other vale. The representative story in the *Graphic* was about Peaches and Daddy Browning, who were involved in a very messy divorce action.

† † †

DADDY BROWNING TELLS HIS STORY

New York Evening Graphic, October 12, 1926.

In an astonishing interview, Edward West Browning, self-anointed "High Priest of the Daddy Cult," stood last night in his pulpit of business and there, amid the ruins of his Temple of Love, revealed to the world through the GRAPHIC the most intimate details of his married life with Peaches Heenan. "I wanted, oh how I longed for a CHILD OF MY OWN," he sobbed out in his heart anguish. Here is his story:

"Peaches did not sleep with me. From the very first night she has always slept with her mother. My marriage was IN NAME only. From our very wedding night Peaches has denied me my rights as a husband. I had hoped to play on the harp of celestial raptures. I thought I would be surrounded by the angels of love. Gnomes alone fluttered about. I don't want to say anything unkind, and even now I won't call my mother-in-law names, but she proved to be no dove of peace. I want Peaches back. I want to be a father. Peaches needs me and my care. I won't say she suffers from epilepsy, but she is a victim of something very close to epileptic fits, she rolls her eyes and froths at the mouth. In her story she charges that mine was a strange and weird love, and intimates that I have lost my virility. I am willing to submit to examination by any reputable group of physicians and they will prove that I am as virile and potent as a youth of 20."

† † †

Such stories were minor league alongside the major news event of 1927. To the 1920s, and to later times as well, the most memorable of all stories was the big one of 1927, the flight made by Colonel Charles A. Lindbergh across the Atlantic, in the little plane he called the *Spirit of St. Louis.* It was a heroic feat, in a time of heroes, in a time when heroes, and heroines, too, could be accepted without making an apology about them. One of the stories about "Lindy" described the welcome the flier received in France.

† † †

A HERO IS WELCOMED IN PARIS

Associated Press, May 23, 1927.

Paris, May 23.—France today gathered "Slim" Lindbergh to its heart.

The young American pilot, who traced a glorious arc through the skies from New York to Paris, to the plaudits of the world, was received in the palace of the Elysee by President Doumergue, and there decorated in the name of the republic with the cross of the Legion of Honor.

Lindbergh still was dressed in ill-fitting borrowed clothes, the tailors and shirtmakers still being busy supplying the wardrobe which he left behind in favor of more fuel for his plane. But the president of France pinned the cross on his breast as though he were arrayed in splendor, and then swept him into his arms and kissed him on both cheeks in the traditional accolade.

"Slim" was moved—even more so when the president presented, through him, the compliments of himself and of all France to the flier's mother, back in Detroit. The bird man's eyes were moist as, accompanied by Mr. Doumergue, Ambassador Herrick and others, he was escorted to the gardens of the palace, where the camera men awaited to record the historic incident.

It was a day of glory for the modest American boy. The Aero Club of France later conferred its great gold medal on him. He was voted an "honorary alumnus" of the highest institution of learning in France, the Superior Normal school.

When Premier Poincare late today congratulated Captain Lindbergh the shy young airman stood by overwhelmed and almost stammered in answer. "I thank you most heartily, Mr. President."

It is some years since Premier Poincare was president of France, but the veteran statesman let the slip pass.

Crowds gathered at the American embassy, his temporary home, and at every other point where he might appear, and vendors along the boulevards shouted a new song, written over night in his honor.

Ambassadors and other notables called to see him and messages of felicitation continued to pour in from all parts of the globe. So many telegrams and cable messages have been received that they have not all been classified, and bushels of letters remain to be opened.

A line-up of motion picture representatives and theatrical promoters waited outside the embassy in an endeavor to get to him, all talking in large sums.

Figures at the Aero Club show that Lindbergh not only is the first man to make an uninterrupted flight between New York and Paris but that he holds the long distance non-stop record, the journey having covered 3,647 miles.

Lindbergh arrived at the Elysee palace promptly at noon, accompanied by Ambassador Herrick and Sheldon Whitehouse, counsellor of the embassy. . . .

"It's just one joy after another," Captain Lindbergh said, referring to the Legion of Honor, "and this is one of the greatest.". . .

† † †

Journalistic legends were being created in the 1920s, too—the legend of Harold Ross and his magazine called the *New Yorker,* the legend of the *New York World*. Though that newspaper was in decline, it was also in what would be known later as its most fabled time, its death coming shortly after the 1930s were underway. Two accounts tell well the story of the last years of the *World*. The first is a memory piece about what it was like, for a young reporter, to be on the staff of that paper in the 1920s.

† † †

THE WORLD—IN THE FABULOUS 1920s

By Herbert Brucker, in Edward W. Barrett, ed., *Journalists in Action* (Manhasset, N.Y.: Channel Press, 1963), p. 147. Reprinted by permission of the author.

. . .our boss told every newcomer, "We have no sacred cows." The boss, as far as we were concerned, was, of course, that race-track devotee Herbert Bayard Swope—erect, ruddy, a big-chested bundle of energy who, as a reporter, had won for *The World* the very first Pulitzer Prize in reporting.

Gradually one got to know who was who; gradually one realized that the journalistic greats with whom one was rubbing elbows were human beings. One day I went to the little window that memory tells me guarded what would now be the library but was then the morgue. There, waiting for the desired dusty envelope of clips, was an unimpressive fellow in shirt sleeves, a cigar stump in his mouth. This, I learned, was F.P.A., the Franklin P. Adams who made his "Conning Tower" column a daily must for intellectual New York. And that great mountain of a fellow in rumpled clothes in the nearby cubbyhole was Heywood Broun. Now and again duty led me up into the sacred dome itself, and there one might see a clean-cut, youthful Ivy League type who presided as editor over the cleanest, punchiest, most literate and most reliable editorial page of the day—Walter Lippmann.

In the corridors and in the news room one would run into the whole galaxy that lit up the Page Opposite: not only Heywood Broun or F.P.A. or William Bolitho, but also Laurence Stallings, Alexander Woollcott, Samuel Chotzinoff, Allison Smith, Wells Root. And so in the news room, where an awed newcomer realized that in one sense he was now the equal of the top reporters of that day: Oliver H. P. Garrett, Ernest K. Lindley, Dudley Nichols, Henry Pringle, and all the rest.

In a corner of the room on a raised platform was the city desk and the attendant assistants' desks, presided over by the owlish Jim Barrett, who after the death of *The World* (which he vainly tried to save with employees' dollars and enthusiasm) ran that extraordinary phenomenon of the battle between newspapers and the upstart radio, the Press-Radio Bureau. . . .

† † †

The other account of the *World* came after the fact. James Barrett, the city editor mentioned by Brucker, tried to save the *World,* and of course he failed. But it was a memorable effort, and his story is one of the moving passages in our journalistic history.

† † †

THE END OF THE WORLD

By James W. Barrett, *The World, the Flesh and Messrs. Pulitzer* (New York: Vanguard Press, 1931), pp. 5-6.

Not until nineteen years after the Denver experience did I learn that it was possible for men and women to cry over the death of a newspaper.

Not until just now did I find out that a newspaper could be as dear to men and women as their wives or husbands or their religions or—to those who have none of these—as dear as their best dog.

I was for fifteen years on the news staff of *The World* and for nearly nine years of that time was city editor, but not until *The World* was gone—not until it had become merely a symbol of possession on the front page of the Scripps-Howard *World-*

Telegram—did I realize how much I was part of *The World* and how much *The World* was part of me.

But my wife knew. . . because she was jealous of *The World*.

Not until I saw editors, reporters, copyreaders, typesetters, compositors, stereotypers, artists, pressmen, mailing-room workers, deliverymen, office boys—rally in a desperate attempt to save *The World* from extinction—until I saw them pledge their savings and their future earnings toward a fund to buy the paper from trustees enjoined by the will of their father to preserve it—till I saw them crowding into the Hotel Astor to back up the plan to save their *World* for them—not until then did I realize that *The World* was to these men and women almost the breath of life.

And when on the last three nights of the paper's existence, I saw these same men and women at their posts of duty, everyone doing the job just as though the paper were going to keep coming out every morning forever and ever; everyone exercising unbelievable care to see that nothing should mar this last issue of the beloved paper—no error of judgment, no inaccuracy of reporting, no bad grammar, no typographical blunder—. . . when I saw all this with my own eyes I knew that it was possible for people to love a newspaper and I thanked God that I was a newspaperman. . . .

† † †

Earlier in the decade T. S. Eliot had given to the world a line in his poem, "The Hollow Men," that would be almost over-quoted in the years to come: "This is the way the world ends, not with a bang, but a whimper." The 1920s ended with a bang—and with a whimper, too. Throughout 1929 there had been portents, but the big boom continued, the financial boom that had been going on for so many years. October 24 and 29, 1929, were the historic dates; the term used since then is "stock market crash." This was the thing that marked the dividing line between the 1920s, and that gave *Variety* magazine its famous headline.

† † †

WALL STREET LAYS AN EGG

Variety, October 30, 1929.

The most dramatic event in the financial history of America is the collapse of the New York Stock Market. The stage was Wall Street, but the onlookers covered the country. Estimates are that 22,000,000 people were in the market at the time.

Tragedy, despair and ruination spell this story of countless thousands of marginal stock traders. Perhaps Manhattan was worst hit in the number of victims. Many may remain broke for the rest of their lives, because the money that disappeared via the ticker tape was the savings of years.

Many people of Broadway are known to have been wiped out. Reports of some in show business losing as much as $300,000 is not hearsay. One caustic comment to that was that the theatre is enough of a gamble without its people to venture into Wall street.

Prominent showmen, several identified with the picture industry on the coast, are said to be in a tight hole. One holding thousands of shares of a blue ribbon security, which dropped over 40 points, is reported having a paper loss of $4,000,000. Another was hit for $1,000,000. That occurred Monday after many thought themselves safe after Thursday's panic.

Yet in the midst of the dizzy panic humorous incidents crept in. Two show fellows hanging out for a year or more without work, stood in front of a theatrical club at supper time. They watched fellows arriving, scanning the market lists with long faces and they laughed. Said one: "Well, it's been a long time, but at last we're even."

A character around a Times Square brokerage office talks with a dialect. Starting with $7,000 he traded in and out for the last three years and ran his pile into a million. He was wiped out Thursday. Friends tried to console him, the man chattering to himself, half loony.

A vaudeville producer, elderly, was found weeping like a child by his son who returned to his office at seven that night by chance. The old boy had lost all his cash, $75,000. Another man lost his all, the amount being similar, but owes the broker an additional $5,000, unable to raise the money.

Any number of girls will probably have to give up expensive apartments and revise their manner of living. Customers' men, harassed by despondent traders, got a few smiles on phone calls from the girls such as: "Is it true my daddy, er ah I mean, has Mr. Soandso really been wiped out?" Some girls planned switching affections even on that terrible Thursday, as indicated by phone calls to the "reserve list."

The story of what happened on Thursday and the further drop of all issues of stock into unthinkable depths early this week, when Wall Street went into pandemonium, probably never will be told. At noon of Thursday it is said that brokerage concerns and bankers did not know how they stood.

As an example: Baldwin Locomotive, a stock that sold at $285 a share, was recently split up four for one, the new price being around $66. It went down to $15.

It was the bitterest blue Monday and the blackest Tuesday ever known to New York. Trading Tuesday totaled 17,000,000 shares, officially the biggest day in history. Stocks like Electric Bond and Share closed at $60. A week previous it was stable at $190.

Monday when the market was tottering and then declined with a worse crash than last week, Wall street was in a state of demoralization. The number of shares traded in exceeded 9,000,000, the third greatest total in a single day on record.

That famous, promised Hoover bull market was converted into a devastating bear rush. . . .

† † †

13

THE ERA OF
THE NEW DEAL

Radio, motion pictures, newsreel—all words that suggest why and how all the basic documents in journalism from the 1930s on cannot be reproduced or even represented in this collection. And in the 1930s the age of television was yet to come. The history of radio goes back to Morse and the telegraph, to Cyrus Field and the Atlantic Cable, through Marconi and the wireless, and the audion tube developed by Dr. Lee De Forest and others. Radio, in so far as journalism is concerned, did not begin until the pioneering stations came into being after World War I, but through the 1920s there were such news stories on the air as political conventions, prize fights, and the Lindbergh flight. Newsreels had been recording history since the 1890s, even though some of the early shows were faked, and some of them censored. Boxing matches, the Boer War, the San Francisco earthquake, Pancho Villa in Mexico, Theodore Roosevelt and Woodrow Wilson, John D. Rockefeller, George Bernard Shaw, the *Spirit of St. Louis* taking off for France—all were recorded on film.

So a *complete* set of documents in journalism would have to include all of these, plus other visual and audio memories of the 1930s: devastating floods, sports events, flaming crashes at the Indianapolis Speedway, the assassination of King Alexander of Yugoslavia, the explosion of the dirigible *Hindenburg,* Edward VIII abdicating the throne for "the woman I love," war breaking out in Spain and Ethiopia and Manchuria, Franklin D. Roosevelt and Huey Long, Hitler coming to power in Germany, and the whole procession of news stories we think of today as the depression.

Like the 1920s, the 1930s present major problems in choice, for the times were crowded with epochal events. The days of the depression offer a kaleidoscope of memories:

The New Deal, the Blue Eagle of the NRA, people standing in breadlines, violence on the picket lines, farm families from the

Midwest and Southwest bound for the promised land in rickety old cars and trucks, the return of beer and legalized alcohol, the WPA, jokes about FDR and Eleanor, Margaret Mitchell's *Gone with the Wind* and the search for stars to play Scarlett and Rhett in the movie, Amos 'n' Andy and Bing Crosby and Jack Benny and Edgar Bergen and Charlie McCarthy on the radio, Charlie Chaplin playing Hitler, Groucho Marx playing a dictator, the acres of dancing girls in the Warner Brothers musicals, Kate Smith singing "When the Moon Comes over the Mountain," the parade of big bands in the era of swing.

For the press of America, it was a coming of age in the coverage of government. Never before had government seemed so important a force, for beginning with the stock market crash, news of government was a standard on the front pages of the land. President Herbert Hoover was unable to hold back the tide of economic trouble; his Reconstruction Finance Corporation was a stopgap only. Franklin D. Roosevelt defeated him by a tremendous plurality in 1932, and Roosevelt won in 1936 with only two states going to his opponent, Alfred M. Landon, in the Electoral College. For the press the New Deal meant the fireside chats of the President; the lame duck amendment; the National Recovery Administration; presidential battles with the "nine old men" of the Supreme Court; the Civilian Conservation Corps; the Tennessee Valley Authority; the Wagner Act; the triple-A of agriculture. To many publishers, Roosevelt was the greatest enemy the press had had in generations, and big majorities of editors opposed him editorially every time he ran for office. He was personally popular with the reporters, however, for he really made the press conference an established institution in both government and journalism.

The New Deal affected the press in many ways, in business operations, in legislation affecting social security and unemployment insurance, in the right to organize labor unions, in child labor regulations, in the stiffening of federal trade regulations. Collective bargaining came with the Wagner Act, bringing the American Newspaper Guild and many long, bitter strikes. In April, 1937, the Supreme Court upheld the constitutionality of the Wagner Act when it ruled in favor of Morris Watson, who, the court held, had been fired by the Associated Press for guild activity.

The story of the depression and its coverage by the press can be told in many ways. A series of vignettes follows.

† † †

VIGNETTES OF THE DEPRESSION YEARS

HUNGER RIOTING, 1931

OKLAHOMA CITY, Jan. 20 (AP).—A crowd of men and women, shouting that they were hungry and jobless, raided a grocery store near the City Hall today. Twenty-six of the men were arrested.

Scores loitered near the city jail following the arrests, but kept well out of range of fire hose made ready for use in case of another disturbance.

The police tonight broke up a second meeting of about one hundred unemployed men and arrested Francis Owens, alleged head of the "Oklahoma City Unemployed Council," who was accused of instigating the raid. . . .

THE BONUS ARMY IN WASHINGTON, 1932

By Jules Sauerwein, the *New York Times.*

WASHINGTON, JUNE 17—For whoever may have a little imagination, Washington today recalls ancient Carthage. Beyond the city, on the banks of the Potomac, in the immense marshy field of the tributary, Anacostia, 17,000 men are encamped just as, in ancient times, were the mercenaries of Hasdrubal. They demand money, but not the arrears of a few months. On the contrary, their claim goes back fourteen years and extends for a dozen years in the future. They are veterans who, not content with their pension, although seven or eight times higher than that of other countries, desire cash from the state today by its sacrificing $2,000,000,000— all that it would pay them as a premium for mobilization up to 1945.

I passed an hour in this camp of revolt, which, this morning, had rather the air of a camp of despair. Rain having fallen in torrents during the night, many of these unfortunates had slept in a veritable marsh. With a prevision of the bad weather they had tried to organize themselves in the region reserved for Pennsylvania Avenue. It was a conglomeration of tented huts made of tattered cloth fixed up on old boards with packing boxes serving as props. Under one of these pitiful shelters men are mournfully lying shivering with fever. They try to comfort themselves by jokes. They have placed at the door a sign, "The Lame, Sick, and Lazy." . . .

AN EMBARGO ON GOLD, 1933

Special to the *New York Times.*

WASHINGTON, March 5.—To prevent the export, hoarding or earmarking of gold or silver, coin or bullion or currency, President Roosevelt issued a proclamation at 11 o'clock tonight, in which he ordered a bank holiday from tomorrow through Thursday, March 9. Earlier in the day he had summoned a special session of Congress to meet on Thursday.

This sweeping action was taken after a day of conferences, among officials and bankers, the President taking recourse to war powers granted under the trading-with-the-enemy act. . . .

A PROGRAM FOR RECOVERY, 1933

Special to The *New York Times.*

WASHINGTON, June 16.—Assuming unprecedented peacetime control over the nation's economic life, President Roosevelt placed in operation today his sweeping program for recovery from the depression.

Within two hours he signed acts of Congress giving him control over industry, power to coordinate the railroads, and authority to start work on a $3,300,000,000 public works program, and then began the active administration of these and other major measures. . . .

AN END TO PROHIBITION, 1933

Chicago Daily Tribune, November 8, 1933.

The thirty-sixth state voted for the adoption of the twenty-first amendment yesterday and by that action sounded the knell of the eighteenth amendment and prohibition in the nation. There now remains only the formality of repeal conventions to be held early next month by several states.

Six states voted yesterday. It required only three of them to vote for repeal to make certain the end of prohibition. But because North and South Carolina voted dry, and because Kentucky will not count its vote until 10 o'clock today, Utah took the spotlight as the returns came in last night. . . .

INVALIDATION OF THE NRA, 1935

By Erwin D. Canham, *Christian Science Monitor,* May 28, 1935.

The era of emergency government in the United States ended yesterday, when the Supreme Court invalidated NRA.

Now that the nation, like the world, is climbing out of the trough of the depression, the supreme tribunal has ruled that instrumentalities which served to facilitate that climb may not be retained as permanent reforms for practices which were believed to have led to that depression. . . .

The NRA decision is of course the severest blow to New Dealers, partly because it ends the "partnership between business and government" which over a period of two years has undeniably put some millions of men and women to work, introduced some more enlightened trade practices, and ended some of the pricecutting which had made the national economy of 1932 largely a regime of tooth and claw. But the decision is an even more severe blow in the threat it gives to other New Deal grants of authority to the President, in particular to AAA with its control of agricultural production.

A MAGNA CHARTA FOR LABOR, 1935

By the Associated Press.

WASHINGTON, July 5.—The Wagner labor disputes bill, intended to guarantee to labor the right to bargain collectively, was signed today by President Roosevelt.

The bill, designed to supersede the now dead section 7A of the National Recovery Act, would set up a new National Labor Relations Board of three members, yet to be appointed.

It gives the labor organization chosen by a majority of employes in a plant the right to speak for all of the employes, and forbids employers from interfering with the self-organization of employes. . .

AN EVICTION IN PORTLAND, 1935

By Harry Steinfeld, *Portland Oregonian,* July 10, 1935.

Harry Miller had finished a day's work yesterday on an SERA road project and was walking home leisurely. About a block from his house at 9499 North Trumbull street his pace quickened. Then he broke into a run.

It had happened. He, his wife and their three young children had been dispossessed. There on the sidewalk was his family, helplessly surveying their few possessions.

Mrs. Miller had been subjected to the same shock, only a bit earlier. Probably hers was more violent. She returned home after an unsuccessful search for a new house—the Millers had been ordered to move because they owed $89 rent—to find her furniture being thrown out into the street. . . .

A CRUSADE OF THE OLD FOLKS, 1936

By Thomas L. Stokes, *New York World-Telegram,* February 17, 1936.

San Francisco—In the heart of San Francisco, along that street where the trolley car climbs on its cable toward the sky, I listened to the new gospel which has gripped the Pacific Coast in a crusade of the old folks.

About sixty or seventy elderly persons were gathered in the weekly meeting of a Townsend Club—one of thousands along the Pacific Coast—in a hall adjoining headquarters of the Northern California Area of "OARP"—Old Age Revolving Pensions, Inc.

Most were fairly well dressed. A few of the women wore fur coats, some of which had seen several seasons. On the back row several old men talked animatedly before the meeting began. . . .

The speaker of the evening was introduced, a lean gentleman of Chautauqua bearing, with hair plastered closely and a heavy gold chain across his front, who explained that he once had been a newspaper man. . . .

The speaker described the Townsend Plan—and as simply and effectively as I've ever heard it described—with homely examples and then, in mock surprise, added:

"And some people don't know yet that it will end the depression!". . .

A BATTLE WITHIN LABOR, 1936

WASHINGTON, Aug. 5.—(A.P.)—The American Federation of Labor's executive council today voted to suspend 10 unions now in the committee for industrial organization unless they withdraw from that group within 30 days.

Otherwise, the council decided, the unions representing more than 1,000,000 workers will be suspended indefinitely.

John L. Lewis, president of the United Mine Workers and leader of the industrial organization committee, immediately retorted:

"We will not disband the committee for industrial organization. The decision of the executive council will not change the policy of the CIO, nor will it have any effect upon the organizing activities of the committee.". . .

† † †

Many of the memories that old-timers have of Franklin D. Roosevelt probably come from radio or newsreel: the election, the assassination attempt, the inaugural, "the only thing we have to fear is fear itself," the visits to Warm Springs, the fireside chats, the campaigns, the ever-on-the-move first lady, the attractive and controversial children. Roosevelt's campaign in 1932 did not suggest the later scope of the New Deal, the controversies that would be so common in the news. But the President became and remained the major news figure in America of the decade.

News of government and its increasing role in the lives of Americans was never a dull story in the 1930s, but the news event that will be remembered by most readers of the time was the one that took place March 1, 1932, at Hopewell, New Jersey—the kidnaping of the 20-month-old son of Colonel and Mrs. Charles A. Lindbergh. It was a horrifying story, and the news, shouted out by newsboys on American streets, will always bring a special twinge. The story lasted over a four-year period, for the events include the arrest of Bruno Richard Hauptmann, his trial, and his execution— and these are shorthand terms only, in a sense, in treating the prolonged story of the Lindberghs and their agony, which was without question the major crime story of the time.

In its shocking impact, the story that described the finding of the body of the little boy may have been greater even than that of the kidnaping itself. One New York newspaper, the *Daily News,* had two words on its front page, in type surpassing in size even that used for a presidential assassination and a moon landing in later years, "BABY DEAD."

† † †

BABY DEAD: THE LINDBERGH BODY IS FOUND

New York Daily News, May 13, 1932. Courtesy of the New York News.

The body of Charles A. Lindbergh Jr. was found four miles from Hopewell at 3:15 P.M. yesterday by a colored truck driver and his assistant. The body was badly decomposed and gave every indication of having lain in a depression a few feet from the Hopewell-Princeton road since a few hours after he was kidnaped seventy-two days ago. A mark resembling a footprint was spread across the tiny form, as if the kidnaper had viciously tried to stamp it into the ground.

An autopsy by County Physician Charles H. Mitchell revealed that the baby had suffered a compound fracture of the skull, "as if it had either been hurled from an automobile or struck over the head." There was a hole in the skull about the size of a quarter, which might have been inflicted by a bullet. But no bullet was found.

The body lay on its face, and its position indicated that a hurried attempt had been made to bury it.

The formal police statement, given out by Col. H. Norman Schwarzkopf, said:

"We have to announce that apparently the body of the Lindbergh baby was found today at 3:15 P.M. William Allen, a colored man, was riding from Mount Rose, N.J., to Hopewell with Orville Wilson on a truckload of timber.

"They stopped the truck near a woods. He, Allen, went into the woods on the Mount Rose Hill in Mount Rose, N.J. Going under the bush he lowered his head and as he raised a branch he saw a skeleton on the ground.

"He called back to Mr. Wilson. Mr. Wilson ran into the woods, saw what it was, and decided to go to Hopewell to get police. They notified Chief Wolf of the Hopewell police, who notified these headquarters. . . ."

Anne Morrow Lindbergh, who expects to give birth to another baby within a few days, had been at the home of her mother, Mrs. Dwight W. Morrow, in Englewood for three days. She and Mrs. Morrow returned to Hopewell Wednesday night—just a few hours before the body was found.

Just when Col. Lindbergh arrived could not be ascertained, but members of the family insisted he was there. . . .

† † †

The 1930s were the years of the famous badmen. The Federal Bureau of Investigation was news, and so was the term "public enemy," and it is likely that many of the children of America could have told you, in 1934, the name of the "most wanted" man in the land—John Dillinger. Jack Lait, of the International News Service, wrote the most vivid story of the stakeout and death of Dillinger in 1934. In so doing Lait beat the press of Chicago, the city where the Number One bad man met his end. Lait's story was not a model of restraint, but it does suggest the color and the vigor of a band of reporters who were not worried about things like objectivity.

† † †

DILLINGER DIES ON A CHICAGO STREET

By Jack Lait, International News Service, July 23, 1934.

John Dillinger, ace bad man of the world, got his last night—two slugs through his heart and one through his head. He was tough and he was shrewd, but he wasn't as tough and shrewd as the Federals, who never close a case until the end. It took twenty-seven of them to end Dillinger's career, and their strength came out of his weakness—a woman.

Dillinger was put on the spot by a tip-off to the local bureau of the Department of Justice. It was a feminine voice that Melvin H. Purvis, head of the Chicago office, heard. He had waited long for it.

It was Sunday, but Uncle Sam doesn't observe any NRA and works seven days a week.

The voice told him that Dillinger would be at a little third-run movie house, the Biograph, last night—that he went there every night and usually got there about 7:30. It was almost 7:30 then. Purvis sent out a call for all men within reach and hustled all men on hand with him. They waited more than an hour. They knew from the informer that he must come out, turn left, turn again into a dark alley where he parked his Ford-8 coupe.

Purvis himself stood at the main exit. He had men on foot and in parked inconspicuous cars strung on both sides of the alley. He was to give the signal. He had ascertained about when the feature film, *Manhattan Melodrama*, would end. Tensely eyeing his wrist watch he stood. Then the crowd that always streams out when the main picture finishes came. Purvis had seen Dillinger when he was brought through from Arizona to Crown Point, Indiana, and his heart pounded as he saw again the face that has been studied by countless millions on the front pages of the world.

Purvis gave the signal. Dillinger did not see him. Public Enemy No. 1 lit a cigarette, strolled a few feet to the alley with the mass of middle-class citizens going in that direction, then wheeled left.

A Federal man, revolver in hand, stepped from behind a telegraph pole at the mouth of the passage. "Hello, John," he said, almost whispered, his voice husky with the intensity of the classic melodrama. Dillinger went with lightning right hand for his gun, a .38 Colt automatic. He drew it from his trousers pocket.

But, from behind, another government agent pressed the muzzle of his service revolver against Dillinger's back and fired twice. Both bullets went through the bandit's heart.

He staggered, his weapon clattered to the asphalt paving, and as he went three more shots flashed. One bullet hit the back of his head, downward, as he was falling, and came out under his eye.

Police cleared the way for the police car, which was there in a few minutes. The police were there not because they were in on the capture, but because the sight of so many mysterious men around the theater had scared the manager into thinking he was about to be stuck up and he had called the nearest station.

When the detectives came on the run, Purvis intercepted them and told them what was up. They called headquarters and more police came, but with instructions to stand by and take orders from Purvis.

Dillinger's body was rushed to Alexian Brothers' hospital in a patrol wagon. There were no surgeons in it. But the policeman knew he was dead, and at the entrance of the hospital, where a kindly priest in a long cassock had come to the door to see who might be in need of help, the driver was ordered to the morgue. . . .

† † †

Perhaps the single most famous magazine article in the history of journalism in America was published in 1935, the year after not only John Dillinger but two other public enemies—Pretty Boy Floyd and Baby Face Nelson—also were killed by the FBI. The article appeared in the *Reader's Digest,* a magazine that had become a kind of phenomenon in journalism, the inspiration of DeWitt and Lila Wallace, who had founded it in 1922 as an adless journal that would reprint, in condensed form, what they thought to be the best writing in other current magazines. J. C. Furnas wrote his article for the *Digest,* and its shock was nationwide. Traffic judges required that driving offenders read the article. Some states mailed out copies with license plates. Paramount made a movie of it. And its impact upon highway safety campaigns remains unquestioned.

† † †

—AND SUDDEN DEATH

By J. C. Furnas, *Reader's Digest*, 27, No. 160 (August, 1935), pp. 21-26. Reprinted with permission from the August, 1935, *Reader's Digest*. Copyright 1935, 1945, and 1966 by The Reader's Digest Association, Inc.

Publicizing the total of motoring injuries—almost a million last year, with 36,000 deaths—never gets to first base in jarring the motorist into a realization of the appalling risks of motoring. He does not translate dry statistics into a reality of blood and agony.

Figures exclude the pain and horror of savage mutilation—which means they leave out the point. They need to be brought closer home. A passing look at a bad smash or the news that a fellow you had lunch with last week is in a hospital with a broken back will make any driver but a born fool slow down at least temporarily. But what is needed is a vivid and *sustained* realization that every time you step on the throttle, death gets in beside you, hopefully waiting for his chance. That single horrible accident you may have witnessed is no isolated horror. That sort of thing happens every hour of the day, everywhere in the United States. If you really felt *that,* perhaps the cold lines of type in Monday's paper recording that a total of 29 local citizens were killed in week-end crashes would rate something more than a perfunctory tut-tut as you turn back to the sports page.

An enterprising judge now and again sentences reckless drivers to tour the accident end of a city morgue. But even a mangled body on a slab, waxily portraying the consequences of bad motoring judgment, isn't a patch on the scene of the accident itself. No artist working on a safety poster would dare depict that in full detail.

That picture would have to include motion-picture and sound effects, too—the flopping, pointless efforts of the injured to stand up; the queer, grunting noises; the steady, panting groaning of a human being with pain creeping up on him as the shock wears off. It should portray the slack expression on the face of a man, drugged with shock, staring at the Z-twist in his broken leg; the insane crumpled effect of a child's body after its bones are crushed inward, a realistic portrait of an hysterical woman with her screaming mouth opening a hole in the bloody drip that fills her eyes and runs off her chin. Minor details would include the raw ends of bones protruding through flesh in compound fractures, and the dark red, oozing surfaces where clothes and skin were flayed off at once. . . .

Last year a state trooper of my acquaintance stopped a big red Hispano for speeding. Papa was obviously a responsible person, obviously set for a pleasant week-end with his family—so the officer cut into papa's well-bred expostulations: "I'll let you off this time, but if you keep on this way, you won't last long. Get going—but take it easier." Later a passing motorist hailed the trooper and asked if the red Hispano had got a ticket. "No." said the trooper, "I hated to spoil their party." "Too bad you didn't," said the motorist,"

I saw you stop them—and then I passed that car again 50 miles up the line. It still makes me feel sick at my stomach. The car was folded up like an accordion—the color was about all there was left. They were all dead but one of the kids—and he wasn't going to live to the hospital.". . .

The automobile is treacherous, just as a cat is. It is tragically difficult to realize that it can become the deadliest missile. As enthusiasts tell you, it makes 65 feel like nothing at all. But 65 an hour is 100 feet a second, a speed which puts a viciously unjustified responsibility on brakes and human reflexes, and can instantly turn this docile luxury into a mad bull elephant.

Collision, turnover or sideswipe, each type of accident produces either a shattering dead stop or a crashing change of direction—and, since the occupant—meaning you—continues in the old direction at the original speed, every surface and angle of the car's interior immediately becomes a battering, tearing projectile, aimed squarely at you—inescapable. There is no bracing yourself against these imperative laws of momentum.

It's like going over Niagara Falls in a steel barrel full of railroad spikes. The best thing that can happen to you—and one of the rarer things—is to be thrown out as the doors spring open, so you have only the ground to reckon with. True, you strike with as much force as if you had been thrown from the *Twentieth Century* at top speed. But at least you are spared the lethal array of gleaming metal knobs and edges and glass inside the car. . . .

If you customarily pass without clear vision on a long way ahead, make sure that every member of the party carries identification papers—it's difficult to identify a body with its whole face bashed in or torn off. The driver is death's favorite target. If the steering wheel holds together it ruptures his liver or spleen so he bleeds to death internally. Or, if the steering wheel breaks off, the matter is settled instantly by the steering column's plunging through his abdomen.

By no means do all head-on collisions occur on curves. The modern deathtrap is likely to be a straight stretch with three lanes of traffic—like the notorious Astor Flats on the Albany Post Road where there have been as many as 27 fatalities in one summer month. This sudden vision of broad, straight road tempts many an ordinarily sensible driver into passing the man ahead. Simultaneously a driver coming the other way swings out at high speed. At the last moment each tries to get into line again, but the gaps are closed. As the cars in line are forced into the ditch to capsize or crash fences, the passers meet, almost head on, in a swirling, grinding smash that sends them caroming obliquely into the others.

A trooper described such an accident—five cars in one mess, seven killed on the spot, two dead on the way to the hospital, two more dead in the long run. He remembered it far more vividly than he wanted to—the quick way the doctor turned away from a dead man to check up on a woman with a broken back; the three bodies out of one car so soaked with oil from the crankcase that they looked like wet brown cigars and not human at all; a man, walking around and babbling to himself, oblivious of the dead and dying, even oblivious of the dagger-like sliver of steel that stuck out of his streaming wrist; a pretty girl with her forehead laid open, trying hopelessly to crawl out of a ditch in spite of her smashed hip. A first-class massacre of that sort is only a question of scale and numbers—seven corpses are no deader than one. . . .

Overturning cars specialize in certain injuries. Cracked pelvis, for instance, guaranteeing agonizing months in bed, motionless, perhaps crippled for life—broken spine resulting from sheer sidewise twist—the minor details of smashed knees and splintered shoulder blades caused by crashing into the side of the car as she goes over with the swirl of an insane roller coaster—and the lethal consequences of broken ribs, which puncture hearts and lungs with their raw ends. The consequent internal hemorrhage is no less dangerous because it is the pleural instead of the abdominal cavity that is filling with blood.

Flying glass—safety glass is by no means universal yet—contributes much more than its share to the spectacular side of accidents. It doesn't merely cut—the fragments are driven in as if a cannon loaded with broken bottles had been fired in your face, and a sliver in the eye, traveling with such force, means certain blindness. A leg or arm stuck through the windshield will cut clean to the bone through vein, artery and muscle like a piece of beef under the butcher's knife, and it takes little time to lose a fatal amount of blood under such circumstances. . . .

It's hard to find a surviving accident victim who can bear to talk. After you come to, the gnawing, searing pain throughout your body is accounted for by learning that you have both collarbones smashed, both shoulder blades splintered, your right arm broken in three places and three ribs cracked, with every chance of bad internal ruptures. But the pain can't distract you, as the shock begins to wear off, from realizing that you are probably on your way out. You can't forget that, not even when they shift you from the ground to the stretcher and your broken ribs bite into your lungs and the sharp ends of your collarbones slide over to stab deep into each side of your screaming throat. When you've stopped screaming, it all comes back—you're dying and you hate yourself for it. That isn't fiction either. It's what it actually feels like to be one of that 36,000.

And every time you pass on a blind curve, every time you hit it up on a slippery road, every time you step on it harder than your reflexes will safely take, every time you drive with your reactions slowed down by a drink or two, every time you follow the man ahead too closely, you're gambling a few seconds against this kind of blood and agony and sudden death.

Take a look at yourself as the man in the white jacket shakes his head over you, tells the boys with the stretcher not to bother and turns away to somebody else who isn't quite dead yet. And then take it easy.

† † †

In the year of "And Sudden Death," two celebrated Americans died in a plane crash in the Alaskan wilds, and their deaths provided one of the most dramatic stories of the decade. The two were Will Rogers and Wiley Post. Rogers, especially, was greatly loved; Post was a highly respected flier. Rogers had obtained journalistic celebrity on the air and with his syndicated column, and in the movies he had been especially popular in *A Connecticut Yankee*, *David Harum*, *Judge Priest*, *State Fair*, and *Life Begins at 40*. When word of the deaths came, the nation went into mourning.

† † †

ROGERS AND POST DIE IN AIR CRASH

By Frank Daugherty, United Press, August 16, 1935.

POINT BARROW, Alaska (UP)—Will Rogers, the cowboy humorist, and Wiley Post, 'round-the-world flier, were killed at 8:18 p.m. Thursday when Post's new plane crashed on the frozen tundra fifteen miles south of here.

The crash occurred as the two were taking off from a native village where they had stopped when forced down by engine trouble and a dense fog that shrouded this northernmost civilized post of Alaska.

During their three-hour stay at the village, they had dinner with the Eskimos and Post repaired his missing motor.

The motors failed again, the natives said, just as the plane took off from the river where it had landed. The ship crashed to the tundra at the edge of the stream and broke up in the frozen moss hummocks.

The craft's right wing was broken and its engine was driven back into the cabin. The plane grounded on its back. Post's body was crushed by the motor. Rogers was thrown out of the plane. Both apparently died instantly.

The country surrounding the scene is almost as low as the river. The moss hummocks, partly frozen, protrude from water. The plane crushed the hummocks when it crashed, and rescuers worked in about two feet of water to extricate the bodies.

Post's watch on his wrist had stopped at 8:18 p.m., fixing the time of the wreck. Rogers' watch was running when Sergeant Stanley Morgan, of the United States Signal Corps, and I reached the wreckage.

We had been notified by a native who came running, terrified, into Point Barrow with news of the tragedy. We reached the scene in a motor-whale-boat manned by natives.

Rogers' body was found lying outside the plane. It was badly battered. It was necessary to pull the wreck to pieces to extricate Post's body, which was completely submerged, as he lay crushed and still beneath the tangle of the wreckage of the motor and controls. Gasoline had spewed on the water and caught fire, flaming briskly for a few moments.

The plane was demolished. . . .

Post, 'round-the-world record holder, and Rogers, the humorist, movie actor and famous air traveler, were on a leisurely trip around Alaska. . . .

While natives and whites struggled to beach the boat carrying the bodies here, an ink-stained piece of paper fell from Rogers' pocket into the sea.

Unfolded, the soggy paper was discovered to be a rotogravure picture of Rogers' daughter, Mary, vacationing in Maine.

One of the natives fell beneath the rollers which were used to beach the heavy whaling boat. He was badly crushed.

Stray bits of wreckage caught in the current of the river on the bank of which the plane landed and floated down into the Arctic Ocean.

† † †

In the newsreels, American filmgoers saw the blowing dust, and many more saw it first-hand. Some Americans, too, saw the *meaning* of the dust, in the Pare Lorentz documentary films, *The Plow That Broke the Plains* and *The River,* in 1936 and 1937, respectively. It became vivid, for those who had not experienced dust bowl days, in the novel by John Steinbeck, *The Grapes of Wrath,* and in the excellent motion picture made from the novel. A powerful description of the blowing dust was provided by Robert Geiger, who came to the Midwest from the Denver bureau of the Associated Press and made a 1,500-mile trip through the dust-afflicted areas: from Denver and through the corners of Kansas, Oklahoma, New Mexico, and Texas.

† † †

A PORTRAIT OF THE DUST BOWL

By Robert Geiger, Associated Press, April 15, 1936.

GUYMON, Okla. (AP)—Three little words—achingly familiar on a Western farmer's tongue—rule life today in the dust bowl of the continent—

If it rains. . .

Ask any farmer, any merchant, any banker what the outlook is, and you hear them—if it rains. . . .

If it rains. . . some farmers will get a wheat crop.

If it rains. . . fresh row crops my flourish.

If it rains. . . pasture and range for livestock may be restored.

If it rains. . . fields quickly listed into wind-resisting clods may stop the dust.

If it rains. . . it always has!

The next three weeks will tell the story.

Black and saffron clouds of dust, spectacular, menacing, intensely irritating to man and beast alike, choking, blowing out tender crops and lasting without mercy for days, have darkened everything but hope and a sense of humor in the dust sector of the Southwest.

The Southwest is big and the dust area is only a small chunk of it. Roughly, it takes in the western third of Kansas, southeastern Colorado, the Oklahoma Panhandle, the northern two-thirds of the Texas Panhandle and northeastern New Mexico.

It always has been a region of sparse rainfall. The World War, with its high wheat prices and urgent demands, sent the plow into the sod and turned this into wheat country. Before then it was range land, and the crop was native buffalo grass, which held the soil firm against insistent winds.

The last three years have been years of droughts, with this Spring's field-eroding dust storms their stifling climax. But dust storms are nothing new in the Southwest. Forty years ago—decades before the wheat farmers came with their combines—a dust storm of such violence swept western Kansas that it stopped trains, just as they were stopped last week.

"This is a tough, hardy country," its farmers say. "It will come back overnight."

"Dusters" approach the prairie country in two ways.

Sometimes they start when a gigantic yellow-and-red cloud floats across the country, high in the air, blotting out the sun.

The wind is gentle, growing in velocity very slowly. This type of storm carries a fine, powdery silt that seems soft and hazy—until you start breathing in it.

The other type starts with a blast, and a huge black cloud approaching across the plains at tremendous speed. It strikes all at once along a well-defined front. It carries sand and on hands and face feels like the blast of chaff from a threshing machine.

When at its height, bright lights in towns are invisible across the street, visibility is zero and, within buildings, lights must be turned on as at night. Motorists continuously crawl along at 5 and 10 miles an hour, unable to peer ahead for more than 10 or 15 feet. Busses are stopped—sometimes trains. . . .

A. L. Thoreson lives over the line in Texas and is a big wheat producer. He raised 90,000 bushels in 1931, got only 25 cents a bushel for it. The best he can hope for, he thinks, is a half crop.

"But we are not suffering acutely," he added. "The Government is paying better than a dollar an acre to us in wheat benefit payments and, in addition, we can sell what wheat we raise. That will keep the farmers going. The Federal wheat program is O.K., and if it wasn't for that the farmers would be in an awful hole. They can hold on indefinitely with wheat payments."

And then there is I. R. Bryan, farmer northwest of Guymon, who could have left 10 years ago, after 30 years of farming in the Panhandle, "with $35,000 in my pockets."

"I made it in row crops and lost it in wheat.

"I could have left here wealthy and I'll be damned if I am going to walk out of here broke now."

† † †

The 1930s had some famous sports figures, but somehow they did not measure up, in flamboyance, at least, to the heroes and heroines of the 1920s, even though some of the personalities of that earlier time, notably Babe Ruth and Lou Gehrig, had extended their careers into the new decade. Two personalities who truly stood out were Negroes—Jesse Owens and Joe Louis. The first of these became the most celebrated performer at the 1936 Olympic Games in Berlin, a black man sweeping to victory in the stadium of the "super race" of Adolf Hitler.

† † †

A BLACK MAN WINS IN BERLIN

By the United Press, August 5, 1936.

OLYMPIC STADIUM, Berlin, Aug. 5.—(United Press.)—Jesse Owens stood on the highest level of the Olympic victory platform today with cold rain pelting his bare head and the cheers of 100,000 spectators ringing in his ears. It was the supreme moment in the life of the 22-year-old Ohio State collegian who was born of humble colored parents in the hamlet of Danville, Alabama.

A few minutes before the streamlined, stout-hearted colored lad had completed the greatest feat of modern athletic history by winning the 200-meter dash in the record-breaking Olympic time of 20.7 seconds for the first Olympic "triple" since Paavo Nurmi, redoubtable Finn, won three championships at Paris in 1924. . . .

† † †

Joe Louis was a young boxer from Detroit, and he disposed of a long string of boxers, first on his way to the championship of the world and then as heavyweight champion himself. One of his opponents was Max Schmeling of Germany, former world champion, who had knocked out Louis in the twelfth round on June 19, 1936. The second fight was a quite different matter, and it is told in the breathless style of that veteran of the Hearst wars, Bob Considine.

† † †

JOE LOUIS DISPOSES OF MAX SCHMELING

By Bob Considine, International News Service, June 22, 1938.

Listen to this, buddy, for it comes from a guy whose palms are still wet, whose throat is still dry, and whose jaw is still agape from the utter shock of watching Joe Louis knock out Max Schmeling.

It was a shocking thing, that knockout—short, sharp, merciless, complete. Louis was like this:

He was a big lean copper spring, tightened and retightened through weeks of training until he was one pregnant package of coiled venom.

Schmeling hit that spring. He hit it with a whistling right-hand punch in the first minute of the fight—and the spring, tormented with tension, suddenly burst with one brazen spang of activity. Hard brown arms, propelling two unerring fists, blurred beneath the hot white candelabra of the ring lights. And Schmeling was in the path of them, a man caught and mangled in the whirring claws of a mad and feverish machine.

The mob, biggest and most prosperous ever to see a fight in a ball yard, knew that here was the end before the thing had really started. It knew, so it stood up and howled one long shriek. People who had paid as much as $100 for their chairs didn't use them—except perhaps to stand on, the better to let the sight burn forever in their memories.

There were four steps to Schmeling's knockout. A few seconds after he landed his only punch of the fight, Louis caught him with a lethal little left hook that drove him onto the ropes so that his right arm was hooked over the top strand, like a drunk hanging to a fence. Louis swarmed over him and hit with everything he had—until Referee Donovan pushed him away and counted one.

Schmeling staggered away from the ropes, dazed and sick. He looked drunkenly toward his corner, and before he had turned his head back Louis was on him again, first with a left and then that awe-provoking right that made a crunching sound when it hit the German's jaw. Max fell down, hurt and giddy, for a count of three.

He clawed his way up as if the night air were as thick as black water, and Louis—his nostrils like the mouth of a double-barreled shotgun—took a quiet lead and let him have both barrels.

Max fell almost lightly, bereft of his senses, his fingers touching the canvas like a comical stew-bum doing his morning exercises, knees bent and the tongue lolling in his head.

He got up long enough to be knocked down again, this time his dark unshaven face pushed in the sharp gravel of the resin.

Louis jumped away lightly, a bright and pleased look in his eyes, and as he did the white towel of surrender which Louis' handlers had refused to use two years ago tonight came sailing into the ring in a soggy mess. It was thrown by Max Machon, oblivious to the fact that fights cannot end this way in New York.

The referee snatched it off the floor and flung it backwards. It hit the ropes and hung there, limp as Schmeling. Donovan counted up to five over Max, sensed the futility of it all, and stopped the fight.

The big crowd began to rustle restlessly toward the exits, many only now accepting Louis as champion of the world. There were no eyes for Schmeling, sprawled on his stool in his corner.

He got up eventually, his dirty gray-and-black robe over his shoulders, and wormed through the happy little crowd that hovered around Louis. And he put his arm around the Negro and smiled. They both smiled and could afford to—for Louis had made around $200,000 a minute and Schmeling $100,000 a minute.

But once he crawled down in the belly of the big stadium, Schmeling realized the implications of his defeat. He, who won the title on a partly phony foul, and beat Louis two years ago with the aid of a crushing punch after the bell had sounded, now said Louis had fouled him. That would read better in Germany, whence earlier in the day had come a cable from Hitler, calling on him to win.

It was a low, sneaking trick, but a rather typical last word from Schmeling.

† † †

It was a radio report that made the *Hindenburg* disaster memorable for all time in our journalism—the report by Herbert Morrison, who had gone to Lakehurst, New Jersey, to make a routine description of the landing of a dirigible. It also was newsreel and newspaper pictures that helped to capture this monumental story for all time. But no account of the 1930s would be complete without the words, too, that appeared in print to tell this story.

† † †

THE CRASH OF THE *HINDENBURG*

New York American, May 7, 1937.

Germany's pride, the dirigible Hindenburg, largest lighter-than-air craft in the world, exploded and fell in a mass of flames as it prepared to land at the Naval Air Station, Lakehurst, N.J., at 7:20 o'clock last night.

Early this morning, after hours of frantic rescue work in the smouldering ruins, the American Zeppelin Transport Corp. announced that 34 of the 97 persons aboard the airliner had lost their lives.

Twenty of the 36 passengers and 43 of the crew of 61 were saved, a total of 63 survivors, it was announced. Many were in critical condition at hospitals throughout the Lakehurst area.

Some escaped death by jumping as the flaming hulk dropped to the ground before the eyes of horrified spectators.

Others, including three children, were hurled from the great luxury airliner by the force of the blast and miraculously escaped.

The cause of the explosion, which came as the proud sky queen was nearing her mooring mast and only a few hundred feet above ground, has not been determined officially.

Federal authorities began an immediate investigation. Dr. Hans Luther, German Amabssador, flew here from Washington to open an independent inquiry to determine whether there was sabotage. . . .

† † †

Many oldsters, searching their memories for the major stories of the depression years, would list the night the Martians came as one of the truly unforgettable events. The Martians came on a CBS radio program called the Mercury Theatre of the Air, and the program was ostensibly a Halloween program offered by the young director-star, Orson Welles. What saved the American people from total—though probably temporary—collapse was the fact that on another network Edgar Bergen and Charlie McCarthy could be heard, and that in 1938 far more Americans listened to Bergen and McCarthy than to the Mercury Theatre of the Air. Of all the stories of the "good old days" of the 1930s, few have the enchantment of this one.

† † †

AN INVASION FROM OUTER SPACE

By George Mawhinney, *Philadelphia Inquirer,* November 1, 1938.

Terror struck at the hearts of hundreds of thousands of persons in the length and breadth of the United States last night as crisp words of what they believed to be a news broadcast leaped from their radio sets—telling of catastrophe from the skies visited on this country.

Out of the heavens, they learned, objects at first believed to be meteors crashed down near Trenton, killing many.

Then out of the "meteors" came monsters, spreading destruction with torch and poison gas.

It was all just a radio dramatization, but the result, in all actuality, was nation-wide hysteria.

In Philadelphia, women and children ran from their homes screaming. In Newark, N.J., ambulances rushed to one neighborhood to protect residents against a gas attack. In the deep South men and women knelt in groups in the streets and prayed for deliverance.

In reality there was no danger. The broadcast was merely a Halloween program in which Orson Welles, actor-director of the Mercury Theatre on the Air, related, as though he were one of the few human survivors of the catastrophe, an adaptation of H. G. Wells' "The War of the Worlds."

In that piece of fiction men from Mars, in meteor-like space ships, come to make conquest of Earth. The circumstances of the story were unbelievable enough, but the manner of its presentation was apparently convincing to hundreds of thousands of persons—despite the fact that the program was interrupted thrice for an announcement that it was fiction, and fiction only.

For the fanciful tale was broadcast casually, for all the world like a news broadcast, opening up serenely enough with a weather report.

The realism of the broadcast, especially for those who had tuned in after it had started, brought effects which none—not the directors of the Federal Radio Theatre Project, which sponsored it, nor the Columbia Broadcasting Co., which carried it over a coast-to-coast chain of 151 stations, nor Station WCAU, which broadcast it locally—could foresee.

Within a few minutes newspaper offices, radio stations and police departments everywhere were flooded with anxious telephone calls. Sobbing women sought advice on what to do; broken-voiced men wished to know where to take their families.

In many neighborhoods of Philadelphia, families packed their belongings and prepared to leave their homes. One small hotel proprietor said every person in the hotel hastily left. . . . .

Station WCAU received more than 4000 calls and eventually interrupted a later program to make an elaborate explanation that death had not actually descended on New Jersey, and that monsters were not actually invading the world.

But calm did not come readily to the frightened radio listeners of the country.

The hysteria reached such proportions that the New York City Department of Health called up a newspaper and wanted advice on offering its facilities for the protection of the populace. Nurses and physicians were among the telephone callers everywhere. . . .

Hundreds of motorists touring through New Jersey heard the broadcast over their radios and detoured to avoid the area upon which the holocaust was focused—the area in the vicinity of Trenton and Princeton. . . .

A white-faced man raced into Hillside, N.J., police station and asked for a gas mask. Police said he panted out a tale of "terrible people spraying liquid gas all over Jersey meadows." . . .

At Princeton University, women members of the geology faculty, equipped with flashlights and hammers, started for Grovers Corners. Dozens of cars were driven to the hamlet by curious motorists. . . .

An anonymous and somewhat hysterical girl phoned the Princeton Press Club from Grovers Corners and said:

"You can't imagine the horror of it! It's hell!". . .

The broadcast began at 8 p.m. Within a few minutes after that time it had brought such a serious reaction that New Jersey State police sent out a teletype message to its various stations and barracks, containing explanations and instructions to police officers on how to handle the hysteria. . . .

Actually, outside the radio stations, the Martians were doing a pretty good job on the Halloween imaginations of the citizenry. The radio stations and the Columbia Broadcasting Co. spent much of the remainder of the evening clearing up the situation. Again and again they explained the whole thing was nothing more than a dramatization.

In the long run, however, calm was restored in the myriad American homes which had been momentarily threatened by interplanetary invasion. Fear of the monsters from Mars eventually subsided.

There was no reason for being afraid of them, anyway. Even the bulletins of the radio broadcast explained they all soon died. They couldn't stand the earth's atmosphere and perished of pneumonia.

† † †

Something else, besides invasions from outer space, was happening to the American people in the 1930s—the invasion of the gossip columnist, of the inside dopester. Editors from the earliest days had known that the reading public would gobble up news, scandal, and rumor about the rich and famous and important; the papers of the age of jazz journalism had capitalized on such reader tastes. In 1931 a book was published anonymously, entitled *Washington Merry-Go-Round*. The authors were two capital reporters named Drew Pearson and Robert S. Allen, and their reporting was frequently on a very high level, even though Pearson, especially, was known to err, and though his later technique of crystal ball-gazing became too basic to his reporting. So successful was the book that the authors began to write a column with the same title, and the columns were a notable publishing success of the time.

† † †

HOOVER: A PORTRAIT FROM *WASHINGTON MERRY-GO-ROUND*

By Drew Pearson and Robert S. Allen, published anonymously (New York: Horace Liveright, 1931), pp. 74-77. Reprinted by permission of Mr. Allen.

In the long and tragic travail of the economic depression, the most tragic thing was the President's fear of admitting that a great disaster had befallen the country. For months, while gloom, unemployment, and deflation settled on the land, he refused to admit their reality or do anything fundamental about the situation. His approach to the problem was wholly that of the boomer, the bull-market operator, concerned only with his own political interests and willing to resort to any device or misrepresentation to further them.

Facts, statistics, plan, organization—there have been none, and when proposed by others have been rejected and stifled, secretly when possible, openly when that was impossible.

One policy alone has dominated his course: not to do or say anything that would reveal the truth about the great catastrophe. Suppression and inaction have been his unshaken rule.

The detailed record of this effort tells the story eloquently:

On December 14, 1929, Mr. Hoover declared that the volume of shopping reported to him indicated that the business of the country was "back to normal." That was some six weeks after the stock market crash.

Early in January, 1930, Secretary of the Treasury Mellon, under pressure from Hoover, announced, "I see nothing in the present situation that is either menacing or warrants pessimism. I have every confidence there will be a revival of activity in the spring." These ebullient assurances were greeted with a drop in stock market prices to new low levels.

A year and five months later Mr. Mellon, addressing a group of international bankers in Washington, and apparently free for the moment from White House restraint, frankly admitted: "I have no means of knowing when or how we shall emerge from the valley in which we are now traveling."

On January 22, the President personally expressed the view that the "trend" of employment had changed upward and then Secretary of Labor Davis, carrying out the refrain, gave it on his word that "every major industry was showing increases and that we can expect a great deal of business in 1930."

In February and early March, Secretary of Commerce Lamont, acting on White House orders, took up the burden and on three occasions solemnly gave assurance that "there is nothing in the situation to be disturbed about."

All this time, according to the most reliable labor statistics available in the United States at present, those of the New York

State Labor Bureau, factories were closing down in increasing numbers and the unemployment line was steadily lengthening.

On March 8, 1930, the President himself again entered the lists with his now famous prediction that the crisis would be over in "sixty days.". . .

On March 16, Julius H. Barnes, close personal friend and under-cover agent for the President, as Chairman of the President's National Business Survey Conference, declared "that the spring of 1930 marks the end of a period of grave concern." Barnes failed to add however that others would follow of even greater gravity.

On May 2, the President, with the expiration of his "sixty days," trimmed his sails very sharply. In a lengthy pronouncement he conceded that things were rather disturbed, but was still irrepressibly optimistic. "We have been passing through one of those great economic storms which periodically bring hardships and suffering to our people," he admitted. "While the crisis took place only six months ago, I am convinced we have passed the worst and with continued unity of effort we shall rapidly recover."

Two months later, in the privacy of his office and under strict and repeated admonitions of secrecy, he petulantly told Amos Pinchot and a group of important business men who had called to urge him to do something drastic to relieve unemployment: "Gentlemen, you are six weeks too late. The crisis is over."

Three months later, with bread lines longer than ever before and facing state and congressional elections, he set up, amid much fanfare, a national unemployment committee to "coordinate" employment activities.

In January, 1931, Colonel Arthur Woods, director of the committee, summoned before a Senate committee to tell about his work, estimated unemployment as around 5,000,000 and informed the Senators that his organization was preparing to disseminate pamphlets on how to stimulate relief. A week later the President issued a proclamation asking the public to contribute $10,000,000 to the Red Cross for food relief.

Three months later the Census Bureau announced that a special unemployment survey it had made showed an estimated 6,050,000 out of work. . . .

The final story of Herbert Hoover is yet to be told. Only time will make available the mass of secret documents and the details of his business career, now so zealously guarded, by which the complete picture can be filled in....

Had Herbert Hoover never gained the presidency, he might well have remained a shimmering hero. The illusion he so skilfully wove never would have been shattered. But before the ruthless realities and the merciless tests of that office his fundamental inadequacy of character undid him and he stands to-day stripped of all his carefully conjured glories. . . .

† † †

Somewhat different from Pearson and Allen was the breezy Walter Winchell, who was born in New York in 1887, went through the sixth grade, became a vaudeville dancer, a writer for something called the *Vaudeville News*, a reporter and columnist for Bernarr Macfadden on the *Evening Graphic*, and finally a columnist for William Randolph Hearst in 1929. Winchell was one of the famous names of the depression years, writing a column called "On Broadway," dwelling on film stars and theatrical stars and sports figures, getting himself punched at ringside by singer Al Jolson, being portrayed in such movies as *Blessed Event, Okay America!*, and *Broadway Through a Keyhole*, and starring in a couple of movies himself. His contributions to our journalism may have been slight (words like Reno-vated, blessed event, Chicagorilla, lohengrined, middle-aisled, debutramp, phfffft, infanticipating), but he was a superlative reporter, and his impact was considerable; a whole new school of similar journalism came into being because of his success.

† † †

WINCHELL GIVES ASSISTANCE TO THE FBI

New York Daily Mirror, August 26, 1939.

NEW YORK, August 25 (INS)—The surrender of public enemy "Lepke" Buchalter to the government last night took place while scores of pedestrians ambled by, and two police radio cars waited for the lights to change, near Twenty-eighth Street and Fifth Avenue.

The time was precisely 10:17 p.m., and the search for the most wanted fugitive in the nation was over. The surrender was negotiated by this reporter, whom G-man John Edgar Hoover authorized to guarantee "safe delivery."

After a series of telephone talks with persons unknown, and with the head of the FBI, Lepke appeared to drop out of the sky, without even a parachute. The time was 10:15. The scene was Madison Square between Twenty-third and Twenty-fourth Streets, where we had halted our car as per instructions.

The following two minutes were consumed traveling slowly north on Fourth Avenue and west on Twenty-seventh Street to Fifth Avenue, where the traffic lights were red—and to the next corner at Twenty-eight Street, where Mr. Hoover waited alone, unarmed and without handcuffs, in a government limousine. Hoover was disguised in dark sunglasses to keep him from being recognized by passersby. . . .

Lepke, who was calmer than this chauffeur, was on the verge of rushing out of our machine into Hoover's arms. The police cruisers, ironically, were the first observed by this reporter in two hours of motoring to complete the surrender.

Not until the final seconds was there a sign of uniformed law. But it was too late. The long arm of the government had reached out and claimed another enemy. The Federal Bureau of Investigation and the city of New York had saved $50,000—the reward offered. . . .

After parking our car behind a machine which was parked behind Hoover's, we shut off the ignition and escorted Lepke into Hoover's car.

"Mr. Hoover," we said, "this is Lepke."

"How do you do?" said Mr. Hoover, affably.

"Glad to meet you," replied Lepke. "Let's go."

"To the Federal Building at Foley Square," commanded Hoover. His colored pilot turned swiftly south. . . .

"You did the smart thing by coming in, Lepke," comforted Hoover.

"I'm beginning to wonder if I did," Lepke answered. "I would like to see my wife and kids, please?"

Mr. Hoover arranged for them to visit him shortly after Lepke was booked, fingerprinted, and Kodaked. . . .

When the government car reached Fourteenth Street, we got out and went to the first phone to notify our editor, who groaned:

"A fine thing! With a World War starting!"

The negotiations which led to Lepke's surrender began in this manner. On Saturday night, August 5 last, a voice on the phone said:

"Don't ask me who I am. I have something important to tell you. Lepke wants to come in. But he's heard so many different stories about what will happen to him. He can't trust anybody, he says. If he could find someone he can trust, he will give himself up to that person. The talk around town is that Lepke would be shot while supposedly escaping."

"Does he trust me?" we inquired.

"Do you really mean that?" said the voice anxiously.

"Sure," we assured. "I'll tell John Edgar Hoover about it and I'm sure he will see to it that Lepke receives his constitutional rights and nobody will cross him."

"O.K., put it on the air tomorrow night if you can get that promise," and then he disconnected. . . .

"You are authorized to state," said Hoover, "that the FBI will guarantee it!". . .

. . . all the dickering abruptly stopped—until last Tuesday night. Then a person we had never seen before, or since, approached us at Fifty-third Street and Fifth Avenue and said: "Where can you be reached on a pay-station phone in an hour?"

We went to the nearest phone booth, where the stranger marked down the number and instructed: "This is about Lepke. This time it's important. Please be here in an hour.". . .

Promptly an hour later, right on the button, that pay-station phone tinkled. We didn't give the voice a chance to talk. "I just spoke to Hoover," we said breathlessly. "He's fed up. If Lepke doesn't surrender by four p.m. tomorrow, Hoover says no consideration of any kind will ever be given him. For every day he stays away it may mean an extra two years added to his sentence."

The voice interrupted: "He's coming in, but you simply have to wait until he can arrange things. He's willing to come in, but it can't be tomorrow. Maybe the next night. Where can you be reached tomorrow night at six?"

We gave him another phone number. He said he'd call—and the call came. But it didn't seem to be the same voice. This time the instructions included: "Drive up to Proctor's Theater in Yonkers.". . . we motored up to Yonkers, and before we reached Proctor's Theater a car loaded with strangers—faces we don't recall ever seeing before—slowly drew alongside. We heard a voice say, "That's him.". . .

"Go to the drugstore on the corner of Nineteenth Street and Eighth Avenue," [one of the men] instructed. "There are some phone booths there. . . ."

At 8:55 p.m. we were in that drugstore. We ordered a coke. The boy behind the counter looked at us as though we seemed familiar. . . . A face met ours as we turned to look through the open door. The stranger jerked his head as though to telegraph "Come here." We joined him outside and walked to our car slowly.

"Go back in there and tell Hoover to be at Twenty-eighth Street on Fifth Avenue between 10:10 and 10:20," he instructed. . .

We took the wheel, turned our eyes left, and noticed many people across the street lounging around. It was very humid. Our clothes were dripping. The butterflies started to romp inside of us.

Suddenly a figure approached our car in haste. Out of the nowhere, it seems. He opened the door, got in, and said: "Hello. Thanks very much."

We released the brake and stepped on the gas. "We'll be with Mr. Hoover in a minute or two," we said. "He's waiting in his car at Twenty-eighth street."

"Yes, I know," said Lepke. "I just passed him."

† † †

Pearson, Allen and Winchell became entertainment figures themselves, in a sense, and helped to change the nature of the press in the depression years. Some press barons remained dominant and served as national figures and national commentators. Two of these were arch-critics of the New Deal—Robert Rutherford McCormick and William Randolph Hearst. By the 1930s the empire of Hearst was on the decline, possibly because Hearst had overextended himself in such ventures as his fabulous San Simeon on the California coast. The number of Hearst newspapers and magazines was becoming smaller; his Cosmopolitan pictures had not been able to make Marion Davies a star in a class with a Greta Garbo or a Norma Shearer. His kingmaking had helped to put Roosevelt in the White House, but the New Deal policies became too much for Hearst. And in early 1935, after looking at America and at the rest of the world, the boss put this signed editorial into all of his newspapers.

† † †

MR. HEARST LOOKS AT THE WORLD

New York American, March 3, 1935.

How is it possible for sane Americans to seek to destroy their own liberties when they see the fearful results of the loss of liberty in foreign lands.

In Italy the Fascist Government has suppressed all freedom of thought and expression, has drilled and dragooned all independent industry and all prosperity out of the country, and has utterly impoverished the people in order to gratify the Government's imperial ambition, and to maintain a nation in arms.

In Germany not only is all liberty lost, and all modern ideas of freedom of thought and speech and publication ended, but as further evidence of complete return of the Dark Ages, the Nazi Government has revived medieval methods of execution and political practices of wholesale assassination.

* * * *

The conditions existing in Russia are the most horrifying of all. There is absolutely no liberty, no security—no prospect but poverty and misery under a government without mercy, no future for subject classes but persecution and starvation. There from eight to ten million farmers in the past two years have been robbed of their grain by the Communist Government and allowed slowly to starve a dreadful death.

Over one million farmers, according to the publication *Time,* have been exiled to Siberia, where half of the men and women and children have died wretchedly from cold and exposure.

Their only crime was that they could not raise enough grain to satisfy the greed of the Communist plunderers.

Nothing in the whole history of despotic Russia even in the days of Ivan the Terrible has in any way equalled the bloody and calculated cruelty of the Communist tyranny.

* * * *

Europe is reverting to tyranny, and with tyranny comes not only the suppression of all popular rights and liberties, but the elimination of all hope of general peace and happiness and individual prosperity.

Communism, the attempt of ignorant and illiberal extremists to establish class government by force and violence, is the primary cause of all these evils.

When the tyranny of Communism threatens the world, Fascism arises to combat it, and in the cruel class conflict which follows force is met with force, violence with violence, and chaos comes again.

We in America should be spared these terrible conditions.

We should scotch the serpent of Communism at its birth. We should suppress the evil class conflict at its beginning.

Otherwise we shall see right here in America Fascism raised to fight Communism—we shall be horrified witnesses of a terrible struggle, in which democracy will surely be destroyed.

*   *   *   *

If the class conflict once gains headway, there can be no victory except for tyranny—the tyranny of Communism or the tyranny of Fascism—and either tyranny means the loss of all our liberties, then end of free thought and free speech and fair trial, the destruction of the fundamental rights of free men, the regimentation of society into a subject state with the scepter held in the bloody hand of despotism.

Then the desolation of the Dark Ages will be here again.

In this free America of ours, in the wholesome hearts of our upstanding independent people, lies the best hope for the survival of liberty and enlightenment and for the conservation of civilization.

We must be worthy of our great opportunity, our great obligation. Our duty is not only to our own people, but to the world.

We must keep the torch of freedom aflame to light the feet of humanity, weary of oppression, back to civilization, back to the free exercise and enjoyment of the elemental human rights of life, liberty, and the pursuit of happiness.

† † †

That other arch-foe of the New Deal was based in Chicago, and he, like Joseph Medill Patterson in New York, was a grandson of Joseph Medill. Robert R. McCormick was the publisher of the *Chicago Tribune,* "the Colonel" to Chicagoans, "Colonel McCosmic" to a cartoonist on the rival *Chicago Daily News.* McCormick's loathing for FDR and the New Deal was surpassing, and to many Americans McCormick was a newspaper publisher whose attitudes and politics were more Middle Ages than twentieth century. But he was a figure of rare fascination, an individualist, a personal journalist in a time when most major editors were known mainly to their colleagues. A *Tribune* editorial of 1940, the year the Democrats nominated the hated Roosevelt for a third time, is instructive for the person wishing to understand the Colonel.

† † †

ON A THIRD TERM FOR ROOSEVELT

Chicago Tribune, July 19, 1940.

For the first time in the history of the United States, and at the most dangerous time in which it could be done, an American party has renominated a man for a third consecutive term in the presidency.

This man, in his second term, undertook to make the Supreme Court a ratifying board for his decrees. In his first term he had been accustomed to issue executive orders which he expected congress to enact into laws by acclaim and without study or discussion. He expected that such a congress would ratify his decree destroying the federal judiciary as a separate branch of government. He demanded that the senators and representatives, without dissent or opposition, give him a Supreme Court of yesmen who would approve any law he issued.

He expected obedience because he had already reduced the national legislature to acceptance of bills as written. If, in his second term, he could have enforced his will, the government of the United States would have consisted in reality of the chief executive and no other independent branch of government. Congress and the court would have disappeared.

When congress, to his astonishment, defeated him in his purpose, he resolved that his supremacy should be reestablished by the ejection of the congressional rebels who had opposed him. He undertook his great purge and failed again. His idea of government was revealed in his second term. Now he is the man to whom the Democratic convention has submitted and for whom it has broken the rule which has kept the presidency from being available to the ambitions of any willful man who wanted prolonged tenure.

The convention did this for this willful man at a time when people in many lands are losing their freedom and being governed as disfranchised subjects of autocratic power, without the vote, without representative assemblies, and without independent judges.

The party which has presented the nation with this shameless historic episode is the party which says that the military forces of oppression are preparing to descend on these shores. It is the war party which has supported in Washington a policy of intervention in world conflict to save democracy in other lands.

The party which has broken down the American safeguard against dictatorship has nominated a man who for seven years has been trying to dictate and who for three years has been preparing his country for war in Europe and in Asia. In a false plank in its platform the party which nominated the war-maker declared for peace. The falseness of that declaration was revealed a few hours after it was made by the nomination of a man who seeks war, has done everything in his power to incite it, and whose record in the

White House is a record of campaign and platform pledges ignored and violated. He alone could tell the country to what degree, by his commitments to France and Great Britain, he is himself responsible for the outbreak of war in September, and how soon after the election America will be drawn into the conflict if he wins.

From what is known of his acts and utterances and of the acts and utterances of his ambassadors to Great Britain, France, and Poland the responsibility seems to be very grave. The Democratic convention has nominated for a third term a man who almost established a dictatorship in his second, and who has already prepared his plan for the conscription of the American people, their resources, and their enterprises, not only in event of war, but when war is imminent.

There were some voices raised against this in the convention, but they were feeble against the roar of the purse-controlled elements of the party and the voice of the mob which had been planted in the hall to drown any protest which might be made. The party, no doubt, has men in it who perceive this event with dismay, who, as citizens, regret not only that any man given power by their party should abuse it, who regret that the national purse should have been used to the disgrace of the party and the peril of the nation. They could not, however, find the spirit or the voice to rebuke the action fittingly. Senator Carter Glass, in spite of infirmities, tried to make his protest, but the man who wanted the nomination had too well prepared the way for it.

As the convention adjourns after its great disservice to the republic the honest public feeling is one of dismay and disgust. The responsible members will bear the reproach of their actions to the end of their days.

† † †

The other document about McCormick is a letter, one that was picked up and published in the *Chicago Daily News*. More than any other item about the Colonel it demonstrates his character, his personality, and his imperious nature.

† † †

A LETTER FROM COLONEL McCORMICK

February 20, 1942, published in the *Chicago Daily News*, March 14, 1942.

Mr. J. H. Sawyer, Jr.
333 North Michigan Avenue
Chicago, Illinois

Dear Mr. Sawyer:
Thank you for your very temperate letter.
What the most powerful propaganda organization in the world has misled you into believing was a campaign of hatred, has really

been a constructive campaign without which this country would be lost.

You do not know it, but the fact is that I introduced the R.O.T.C. into the schools; that I introduced machine guns into the army; that I introduced mechanization; I introduced automatic rifles; I was the first ground officer to go up in the air and observe artillery fire. Now I have succeeded in making that the regular practice in the army. I was the first to advocate an alliance with Canada. I forced the acquiring of the bases in the Atlantic Ocean.

On the other hand I was unsuccessful in obtaining the fortification of Guam; in preventing the division of the navy into two oceans. I was unable to persuade the navy and the administration that airplanes could destroy battleships.

I did get the marines out of Shanghai, but was unsuccessful in trying to get the army out of the Philippines.

Campaigns such as I have carried on inevitably meet resistance, and great persistence is necessary to achieve results. The opposition resorts to such tactics as charging me with hatred and so forth, but in view of the accomplishment I can bear up under it.

Yours sincerely,
Robert R. McCormick

† † †

14

THE PRESS AND WORLD WAR II

Of the British people, Winston Churchill ventured the opinion that a future time would regard 1940 as "their finest hour." Of American journalism in World War II, it also could be said that the war brought journalism its finest hour. In newspapers, in magazines, on the air, in photography, our journalists excelled. Singling out the most representative work of journalism in World War II was the most difficult task in this anthology.

The problem lay in part in the very defining of the word "beginning," in making reference to the beginning of the war. The seeds of war surely were sown in that war to end wars, 1914-1918. Long before the official outbreak of war in Europe there had been many wars to report, somewhere in the world, and from 1918 on the American journalist had been continuously on the job. Walter Duranty stayed in Russia to report the Soviet experiment for the *New York Times*. Edgar Snow went into China to write about Mao Tse-tung and the Communists. Webb Miller called his memoirs *I Found No Peace*, because his experience was that of covering wars from World War I until his death in a London blackout in 1940. Vincent Sheean saw his experience as a *Personal History;* he, like Miller, traversed the Middle East, North Africa, and the Orient in pursuit of his stories. To Pierre van Paassen it was *Days of Our Years;* he was a reporter who covered much of the same ground as Miller and Sheean. From the early 1930s on, John Gunther seemed to be "inside" everywhere, contributing a new kind of journalism, that which was enclosed within the covers of a book. Often outstripping all these reporters was Dorothy Thompson, who was in Europe from the 1920s on.

Reporters covered the aggression of the Japanese in Manchuria, that province of China which the conquerors then would label "Manchukuo." They were in Italy for the rise of Mussolini, in

Germany for the rise of Hitler, the biggest stories of all in pre-war years. When Italy invaded Ethiopia in 1935 representatives of the press were there. They covered the civil war in Spain—not a civil war alone, for the Fascists and the Communists from the outside used the war as a laboratory for a greater one to come. The press covered the full-fledged war that broke out between Japan and China in 1937. When the Munich meeting took place in 1938 reporters were there to describe the return of Prime Minister Neville Chamberlain to England, umbrella in hand. The invasion of Poland in 1939, the "overt act" of the war, became the culminating story of pre-war years. American newsmen, then, were not merely waiting for their own country to enter the conflict; they had been on the scene for years. (Recent scholarship, notably Phillip Knightley's *The First Casualty*, damns some of these reporters for being propagandists or willing tools of governmental censors.)

Domestic stories of the 1939-1945 years pale in comparison to the war stories, so this section is mainly a depiction of how the press covered a world at war. The major story on the "home front" was mobilization. The United States had been reluctant to become involved in the European affair, even though there was considerable sympathy for the invaded people of Scandinavia, the Lowlands and France, the peoples of the Mediterranean, and for the beleaguered British, like the French an ally in a war that had seemed so recent. It took the bombing of Pearl Harbor to unite a people who were basically quite pacifist.

An important domestic story was rationing, another was price controls. Neither is the kind of story that makes the bells ring. There were home-front heroes and heroines like Rosy the Riveter and the air raid wardens. Neither was a type likely to stir legend-making. There were "victory gardens" and greatly congested travel, and unbelievably tight housing accommodations in the major cities. There were many books about the war, and there were many movies. Popular songs were sentimental; there were few rousers, like "Over There" in World War I, but there were bluebirds over the White Cliffs of Dover, and a nightingale in Berkeley Square, and girls were told not to sit under the apple tree. One song urged us to "heil" right in "der Führer's face," and one informed us that the sun would soon be setting on the land of the rising sun. Long lines of teen girls waited to hear the new singing sensation, Frank Sinatra. Others wondered where all the sports heroes had gone; the answer, of course, was that they had gone to war—even a comic strip prize fighter, Joe Palooka, fought for democracy. So the heroes, on the news pages, were mainly President Franklin D. Roosevelt, who had been in the White House forever, some Republicans believed; his constant companion, Prime Minister Winston Churchill; their associates in the allied forces, linked in an arrangement that even then seemed uneasy, Premier Josef Stalin and Generalissimo Chiang Kai-shek; and the villains—Adolf Hitler, Benito Mussolini, and the Emperor Hirohito. Plus, of course, such military figures as Douglas MacArthur, Dwight Eisenhower,

Omar Bradley, George Marshall, George Patton, William Leahy, Ernest King, and Chester Nimitz. And an anonymous, but ever-present figure in most of the news stories—the GI.

Certain newspapers, inevitably, did especially distinguished reporting of the war: the *New York Times,* the *New York Herald Tribune,* the *Chicago Daily News,* the *Chicago Tribune,* the *Christian Science Monitor,* and those two new journals, *PM* and the *Chicago Sun. Time, Life,* and *Newsweek* reporters were at work; the photography in *Life* is among the best of the period. Pictures taken by Robert Capa, Bert Brandt, and Margaret Bourke-White deserve places in any collection of photography; the D-Day photography was superior; Joseph Rosenthal's shot of the flag-raising on Iwo Jima is almost *the* symbol of the Pacific war. The Signal Corps made available its men and its photographs. Some of the radio journalism finds a place in these pages, as does some of the soldier journalism, for *Stars and Stripes* was back, and there was a highly popular magazine called *Yank.* Such work as Bill Mauldin's cartoons of Willie and Joe is, of course, not here. Notable novelists—Ernest Hemingway, John Steinbeck, John Dos Passos—engaged in war correspondence. Some of the journalism appeared in book form: Robert Trumbull's *The Raft;* W. L. White's *Journey for Margaret* and *They Were Expendable;* Richard Tregaskis's *Guadalcanal Diary.* Reporters had adventures of almost swashbuckling scope, and some of them became national celebrities in the process. And to the credit of both press and government, it was in great part a war free from controversy, except for the most celebrated dispute of all, one at which we shall look later. (The very freedom from controversy may be to the *discredit* of the press, some critics contend.)

The story of press coverage of World War II could begin with the work of Vincent Sheean, who wrote *Personal History,* an autobiography so popular that it was purchased for the movies and became (though only incidentally) Alfred Hitchcock's thriller, *Foreign Correspondent.* Sheean became especially known for his coverage of the Moroccan rebellion in the early 1920s. He was also in China for the 1927 fighting between Nationalists and Communists. A friend and colleague of Vincent Sheean was Dorothy Thompson, as authentic a celebrity as her journalistic times offered, a foreign correspondent and later a syndicated columnist, one who received fan mail in such amounts as to rival Joan Crawford or Clark Gable. In her heyday she was married to another celebrity, the novelist Sinclair Lewis, and it was Sheean who recorded the story of that marriage—not one of history's happiest. Dorothy Thompson's foreign correspondence began in 1920, after she had received a college education at Syracuse University and had been what was then called a "suffragette." She talked her way into covering a Zionist convention in London, and from then on was a reporter of note.

As a syndicated columnist Miss Thompson was usually of a somewhat conservative persuasion. She was not enamored of

Franklin D. Roosevelt, but in 1940 she changed her mind, and in so doing lost her job with the *New York Herald Tribune,* then the kingpin Republican paper of the land. For how could a *Herald Tribune* columnist support anything as bad as a third term for Roosevelt?

† † †

A COLUMNIST COMES OUT FOR ROOSEVELT

By Dorothy Thompson, *New York Herald Tribune,* October 9, 1940. Copyright New York Herald Tribune.

. . . I shall support the President because I think he has assets on his side that nobody can match—assets for this nation in this time.

The President *knows* the world. He knows it, in the most particular minutiae, better than any other living democratic head of a state or ex-head of a state. . . .

The President is a man of peace. No one who saw and talked with him, as I did, after the outbreak of the war, and in June, in the midst of the collapse of France, and saw how the war had stricken that naturally insouciant personality, marking his face with suffering, could ever dare to say that he is a warmonger. . . .

The President can be a very great man in times of emergency. He was a great man in 1933, and he has been a great man since the overwhelming crisis in June. . . .

He is the first President in our whole history to dare to call for conscription in the midst of an election campaign. In that he threw his political career into the scales. . . .

The President gave two of the most critical Cabinet posts—War and Navy—to two great patriots and two Republicans, one of them the man who, as Vice-Presidential candidate four years ago, made the sharpest attacks upon his policy. . . .

He unified the defense with Canada, making a military and political move of first-class statesmanship and importance.

He made a deal on air bases which is worth billions for the defense of these shores. . . .

He possesses the greatest single asset that any leader of a democratic state can have in a crisis like this: the confidence of the rank and file of workers that he will not use conscription and defense to betray democracy itself and destroy their freedom. . . .

Finally, the prestige of the President throughout the democratic world, what is left of it, free, and what still hopes and believes and struggles under tyranny, is immense. . . .

† † †

Some of her contemporaries thought Dorothy Thompson to be the prime globetrotter of them all, but surely she would have had to yield to John Gunther on that score. The first place Gunther went inside was Europe—*Inside Europe,* of course. He took a look at Germany as Hitler was rising to power; he went to Italy and saw what Benito Mussolini was like—Mussolini, who had been a journalist himself and was still directing his newspaper, *Popolo d'Italia.* Gunther wrote in a crisp, factual, entertaining style; his books became highly popular, and he was still reporting inside various world trouble spots in the 1960s.

† † †

INSIDE BENITO MUSSOLINI

By John Gunther, *Inside Europe* (New York: Harper, 1937 rev.), pp. 177-178. Copyright by John Gunther.

Most people meeting Mussolini are surprised at his shortness of stature. He is, like Napoleon, only five feet six. His shoulders are powerful and his hands are finely formed and almost delicate. His smile is gritty. Usually he wears the uniform of a corporal in the Fascist Militia. He works in the Palazzo Venezia, in the center of Rome, and lives about ten minutes away by car, in the Villa Torlonia, a comfortable villa with a luxuriant garden on the Via Nomentana, near the Porta Pia. . . .

At fifty-two Mussolini is in powerfully good health, partly as a result of attention to severe regime. Shortly after he became prime minister he was desperately ill with a stomach ailment; he eats very little nowadays but milk and fruit. He told a recent American interviewer, pointing to a basket of fruit on the table, "That is the secret of my continued health—fruit, fruit, fruit. In the morning I have a cup of coffee and fruit; at noon I have soup or broth and fruit, and at night I have fruit. I never touch meat, but sometimes I have a little fish." He loves exercise, and takes a lot of it: riding in the Torlonia gardens, fencing, swimming, hiking. He neither drinks nor smokes. He was fond of women in his younger days, but for the last few years he has paid little attention to them. . . .

† † †

Of the war correspondents of his generation Webb Miller may have been the gentlest, a reporter somehow ill-suited—at least by conventional stereotypes—to the role he was playing. He was sensitive even to the police stories he had covered in Chicago, but his beat still became war, wherever the little brushfire wars were taking place in the 1920s and 1930s. Miller was in an African country, one known to Americans as Abyssinia but soon as mainly Ethiopia, when war began there in 1935, with the invasion by the forces of Mussolini. Soon the face and figure of Ethiopia's Emperor Haile Selassie became familiar to Americans in the newsreels and newspapers—Selassie before the League of Nations, pleading the case of his country. With Webb Miller in Ethiopia was Floyd

Gibbons, the same Gibbons who had become a celebrity in World War I.

† † †

WAR BEGINS IN ETHIOPIA

By Webb Miller, United Press, October 3, 1935. Copyright United Press, 1935.

WITH ITALIAN ARMIES IN THE FIELD, Oct. 3.—The Italian advance into Ethiopia was started this morning.

The initial objective was Aduwa, to the south of the main Italian concentration area, for Aduwa was where an Italian army was ripped to pieces 39 years ago.

The Italians crossed the Mareb River frontier at widely separated points, all converging in heavy columns toward Aduwa.

Squadrons of bombing airplanes, fighting airplanes and scout airplanes roared southward from the Asmara area and over the Mareb River, topping great rugged mountain peaks, for the ancient empire of the Ethiopians, never conquered.

The planes and the men under them were headed for Aduwa as the chief objective with Adigrat, to the east, and other similar points as minor objectives whose occupation was essential to the plan of strategy of General Emilio De Bono, commander-in-chief of the colonial armies. . . .

† † †

September 1, 1939, was the date, and the story as reported in our newspapers was factual and unsentimental: Germany had invaded Poland. The invasion came in time for Labor Day in America, an invasion that followed a summer of nerve-fraying developments, especially the treaty signed by those long-time antagonists, Germany and the Soviet Union—two dogs no longer chewing at each other's throats. In Berlin for the Columbia Broadcasting System was William L. Shirer, who was keeping what he was later to publish as his *Berlin Diary*.

† † †

A BROADCASTER REPORTS THE START OF WAR

By William L. Shirer, *Berlin Diary* (New York: Knopf, 1941, Popular Library ed., 1961), pp. 148, 149. Copyright 1941 and renewed 1969 by William L. Shirer. Reprinted by permission of Alfred A. Knopf, Inc.

BERLIN, September 1, later

It's a "counter-attack"! At dawn this morning Hitler moved against Poland. It's a flagrant, inexcusable, unprovoked act of aggression. But Hitler and the High Command call it a "counter-attack." A grey morning with overhanging clouds. The people in the street were apathetic when I drove to the *Rundfunk* for my first broadcast at eight fifteen a.m. Across from the Adlon the morning shift of workers was busy on the new I. G. Farben building just as if nothing had happened. None of the men brought the extras which the newsboys were shouting. Along the east-west axis the Luft-waffe were mounting five big anti-aircraft guns to protect Hitler when he addresses the Reichstag at ten a.m. Jordan and I had to remain at the radio to handle Hitler's speech for America. Throughout the speech, I thought as I listened, ran a curious strain, as though Hitler himself were dazed at the fix he had got himself into and felt a little desperate about it. . . .

†   †   †

Shirer's boss in London was Edward R. Murrow, a North Carolinian transplanted to Washington state, a journalist with no formal training in journalism but with all the best instincts of the newsman, a man with a voice that still reverberates in the memories of many of his listeners. Murrow would say "This. . . is London," and then would come his description, fading out at times as short wave reports were known to do, punctuated sometimes by the sounds of bombing, gunfire, aircraft—or merely walking people. Murrow's reports have been collected, on recordings and in published form; they really have to be heard to be appreciated, but they read beautifully, too. Here he is, in the first month of war.

†   †   †

THIS. . . IS LONDON

By Edward R. Murrow, September 22, 1940, in Edward W. Bliss, Jr., *In Search of Light: The Broadcasts of Edward R. Murrow* 1938-1961 (New York: Knopf, 1967), pp. 37-38. Copyright © 1967 by the Estate of Edward R. Murrow. Reprinted by permission of Alfred A. Knopf, Inc.

I'm standing again tonight on a rooftop looking out over London, feeling rather large and lonesome. In the course of the last fifteen or twenty minutes there's been considerable action up there, but at the moment there's an ominous silence hanging over London. But at the same time a silence that has a great deal of dignity. Just straightaway in front of me the searchlights are working. I can see one or two bursts of antiaircraft fire far in the distance. Just on the roof across the way I can see a man wearing a tin hat, a pair of powerful night glasses to his eyes, scanning the sky. Again, looking in the opposite direction, there is a building with two windows gone. Out of one window there waves something that looks like a white bed sheet, a window curtain swinging free in this night breeze. It looks as though it were being shaken by a ghost. There are a great many ghosts around these buildings in London. The searchlights straightaway, miles in front of me, are still scratching that sky. There's a three-quarter moon riding high. There was one burst of shellfire almost straight in the Little Dipper. . . .

Down below in the streets I can see just that red and green wink of the traffic lights; one lone taxicab moving slowly down the street. Not a sound to be heard. As I look out across the miles and miles of rooftops and chimney pots, some of those dirty-gray fronts of the buildings look almost snow-white in this moonlight here tonight. And the rooftop spotter across the way swings around, looks over in the direction of the searchlights, drops his glasses and just stands there. There are hundreds and hundreds of men like that standing on rooftops in London tonight watching for fire bombs, waiting to see what comes out of this steel-blue sky. The searchlights now reach up very, very faintly on three sides of me. There is a flash of a gun in the distance but too far away to be heard.

† † †

It was sometimes the veteran, the aging reporter, who was there to cover the action in World War II, and American journalism has no better example of such a veteran than Leland Stowe, of the *Chicago Daily News*. Stowe's great accomplishment was to be there when the Nazis invaded Norway and to tell the story of the selling out of his country by a man named Quisling. Stowe got his story in part through instinct; he felt that something important was about to happen, and he stayed to get that something important. Later he was in another dramatic setting: he was the only American to be with the Russians at the front after Germany invaded the Soviet Union in June, 1941.

† † †

A REPORTER IN NORWAY

By Leland Stowe, *Chicago Daily News,* April 25, 1940.

GADDEDE, NORWEGIAN-SWEDISH FRONTIER, APRIL 25— Here is the first and only eyewitness report on the opening chapter of the British expeditionary troops' advance in Norway north of Trondheim. It is a bitterly disillusioning and almost unbelievable story.

The British force which was supposed to sweep down from Namsos consisted of one battalion of Territorials and one battalion of the King's Own Royal Light Infantry. These totaled fewer than 1500 men. They were dumped into Norway's deep snows and quagmires of April slush without a single antiaircraft gun, without one squadron of supporting airplanes, without a single piece of field artillery.

They were thrown into the snows and mud of sixty-three degrees north latitude to fight crack German regulars—most of them veterans of the Polish invasion—and to face the most destructive of modern weapons. The great majority of these young Britishers averaged only one year of military service. They have already paid a heavy price for a major military blunder which was not committed by their immediate command, but in London.

Unless they receive large supplies of antiaircraft guns and adequate reinforcements within a very few days, the remains of these two British battalions will be cut to ribbons.

Here is the astonishing story of what has happened to the gallant little handful of British expeditionaries above Trondheim:

After only four days of fighting nearly half of this initial BEF contingent has been knocked out—either killed, wounded, or captured. On Monday, these comparatively inexperienced and incredibly underarmed British troops were decisively defeated. They were driven back in precipitate disorder from Vist, three miles south of the bomb-ravaged town of Steinkjer.

As I write, it is probable that the British field headquarters has been withdrawn northward and that the British vanguard has been compelled to evacuate one or several villages. Steinkjer was occupied by the Germans Tuesday.

I was in Steinkjer Monday evening just before the British lines were blasted to pieces. I was the only newspaper correspondent to enter the burning town and the only correspondent to visit British advance headquarters and to pass beyond to the edge of the front's heavy firing zone.

A score of buildings were flaming fiercely on the town's water front from a bombing two hours earlier. In the midst of the smoky ruins I heard machine-gun cracking at high tempo in the hills just beyond the town. Shell explosions rapped the valley regularly with angry echoes. This was the first sustained battle between German and British troops on Norwegian soil. Already the conflict was snarling hot.

A battalion of six hundred Territorials was fighting desperately to hold Vist, the point of their farthest southwest advance toward Trondheim. As Monday's twilight closed they were completely done in. For hours they had been torn and broken under the terrible triple onslaught of German infantry, trimotored bombers, and naval firing from destroyers at the head of Breitstadfjord.

Within two hours the British troops were in flight. They had no chance whatever of standing off from bombs and three- or six-inch shells with nothing but Bren machine guns and rifles. Before eleven o'clock that night I talked with the nerve-shattered survivors of the British battalion. We found two truckloads of them several miles above their headquarters and on their way north away from the front. . . .

† † †

In the mold of Vincent Sheean, Webb Miller, and John Gunther was a reporter named Quentin Reynolds, another of those war correspondents who became almost celebrities in the 1939-1945 period. Reynolds was a big, easygoing, unruffled-appearing man, and he told of the fall of Paris in his book, *The Wounded Don't Cry*, published in 1941. Paris was not supposed to fall; nor was France, for that matter. When that supposedly impregnable nation went under, there was a shock around the world, and the song composed by Jerome Kern and Oscar Hammerstein II, "The Last Time I Saw Paris," was one that could move many a listener.

France fell on June 22, 1940; the French capitulation was the major story that helped to inaugurate one of the most interesting experiments in the history of American journalism. This was the newspaper *PM*, begun on June 23, the inspiration of a veteran of both *Time* and the *New Yorker,* Ralph Ingersoll, who was joined by a corps of able newsmen from clear across the land. Their dream was to publish a newspaper that would be free of advertising, one that would freely interpret the news—and *PM* was such a newspaper, for a time. A series of vignettes from that first issue tells the story of *PM,* in part, a paper that perished in the postwar period, long after it had been taken over by Marshall Field III of Chicago.

† † †

FROM THE FIRST ISSUE OF A NEW PAPER

PM, June 23, 1940. Copyright PM, 1940.

France signed an armistice with Germany at 12:50 p.m. EDT Saturday after less than ten months of war.

The agreement, imposed on the defeated French, is to take effect when France agrees to Italian armistice terms. . . .

* * * * *

A two-headed Janus stood at the microphones when Germany gave the world her story of what happened in the Compiegne Forest. The mouth of one, speaking for the German public, spat verbal venom, hate and vengeance. The other, solemnly chivalrous, was addressed to the world—to the populations Germany would like to convince that only a just and real peace is their desire. . . .

* * * * *

Tomorrow at Philadelphia the Republican National Convention begins the serious business of nominating candidates for President and Vice-President of the United States. There are four major candidates—Dewey, Willkie, Taft, Vandenberg—but no one of them today can claim a majority of the 1000 delegates. . . .

* * * * *

Being mistaken for an escaping bank robber was a new experience for H. V. Kaltenborn, radio commentator, when his plane landed him in the arms of waiting cops at Denver's airport. His train having stalled, Kaltenborn had chartered a plane. He talked his way out of trouble and made his broadcasting date by a two-minute margin.

* * * * *

The war boomlet in America has survived the defeat of France and is spreading into the light consumption industries, the big job-makers in New York City.

By July 1, total industrial output will probably be within striking distance of the summit of last fall's short-lived war spurt. By now, the Federal Reserve Board's index of production has already recovered to at least 118, according to PM estimates. The April low was 102. . . .

* * * * *

Bobby Feller, the best pitcher in baseball today, is a living example of the fact that America is still the land of opportunity. Feller won't be 21 in time to vote this fall but he already has banked $60,000 on the strength of his high hard one.

Not every American boy who has the stuff can become president but any American boy who has a high hard one can become a big league pitcher. Feller's case history proves that. . . .

* * * * *

Dear Editor:

This is the first chance I have had to secure a copy of PM. It certainly is easy on the hands, holding it in the crowded subway, but there is so much in it, it is rather hard on the head.

RUSSELL S. GILBERT

Try wearing it slightly at an angle, with brim down.—ED.

† † †

Until December, 1941, it had seemed to be somebody else's war, but then came Pearl Harbor. Japan invaded the Hawaiian Islands on a Sunday morning, and because most papers in this country did not publish in those days from late Saturday night until Monday morning, the story that appeared in the 144-point type in some papers was that of the invasion of the Philippines, with Pearl Harbor a secondary story. Most Americans got the news by radio, or by word of mouth, but the wire services were, as always, operating twenty-four hours a day. If a newspaper published an extra that Sunday it was likely to use stories like these.

† † †

WAR COMES TO AMERICA

By the Associated Press, December 7, 1941.

WASHINGTON, Dec. 7 (AP)—The president decided today after Japan's attack on Pearl Harbor and Manila to call an extraordinary meeting of the cabinet at six-thirty p.m. (M.S.T.) tonight and to have congressional leaders of both parties join the conference at seven p.m.

WASHINGTON, Dec. 7 (AP)—Japanese airplanes today attacked American defense bases at Hawaii and Manila, and President Roosevelt ordered the army and navy to carry out undisclosed orders prepared for the defense of the United States.

The White House said that Japan had attacked America's vital outposts in the Pacific—Hawaii and Manila—at three-twenty p.m. (EST) and that so far as was known the attacks were still in progress.

Announcing the President's action for the protection of American territory, Presidential Secretary Stephen Early declared that so far as is known now the attacks were made wholly without warning—when both nations were at peace—and were delivered within an hour or so of the time that the Japanese ambassadors had gone to the state department to hand to the secretary of state Japan's reply to the secretary's memorandum of the twenty-sixth. . . .

HONOLULU, Dec. 7 (AP)—At least two Japanese bombers, their wings bearing the insignia of the Rising Sun, appeared over Honolulu at about seven-thirty-five a.m. (Honolulu time) today and dropped bombs. Unverified reports said a foreign warship appeared off Pearl Harbor and began firing at the defenses in that highly fortified post. . . .

LONDON, Dec. 7 (AP)—President Roosevelt's announcement of Japanese air attacks on United States Pacific bases staggered London tonight, which awaited fulfillment of Prime Minister Churchill's promise to declare war on Japan "within the hour" if she attacked the United States.

The prime minister's promise, made in a speech Nov. 11, was recalled on every hand. . . .

† † †

So America was at war. Of the columnists and Washington observers operating at that time, one of the best was Raymond Clapper. He was a Kansan, a United Press man who had been covering the Washington scene for many years, and who was later killed in a plane crash in the Marshall islands in 1944. One of his columns appeared the day Roosevelt addressed Congress, the day war was declared upon the axis.

† † †

A COLUMNIST REFLECTS ON WAR COMING TO AMERICA

By Raymond Clapper, *Cincinnati Post,* December 8, 1941.

Americans can be proud today. We can be proud that we tried to the bitter end to avoid war.

In the face of advancing savagery the Government of the United States continued to labor for peace. We tried to throw our moral weight against aggression and for the protection of all nations and for equal opportunity. We can be proud that we continued to do this until Japan struck.

Twelve hours before Japanese planes appeared over Honolulu, President Roosevelt appealed personally to the Emperor of Japan to join him in a peaceful adjustment. Even as the news of the attack was flashed to Washington, Secretary Hull was talking with the two Japanese representatives in his office. We were shot at while still in the act of seeking peace.

A strong nation can take pride in that, and in the record of patience and fair dealing. We can be proud of President Roosevelt and Secretary Hull, and of their cool and steady loyalty to those basic principles that must, after the last drop of blood has been spilled, rise again to guide nations. Our efforts failed. But we can be proud that those efforts were made, and that no American gun fired before we were attacked. Only today have we put on the uniform of war.

Japan has made our decision for us. This nation hates war so deeply, is so convinced of its futility as a method of adjusting differences, that we could not take the initiative. Within the last few days I have heard diplomats who have participated in some of the Far Eastern discussions express doubt that the United States would go to war even if Thailand were attacked by Japan. It would have been easy for Japan to avoid war with the United States.

But now all of our doubts, all of our reluctance, all of our hesitations, have been swept away from us. Practically every leading isolationist already has been heard from. Their answer to the attack on Honolulu is that we must fight. Wheeler and Taft, and McNary, leader of the Senate Republicans, have taken their stand with the Government. Japan has united this country for us. Congress will very soon register the unity of this nation.

This is suicide for Japan. A desperate, fourth-rate nation, the spoiled little gangster of the Orient will have to be exterminated as a power. Japan has asked for it and now she will get it.

Japan could have joined the United States and Britain as one of the three controlling sea powers of the globe. Her geography and economic situation made that her logical course. Japan can live only by sea trade. But she has chosen to war with the two other sea powers. She preferred to take her chances with armed force just as Germany has done. Japan chose to live by the sword and she will die by the sword. Japan will be blasted, bombed, burned, starved. Her people will suffer ghastly tortures. A nation which has possibilities of becoming one of the rulers of the world will be reduced to a pitiful huddling people on a poor little group of islands.

The modern world can no longer tolerate the anarchy of conquest by force. The two nations most addicted to this barbarism are Germany and Japan. They must be disarmed. Force must be hereafter kept in the hands of nations that will use it to bring about a peaceful world.

We shall come out of this war with fighting strength the like of which has never been seen. We shall have plenty of it for our protection. I hope we shall use it also in cooperation with other nations so that no power again can commit such an assault against the peace as Japan has just been guilty of.

This war must be fought until Japanese military strength is exterminated.

But more than that must come out of it. Our victory must be used to bring about a new era of benevolent force which will secure for all men and women and their children a new kind of peace in which the human race can progress toward that happier life which science and industry have made possible.

America can open that door.

†   †   †

Raymond Clapper's column is pure 1941, marked by the mood that so penetrated the air that December 7 and 8. Bill Vaughan wrote differently, and few journalists have the prescience or the ability to offer a record like the one that follows. Vaughan wrote for the *Kansas City Star,* especially a column of short commentaries called "Starbeams," but he also wrote one-subject columns. A few days after Pearl Harbor he assessed the meaning of what was taking place, and he did so with wit, charm, good taste, and an amazing sense of history.

† † †

THAT SLEEPY SUNDAY IN '41 WHEN WE WENT TO WAR

By Bill Vaughan, *Kansas City Star,* December 12, 1941.

This is for your scrapbook, and for the curious citizen who will want to know what it was like in Kansas City in 1941 when war came. How did it feel to sit down to a pleasant Sunday dinner in a world where war was a headline and push back your chair at the end in a world, whether you knew it or not, in which the dive bombers were killing your neighbors' sons? Your children's children will want to know that.

December 7 dawned to clouds. It was a day for sleeping late. If you went to church it was under a dappled sky.

In your newspaper that morning you had read that Japan was massing troops in an apparent threat against a place called Thailand and that Franklin D. Roosevelt, our President, had sent a note to Emperor Hirohito in an effort to save the peace in the Pacific. The article was full of grave portents, but the Japanese emissaries still were conferring with the State department in Washington. There had been so much diplomatic seesawing, so many changes in position, the final plunge into war had been skirted so often, that although you shook your head, you really were not alarmed.

Besides, in two years of war in Europe, you had come to accept cities bombed with your grapefruit, grave conferences of foreign ministers with your luncheon and destroyers sunk with your after-dinner coffee. The picture of a lost child on the front page really was more interesting, and your casual talk that quiet morning was as likely to be of the Missouri Tigers' chances against Fordham in the Sugar Bowl as of the course of the empire in the Far East. (Note to future historians: If you don't get that part about the Sugar Bowl, just skip it.)

Your country had passed more than a year of intensive preparation, including the compulsory training of its young men, yet here in the Middle West it had not touched you very deeply. You knew many men in the Army or the Navy, but their problems seemed to be one of morale—whether they were getting enough table tennis equipment and magazines—rather than anything that struck you as very vital.

Defense industries were expanding, you knew, but booms, housing problems and vaulting prices were things which affected you less than they would have if you had lived elsewhere. You were against strikes in defense industries, you were against Hitler and you had a "V for Victory" sticker on your car to show your approval of the desperate protest of the oppressed peoples of Europe—or because it was fashionable. You applauded such slogans as "Keep 'Em Flyin'," but it all seemed a little remote, a confusing picture you read about, but which had little bearing on your own daily business as usual.

It was with a good feeling that you sat down to dinner with your family at 1 o'clock. Sunday dinner, a tradition all the years of your life, seemed a firm and stable thing, a million miles away from men who died in snow or sand.

But by the time you were starting on your dessert and the children were squirming to get out of doors, a copy editor of The Star, shuffling through a stack of news reports in the nearly deserted office, stifled a yawn as he reached for a ringing telephone.

It was the office of the Associated Press on the third floor of The Star building calling.

"Japan has bombed Hawaii!" an excited A.P. man cried. "The flash is in the tube."

Before The Star man could understand fully, he heard one of the leather cylinders which carried the news through a pneumatic tube hit the desk beside him. He unsnapped the flap, and pulled out the thin, white paper. That was at 1:22 p.m.

"FLASH—WHITE HOUSE SAYS JAPS ATTACK PEARL HARBOR."

Those were the eight words on the slip, to be followed by the additional flash two minutes later that the Philippines also had been bombed, a report which later developed to be premature.

After a quick call to the managing editor at his home, the telegraph desk man sprinted up a flight of stairs to the studio of station WDAF and handed the paper to an announcer.

At 1:33 o'clock WDAF broke in on the University of Chicago Round Table, a program in which various pundits were discussing "Canada, Neighbor at War." The interruption apparently was Kansas City's first news of the almost unbelievable events in the East, although the other radio stations carried it within a few minutes.

If you were paying strict attention to your dinner, however, the chances are you did not hear that bulletin. It may have been during the New York Philharmonic broadcast that you first heard what was happening, the news flashes breaking in as a macabre counterpoint to Brahms.

Or perhaps you were out for a drive or taking a nap and didn't know that Japan had declared war on the United States until The Star's first extra hit the street at 6:12 o'clock.

These editions were the result of quick, exacting work by a staff hastily organized to quicken the pulse of the newspaper plant, which had slowed to its customary Sunday afternoon beat—slowest of the week.

It was the work of men, many of whom recalled America's entry into the last war, much less dramatic, lacking the sharp, shattering event which started this one. And it was the work of young men who, even in their time, had printed much of many wars. The formal vote in Congress, of course, did not come until Monday, but these men knew the war had come, and you, in your home or in your motor car, knew it too, when you heard the news. You all knew that the people of the United States could choose nothing but war with a foe who hissed politely the while he laid his plans for stealthy murder from the sky.

"Gotta whip those Japs!" the strong-lunged newsboys bawled. At the doors of theaters, men and women emerging from the unreality within, from "Swamp Water" and Fibber McGee in "Look Who's Laughing," or from seeing Sally Rand dance with her fan and bubble at the Tower, saw the big, black headlines and rushed to buy a paper. At Loew's Midland, the manager, John McManus, seizing an opportunity in the middle of a B picture (Have they forgotten B pictures, lucky historian?) called "Niagara Falls," when the action was scenic rather than dramatic, spoke the shocking news briefly through the screen's loudspeaker.

In the lobbies of theaters and hotels and in restaurants radios were going. Men took the news differently, of course, according to their several natures. There was surprise and indignation, covered often by a rough humor. There even seemed to be some of that strange relief, the feeling of "Well, here it is at last," which had been reported from nation after nation as the war of arms replaced the war of nerves.

To others, however, the news struck too deep even for the appearance of levity. From the time of the first flash until 7 o'clock that night the switchboard of The Star's city desk handled a steady flow of calls. Mothers, many of them in tears, asked for word of their sons at Manila or on the U.S.S. Oklahoma, reported struck by bombs. Others wondered if their boys would be home for long-anticipated Christmas furloughs.

If you were like many Kansas Citians the coming of war upset you rather less than you might have expected. As you listened to the bulletins and read the extras, however, you had the urge to get out and see and talk to people. You may have taken the family for a drive through the downtown district which, strangely, was not changed from the way it had been in peace. You smiled at the irony of the signs which said: "It's Christmastime," as you drove by the gay windows full of holiday presents, and you tooted the horn of your car, not exactly knowing why you did it.

At 9:12, according to the weather bureau, the moon came up. It was a bomber's moon, bright and only four days past full. The stars were out and in the Country Club Plaza the colored lights picked out the skeleton lines of shops and restaurants, familiar, cheerful and reassuring in the night on which you went to war.

† † †

That was December, 1941. There was as yet no realization in the land of what lay ahead, of the grim accounts of battles and heroism and treachery. One author who made the war vivid was Richard Tregaskis, in his book, *Guadalcanal Diary,* another of those pieces of reporting lodged between covers. He offered a description of some of the most terrible fighting that took place during the Pacific campaigns, on a tiny island in the South Pacific. The book had enormous sales, became a standard of war reporting, and was made by 20th Century-Fox into a successful film.

† † †

THE DEVASTATION OF GUADALCANAL

By Richard Tregaskis, *Guadalcanal Diary* (New York: Popular Library ed., 1962), pp. 120-121. Copyright, 1943 by Random House, Inc. Reprinted by permission of the publisher.

. . . The stench of bodies strewn along Hell Point and across the Tenaru spit was strong. Many of them lay at the water's edge, and already were puffed and glossy, like shiny sausages. Some of the bodies had been partially buried by wave-washed sand; you might see a grotesque, bloated head or twisted torso sprouting from the beach.

It was not pleasant to look at the piles of bodies on the spit. But that carnage was a pale painting, compared to the scene in the grove across the spit. That was a macabre nightmare. We saw groups of Jap bodies torn apart by our artillery fire, their remains fried by the blast of the shells. We saw machine-gun nests which had been blasted, and their crews shredded, by canister fire from our tanks. The tread tracks of one of our tanks ran directly over five squashed bodies, in the center of which was a broken machine gun on a flattened bipod.

Everywhere one turned there were piles of bodies; there one with a backbone visible from the front, and the rest of the flesh and bone peeled up over the man's head, like the leaf of an artichoke; there a charred head, hairless but still equipped with blackened eyeballs; pink, blue, yellow entrails drooping; a man with a red bullet-hole through his eye; a dead Jap private, wearing dark, tortoise-shell glasses, his buck teeth bared in a humorless grin, lying on his back with his chest a mess of ground meat. There is no horror to these things. The first one you see is the only shock. The rest are simple repetition. . . .

† † †

One of the reporters of the war, Ernie Pyle, became to his generation and to later ones the best-loved of all chroniclers of World

War II. He was a Midwesterner, a Hoosier, and, working for Scripps-Howard, a long-time observer of the American scene. He slogged with the foot soldiers through North Africa, through Italy, through France, and was then assigned to the Pacific, where he was killed by a sniper's bullet on Ie Shima, off Okinawa, in April of 1945. His death hit many Americans the way the death of Will Rogers had hit them, even amidst the many other reports of dead men. Pyle had been a different kind of reporter, one who did not cover the great generals and the great strategies but was with the "dogfaces," despite the fact that he was small, frail, and ill much of the time. This column may be the best thing he ever wrote.

† † †

THE STORY OF CAPTAIN WASKOW

By Ernie Pyle, Scripps-Howard, January 10, 1944. Reprinted by permission of Scripps-Howard and the Scripps-Howard Foundation.

In this war I have known a lot of officers who were loved and respected by the soldiers under them. But never have I crossed the trail of any man as beloved as Captain Henry T. Waskow, of Belton, Texas.

Captain Waskow was a company commander in the Thirty-sixth Division. He had led his company since long before it left the States. He was very young, only in his middle twenties, but he carried in him a sincerity and a gentleness that made people want to be guided by him.

"After my father, he came next," a sergeant told me.

"He always looked after us," a soldier said. "He'd go to bat for us every time."

"I've never known him to do anything unfair," another said.

I was at the foot of the mule trail the night they brought Captain Waskow down. The moon was nearly full, and you could see far up the trail, and even partway across the valley below.

Dead men had been coming down the mountain all evening, lashed onto the backs of mules. They came lying belly-down across the wooden packsaddles, their heads hanging down on one side, their stiffened legs sticking out awkwardly from the other, bobbing up and down as the mules walked.

The Italian mule skinners were afraid to walk beside dead men, so Americans had to lead the mules down that night. Even the Americans were reluctant to unlash and lift off the bodies when they got to the bottom, so an officer had to do it himself and ask others to help.

I don't know who that first one was. You feel small in the presence of dead men, and you don't ask silly questions.

They slid him down from the mule, and stood him on his feet for a moment. In the half-light he might have been merely a sick man standing there leaning on the others. Then they laid him on the ground in the shadow of the stone wall alongside the road. We left him there beside the road, that first one, and we all went back into the cowshed and sat on water cans or lay on the straw, waiting for the next batch of mules.

Somebody said the dead soldier had been dead for four days, and then nobody said anything more about it. We talked soldier talk for an hour or more; the dead man lay all alone, outside in the shadow of the wall.

Then a soldier came into the cowshed and said there were some more bodies outside. We went out into the road. Four mules stood there in the moonlight, in the road where the trail came down off the mountain. The soldiers who led them stood there waiting.

"This one is Captain Waskow," one of them said quietly.

Two men unlashed his body from the mule and lifted it off and laid it in the shadow beside the stone wall. Other men took the other bodies off. Finally, there were five lying end to end in a long row. You don't cover up dead men in the combat zones. They just lie there in the shadows until somebody comes after them.

The unburdened mules moved off to their olive grove. The men in the road seemed reluctant to leave. They stood around, and gradually I could sense them moving, one by one, close to Captain Waskow's body. Not so much to look, I think, as to say something in finality to him and to themselves. I stood close by and I could hear.

One soldier came and looked down, and he said out loud, "God damn it!"

That's all he said, and then he walked away.

Another one came, and he said, "God damn it to hell anyway!" He looked down for a few last moments and then turned and left.

Another man came. I think he was an officer. It was hard to tell officers from men in the dim light, for everybody was bearded and grimy. The man looked down into the dead captain's face and then spoke directly to him as though he were alive, "I'm sorry, old man."

Then a soldier came and stood beside the officer and bent over, and he too spoke to his dead captain, not in a whisper but awfully tenderly, and he said, "I sure am sorry, sir."

Then the first man squatted down, and he reached down and took the captain's hand, and he sat there for a full five minutes holding the dead hand in his own and looking intently into the dead face. And he never uttered a sound all the time he sat there.

Finally he put the hand down. He reached over and gently straightened the points of the captain's shirt collar, and then he sort of rearranged the tattered edges of the uniform around the wound, and then he got up and walked away down the road in the moonlight, all alone.

The rest of us went back into the cowshed leaving the five dead men lying in a line end to end in the shadow of the low stone wall. We lay down on the straw in the cowshed, and pretty soon we were all asleep.

† † †

Newspaper and magazine press, camera, and radio were there to cover the key invasion of the war, that which we call D-Day, June 6, 1944, when General Dwight D. Eisenhower played a hunch and went ahead with the invasion of Europe despite ominous weather forecasts. The invasion was on that northwest sector of France called Normandy, and the main beaches were designated Utah and Omaha. As with the reports of Edward R. Murrow it really is better to hear the voice of the commentator—in this case George Hicks of ABC—but this excerpt will suggest how some reporters can present dramatic yet unified and even literary reports while operating under fire.

† † †

A GLIMPSE OF D-DAY

By George Hicks, American Broadcasting Corporation, June 6, 1944, from Louis L. Snyder and Richard B. Morris, *A Treasury of Great Reporting* (New York: Simon and Schuster, 1949), p. 646.

One battleship is in as close as three miles, and one of the famous American battleships, the *Texas,* was [static]...finally in her firing position. [static]... battleships lying just a couple of miles off the French shore, and firing broadsides into the land. The Germans are replying from the land with flashes, and then the battleship lets go with its entire broadside again. The whole side of the battlewagon lights up in a yellow flare as a broadside goes off, and now we can see brown and gray smoke drifting up from her, from her gun barrels... and now batteries are firing from the beach... the broadsides of the battleship are pouring it back at them. Overhead, high, planes are roaring . . . they just came in and dropped a salvo of bombs. . . .

The [static]... one of America's famous cruisers, is in off the shore near [static]... as well as the *Texas,* the *Nevada,* and the *Arkansas;* old battleships . . . They're just anchored offshore and blowing into the Nazi batteries on shore... The first Allied forces are reaching the beaches in France . . .

That baby was plenty low!

I think I just made the statement that no German planes had been seen, and I think there was the first one we've seen so far. . . . just cleared our stack... let go a stream of tracers that did no harm...

[Sound of ship's whistle]

Our own ship has just given its warning whistle, and now the flak is coming up in the sky . . .

† † †

The beginning of World War II... the invasion of Pearl Harbor... the death of Franklin D. Roosevelt. These were the major events, the "remember where you were?" events of the war. Roosevelt had been ill during the 1944 election campaign; that had been obvious, even though the fact was not advertised. But most people were too absorbed in the war to be worrying much about the President, despite the shocking photographs carried in some newspapers. What made the President's death so stunning, in a sense, was the thought in the minds of many Americans that his successor would be the unknown, untrained Harry S. Truman.

† † †

THE DEATH OF FRANKLIN D. ROOSEVELT

By Merriman Smith, United Press, April 12, 1945.

WARM SPRINGS, GA., April 12.—Death gave Franklin D. Roosevelt short notice.

At about 1 o'clock this afternoon (Chicago time), sitting in the "Little White House" here, he felt a sudden pain in the back of his head.

At 1:15 p.m. he fainted. He never regained consciousness. At 3:35 p.m. he died of what the doctor called a "massive cerebral hemorrhage."

Only three persons were with the President when he died in his quarters at the Warm Springs Foundation for Infantile Paralysis Victims. They were Cmdr. Howard G. Bruenn on the staff of Vice-Adm. Ross T. McIntire, Navy surgeon general and Mr. Roosevelt's personal physician; Lt. Cmdr. George Fox, a White House medical aide, and Dr. James Paullin, Atlanta physician, who had been summoned when the President was stricken.

Mrs. Roosevelt and their daughter, Mrs. Anna Boettiger, were in Washington; his four sons were on duty with the armed forces.

In the "Little White House," but not in the room where he died, were the President's cousins, Miss Margaret Suckley and Miss Laura Delano. With them was his private secretary, Grace Tulley, and William Hassett, White House secretary.

Death came on a pleasant spring day. The scene was a little room overlooking a green and lovely Georgia valley.

So far from death were the President's thoughts when he began his last day that he had planned an unusually busy afternoon and evening. He was posing for a portraitist's sketch when the pain came. He had planned to attend a minstrel show a few hours later.

The President had been in Warm Springs—which he called his "second home"—since March 30. Most of the preceding week he had spent at his home in Hyde Park, N.Y.

The news of Mr. Roosevelt's death came from Hassett. He called in three press association reporters who had accompanied the President here and said:

"It is my sad duty to inform you that the President died at 3:35 of a cerebral hemorrhage."

The news was telephoned simultaneously to Washington.

Mr. Roosevelt's last words were, "I have a terrific headache."

He put his hand suddenly to the back of his head. A few minutes later he slumped over unconscious. . . .

His last official act was to sign legislation extending the life of the Commodity Credit Corp. As he signed the bill, he remarked to Hassett, "Here's where I make a law.". . . .

† † †

One of the newspapers that took special note of the death of the President was a relatively new one, the *Chicago Sun,* which had been launched shortly before Pearl Harbor. The *Sun* represented an important adventure in our journalism; it was a close relative of the one in New York called *PM,* but where Marshall Field III had served mainly as an angel for *PM,* he was the founder of the *Sun,* and his objective was to provide stiff morning competition for Colonel McCormick's *Tribune.* Later in 1947 the *Sun* merged with the *Chicago Times,* but in its day it was a newspaper of excitement and singular courage, one that tackled many of the hard issues of its time, issues ignored by most newspapers. As the war was ending in Europe, delegates were founding the United Nations at a conference in San Francisco, and a new president was taking over from the dead FDR. It is appropriate that a newspaper which so strongly supported Roosevelt should be quoted on the occasion of his death.

† † †

HIS COUNTRYMEN MUST CARRY HIS BURDEN

Chicago Sun, April 13, 1945. Reprinted by permission of the *Chicago Sun-Times.*

Our great and beloved President has laid down his life for victory, decency and peace.

His task was always the task of all of us. Henceforth, because he is gone, it is, in incomparably greater degree, ours to serve, with mind and heart and will, the noble ends for which he died.

We, his countrymen, will long sorely miss Franklin Delano Roosevelt, and he will be sorely missed by the world. More men looked up to him than to any other living man. More confidence was placed in him than in any other. More inspiration came from him.

Franklin Roosevelt's was a buoyancy, a boundless faith in man and God, a courage in the face of every evil, a warmth of love for human beings, a genius of understanding for human needs, and a leadership in serving them, which made him the peer of the very greatest of our Presidents.

No other statesman in this epic period of crisis for mankind has equaled him in the art of co-operation, and of leading others to it. . . .

† † †

The horror of war, especially the horror of what the Nazis had done on the European continent, became manifest as the armies of the Allied nations moved into Germany in 1945. Dachau, Auschwitz, Buchenwald—all were revealed to the world. It became known that many other such camps had existed during the war, and later revelations were made when the war crimes trials convened at Nuremberg. Buchenwald was near Weimar, the city of Goethe and Schiller. The camp was liberated by the U. S. 80th Division on April 10, 1945, and an early visitor was the CBS correspondent, Edward R. Murrow.

When the war ended in Europe many readers were treated to a dispatch that still can stir controversy. The war was ended; there was no question about that. The question was whether it was ethical for Edward Kennedy, chief of the Associated Press on the western front, to violate an understanding on the release time and tell the story to the world. Kennedy told the story, was suspended, shunned by the Associated Press, and bore the stigma the rest of his days.

† † †

THE END OF THE WAR IN EUROPE

By Edward Kennedy, Associated Press, May 7, 1945.

REIMS, FRANCE, MAY 7—Germany surrendered unconditionally to the Western allies and the Soviet Union at 2:41 A.M. French time today. This was at 8:41 P.M. Eastern war time, Sunday, May 6, 1945.

The surrender took place at a little red schoolhouse that is the headquarters of General Dwight D. Eisenhower.

The surrender was signed for the Supreme Allied Command by Lieutenant General Walter Bedell Smith, chief of staff for General Eisenhower.

It was also signed by General Ivan Susloparov of the Soviet Union and by General Francois Sevez for France.

General Eisenhower was not present at the signing, but immediately afterward General Jodl and his fellow delegate, General Admiral Hans Georg Friedeburg, were received by the Supreme Commander.

They were asked sternly if they understood the surrender terms imposed upon Germany and if they would be carried out by Germany.

They answered yes.

Germany, which began the war with a ruthless attack upon Poland, followed by successive aggressions and brutality in concentration camps, surrendered with an appeal to the victors for mercy toward the German people and armed forces.

After having signed the full surrender, General Jodl said he wanted to speak and received leave to do so.

"With this signature," he said in soft-spoken German, "the German people and armed forces are for better or worse delivered into the victor's hands.

"In this war, which has lasted more than five years, both have achieved and suffered more than perhaps any other people in the world."

† † †

It was a summer for holding one's breath, that summer of 1945. The war was over in Europe, but it seemed a long time from being over in the Pacific. The American people did not know the background of the mighty story that soon would cover the front pages, the story of the development of the atomic bomb. They did not know about the horrifying explosion that had taken place on the New Mexico desert in July. On August 6, 1945, President Harry Truman told his people about the devastating bomb that had been dropped on the Japanese city, Hiroshima. And the most dramatic news story of the age was published, several weeks after the fact, when the *New York Times* told the story of the bomb that fell on Nagasaki, two days after the one that destroyed Hiroshima. William L. Laurence was the reporter, a man who had been in on the development of atomic power from the beginning.

† † †

A REPORTER DESCRIBES A MUSHROOM CLOUD

By William L. Laurence, *New York Times,* September 9, 1945. Copyright 1945 by The New York Times Company. Reprinted by permission.

... We flew southward down the channel and at 11:33 crossed the coastline and headed straight for Nagasaki, about one hundred miles to the west. Here we again circled until we found an opening in the clouds. It was 12:01 and the goal of our mission had arrived.

We heard the prearranged signal on our radio, put on our arc welder's glasses, and watched tensely the maneuverings of the strike ship about half a mile in front of us.

"There she goes!" someone said.

Out of the belly of *The Great Artiste* what looked like a black object went downward.

Captain Bock swung around to get out of range; but even though we were turning away in the opposite direction, and despite the fact that it was broad daylight in our cabin, all of us became aware of a giant flash that broke through the dark barrier of our arc welder's lenses and flooded our cabin with intense light.

We removed our glasses after the first flash, but the light still lingered on, a bluish-green light that illuminated the entire sky all around. A tremendous blast wave struck our ship and made it tremble from nose to tail. This was followed by four more blasts in rapid succession, each resounding like the boom of cannon fire hitting our plane from all directions.

Observers in the tail of our ship saw a giant ball of fire rise as though from the bowels of the earth, belching forth enormous white smoke rings. Next, they saw a giant pillar of purple fire, ten thousand feet high, shooting skyward with enormous speed.

By the time our ship had made another turn in the direction of the atomic explosion the pillar of purple fire had reached the level of our altitude. Only about forty-five seconds had passed. Awe-struck, we watched it shoot upward like a meteor coming from the earth instead of from outer space, becoming ever more alive as it climbed skyward through the white clouds. It was no longer smoke, or dust, or even a cloud of fire. It was a living thing, a new species of being, born right before our incredulous eyes.

At one stage of its evolution, covering millions of years in terms of seconds, the entity assumed the form of a giant square totem pole, with its base about three miles long, tapering off to about a mile at the top. Its bottom was brown, its center was amber, its top white. But it was a living totem pole, carved with many grotesque masks grimacing at the earth.

Then, just when it appeared as though the thing had settled down into a state of permanence, there came shooting out of the top a giant mushroom that increased the height of the pillar to a total of forty-five thousand feet. The mushroom top was even more alive than the pillar, seething and boiling in a white fury of creamy foam, sizzling upward and then descending earthward, a thousand Old Faithful geysers rolled into one.

It kept struggling in an elemental fury, like a creature in the act of breaking the bonds that held it down. In a few seconds it had freed itself from its gigantic stem and floated upward with tremendous speed, its momentum carrying it into the stratosphere to a height of about sixty thousand feet.

But no sooner did this happen when another mushroom, smaller in size than the first one, began emerging out of the pillar. It was as though the decapitated monster was growing a new head.

As the first mushroom floated off into the blue it changed its shape into a flowerlike form, its giant petals curving downward, creamy white outside, rose-colored inside. It still retained that shape when we last gazed at it from a distance of about two hundred miles. The boiling pillar of many colors could also be seen at that distance, a giant mountain of jumbled rainbows, in travail. Much living substance had gone into those rainbows. The quivering top of the pillar was protruding to a great height through the white clouds, giving the appearance of a monstrous prehistoric creature with a ruff around its neck, a fleecy ruff extending in all directions, as far as the eye could see.

† † †

When word of the bombing of Hiroshima came, even the popular radio news commentator, Gabriel Heatter, found it difficult to offer his usual "There's good news tonight!" Not for some time would the American people know the true import of the bomb, of the deadly age into which they had been ushered, without really knowing where they were going. Most Americans were satisfied to see the war come to an end. And it ended—on August 14, 1945. Vignettes tell the story.

† † †

THE END OF WORLD WAR II

Chicago Tribune, Associated Press, International News Service.

Washington, D.C., Aug. 14—The war is over.

President Truman at 6 o'clock tonight (Chicago time) announced the unconditional surrender of Japan on the terms dictated by the allied powers.

The Japanese empire fell before the military and industrial might of the United States, climaxed last week by the projection of two atomic bombs—America's terrible, new secret weapon—upon two Japanese cities with devastating effect. . . .

* * * * *

By the Associated Press

A Domei dispatch broadcast by the Tokyo radio said last night that Emperor Hirohito, speaking for the first time by radio, had told the Japanese people that "the enemy has begun to employ a new and most cruel bomb" and should Japan continue to fight "it would lead to the total extinction of human civilization." This, he said, caused him to accept the Potsdam declaration. . . .

* * * * *

Chicago's loop today took on the aspect of a holiday—in the quiet sense—after the hysterical celebration that followed the announcement of cessation of war.

An army of sweepers, who went to work at dawn, had the debris situation well in hand. By 10 a.m. the streets were fairly well cleared of the snowfall of waste paper which celebrants insisted on throwing, despite advice from the salvage committee. . . .

* * * * *

WASHINGTON, Aug. 15.—(INS)—Price Administrator Bowles announced today that gasoline and canned fruits and vegetables have been freed from rationing, effective immediately.

Bowles also announced that fuel oil rationing and rationing of oil stoves likewise has been suspended, effective at once.

Bowles said meats, fats and oils, butter, sugar, shoes, men's rubber footwear and tires will stay on the ration list for the time being. . . .

* * * * *

U.S.S. MISSOURI, Tokyo Bay, Sept. 2 (Sunday)—(AP)—Two nervous Japanese formally and unconditionally surrendered all remnants of their smashed empire to the allies today, restoring peace to the world.

Surrender hour was cool and cloudy, but the sun broke through the overcast 20 minutes later as Gen. MacArthur intoned "These proceedings are closed. The entire world is quietly at peace. A new era is upon us.". . .

† † †

Stars and Stripes, created in World War I for the Americans fighting in France, had a rebirth in World War II. It was given new life in 1942, and by the end of the war it had editions published for the men and women in the several theaters of action. Many popular features appeared in the newspaper, and it was singular in that it was virtually uncensored and that it provided an outlet for the servicemen to express their opinions and frustrations. The Pacific edition of *Stars and Stripes* described the joy of GIs in Hawaii when word came of the surrender offer by the Japanese in August, 1945.

† † †

SOLDIERS HEAR NEWS OF THE END OF WAR

Stars and Stripes, Pacific Edition, August 10, 1945.

Singing, shouting, delirious GIs the island over let loose with four years of pent-up emotions as they looked at peace in the early hours of Aug. 10, 1945.

MPs, night crews and optimists glued to radios got the first flash at 2:31 a.m. Self-appointed committees of one headed for barracks to rout unbelieving men from beds.

The cry "It's Over," swelled to a roaring crescendo from Kuhuku to Pearl Harbor.

Guards at Hickam field's gate saw a quick reunion with their families—and a rough 24 hours before them.

"I'm about the happiest guy in the world," said Pvt. Joe Czysz of Erie, Pa., "I can now get to see my year-old baby boy."

"I have a cold chill I can't get rid of," said Sgt. Edward Platter of Newark.

Lt. John L. Miller of Cleveland was Hickam O. D., "And what a night to be on this kind of job," he said. "I'm dumbfounded at the news. I expected it shortly, but it came so sudden it bowled me over.". . .

The Moana hotel, hangout for many servicemen in Honolulu, maintained its usual 3 a.m. quiet because the hotel manager refused to allow any radios to tell occupants the news, but the nearby Kau Kau coffee shop was in a turmoil.

The bugler was the forgotten man at Pearl Harbor. His customers were up way ahead of time as peace or the rumor of peace swept through barracks, Navy Yard shops, and dry docks several hours before dawn.

Here at the spot where the Jap attacked 3 years, 8 months and three days before, there was shouting, laughter, tears. . . and unbelief.

It came first in a single shout: "It's over."

It became a quartet, a gigantic chorus as sailors and civilian workers took up the cry. Ships in the harbor punctuated the roaring crescendo with deep-throated whistles. Word was passed from deck to deck that the good news was here. . . .

† † †

The army weekly, *Yank,* was given its honorable discharge by General Eisenhower in the issue of December 28, 1945. It had been a vastly popular magazine since its founding in 1942, a magazine that carried fiction, nonfiction, cartoons, and some famous pinups—two pages of which were reproduced in that final issue. *Yank* tells its own story, and that story is in many respects the story of the war itself, and how American journalists covered that war.

† † †

A CHRONICLE OF A MAGAZINE AND A WAR

Yank, December 28, 1945, pp. 2-3.

"In YANK you have established a publication which cannot be understood by our enemies. It is inconceivable to them that a soldier should be allowed to express his own thoughts, his ideas and his opinions. It is inconceivable to them that any soldiers—or any citizens, for that matter—should have any thoughts other than those dictated by their leaders. . . . .

"Upon you, and upon your comrades in arms of all the United Nations, depend the lives and liberties of all the human race. You bear with you the hopes of all the millions who have suffered under the oppression of the war lords of Germany and Japan. You bear

with you the highest aspirations of mankind for a life of peace and decency under God."
—Franklin Delano Roosevelt
From YANK, Volume 1, Number 1.

* * *

At the time when President Roosevelt wrote this message to GIs for the first issue of YANK, in June 1942, the Japanese were settling down on Kiska and Attu and German Gen. Erwin Rommel had just captured Tobruk, Bardia and Bir-el-Gobi. Hulks of American ships were gathering slime under the waters of Pearl Harbor. The Philippines were lost. The Red Army had evacuated the Kerch Peninsula, and all along a heart-breakingly extended front its troops fought a delaying action, an armed retreat. Japs swarmed all over the East—New Guinea, the Netherlands East Indies, Malaya, the Solomons.

The American soldier of that June who had seen any action at all, who had even served overseas, was an exception. There were a few GIs in England and Northern Ireland. Engineers had been stationed in Iceland and Greenland for some months. There were GIs guarding the bauxite mines at Dutch Guiana and British Guiana. There were several shipments of U.S. troops in Australia. There were too many American soldiers prisoners of the Japs.

The GIs at home were training at a speeded-up rate with the best equipment they could find to train with. Factories were working overtime to break production records that had to be broken and then broken again. Of course, nobody actually thought we might lose the war, but everybody knew we were in a fight. Line after line of confused civilian males filed into railway terminals, waving good-bye to their families, headed for something strange called camp. There were rumors of worse defeats to come and, ranged alongside rumors, the uncomfortable fact that the enemy had a corner on oil and rubber—and trained manpower. There was a battle going on in the air above Britain while we stumbled about the drill fields of Fort Jackson and Fort Belvoir and Fort Benning and dozens of other posts, learning to move our feet according to a new rhythm and to sight an M1 and eat SOS and walk and work and walk and work and sleep like the dead.

YANK was founded to be the publication of the enlisted men of this new Army of ours. It was to be written and edited by enlisted men for enlisted men all over the world. It was to spread both news and entertainment; not to point official morals. It was to be a free organ for the legitimate gripes of enlisted men.

It was just as stumbling and hopeful as any other part of the new Army it joined. YANK was sold first only to GIs serving overseas. By its eighth issue it was authorized to sell in the U.S. PXs as well. By YANK's eighth issue U.S. Marines were fighting on Guadalcanal, and there was something new in the air as we showed our stuff in an offensive action. There was a commando raid on Nazi-held Dieppe across the English Channel that fall, and U.S. Rangers took part in it.

YANK had an edition being printed in England by November 1942, and another in Puerto Rico. England was an island staging area for nobody yet knew what invasion. And in the waters off Puerto Rico, German submarines sank Allied ships.

In November, too, the secret of the invasion was out. American and Allied forces landed in North Africa under the command of Lt. Gen. Dwight D. Eisenhower. They had just barely enough men to push through to a successful landing, just barely enough ships to carry them. But the invasion worked. The battle for North Africa was on. And the Germans in Russia were finding out they couldn't take Stalingrad. In a sea battle off the Solomons, 28 Jap ships were sunk.

There were U.S. troops spreading all over the globe. GIs from Arkansas and Oklahoma were standing guard or loading trucks or fighting in places with exotic names like Bandar Shapur, Iran, Karachi, India, Tripoli, North Africa.

The war was still see-sawing. In Burma we hadn't recovered from the "one hell of a beating" Gen. Joseph Stilwell had taken in the early summer. The Germans still had France, even if the British were chasing them out of Egypt, and the Japs still had so much of the Pacific that our gains hardly showed up on the map. But we knew now, surely, and by actual sampling, what we had never doubted— that we could lick the enemy on their own grounds.

In the summer of 1943, six new overseas editions of YANK were started—in Hawaii, in Trinidad, in Egypt, in India, in Australia and in Iran. That fall another was added in Panama.

We could look at the war with a growing impatience, a heightened sense of progress, instead of with the dogged resolution we had had to live on in those first long months. We had sewed up North Africa and had taken Sicily. We had landed in Italy, kept our toe-hold and moved successfully north, until the Italian Government, in defiance of a fleeing Mussolini, sued for peace. We had taken back Kiska and Attu from the Japs. We were pushing back other Japs the hard way in New Guinea and on Bougainville and in New Britain, and our airmen were pounding Jap supply lines in China.

The year 1944 opened slowly as a war year. There were gains in the Pacific in January on Kwajalein and Majuro. In Italy, GIs landed at Anzio beachhead to lie there week after week, holding a strip of shore under enemy fire. There was another Pacific landing on Eniwetok Atoll in the Marshalls, and Sgt. John Bushemi, YANK photographer, was killed there.

YANK's tenth overseas edition was printed in Italy in March. The war in Italy was still slow. Allied forces to the south finally connected with the orphans of Anzio in May, and the front moved north in June and July. The Pacific war was still a war of strange names and infrequent headlines which didn't mean much except to the men who earned them. In June we landed on Saipan in the Marianas.

And in June the big jump came, the invasion of Europe from across the channel. There were landings in Normandy, and Easy Red Beach and Omaha Beach were added to the war names Americans will always remember. Sgt. Pete Paris, YANK photographer and artist, was killed on D-Day.

That invasion took, too. It pushed from Cherbourg to Caen to Le Mans, and in August another invasion hit France in the south, launched from Italy, landing between Marseilles and Cannes. It pushed to Belfort and met the Normandy invaders in the middle. In the Pacific there were landings on Peleliu and Morotai, Angaur and Ulithi Atoll. It was more and more our winning war.

YANK was printing in Paris by September and in Strasbourg by November. The Allies were sweeping through France like the happy ending of a movie. In Italy we had passed and taken Florence.

The Philippines were the hardest, biggest loss of 1942, and in October 1944 we invaded Leyte to begin to win them back. We landed and stayed.

In the China-Burma theater we took Bhamo and lost Kweiling. From the Marianas, raiding B-29s struck Tokyo. The Red Army steam roller, which started its first big push back in June, had never stopped and was now in East Prussia.

At the end of 1944 there was a cornered-rat lunge from the German forces in the Ardennes sector and, caught off-balance, we were knocked groggy. But we hit back. We had regained our losses by the end of January and, in the Pacific, we had wiped up both Leyte and Samar and were striking at Luzon.

We didn't move backwards again for the rest of the war. We crossed the Rhine and pushed on until we met the Red Army at the Elbe and Germany was licked. YANK correspondent Cpl. Bob Krell was killed in the airborne Rhine crossing.

The Philippines were contested all the way, but we took them, and Marines on Iwo Jima and Marines and GIs on Okinawa carved two more names on our military roll of honor. B-29s pounded hell out of the Jap mainland, and the atomic bomb and the entry of Russia into the Jap war hastened an end already certain.

The Germans surrendered unconditionally on May 7 at Rheims. The Japs surrendered on August 14 aboard the U.S.S. Missouri in Tokyo Bay.

YANK's last four overseas printings were set up on Saipan in February, in Manila in July, on Okinawa in August and in Tokyo in September—the last one just in time to serve incoming occupation troops.

* * *

The fighting part is over now and we are winners. If you ever begin to wonder about what we were fighting for, look back to those words of President Roosevelt's at the beginning of this editorial. Read them and try to remember everything that Jap and German domination meant that made us fight it.

We fought it starting from damn near scratch and we beat it. YANK is proud to have been part of the Army that beat it.

✝   ✝   ✝

15

THE MASS MEDIA IN THE POST WAR WORLD

What can one say about a period in history that gave the world Joseph McCarthy, Elvis Presley, hula hoops, and the word "media"? Such was the one that followed World War II, a period that is difficult to separate into "late 1940s" and "1950s." One theme was common to the whole period—domestic communism. The administration of Harry Truman embraced years in both decades. Television came on the scene in the late 1940s and had its flowering in the 1950s. For these reasons the journalistic documents of the period roughly from 1945 to 1960 are included in this one section.

Old-timers had never heard of the term "mass media"; the media came into being, really, in this period. And despite the recent demotion of that plural word *media* to the singular, it is still descriptive of much more than television, for it also meant the more traditional newspapers, the magazines, radio, motion pictures, phonograph records, paperback books. For obvious reasons this anthology is concerned mainly with the printed word, but a description of journalism in the 1945-60 period must take into account all of these "media," and the entire American scene. For there was an economic boom of great scope that followed the war, and an age of leisure appeared for all to enjoy, even though there remained great pockets of poverty alongside the plenty. It seemed of some significance that major books in the period after the war should bear titles like *The Affluent Society,* by John Kenneth Galbraith, and *The Other America,* by Michael Harrington.

Radio and the newsreel had been part of an earlier journalism; now a new image, that of television, became even more a document of the times, a document that unfortunately was often not recoverable. If the story of Joseph McCarthy is important in the memories of many Americans it is largely attributable to the fact that what is recalled most of all is the hearings on television in the spring of 1954 and the droning words from McCarthy, "Point of order." If the return of Douglas MacArthur in 1951 looms large in our memories it may be not the newspaper story that we recall but instead hearing MacArthur tell us, on radio or television, that "Old soldiers never die, they just fade away." It is the voice of Richard Nixon explaining the California fund matter in his "Checkers" speech (and the earnest, sincere face); it is a memory of the hands of Frank Costello during the Senate crime hearings; it is the face and voice of Adlai E. Stevenson at the 1952 Democratic convention; it is Charles Van Doren sweating in a quiz show isolation booth; it is Elvis Presley gyrating on the Ed Sullivan television show. There is no real *printed* counterpart of these memories.

Television, and all the other segments of the big media of the postwar age, altered many relationships. This was in part the theme of that important book of 1958, Douglass Cater's *The Fourth Branch of Government,* in which Cater seemed to equate the new power of the press with the powers of the three traditional branches of government—executive, legislative, judicial. By the time Cater wrote the book he had been able to assess the growing publicity powers of Congress and of its committees, of the prevalence of the idea of security, of the suppression of news, of the development of the presidential press conference so that it was greatly changed from the casual give-and-take of the days of FDR; of the circuses called hearings: communism in Hollywood, crime and government, the promotion of a "pink dentist" in the army. An excerpt from the book follows.

† † †

THE PRESIDENT AND THE PRESS

By Douglass Cater, *The Fourth Branch of Government* (Boston: Houghton Mifflin, 1959), pp. 22-225. Reprinted by permission of the author.

No monarch in history has had a retinue like that which gathers about the American President and calls itself the White House press corps. The reporters hang about his antechamber with the indolence of courtiers at some feudal court keeping those who pass in and out— Governors, Cabinet members, Senators, Ambassadors—under constant surveillance and interrogation. They dog the President's every step and turn his most casual public conversation into a mass meeting. They follow him wherever he goes. Their special plane takes off after the one carrying him and alights just in advance of it. Thus even the contingency of a fatal crack-up has been calculated so as not to interrupt the flow of prompt and plentiful publicity about our President.

No television idol, axe-murderer, or foreign head of state lives in the glare of continual publicity that is the accepted fate of our

President. His ordinary habits of work and play are the grist of ever fresh "news" from the White House. His most minor indispositions turn the place into a mecca for journalistic pilgrims prepared to maintain a twenty-four-hour-a-day vigil until the sickness passes. Even the bowel movements of an ailing Chief Executive has been considered fit subject for a press communique.

Just to the right of the entrance to the White House west wing, where the President has his office, a special room has been set aside for the press, its typewriters, its telephones, its poker table. Twenty to thirty White House "regulars"—reporters whose sole assignment is to cover this tiny beat—spend much of their day there. Just across the entrance hall, the Press Secretary has offices, connected by private corridor to the President's own office. He is the hourly spokesman of the President, the constant stand-in for the public image of the Presidency. Two and three times daily he meets with the regulars and any other reporters who may wander in. These sessions may drone along on humdrum matters or just as suddenly erupt in high drama.

To the outsider there seems almost unhealthy interest in the trivial routine of the White House and its chief occupant. Throughout the day the reporters pay constant court to the Press Secretary and his assistants, checking leads, listening for tips, or simply passing the time of day. It is their consuming preoccupation to sift the heaps of ore, isolate the nuggets of news, and yearn for the quick wealth of a rich vein. Mining the news at the White House is a major industry employing a sizable body of prospectors.

But the chief event of the week occurs when the reporters, one hundred and fifty to two hundred strong, file into the ornate little room in the old State Department Building once used for signing treaties. They pack themselves row on row in tightly spaced steel folding chairs and overflow onto the rococo balcony up near the ceiling. Along the back of the room a solid bank of floodlights and cameras adds to the congestion. In the heat of Washington summer it is almost unbearable.

At the appointed hour, the doors are closed against the laggards and the nation's leading citizen hurries in from a side entrance to meet the press, figuratively wearing his several hats as head of state, chief executive, commander-in-chief, leader of his party, and the rest. He greets his audience with the habitual familiarity of one dealing with long-time intimates. His assistants march in behind him to listen but seldom to interrupt the ritual that follows.

There may be a few prepared words and then with a barely perceptible nod it begins. Reporters rise and vie for recognition. For the next half hour, the President's gaze scans the assemblage and the President's nod designates who shall be his interrogators. His choice is generally random and as a consequence the interchange of question and answer is apt to be quite haphazard. But the underlying solemnity of the occasion can never be entirely forgotten. For a time the President of the United States stands alone, unshielded by the layers of officialdom that lie between him and the public. The reporters present themselves with a reverence of manner as would intercessors before a monarch. The content of their questions, however, is not always so reverent.

The spirit of the President's press conference varies from week to week and year to year and President to President. The conference may follow a smooth and gentle course. Or it may explode with unabashed savagery, the reporters probing relentlessly into a touchy subject and the President lashing back angrily at question and questioner.

Then at a signal from the press itself, it is all over. The grand finale is a scene of frenzy. Turning their backs on the standing President, the reporters from the wire services and networks who occupy the front seats charge down the center aisle in a pushing, shoving race to reach the telephone booths just outside the door. So keen is this competition that one time a veteran correspondent broke a leg in the stampede.

Foreign visitors to the President's press conference depart from this undisciplined ritual with a feeling of awe, consternation, or outright disgust. But they rarely fail to be impressed by its importance as a central act in the high drama of American government.

Why such mutual fascination between the President and the press? What prompts the editor and publisher to devote so much money and space to the subject? And what, in turn, causes the President to put up with the incessant inroads on his privacy? No other head of government feels the obligation to suffer as great an intrusion. No other chief of state finds the publicity role of the office such a continual burden.

The answer goes beyond the publisher's need for filler material to provide an offset for the advertisements. It cannot be attributed simply to the heady thrill of being in the limelight which affects most men and particularly those whose ambitious direct them toward public office. The answer lies, I submit, in the very nature of modern American government. Publicity is as essential to its orderly functioning as the power to levy taxes and pass laws.

For the President of the United States his press conference, which is his primary and most systematic effort to converse with the people on a variety of major and lesser matters, offers a challenge and an opportunity. It provides a major measure of his leadership if, as Sidney Hyman has argued in *The American President,* the distinction between "strong" and "weak" presidents can be drawn in terms of "how they manage the slippery imponderables of public opinion.". . .

† † †

Douglass Cater and other observers saw that the very process of a presidential convention had changed because of television, that politicians—with the eyes of the world upon them—no longer could engage in the convention tomfoolery of a more naive age. And now, with those eyes of the world also looking at a president, that president had to be careful, much more careful, of his words, had to look just right, avoid flares of temper, keep in mind public opinion polls and the word that was becoming so popular, "charisma." Campaigning itself had to be changed; it was singular that both Dwight Eisenhower and Adlai Stevenson, in 1952—America's first full-scale television year in presidential campaigning—had to put in a dutiful appearance at a church each Sunday.

Manipulation of the media became a game for many, especially for Joseph McCarthy—more on him later. The media helped to promote political careers, though not always as extensively as some had hoped; Estes Kefauver's investigation of crime in America, a relatively low key governmental hearing, did not catapult that political leader into the presidency, though on hindsight such an eventuality in the age of the fabulously popular Eisenhower would have been unlikely. Television undoubtedly did help the temporarily waning fortunes of Richard Nixon in 1952. It helped to build the anti-Truman feeling so strong when Douglas MacArthur was brought back from Korea. And television—plus the slipping movies, and the vastly popular phonograph records of the time—was there to record the fortunes of the talented new actors, Marlon Brando and James Dean; the sex goddess of the 1950s, Marilyn Monroe; the cool, patrician Grace Kelly of Philadelphia and Hollywood, who became a royal princess with some assistance from the press; the many singers and groups that were part of the phenomenon known as rock 'n' roll; and such television favorites as Lucille Ball, Milton Berle, Sid Caesar, Phil Silvers, Jackie Gleason, and actors and actresses on horseback and in operating rooms in that place FCC Commissioner Newton Minow later called the "vast wasteland." In bound volume, on microfilm, on tape, or merely in memory, one can call back the excitement of Bridey Murphy and reincarnation; flying saucers; pink shirts and Mohawk hairdos; jive language; the Mickey Mouse Club; game shows; books about men in gray flannel suits; Dragnet; dance crazes; and always communism, international or domestic, in the background like a sick phantom out of a ghastly science fiction adventure, poisoning the air of the postwar world.

The fall of 1945 was a curious time in our lives. Demobilization was underway, but it was still hard to believe that the war was over. Not for a year, when the euphoria began to sour, did the American people truly enter a postwar world and mood. In our literature, on the stage, in the press, democratic affirmations related to a war designed to make the world safe for democracy were still popular, as in plays like Garson Kanin's *Born Yesterday* and Howard Lindsay and Russel Crouse's *The State of the Union,* and movies like William Wyler's *The Best Years of Our Lives* and Frank Capra's *It's a Wonderful Life.* In Norman Cousins' *Saturday Review* piece, *Modern Man Is Obsolete,* however, there already was the alarming suggestion that mankind had entered a new age. In the summer of 1946 such a suggestion became ominous fact, when the *New Yorker* published John Hersey's brilliant report, *Hiroshima.* Part of the postwar mood of affirmation was represented in a greater sensibility to the question of racial understanding. In August of 1945, a splendid editorial was published in the little paper called the *Delta Democrat-Times*, in Greenville, Mississippi, published by an eloquent editor named Hodding Carter, who had fought against Huey Long in Louisiana and been one of the idealistic group briefly associated with *PM*. Carter made a plea in the editorial, and the plea won him a Pulitzer prize. The plea was for racial tolerance, and though Carter wrote about the Nisei there is little doubt that he was applying the theme, too, to the black race of his own Mississippi.

† † †

A PLEA TO "GO FOR BROKE!"

By Hodding Carter, *Delta Democrat-Times*, August 27, 1945.

Company D of the 168th Regiment, which is stationed in Leghorn, Italy, is composed altogether of white troops, some from the East, some from the South, some from the Midwest and West Coast. Company D made an unusual promise earlier this month. The promise was made in the form of a communication to their fellow Americans of the 442nd Infantry Regiment, whose motto is "Go for Broke," and it was subscribed to unanimously by the officers and men of Company D.

In brief, the communication pledged the help of Company D in convincing the folks back home that "you are fully deserving of all the privileges with which we ourselves are bestowed." The soldiers to whom that promise was made are Japanese-Americans in the United States Army, and no troops have chalked up a better combat record. Their record is good.

These Nisei were selected by Gen. Francis H. Oxx, commander of the military area in which they are stationed, to lead the final victory parade, so they marched 3000 strong at the head of thousands of the other Americans. Their battle flag with three presidential unit citation streamers floating above them, their commander, a Wisconsin white Colonel, leading them, some of the Nisei must have been thinking of the soulcarking days last October when they spearheaded the attacks that opened the Vosges Mountain doorway to Strasbourg.

Some of them were probably remembering how they, on another bloody day, had snatched the Thirty-sixth Division's lost battalion of Texans from the encircling Germans, and how many of them were bearing scars from those two engagements which alone had cost the Nisei boys from Hawaii and the West Coast 2300 casualties.

Perhaps these yellow-skinned Americans, to whose Japanese kinsmen we have administered a terrific and long overdue defeat, were holding their eyes higher because of the pledge of their white fellow soldiers and fellow Americans of Company D. Perhaps when they gazed at their combat flag, the motto, "Go for Broke," emblazoned thereon took on a different meaning. "Go for Broke" is the Hawaiian-Japanese slang expression for shooting the works in a dice game.

The local Nisei have shot the works. From the beginning of the war they have been on trial, in and out of uniform, in the Army camps and relocation centers, as combat troops in Europe and as front-line interrogators, propagandists and combat intelligence personnel in the Pacific, where their capture meant prolonged and hideous torture. And even yet they have not satisfied their critics.

It is so easy for a dominant race to explain good or evil, patriotism or treachery, courage or cowardice in terms of skin color. So easy and so tragically wrong. Too many have committed a wrong against the loyal Nisei, who by the thousands have proved themselves good Americans, even while others of us, by our actions against them, have shown ourselves to be bad Americans.

Nor is the end of this misconception in sight. Those Japanese-American soldiers who paraded at Leghorn, in the commemoration of the defeat of the nation from which their fathers came, will meet other enemies, other obstacles as forbidding as those of war. A lot of people will begin saying, as soon as these boys take off their uniforms, that "a Jap in a Jap," and that the Nisei deserve no consideration. A large majority won't say or believe this, but an active minority can have its way against an apathetic majority.

It seems to us that Nisei slogan, "Go for Broke," could be adopted by all Americans of good will in the days ahead. We have got to shoot the works in a fight for tolerance. Those boys of Company D point the way. Japan's surrender will be signed aboard the Missouri and Gen. MacArthur's part will be a symbolic "Show Me."

† † †

In the historical accounts of the time, the story of Jackie Robinson and Branch Rickey takes little space, but it may have been one of the major domestic news stories of the postwar age. Robinson was a Negro, a tough, rather pugnacious man who had been spectacular as a football star at UCLA. Rickey was general manager of the Brooklyn Dodgers, and he believed that Robinson could play major league baseball and that the ancient color line could be removed. So Rickey and Robinson, with considerable difficulty, made Robinson a baseball superstar. In the 1970s, looking back on the story, it seems strange in a way that race could have been such a problem. One who did look back, when Jackie Robinson died in 1972, was a columnist who had seen it all happen.

† † †

THE MAN WHO ALMOST RUINED BASEBALL

By Mike Royko, *Chicago Daily News,* October 25, 1972. Reprinted by permission of the publisher and the author.

Chicago—All that Saturday, the wise men of the neighborhood who sat in chairs on the sidewalk outside the tavern, had talked about what it would do to baseball.

I hung around and listened because baseball was about the most important thing in the world, and if anything was going to ruin it, I was worried.

Most of the things they said, I didn't understand, although it all sounded terrible. But could one man bring such ruin?

They said he could and he would. And the next day he was going to be in Wrigley Field for the first time, on the same diamond as Hack, Nicholson, Cavaretta, Schmidt, Pafko and all my other idols.

I had to see Jackie Robinson, the man who was going to somehow wreck everything. So the next day, another kid and I started walking to the ball park early.

We always walked to save street-car fare. It was five or six miles, but I felt about baseball the way Abe Lincoln felt about education.

Usually, we could get there just at noon, find a seat in the grandstands, and watch some batting practice. But not that Sunday, May 18, 1947.

By noon, Wrigley Field was almost filled. The crowd outside spilled off the sidewalk and into the streets. Scalpers were asking top dollar for box seats and getting it.

I had never seen anything like it. Not just the size, although it was a record, more than 47,000. But this was 25 years ago, and in 1947 few blacks were seen in downtown Chicago, much less up on the white North Side at a Cubs game.

That day, they came by the thousands, pouring off the northbound els and out of their cars.

We managed to get in, scramble up a ramp and find a place to stand behind the last row of grandstand seats. Then they shut the gates. No place remained to stand.

Robinson came up in the first inning. I remember the sound. It wasn't the shrill, teen-age cry you now hear, or an excited gut roar. They applauded, long, rolling applause. A tall, middle-aged black man stood next to me, a smile of almost painful joy on his face, beating his palms together so hard they must have hurt.

When Robinson stepped into the batter's box, it was as if someone had flicked a switch. The place went silent.

He swung at the first pitch and they erupted as if he had knocked it over the wall. But it was only a high foul that dropped into the box seats. I remember thinking it was strange that a foul could make that many people happy. When he struck out, the low moan was genuine.

I've forgotten most of the details of the game, other than that the Dodgers won and Robinson didn't get a hit or do anything special, although he was cheered on every swing and every routine play.

But two things happened that I'll never forget.

Robinson played first, and early in the game a Cub star hit a grounder and it was a close play.

Just before the Cub reached first, he swerved to his left. And as he got to the bag, he seemed to slam his foot down hard at Robinson's foot.

It was obvious to everyone that he was trying to run into him or spike him. Robinson took the throw and got clear at the last instant.

I was shocked. That Cub, a home-town boy, was my biggest hero. It was not only an unheroic stunt, but it seemed a rude thing to do in front of people who would cheer for a foul ball. I didn't understand why he had done it. It wasn't at all big league.

I didn't know that, while the white fans were relatively polite, the Cubs and most other teams kept up a steady stream of racial abuse from the dugout. I thought that all they did down there was talk about how good Wheaties are.

Later in the game, Robinson was up again and he hit another foul ball. This time it came into the stands low and fast, in our direction. Somebody in the seats grabbed for it, but it caromed off his hand and kept coming. There was a flurry of arms. The ball kept bouncing, and suddenly it was between me and my pal. We both grabbed. I had a baseball.

The two of us stood there examining it and chortling. A genuine, major league baseball that had actually been gripped and thrown by a Cub pitcher, hit by a Dodger batter. What a possession

Then I heard the voice say: "Would you consider selling that?"

It was the black man who had applauded so fiercely.

I mumbled something. I didn't want to sell it.

"I'll give you $10 for it," he said.

Ten dollars. I couldn't believe it. I didn't know what $10 could buy because I'd never had that much money. But I knew that a lot of men in the neighborhood considered $50 a week to be good pay.

I handed it to him, and he paid me with 10 $1 bills.

When I left the ball park, with that much money in my pocket, I was sure Jackie Robinson wasn't bad for the game.

Since then, I've regretted, a few times, that I didn't keep the ball. Or that I hadn't given it to him free. I didn't know, then, how hard he probably had to work for that $10.

But yesterday I was glad I had sold it to him. And if that man is still around, and has that baseball, I'm sure he thinks it was worth every cent.

† † †

Most of the big newspapers and magazines had survived the war, and some of them were about to come under a barrage of criticism, even though the criticism they received would seem little more at the time than a mild rapping of knuckles. The *New York Times,* the *St. Louis Post-Dispatch,* the *Chicago Tribune*—these were among the mighty and influential at war's end. As imperious as ever was

Robert R. McCormick of the *Tribune,* and his paper especially was being called upon to defend certain of its chosen practices—such as the way it spelled certain words. The *Tribune* offered a good-humored defense of its idiosyncracies.

† † †

TO PHYLLIS WHO MIGHT SPELL IT PHREIGHT

Chicago Tribune, August 7, 1946.

A girl in the sixth grade named Phyllis who lives in California, wrote us a letter the other day, asking why we used the spelling *frate.* As a number of other readers have asked the same question, we publish our reply as the answer to all of them:

Dear Phyllis:

We think that the spelling of words in our language is very disorderly and we are trying to clean up the mess, a little at a time. That is why we have adopted simplified spellings of a few dozen words, including *frate,* in the hope that our readers, including the editors of other publications, will come to accept the changes.

If the changes annoy our readers too much, we go back to the old forms. The readers didn't like *iland* because they said it made them think of an African antelope; so we went back to *island. Frate* seems to be winning acceptance and we hear very few objections to *tho, thru, altho* and some others of the sort. Recently, we adopted *telegraf, geografy,* etc., but it is still too early to say how well or ill they have been received.

As you know, there is no official spelling authority in this country. Spelling is a matter of custom; when you get 100 in spelling, you have spelled all your words the way they are customarily written in 1946, but that doesn't mean that the customary forms can't be improved. In fact, ever since there has been an English language, spelling has been changing and most of the changes have been simplifications. All we are trying to do is to carry along the work.

To show you that *frate* is not exactly a new spelling, and also to show you how much change has taken place in spelling in a few hundred years, we quote a sentence which we found in the Oxford English dictionary. It comes from Starkey's "England," published in 1538 and reads as follows:

"Specyally yf to that were joyned a nother ordynance. . . wych ys, concernyng the frate of marchandyse."

There is a very good chapter on spelling in the big book called "The American Language" by H. L. Mencken. In our copy, this chapter begins at page 379. You can find this book in almost any public library (but be sure to ask for "The American Language" and not for "The American Language: Supplement One" which is a wholly different book by the same author). If you will read the chapter, you will find that the movement for simplified spelling had the approval of Benjamin Franklin, Theodore Roosevelt, and a lot of other distinguished men. You will learn, also, how much Noah Webster, the dictionary man, did to improve spelling when this country was young. You will find that the same kind of people who today fuss about *frate* used to throw fits about *honor* and *labor,* which, they thought, must be spelled *honour* and *labour.* Maybe in a few years, people will think *freight* is a silly way to spell the word.

We hope this answers your question.

We may add that we are always glad to receive suggestions on spelling from readers. We can't promise to adopt all the proposals but we'll give them careful consideration.

† † †

One of the newer newspapers, *PM,* was in trouble. Its editor, Ralph Ingersoll, had had a long and unseemly fight with his draft board. The paper was in financial trouble and was even accepting some advertising. *PM* appeared to some critics to be much too friendly toward Communists, and in the fall of 1947 such friendliness was not a popular position. But the paper had maintained its essentially optimistic view of life and had continued to push for reform. A writer in 1947 asked a question that was especially relevant at the time, "How Free Is the Free Press?"

† † †

REFLECTIONS ON FREEDOM OF THE PRESS

By Saul Padover, *PM,* October 27, 1947. Copyright PM, 1947.

. . . It is. . . wrong to say that freedom of the press does not exist in this country. It does exist—to a degree of near-anarchy and irresponsibility. There is no body or agency or censor or official or law to tell a newspaper what to publish or what to leave out. Every paper and magazine is on its own, guided by the conscience, self-interest or bias of its own editor and publisher. In his own publication Henry Luce is free to preach holiness and religion, William Randolph Hearst is at liberty to battle against Russia and sin, and Robert McCormick is allowed to fight the British Empire. This unhampered freedom may be good or bad, depending upon the point of view, but it is senseless to deny that it exists.

Complete freedom of the press reigns because American newspapers are private businesses, not governmental instruments. Like any other business in a free enterprise economy, the press is organized and owned by businessmen for the purpose of making money—a process which under the Constitution of the United

States may not be interfered with. "A newspaper," the *Wall Street Journal* said (Jan. 20, 1925), "is a private enterprise, owing nothing to the public, which grants it no franchise. It is therefore afflicted with no public interest. It is emphatically the property of its owner, who is selling a manufactured product at his own risk."

But while the Russians are wrong in denying the existence of freedom, they are right in accusing the American press of monopolistic tendencies and big business control. . . .

† † †

The question about the free press asked by Saul Padover in *PM* was timely because 1947 was the year in which the report of the Commission on Freedom of the Press was issued. The report— usually referred to in later years as the Hutchins Report, taking its name from Robert M. Hutchins of the University of Chicago, chairman of the commission—had been subsidized by Henry Luce of *Time-Life*. It said some important things about what the press should be in a free society. There was righteous indignation, especially from those who, in the analogy once offered by Tom Wallace of the *Louisville Times,* thought freedom of the press guaranteed a newspaper the right to drive a circulation truck through a red light. Still others thought the commission should have taken a much sterner position. A quarter of a century after the report was issued it seemed to have even more meaning than when it first burst upon the world of the press.

The euphoria that disappeared in the years immediately after the war had come about because of the great expectations for peace that normally accompany the end of a conflict such as World War II. But soon the news stories seemed to be related, one after the other, to communism, to the nations of eastern Europe that went behind what Winston Churchill labeled in his speech at Fulton, Missouri, as the "iron curtain"—Poland, Czechoslovakia, Hungary, Romania, Bulgaria, Yugoslavia. There were stories of spies and of rumored espionage—Alger Hiss and Whittaker Chambers, Judith Coplon, the Rosenbergs. From 1947 on committees in both House and Senate were investigating domestic communism. Then, at the end of 1949, China, the great wartime ally, had become a Communist power, and the government of Chiang Kai-shek was driven to the island of Formosa. On June 25, 1950, the Communists of North Korea crossed the 38th parallel into South Korea, and a new war, a hated war, a misunderstood war, a politically abused war, began. Hal Boyle, Don Whitehead, Keyes Beech, Fred Sparks, Jim Lucas, Homer Bigart, and Marguerite Higgins were among the reporters, some veterans of World War II, who covered the unpopular new war. This is one of the stories that helped to win the Pulitzer prize for Marguerite Higgins.

† † †

THE LANDING AT INCHON

By Marguerite Higgins, *New York Herald Tribune,* September 18, 1950.

WITH THE U.S. MARINES AT INCHON, KOREA, Sept. 15 (Delayed)—Heavily laden U.S. Marines, in one of the most technically difficult amphibious landings in history, stormed at sunset today over a ten-foot sea wall in the heart of the port of Inchon and within an hour had taken three commanding hills in the city.

I was in the fifth wave that hit "Red Beach," which in reality was a rough, vertical pile of stones over which the first assault troops had to scramble with the aid of improvised landing ladders topped with steel hooks.

Despite a deadly and steady pounding from naval guns and airplanes, enough North Koreans remained alive close to the beach to harass us with small-arms and mortar fire. They even hurled hand grenades down at us as we crouched in trenches which unfortunately ran behind the sea wall in the inland side.

It was far from the "virtually unopposed" landing for which the troops had hoped after hearing of the quick capture of Wolmi Island in the morning by an earlier Marine assault. Wolmi is inside Inchon harbor and just off "Red Beach." At H-hour minus seventy, confident, joking Marines started climbing down from the transport ship on cargo nets and dropping into small assault boats. Our wave commander, Lieutenant R. J. Schening, a veteran of five amphibious assaults, including Guadalcanal, hailed me with the comment, "This has a good chance of being a pushover."

Because of tricky tides, our transport had to stand down the channel and it was more than nine miles to the rendezvous point where our assault waves formed up.

The channel reverberated with the ear-splitting boom of warship guns and rockets. Blue and orange flame spurted from the "Red Beach" area and a huge oil tank, on fire, sent great black rings of smoke over the shore. Then the fire from the big guns lifted and the planes that had been circling overhead swooped low to rake their fire deep into the sea wall. . . .

† † †

Perhaps the biggest story of the Korean War was the one so full of political implications, the shocking removal of General Douglas MacArthur as commander in the Far East in April of 1951. The American people seemed to go temporarily crazy. Forgotten was the unhappy reputation MacArthur had had with many during World War II, when he was known bitterly as "Dugout Doug." For Truman was "the little man from Missouri," an unpopular president who was unwilling to let a popular and great general win an unpopular war. Truman based his decision on recommendations of the Joint Chiefs of Staff, and MacArthur was fired, technically, at least, for insubordination—a fact ignored in the hysteria of the time. Coast to coast there was pro-MacArthur frenzy, and in a few days everything from MacArthur dolls to recordings of "Old Soldiers Never Die"—the song MacArthur quoted in his speech to Congress—could be purchased. The country recovered and regained its sanity, and a year later the general occasioned only a flutter when he was the keynote speaker at the Republican national convention.

† † †

TRUMAN FIRES MacARTHUR

By Ernest B. Vaccaro, Associated Press, April 11, 1951.

Washington, April 11 (Wednesday). (AP)— President Truman early today forced General Douglas MacArthur from all his commands.

The President said he had concluded that MacArthur "is unable to give his wholehearted support" to United States and United Nations policies.

In a statement, Mr. Truman asserted that "military commanders must be governed" by policies and directives of the government and "in time of crisis, this consideration is particularly compelling."

Mr. Truman immediately designated Lieut. Gen. Matthew B. Ridgway as MacArthur's successor as supreme commander, Allied powers, commander in chief, United Nations command; commander in chief, Far East; and commanding general, U.S. Army, Far East.

The President appointed Lieut. Gen. James A. Van Fleet to succeed Ridgway to take over active command of the Eighth army.

Announcement of the almost unprecedented dismissal of the hero-general was made at a rare news conference at the White House at 1 a.m. The time was fixed to coincide as nearly as possible with the delivery to MacArthur at Tokyo of the order relieving him of his commands, "effective at once."

The White House released, with the President's statement, a memorandum purporting to show differences between MacArthur's statements and action and presidential policy. . . .

The President's action came as the aftermath of a series of differences with MacArthur over policy in the Far East and raised prospects that MacArthur might return to this country to deliver a series of blasts against the administration, probably under auspices of Republican supporters of the general.

These differences embraced not only the question of MacArthur's sympathy with the administration's policy but also fundamental views toward the struggle against communism.

MacArthur is on record in favor of waging a more vigorous war in Asia. He said the West was fighting Europe's battles in the Far East.

The general wanted to bomb Red Chinese bases in Manchuria and also wanted Nationalist Chinese troops released from Formosa to fight the Reds. . . .

Aware of political reverberations certain to follow in the wake of his action, the President made public a series of heretofore secret directives tending to show how MacArthur failed to follow administrative foreign policy.

These included one from the Joint Chiefs of Staff to MacArthur and other commanders on December 6, 1950, embracing a presidential order that "No speech, press release, or other public statement concerning military policy should be released until it has received clearance from the Department of Defense."

To this was attached another memo from the Joint Chiefs of Staff to MacArthur March 20, 1951, asserting that the State department was planning an announcement shortly that "with clearing of bulk of South Korea of aggressors, United Nations now prepared to discuss conditions of settlement in Korea" and adding:

"Strong U.N. feeling persists that further diplomatic efforts toward settlement should be made before any advance with major forces north of thirty-eighth parallel.

"Time will be required to determine diplomatic reactions and permit new negotiations that may develop.". . .

† † †

The popularity of Harry S. Truman reached a low point in that confrontation with MacArthur. But his popularity had been in decline for some time, even though he had defeated Thomas E. Dewey in 1948. The Truman document most representative of that event is the broadcast in which the President recalled that election night and gave his delightful impersonation of the newscaster, H. V. Kaltenborn—Austrian accent and all. (The photograph of Truman holding up the *Chicago Tribune* front page—DEWEY DEFEATS TRUMAN—is another of the memories Americans have of the feisty president.) Truman's term in office had been a troubled one, despite the history-making bombing of Japan, the Greek-Turkish aid program, and the Marshall Plan. Corruption had come to mar his administration, and much of the low repute into which Truman fell, and part of the defeat of Adlai Stevenson in 1952, can be traced to a succession of scandals. In the early 1950s scandals were coming to seem a way of life, and there was still an old-fashioned concern in some quarters for morality and decency. Among the troubled was a St. Louis editorial writer, who won a Pulitzer prize for his 1951 commentary.

† † †

THE LOW ESTATE OF PUBLIC MORALS

By Louis LaCoss, *St. Louis Globe-Democrat,* August 6, 1951.

The discharge of 90 West Point cadets for cheating at examinations is only one facet of the many-sided problem of moral disintegration nationally that is causing many persons to wonder whether America is going down the path of decay that caused the Roman empire to fall. It is a sobering thought. But the facts must be faced.

The West Pointers were dishonest. They cheated. Some did so because they couldn't play football and keep up with their studies. Others who were not athletes cheated because that was the easy way to make passing grades.

The excuse of the athletes accents the abnormality of thinking in many institutions of higher education as to the part sports should play in college life. The necessity of having a good team to assure big revenue to build a bigger stadium to make more money has led many of our colleges into the evil devices of buying players, of combating in the open market for a star halfback. Some colleges have recognized the error and have de-emphasized sports, as should be done.

At West Point the incentive was a bit different because Uncle Sam foots the bills there, but there was the incentive for the individual to "make" a team that was tops or near it in the nation. So, if practice on the field interfered, cheat a little and make the necessary grades.

But fundamentally what happened at West Point reflects a present distorted attitude toward old-fashioned honesty and integrity that pertains not only in our schools but in America's social and political life.

It is seen in the high places in government, which after World War II practiced plain deception on the people. We were told no secret agreements had been made with anybody. Later, we discovered pacts were signed at Tehran, Yalta and Potsdam that made the Korean war inevitable.

In the New Deal era was born the idea that an administration can perpetuate itself in the power by buying the voters with handout money. Remember how Harry Hopkins tapped the WPA till to win an election in Kentucky? During that era was born the fiction that cities and states as well as individuals need not look to their own resources or ingenuity to survive—let Washington do it. Out of the mating of depression and political trickery, came the insidious thinking by millions of Americans that hard work is positively silly; that if one does work, do the least possible, draw the biggest pay possible—and strike for more.

The youths, such as the West Pointers, with whom we are concerned today, were babies then. They have grown into manhood in an environment of take-it-where-I-find-it entirely alien to the

American tradition. They are the unpretty fruit of the mistakes of the past two decades.

What do we see in Washington today? Corruption and scandals. The close link between the underworld and politics was revealed by the Kefauver committee. The Fulbright committee turned the spotlight on the RFC and the influence peddlers, some within the shadow of the White House, who sold their contracts for a price.

We hear of doubtful goings-on in the government department that collects our income taxes. We hear of patronage bought and sold like so much goods over the counter.

An army General sees no wrong in accepting gifts from those with whom he does government business, nor in diverting government materials to private use.

The chairman of the Democratic National Committee yells "smear" when it is discovered that he is on the payroll of a St. Louis company for the ostensible reason that he has influence on RFC loans.

The close personal friend of the President, a Major General, has a desk in the White House where he conveniently hands out receipts for deep freezers, presented him gratis and which he distributes where they will do good politically.

Campaigns for the Senate in Ohio and Maryland last year were conducted along lines that set a new political low.

So, when 90 West Point cadets stray from paths of honesty, when nauseous revelations are made of the bribing of college basketball teams, when youths charged with robbery stand up in court, as they did in New York, and brazenly admit their guilt, but excuse it by saying that "everybody's doing it," when teenagers become delinquent via the narcotics road, when too many youths of both sexes flout the laws of chastity and decency—when these derelictions of the youths of our lands totaled up, there comes a time for sober questioning among the adults.

Where does the fault lie? In the home? Perhaps. In the schools? In part. In the churches? In part. But in the main the fault lies in that nebulous field of public morals and spirituality which was so highly cultivated by the founding fathers and which of late has been so scantily tilled. Among too many of us the accepted premise is that anything is fair unless we are caught; that each of us is entitled to something for nothing; that the world owes us a living; that an honest day's work for an honest day's pay is almost unethical; that gypping the other fellow before he gyps you is the only policy that pays off.

The level of public morals is low. Unfortunately, the good example is not set in Washington. The President is victimized by his friends, but a false sense of loyalty prevents him from moving forthright against them. His reluctance condones wrong doing. Leadership in both parties is weak, because it is consistently attuned to the next election, not to what is best for the public welfare. In fact, public morals are low because politics at all levels is played at a historic low. The one is the coadjutor of the other.

370

Yet, we strut the earth telling everybody else to look at us and see democracy in fairest flower—and please copy; we'll foot the bill. We wonder, for instance, what Pravda will have to say about the 90 West Point cadets.

The time is here for moral regeneration. West Point is just one item in the sad chronology. The Roman empire fell, not because it was overwhelmed from without but because it decayed from within. If this is an appeal for a return to the day-to-day practice of old time religion, and respect for God's moral law, so be it. When the moral fabric of a nation begins to unravel, it is time to do some patching before the entire garment is gone. The cause and effect of this deterioration nationally will be issues in next year's presidential campaigns.

† † †

There was a historic passing from the public scene in 1951 when William Randolph Hearst, a major figure in journalism since the 1880s, died. In some newspapers there was the conventional utterance of piety, praise for Hearst and all that he had done. One editor who refused to treat the Hearst career in a conventional way was a small-town editor, one who had achieved national recognition, Houstoun Waring of the *Littleton Independent,* a paper in a suburb of Denver. His editorial was a refreshing and meaningful commentary.

† † †

THE MEANING OF HEARST

By Houstoun Waring, *Littleton Independent,* August 24, 1951.

The most baneful influence in American journalism came to a close last week with the death of William Randolph Hearst. For 65 years Hearst was a mighty force in this nation. To increase his circulation in 1898, he whipped up a frenzy of feeling against Spain and brought on the unnecessary Spanish-American war.

So stirred with hatred were the people of this country that President McKinley did not have the courage to tell Congress about Spain's apologies when he asked for war.

Hearst's circulation shot skyward.

Most of the men on Hearst's newspapers have grumbled about their lot and despised themselves for prostituting their talents in his behalf. They have always pleaded economic necessity. We recall one of Hearst's editors asking Ilya Ehrenberg, the noted Russian journalist, if the Soviet Union would tolerate a man like Hearst. Ehrenberg dodged the question (it was in the days of American-Soviet friendship), but the inquiry was revealing.

George Sokolsky has written an encomium about Hearst, and this appeared in many newspapers on Sunday.

"His cause was Americanism—fundamentalist, understandable, patriotic Americanism," Sokolsky says.

At the bottom of the article is the revealing line: "Distributed by King Features Syndicate."

The American public generally was unaware that Hearst's un-American ideas were being pumped into their minds by his King Features Syndicate and other media. Besides his 19 newspapers, Hearst utilized his International News Service to widen his power. And he entered the homes and hearts of millions of unsuspecting Americans who never knew that the Hearst line is followed to the letter in his magazines; namely, Good Housekeeping, Harper's Bazaar, Cosmopolitan, Junior Bazaar, House Beautiful, Town and Country, Motor, Motor Boating, American Druggist, and the British Connoisseur.

While the American press has been delicate with Hearst in death the two most respected English newspapers have been more forthright. Said the London Times: "His exploits. . . were perhaps the largest factor in lowering the tone of the press of the English-speaking world." And the Manchester Guardian declared: "It is hard even now to think of him with charity. Perhaps no man ever did so much to debase the standards of journalism."

Thinking people of America are now asking whether another Hearst could rise in the middle of the Twentieth Century. We doubt it. This nation has accepted men like Henry Luce and DeWitt Wallace because they use their tremendous power tastefully al-though with doubtful benefit to society. But we believe the new forces in this nation, such as a stronger federal government, and aggressive national labor unions, will prevent the future develop-ment of a buccaneer like Hearst.

A free press prevails in our country because its citizens realize that a free press serves their interests. If ever the Hearsts and McCormicks should outweigh the Barry Binghams and the Eugene Meyers, citizens will seek some better means of informing them-selves—possibly with government-operated periodicals.

This day may never come, but if it does we can blame the irresponsible members of the profession.

† † †

For the press of America, the big story of 1952 was the presiden-tial campaign, the one that pitted the vastly popular General Dwight D. Eisenhower against the popular, though not vastly popular, Governor Adlai E. Stevenson of Illinois. Before the campaign, however, there came the story that broke on a March night, when President Harry S. Truman abandoned his prepared text at a political dinner and made an announcement of great

372

portent. Newspapers that published the conventional prepared text in their first editions missed one of the year's major stories.

† † †

TRUMAN CHOOSES NOT TO RUN

By the Associated Press, March 29, 1952.

Washington, March 29 (AP)—Harry S. Truman, President of the United States, announced tonight he would not accept another nomination.

He threw the annual Jackson-Day dinner of his party into surprised turmoil with the flat announcement:

"I shall not be a candidate for re-election. I have served my country long and, I think, efficiently and honestly.

"I shall not accept a renomination. I do not feel that it is my duty to spend another four years in the White House."

(Cries of no, no! from the floor.)

"We must always remember the things the Democratic party has done, and the high ideals that have made it great.

"We must be true to its principles and keep it foremost in service to the people.

"If we do that, we can be sure there will be a Democratic President in the White House for the next four years."

Thus the nation's thirty-third chief executive bowed himself out of the presidential picture seven years and seventy-nine days after he entered the country's highest office on the death of Franklin D. Roosevelt. . . .

† † †

In July, the Republicans nominated Dwight D. Eisenhower, after a spirited competition between Eisenhower and "Mr. Republican," Robert A. Taft of Ohio. Eisenhower, like Harry Truman, was earthy, a man of the Midwest, a man of the people. His opponent, Adlai Stevenson, nominated by the Democrats the same month, was midwestern, too, but he was much more sophisticated, much more intellectual, and even though many were thus attracted to him, the victory that took place in November seemed preordained. But one affair was temporarily shocking to the Republican party, for the vice presidential candidate, Richard M. Nixon, was called upon to defend his secret $18,000 political fund, and his defense became one of the shrewdest pieces of political propaganda in American history. This is an excerpt.

† † †

THE "CHECKERS" SPEECH

By Richard M. Nixon, September 23, 1952, excerpted from *New York Times*, September 24, 1952.

... Now, that's what we have. What do we owe? Well, in addition to the mortgage, the $20,000 mortgage on the house in Washington, the $10,000 one on the house in Whittier, I owe $4,500 to the Riggs Bank in Washington, D.C., with interest 4½ percent.

I owe $3,500 to my parents and the interest on that loan which I pay regularly, because it's the part of the savings they made through the years they were working so hard. I pay regularly 4 percent interest. And then I have a $500 loan which I have on my life insurance.

Well, that's about it. That's what we have and that's what we owe. It isn't very much but Pat and I have the satisfaction that every dime that we've got is honestly ours. I should say this—that Pat doesn't have a mink coat. But she does have a respectable Republican cloth coat. And I always tell her that she'd look good in anything.

One other thing I probably should tell you, because if I don't they'll probably be saying this about me too, we did get something—a gift—after the election. A man down in Texas heard Pat on the radio mention the fact that our two youngsters would like to have a dog. And, believe it or not, the day before we left on this campaign trip we got a message from Union Station in Baltimore saying they had a package for us. We went down to get it. You know what it was? It was a little cocker spaniel dog in a crate that he sent all the way from Texas. Black and white spotted. And our little girl—Trisha, the 6-year-old—named it Checkers. And you know the kids love the dog and I just want to say right now, that regardless of what they say about it, we're gonna keep it. ...

† † †

In retrospect, one must conclude that neither Nixon nor Eisenhower should have been greatly worried. Eisenhower swamped Stevenson in November, after a large majority of newspapers had given the Republican candidate their editorial support. For most Americans, obviously, it was a highly popular victory.

† † †

EISENHOWER WINS THE PRESIDENCY

By the Associated Press, November 5, 1952.

Gen. Eisenhower won the Presidency by a landslide early today and brought to a crashing end the 20-year era of Democratic political reign.

Eisenhower even split the Southland.

Down to galling defeat went Gov. Stevenson of Illinois. The Democratic nominee conceded it was all over at 1:44 a.m.

"My fellow citizens have made their choice. . . and I gladly accept it," Stevenson said.

Praising Eisenhower as a great leader in time of war, the beaten governor read a statement at Springfield, Ill., urging all Americans to unite behind the winner.

"I urge you all to give Gen. Eisenhower the support he will need," Stevenson said. "With a united people, with faith in Democracy. . . we shall move forward with God's guidance. . . in freedom and dignity and peace.". . .

As Stevenson spoke the fateful words of concession, this was the scope of the Eisenhower sweep:

Ike had ripped Virginia and Florida away from the traditionally "Solid South" and was leading in Texas and Tennessee. He had captured Oklahoma and Maryland along the border and was out front in Missouri.

New York, New Jersey, Ohio—all big vote states—were solidly in the G.O.P. column. So were Illinois and California. Michigan and Pennsylvania were moving in that direction.

Farm states—many of those that sealed President Truman's upset victory four years ago—swung to the G.O.P. and the victory surge boiled westward to the coast.

It all added up to the Eisenhower lead in 39 states with 442 electoral votes out of the 531—and only 266 had been needed for victory. Stevenson was ahead in a mere nine states with 89 electoral ballots—Alabama, Arkansas, Georgia, Louisiana, Mississippi, North Carolina, South Carolina, Kentucky and West Virginia.

At one mighty blow Eisenhower had demolished political ramparts which had securely sheltered Franklin D. Roosevelt and Harry S. Truman while they built their New Deal and Fair Deal. . . .

† † †

Harry S. Truman spent his last year in relative obscurity; the triple problem advertised on Republican bumper stickers—Communism, Corruption, and Korea—had been harmful, of course, and he was not popular with some of the people who were coming to power in his party. When he left the White House in January, 1953, few editorial writers were given to laments, but one publication that offered thoughtful historical insights was the one Harold Ross had founded in 1925, the *New Yorker,* a magazine of wit and sophistication whose "Talk of the Town" section was presenting in the postwar years some of the finest editorial writing in America.

† † †

ON TRUMAN AND HIS PLACE IN HISTORY

New Yorker, XXVIII, No. 48 (January 17, 1953), pp. 17-18. Reprinted by permission.

Harry Truman's swan song about the state of the union was delivered in droning fashion by clerks, but there was nothing monotonous about the message itself. It was an ominous statement —if anything, an *under*statement. The hydrogen bomb releases Carbon 14, which has a half life of 5,600 years. When the planet has enough Carbon 14 kicking around, the so-called higher forms of life find that their reproductive powers either vanish or take odd turns, and at this point the planet becomes habitable only for the so-called lower forms, such as the cockroach, who can make a nice meal out of Carbon 14 laced with desk paste. This news is beginning to get around, via the grapevine.

Mr. Truman's essay on fear was excellent in every respect and belongs alongside Learned Hand's pronouncement of a few weeks ago, when he spoke the most haunting sentence of 1952: "I believe that that community is already in the process of dissolution where each man begins to eye his neighbor as a possible enemy, where nonconformity with the accepted creed...is a mark of disaffection, where denunciation, without specification or backing, takes the place of evidence."

Harry Truman has only a few days to go in office. He has been a much-reviled President, an object of perhaps a record-breaking amount of attention from the Bronx-cheering sections of the nation. He came into office scared to death (he hadn't even known that Roosevelt was sick), and he soon found himself trying to run the biggest country in the world in what is probably the toughest sort of period—a cold war. A cold war is more trying for a president than a hot one; in hot times the people are united, everything moves forward on a tremendous surge of national spirit, impossible deeds are accomplished. In cold times the opposite is true; for resolution read fear, for unity read disunity, for accomplishment read frustration, bumbling, corruption. Harry Truman, in our opinion, did remarkably well. At moments he was great. His two top decisions were of the first order of toughness: the use of the A-bomb, the intervention by the United Nations in Korea. Both decisions imposed an almost unbearable burden of responsibility and they took enormous guts—guts and a good sense of history. In his petty moments, Harry Truman broke records, too. But his flights of short temper and his bursts of bad spirit were overbalanced by his sincerity, by his cheerful belief in the facts of democratic life, and by his fortitude. In his failure to turn back the strong tide of political corruption, he was, we think, a victim of circumstances; we doubt that anybody could have done it at the tag end of a twenty-year stretch of one-party rule and with a cold war on his hands. We may have had bigger presidents and we may have had wiser ones, but we've had none more doughty and few with so tough an assignment.

We send Harry Truman our thanks and wish him Godspeed in Independence.

To Mr. Stalin we address just another sentence or two, an addendum to the Presidential message: The cockroach—the brown-banded cockroach—has already begun acting uppity. He has been found, of late, in television sets, gnawing away at the excess glue at the connections. Put this in your pipe and smoke it. Nothing else has been able to bring peace and order to the world, but we're beginning to think that Carbon 14, in collaboration with the brownbanded cockroach, is going to swing it.

† † †

The early 1950s were the years of McCarthy even more than years of Truman or Eisenhower. Joseph R. McCarthy was elected to the Senate from Wisconsin in 1946, and he was not expected to make history in the upper house. He began to look for an issue to aid his sagging career and seized upon the matter of domestic communism, giving a speech in February, 1950, in Wheeling, West Virginia, about "communism in the State Department"—205 card-carrying Communists, or any other figure that would strike his fancy; on one occasion, perhaps after seeing a Heinz advertisement, he gave the figure "57." He became an expert at distracting the national audience and learned well how to use the press, especially in loosing an attack at deadline time. Soon the word "McCarthyism" became commonly known, and by the spring of 1954 the nation was watching the hearings on television involving the Army's charge that McCarthy had used his influence in behalf of an aide named G. David Schine and McCarthy's charge that the Army had promoted a Communist dentist named Irving Peress. On March 9, 1954, Edward R. Murrow devoted his *See It Now* broadcast to a report on McCarthy. These were the concluding words.

† † †

SEE IT NOW—A LOOK AT JOSEPH McCARTHY

By Edward R. Murrow, March 9, 1954, in Edward W. Bliss, Jr., *In Search of Light: The Broadcasts of Edward R. Murrow 1938-1961* (New York: Knopf, 1967), pp. 247-248.

. . . No one familiar with the history of this country can deny that congressional committees are useful. It is necessary to investigate before legislating. But the line between investigation and persecuting is a very fine one, and the junior senator from Wisconsin has stepped over it repeatedly. His primary achievement has been in confusing the public mind as between the internal and the external threat of Communism. We must not confuse dissent with disloyalty.

We must remember always that accusation is not proof and that conviction depends upon evidence and due process of law. We will not walk in fear, one of another. We will not be driven by fear into an age of unreason if we dig deep in our history and our doctrine and remember that we are not descended from fearful men, not from men who feared to write, to speak, to associate and to defend causes which were for the moment unpopular.

This is no time for men who oppose Senator McCarthy's methods to keep silent, *or* for those who approve. We can deny our heritage and our history, but we cannot escape responsibility for the result. As a nation we have come into our full inheritance at a tender age. We proclaim ourselves, as indeed we are, the defenders of freedom— what's left of it—but we cannot defend freedom abroad by deserting it at home. The actions of the junior senator from Wisconsin have caused alarm and dismay amongst our allies abroad and given considerable comfort to our enemies. And whose fault is that? Not really his; he didn't create this situation of fear, he merely exploited it and rather successfully. Cassius was right. "The fault, dear Brutus, is not in our stars but in ourselves."

† † †

The high point of the Army-McCarthy hearings themselves came in an encounter between the Wisconsin senator and another Joseph—Joseph Welch, lawyer for the Army. The encounter seemed, to many television viewers, the very moment when the rapidly rising star of Joseph McCarthy began to descend. For McCarthy it was a monumental blunder; one sensed that his aides were trying to stop him from saying the words that would be so destructive to his ambitions.

† † †

A FAMOUS ENCOUNTER ON NATIONWIDE TELEVISION

By John R. Cauley, *Kansas City Star,* June 10, 1954.

Washington, June 9.—The controversy between Senator McCarthy and the army exploded into an electrifying session late today.

Joseph N. Welch, special counsel for the army, accused McCarthy of "cruelly and recklessly" smearing a young lawyer in Welch's office and McCarthy himself took the witness stand to testify it would be a "waste of time, money and blood" to fight communism abroad unless they are routed out of the government here at home.

McCarthy said more persons had been brought under the hammer of communism in its 106 years than had been converted to Christianity since its inception and predicted:

"Unless we make sure there is no infiltration of government, just as sure as you are sitting there, in the period of our lives you will see a Red world."

The exchange between Welch and McCarthy came after the senator had accused the counsel of "trying to foist off on the committee" as one of Welch's assistants a "young man named Fisher" who, McCarthy charged, once belonged to a Communist-front organization.

Welch identified the young man as Fred Fisher and said Fisher once had belonged to the National Lawyers guild.

His face flushed with anger and his voice quivering with emotion, Welch stared across the table at McCarthy and said:

"Until this moment, I think I never really gauged your cruelty and recklessness. Little did I dream you could be so reckless and cruel as to do injury to this lad.

"He will always bear a scar needlessly inflicted by you. I wish it were in my power to forgive you but your forgiveness will have to come from someone other than me."

McCarthy came back bitterly at Welch. Then the army counsel refused to discuss Fisher further with McCarthy, abruptly broke off his cross-examination of [Roy] Cohn and asked the chairman to call the next witness.

There was a heavy burst of applause from the packed hearing room as Welch finished. . . .

† † †

In the same month that the Army-McCarthy hearings were nearing their end, another historic event was making the front pages. News reports of that story, the Supreme Court decision of segregation in public schools, were factual and not very exciting; the more dramatic stories in the civil rights saga lay ahead. But the ruling was perhaps the major domestic event between the end of the war and the assassination of John F. Kennedy in 1963, a ruling that was known, prosaically, as Brown *vs.* Board of Education of Topeka. What the case involved, quite simply, was black students—in the Topeka instance, one student—who were denied the right to attend "white" schools; the Topeka girl had to be bused far across the city although there was a perfectly good school near her home.

† † †

SUPREME COURT STRIKES DOWN SCHOOL SEGREGATION

By the Associated Press, May 17, 1954.

WASHINGTON, May 17 (AP)—The Supreme Court today unanimously struck down segregation in the nation's public schools. The tribunal said that to separate Negro and white pupils violates the constitutional guarantee of equal protection of the laws.

Chief Justice Earl Warren read the court's opinion, which declared:

"We conclude that in the field of public education the doctrine of separate but equal has no place. Separate educational facilities are inherently unequal.

"Therefore,we hold that the plaintiffs (Negro parents) and others similarly situated for whom the action has been brought are, by reason of the segregation complained of, deprived of the equal protection of the laws guaranteed by the 14th Amendment.

"This disposition makes unnecessary any discussion whether such segregation also violates the due process clause of the 14th Amendment."

The 14th Amendment was adopted after the Civil War, primarily for the benefit of slaves freed by President Lincoln. It says no state may deny any person due process and equal protection of the law, nor abridge their privileges or immunities.

Chief Justice Warren, reading the court's opinion, said that to separate children solely because of race, generates feelings in their hearts and minds which might never be undone.

Today's historic decision overturned the segregation doctrine established by the Supreme Court 57 years ago.

And, if advance threats are carried out, today's ruling will lead eventually to the abolition of public school systems as they now exist in South Carolina, Georgia and Virginia.

Justice Warren said that because of the complex questions involved, the formulation of Supreme Court decrees backing up the ruling will be delayed.

"But," he declared, "we have announced that segregation has no place in education. . . .

The cases decided today involve schools in South Carolina, Virginia, Kansas, Delaware and the District of Columbia. . . .

† † †

A man named Robert S. Abbott was the founder of the *Chicago Defender* in 1905, a black newspaper that had become one of the acknowledged leaders of the ethnic press. Abbott's paper had fit into the typical formula of the black press of its time—sensationalism on behalf of blacks, stories angled toward his race, advertising that seemed designed to move blacks into the white culture. It was one of several notable such journals, others including the *Pittsburgh Courier* and the *Baltimore Afro-American,* all of which were speaking authoritatively as the black-crises developed in the 1940s and 1950s. When the Supreme Court story broke in May of 1954, the *Defender* offered a front page story that clearly had editorial overtones.

† † †

A BLACK NEWSPAPER COMMENTS ON THE DECISION

Chicago Defender, May 22, 1954.

The South is in an ugly mood this week, still rocking under the historic Supreme Court ruling banning public school segregation.

In its implication, the high court's decision ranks in importance with the Emancipation Proclamation. It held that school Jim Crow is contrary to the constitutional guarantee of equality of all Americans.

High and low officials from cities as large as Atlanta, Ga., to burgs as small as Cowpens, S.C., denounced the sweeping ruling which will eventually put white and Negro children in the same classrooms.

Plans to circumvent the court's decision ranged from an Alabama lawmaker's suggestion that lessons be televised to the students' homes to one for setting up a triple, rather than dual school system. Under the latter system, counties would have schools for whites, schools for Negroes and schools for those who desired to attend integrated institutions.

But most Southern leaders who seek a path of resistance looked to two alternatives.

One plan would create a system of "private schools" which proponents say would not come under provisions of the high court's ruling.

The chief alternative would seek to preserve both public schools and segregation, by giving local officials full authority to assign students to classrooms.

One thing seems certain, however: the transition to non-segregated schools will be slow. Long, drawn-out court battles loom and violence may accompany integration attempts in any one of the 31 states affected by the decision.

Gov. James F. Byrnes of South Carolina has declared that his state will never permit integration. Gov. Herman Talmadge of Georgia has threatened he will call out the militia to prevent intermingling of Negro and white pupils.

Virginia, which with South Carolina is directly involved in cases on which the ruling came, is not expected to resist to the extent that will South Carolina and Georgia. Gov. Thomas Stanley has called a meeting of representatives of both races to discuss the ruling. Virginia's legislators previously rejected the private school idea.

Talmadge has called a policy subcommittee meeting for next Tuesday to draw up an agenda for the full state commission on education to consider. The commission was created to find ways to keep school segregation.

A similar approach was indicated in Mississippi where Gov. Hugh White named eight members of a 25-man committee set up for the same purpose as Georgia's commission. Political leaders indicate the group will meet some time this summer.

South Carolina's similar committee was expected to meet in the next few days.

Florida's cabinet directed Atty. Gen. Richard Ervin Tuesday to submit a brief bearing on ways of implementing the high court's decision.

The court decision became an issue in North Carolina's senatorial race. Incumbent Sen. Alton Lennon attacked the decision and accused his opponent, ex-Gov. Kerr Scott, of having encouraged the abolition of segregation in schools. Scott said he has "always been opposed" to school integration.

† † †

The ruling by the high court came in 1954; not until the autumn of 1957 was there an explosion over the issue. In much of the South, after the decision, there was continued circumvention of the decision, and some lawyers even dug out the old "interposition" argument that Jefferson and Madison had used in the Virginia and Kentucky Resolutions of 1798. The school that made news was Central High School, in Little Rock, Arkansas, where nine black pupils were to be admitted. Governor Orval Faubus, the day before school was to open, ordered National Guardsmen to surround the school and keep the black children from entering. There to cover the story, after the school had opened its doors after a federal injunction was obtained by the Department of Justice, was an Associated Press veteran.

† † †

A SEGREGATION DISPUTE IN LITTLE ROCK

By Relman Morin, Associated Press, September 23, 1957.

LITTLE ROCK, ARKANSAS, SEPTEMBER 23 (AP)—A howling, shrieking crowd of men and women outside Central High School, and disorderly students inside, forced authorities to withdraw eight Negro students from the school Monday, three and one-half hours after they entered it.

At noon, Mayor Woodrow Wilson Mann radioed police officers on the scene, telling them to tell the crowd: "The Negro students have been withdrawn."

Almost immediately, the three Negro boys and the five girls left the school under heavy police escort. The officers took them away in police cars.

Crowds clustered at both ends of the school set up a storm of fierce howling and surged toward the lines of police and state troopers. They were beaten back.

The explosive climax came, after the school had been under siege since 8:45 a.m., when the Negroes walked quietly through the doors. Police, armed with riot guns and tear gas, had kept the crowd under control.

Inside, meanwhile, students reported seeing Negroes with blood on their clothes. And some whites who came out—in protest against integration— pictured wild disorder, with policemen chasing white students through the halls, and attacks on Negroes in the building.

The break came shortly before noon.

Virgil Blossom, school superintendent, said he asked Gene Smith, assistant chief of police at the scene, if he thought it would be best to pull out the Negroes. Smith said he did.

Mann's announcement, ordering the police to notify the crowd, came minutes afterward.

Three newspapermen were beaten by the crowd before the sudden turn in the situation. They were Paul Welch, a reporter, and Gray Villette and Francis Miller, photographers. All three are employed by *Life* Magazine. A man smashed Miller in the face while he was carrying an armful of camera equipment. Miller fell, bleeding profusely.

Even after the Negroes left the school, the crowds remained. Teenagers in two automobiles cruised on the outskirts yelling, "Which way did the niggers go?"

During the hours while the Negroes were in the school an estimated thirty to fifty white students left. The crowd yelled, cheered, and clapped each time a white student left the school. "Don't stay in there with the niggers," people yelled.

Four Negroes were beaten and some arrests were made before the eight students went into the school.

The initial violence outside the school was a frightening sight. Women burst into tears and a man, hoisted up on a wooded barricade, roared, "Who's going through?"

"We all are," the crowd shouted. But they didn't.

The drama-packed climax of three weeks of integration struggle in Little Rock came just after the buzzer sounded inside the 2,000-pupil high school at 8:45, signaling the start of classes.

Suddenly, on a street leading toward the school the crowd spotted four Negro adults, marching in twos, down the center of the street. A man yelled, "Look, here come the niggers!"

They were not the students. One appeared to be a newspaperman. He had a card in his hat and was bearing a camera.

I jumped into a glass-windowed telephone booth on the corner to dictate the story. As the crowd surged toward the four Negroes they broke and ran.

They were caught on the lawn of a home nearby. Whites jumped the man with the camera from behind and rode him to the ground, kicking and beating him. They smashed the camera.

This, obviously, was a planned diversionary movement to draw the crowd's attention away from the school. While I was dictating, someone yelled, "Look! They're going into the school!"

At that instant, the eight Negroes—the three boys and five girls— were crossing the schoolyard toward a side door at the south end of the school. The girls were in bobby sox and the boys were dressed in shirts open at the neck. All were carrying books.

They were not running, not even walking fast. They simply strolled toward the steps, went up and were inside before all but a few of the two hundred people at that end of the street knew it.

"They're gone in," a man roared. "Oh, God, the niggers are in the school."

A woman screamed, "Did they get in? Did you see them go in?"

"They're in now," some other men yelled.

"Oh, my God," the woman screamed. She burst into tears and tore at her hair. Hysteria swept the crowd. Other women began weeping and screaming.

At that moment a tall, gray-haired man in a brown hunting shirt jumped on the barricade. He yelled, waving his arms: "Who's going through?"

"We all are," the people shouted.

They broke over and around the wooded barricades, rushing the policemen. Almost a dozen police were at that corner of the street. They raised their billy clubs.

Some grabbed men and women and hurled them back. Two chased a dark-haired man who slipped through their line, like a football player. They caught him in the schoolyard, whipped his coat down his arms, pinning them, and hustled him out of the yard.

Another man, wearing a construction worker's hard hat, suddenly raised his hands high in front of a policeman. It was only a dozen yards or so in front of the phone booth.

I couldn't see whether the officer had a gun in the man's stomach, but he stopped running abruptly and went back. Two men were arrested.

Meanwhile, a cavalcade of cars carrying state troopers, in their broad-brimmed campaign hats and Sam Browne belts, wheeled into the street from both ends. They came inside the barricades, and order was restored for a moment.

The weeping and screaming went on among the women. A man said, "I'm going in there and get my kid out."

An officer said, "You're not going anywhere."

Suddenly another roar—and cheering and clapping—came from the crowd. A white student, carrying his books, came down the front steps. He was followed by two girls wearing bobby sox. In the next few minutes, other students came out. Between fifteen and twenty left the school within the next half hour.

Each time they appeared, the people clapped and cheered. "Come on out," they yelled. "Don't stay in there with the niggers. Go back and tell all of them to come out."

Inside, it was reported, the eight Negro students were in the office of the principal. A moment later, two policemen suddenly raced into the building through the north door. When they came out, they were holding a girl by both arms, rushing her forcibly toward a police prisoners' wagon.

For an instant it looked as though the crowd would try to break the police lines again to rescue her. But the police put her in the car and drove swiftly down the street. Screams, catcalls, and more yelling broke out as the car raced down the street.

A man, distraught, came sprinting after it. "That's my kid in there," he yelled. "Help me get my kid out."

But the car was gone. Soon afterward four white students ran down the steps of the school and across the street. Policemen were chasing them.

One of the boys said they had caught a Negro boy outside the principal's office in the school. "We walked him half the length of the building and we were going to get him out of there," they said. They refused to give their names.

Meanwhile, on the streets, at both ends of the school, clusters of troopers took up their stations, reinforcing the police. The crowd heckled them, hurling insults and some obscenity.

"How you going to feel tonight when you face your neighbors?" a man shouted.

The people called the police "nigger lovers" and insulted them. The officers stood, poker-faced, making no response.

Then the crowd, lacking any other object, turned on the newspapermen and photographers. A boy jumped up, caught the telephone wire leading from one of the three booths to the main wire and swung on it, trying to break it. The booth swayed and nearly toppled to the street.

Someone said, "We ought to wipe up the street with these Yankee reporters."

"Let's do it right now," another replied.

But it was only words. Nothing happened. The same woman who had first burst into tears buttonholed a reporter and said, "Why don't you tell the truth about us? Why don't you tell them we are peaceful people who won't stand to have our kids sitting next to niggers?"

People in the crowd reported gleefully—and shouted it at the other officers—that one policeman had torn off his badge and had thrown it on the ground.

"There's one white man on the police force," a burly slick-haired youth in a T shirt yelled at the policeman in front of him.

Sporadic tussles broke out, from time to time, when men tried to pass the police and trooper lines. The police wrestled one man to the street and then, taking him by the hands and arms, hauled him into the squad car and drove off.

A number of plainclothesmen—some reported to be FBI agents—kept circulating up and down in front of the school.

Inside there was no sign that this was different from any other school day. Students who came out at the 10:30 recess said that, in one class of thirty students, only one stayed in the classroom when a Negro entered.

† † †

Thanks to the *Arkansas Gazette,* a Little Rock newspaper, and its editor, Harry Ashmore, the city of Little Rock had one spokesman that deplored the action of the governor. The newspaper won a Pulitzer prize for its work. To some observers in a later time, Ashmore did not take a position as militant as they would have wished, but in 1957 his words were courageous, and they may have helped to still the troubled air, even though Little Rock would prove to be only the beginning of racial troubles in the schools.

† † †

THE HIGH PRICE OF RECKLESSNESS

Arkansas Gazette, September 25, 1957.

This is a tragic day in the history of the republic—and Little Rock, Arkansas, is the scene of the tragedy.

In one sense we rolled back our history to the Reconstruction era when federal troops moved into position at Central High School to uphold the law and preserve the peace.

Yet there was no denying the case President Eisenhower made in solemn words on television last night.

Law and order had broken down here.

The local police could not restore the peace with their own resources.

Governor Faubus had refused to use his state forces to enforce the law, and instead has used them to defy the order of a federal court,— and in so doing had made this last, painful step inevitable.

And so the reckless course the governor embarked upon three weeks ago has raised old ghosts and tested the very fiber of the Constitution. And, the greatest irony of all, he has by his acts and words dealt a major and perhaps a lethal blow to the cause of segregation which he purported to uphold.

We in Little Rock had perfected a plan to meet the Supreme Court's new racial requirements in education gradually and largely on our own terms. The federal courts had sustained us. But now Mr. Faubus and the angry, violent, and thoughtless hand of agitators who rallied to his call may well have undone the patient work of responsible local officials.

We can still hope that this will not be the case. Unhappy though it may be, the action of the President in using federal force will serve to restore the calm that is essential to an orderly approach to any problem. In the days ahead we, as a people, will, we believe, regain our perspective and accept the clear course of duty.

That is the job for all of us now—to restore the peace and sustain the law.

† † †

Amidst all the turmoil of presidential elections, McCarthyism, and racial disturbances, one story, in 1956, came as an echo of the sinking of the *Titanic*, and a reminder that the old-fashioned kind of news story, one unrelated to politics, was still exciting to report and to read. The story was about a collision of two mighty vessels in the Atlantic, off Nantucket.

† † †

THE *STOCKHOLM* AND THE *ANDREA DORIA*

By the Associated Press, July 25, 1956.

Boston, July 25. (AP)—The Trans-Atlantic liners Andrea Doria and Stockholm, with a combined passenger total of about 2,000, collided tonight in a dense Atlantic fog off Nantucket Island. The Coast Guard reported the 29,000-ton Andrea Doria listing so badly life boats could not be lowered.

The first SOS was flashed from the Andrea Doria, an Italian liner out of Genoa, about 9:30 o'clock (Kansas City time). The ship was due to dock in New York City tomorrow with 1,134 passengers aboard.

Minutes later, the Coast Guard said, the Stockholm, operated by the Swedish American line, sent out a distress signal.

The Coast Guard said the Stockholm, a 12,600-ton, 510-foot motor ship, reported its bow stove in and its No. 1 hold flooded. But the vessel appeared to be in less danger than the stricken Italian ship, built in 1953.

The Coast Guard first reported that the Andrea Doria passengers were abandoning ship.

The passengers reportedly were using ladders to go over the side of the stricken ship. There were no indications that any passengers had jumped into the water.

The Stockholm radioed the French liner Ile de France that her foreship was damaged and her number one hold flooded.

But the Stockholm was otherwise tight and the crew was making plans to proceed to New York at slow speed.

The Coast Guard said the Andrea Doria reported:

"Unable to use our boats. Passengers leaving ship by assistance of other ships."

The Stockholm was reported lowering lifeboats.

Another liner, the Cape Ann, was reported at the scene and lowered all eight of its lifeboats in a rescue operation.

Four Coast Guard vessels from the metropolitan New York area were dispatched to the scene, 60 miles southeast of Nantucket island. . . .

† † †

The 1950s—a time for exciting new magazine journalism. Recognizing that many people did not agree with Henry Ford that history was "bunk," the American Association for State and Local History founded *American Heritage,* and later a sister publication, *Horizon*—expensive, slick-paper, hard-cover, extremely attractive publications. Building on the popularity of a surge of trashy publications exposing low life in major cities and in the nation, the *Confidential* magazines appeared, and then disappeared in the wake of libel suits. Movie magazines enjoyed the boom days of Marilyn Monroe, Elizabeth Taylor, and Debbie Reynolds. Time Inc. brought out *Sports Illustrated.* Among the successful newer magazines was one published by John Johnson called *Ebony,* pointed to the black reading audience. Hugh Hefner started the phenomenally popular *Playboy,* which capitalized on the hedonistic strain in the American male and demonstrated that moral values had changed sufficiently so that naked women could be revealed— *truly* revealed—in double-page spreads. One of the first of Playboy's "playmates" was none other than Marilyn Monroe, and soon the young women were well identified for readers back home: local girl makes good. *Playboy* became one of the astonishing success stories in the history of journalism.

Such magazines, along with newspapers and television, paid special attention to such rising phenomena of the time as a musical movement called "rock 'n roll" and to its practitioners, Elvis Presley, Bill Haley, Little Richard, Chuck Berry, Fats Domino, all foreign in their sounds and approaches to those attuned to the Mills Brothers or Bing Crosby. The mass media were making, and breaking, many such heroes in the years after the war. A pianist named Van Cliburn took Russia by storm. Baseball stars continued to reign, even as professional football began to seize the spectators. Many movie fans could not really believe that an actor named James Dean had died in an automobile crash in the fall of 1955, and some of them continued to send him fan mail. A politician named John Kennedy became a popular favorite after his attempt to receive the vote of his fellow Democrats as vice presidential candidate in 1956.

One symptom of hero worship seemed beyond commendation— the quiz show scandals, in which such celebrities as the handsome young professor, Charles Van Doren, revealed that, as they sweated in their "isolation booths," they had already been given the answers. Similar scandals touched the recording industry, especially a disk jockey named Dick Clark. One teenager plaintively moaned, "Why do we care if Dick Clark takes payola? He makes us happy." One editor ready to comment on all this was Ralph McGill of the *Atlanta Constitution,* through the years a kind of moral chorus in his state, a notable conscience, especially, in the racial questions of his time. One of his best columns was on the matter of the television quiz stars, the isolation booths, and the slobs out there in TV-land who watched, envied, and in many cases could see nothing wrong about lying for cash.

† † †

THE CULT OF THE GOLDEN CALF

By Ralph McGill, Consolidated News Features, November 7, 1959.

Worshipers of the Golden Calf, set up by Americans wandering in the wilderness of their public values in this last half of the 20th century, will not be greatly disturbed by Charles Van Doren's forthright confession. His great crime, they are already saying, in their world of the fast buck and of anything goes, was getting caught.

If someone hadn't sung to the law, all would have been well. No one would have been hurt. The people would have been entertained. The Cult of the Golden Calf does not believe that human art and intelligence can entertain. Only a "fix" will assure the sweet smell of success.

Van Doren's story is a genuine human document. He poured out all his sufferings and admitted all his pangs.

He may be left to his own troubles, he is the one most shamed. The producers are the ones most guilty.

They decided, by their rituals of polls, that the people are boobs who enjoy to the hilt being treated like boobs. They also determined, by the sorcery of "motivation," that what motivates the majority of American people is the big dough. And so, they dropped all the quizzes which gave away candy bars and small change and placed on the horizon a look at Mahomet's heaven—a sort of big rock candy mountain where money grows on trees.

They had millions of us panting like lizards on a wall in July, as we looked at all the sufferers in the booths. This was a sort of jazz crucifixion in modern dress. "Boy, did you see him sweat?"

A nation of boobs sweated and writhed with the contestants. And the producers, with one careful eye on the ratings, wriggled with joy.

They know us all too well—and that is the worst part of it—much worse than Van Doren, red-eyed and sorry for what he did, apologizing for debasing education and teaching. He is but an incident, an apostate to the Cult of the Golden Calf.

† † †

One other notable national conscience was the *Christian Science Monitor,* founded in 1908 by Mary Baker Eddy. This newspaper had become one of the quite remarkable journals of America—honest, dependable, conservative, extraordinarily attractive in format, publishing full interpretative accounts without resorting to any kind of sensationalism. In 1958 its editor was Erwin D. Canham, a veteran on the paper, and he wrote that year a history of the *Monitor* called *Commitment to Freedom,* on the occasion of the newspaper's fiftieth birthday. In its anniversary edition the paper editorialized on the question of peace.

† † †

THINKING OUR WAY TOWARD PEACE

Christian Science Monitor, October 18, 1958. Reprinted by permission from The *Christian Science Monitor.* Copyright 1958 The Christian Science Publishing Society. All rights reserved.

Fundamentally related to all the great issues dealt with in our anniversary edition is the question of peace.

Deep, strong, and remarkably united are humanity's aspirations for peace. But its thinking about peace leaves much to be desired. And since thought precedes and produces action, we should be giving more attention to clear, constructive, and peaceable thinking.

First of all, what kind of peace do we seek? An absence of human strife? Yes. But is that enough? The Hungarians didn't think so. In the end few men who have even tasted freedom will settle for the "peace" of a dungeon. The goal is peace with freedom, justice, and opportunity.

Plainly there are some prices we cannot pay for peace. But there are prices we can and should pay. Ignorance, prejudice, fear, hate, greed—these are imperative sacrifices. Few of us have yet paid all we can in this coin.

What instruments shall we use in pursuit of peace? We are much concerned these days with weapons, military and material weapons. In the present stage of human thought they are required for defense. They represent deterrent power. But this must be used in the manner of a policeman's power.

Let us recognize the limitations of such weapons. They do not make either war or peace; it is the thought directing them which does that. Real disarmament begins with aims, not arms. Weapons may help to maintain order and check tyranny; they cannot create the positive essence of peace found in harmony and amity. For that we must rely on spiritual weapons—truth, reason, enlightenment, compassion, brotherhood. Will not this kind of offense ultimately prove the best defense?

Too much of the world is hoping for peace but expecting war—thinking, perhaps unconsciously, toward war. Positive peace thinking will reject this mesmeric fatalism. Peacemakers realize that their work will proceed most naturally and effectively where it spreads outward from a sound core.

Mutual understanding and helpfulness, obedience to law, peaceable adjustment of differences must be developed first in the family, the school, the industry, the community, the nation, and among trustworthy, liberty-loving like-minded nations before they will take effect in the wider neighborliness required for world peace. Like charity, this peacemaking begins at home and affords the individual daily opportunity. If he cares enough about peace, nothing will stop him praying for it, thinking toward it, working for it.

One kind of work for peace is expressed in organizations. This can be useful at every level. But it should be more often remembered that organizations provide only machinery. The motive power must come from the nations and individuals involved. The spirit animating them will determine results.

Indeed, the indispensable ingredient is the individual imbued with true brotherhood, derived from spiritual understanding of God's Fatherhood. In the measure that his tribe increases genuine peace will be won.

† † †

By the late 1950s, ten years after the war in Europe had ended, there were some perceptive backward glances. Anne Frank's diary had become a big seller and had been made into a play and a movie. War stories had continued to be highly popular, and some of them were made into worthwhile films, such as James Jones' *From Here to Eternity*. In early 1955, William H. Stringer of the *Monitor* had written, in blank verse, a moving memory piece on the battle of the Bulge of ten years before. It took an entire page in the newspaper, and this is only the first stanza.

† † †

THIS WAS THE DREAR DECEMBER

By William H. Stringer, *Christian Science Monitor,* January 10, 1955 Reprinted by permission from The *Christian Science Monitor.* Copyright 1960 The Christian Science Publishing Society. All rights reserved.

This was the drear December
Ten distant, vanished years ago
When through the Ardennes mist and drizzle
Unexpected, clanked the Nazi panzers.
This, Hitler's final try for triumph,
Biggest pitched battle of World War Two
On any American front.
Scream the eagle, roar the lion,
Ride the Valkyrie maidens!
We hardly remember all of it now—
When Paris went on curfew and New York prayed,
When hopes wrote small and headlines large,
Bastogne became a legend like Verdun,
When Georgie Patton and his star-spangled jeep
And pearl revolvers wrought like Paul Bunyan.
When Eisenhower, the general's general,
And Bradley, the soldier's soldier,
And Monty, who said "This won't do. . ."
Worked to hold the shoulders, block the surge
Of the rampant tanks, the gray-clad infantry,

When the foot-slogging GIs, rallying,
And the tank commanders, driving
The Shermans slithering over icy roads,
Resourceful, resilient, did themselves proud. . .
Heroes, heroes, enough and to spare,
Among the dark hills and the falling snow.
This was the drear December
This was the Battle of the Bulge
Ten swift-receding years ago.

† † †

Looking backward, too, was A. M. Rosenthal of the *New York Times*. He visited a place called Auschwitz, while covering Poland in 1958, and wrote a Pulitzer prize-winning article that became one of the most celebrated pieces of journalism in its time. It is a piece of writing that requires no further commentary.

† † †

THERE IS NO NEWS FROM AUSCHWITZ

By A. M. Rosenthal, *New York Times Magazine,* August 31, 1958. Copyright 1958 by The New York Times Company. Reprinted by permission.

BRZEZINKA, POLAND—The most terrible thing of all, somehow, was that at Brzezinka the sun was bright and warm, the rows of graceful poplars were lovely to look upon and on the grass near the gates children played.

It all seemed frighteningly wrong, as in a nightmare, that at Brzezinka the sun should ever shine or that there should be light and greenness and the sound of young laughter. It would be fitting if at Brzezinka the sun never shone and the grass withered, because this is a place of unutterable terror.

And yet, every day, from all over the world, people come to Brzezinka, quite possibly the most grisly tourist center on earth. They come for a variety of reasons—to see if it could really have been true, to remind themselves not to forget, to pay homage to the dead by the simple act of looking upon their place of suffering.

Brzezinka is a couple of miles from the better-known southern Polish town of Oswiecim. Oswiecim has about 12,000 inhabitants, is situated about 171 miles from Warsaw and lies in a damp, marshy area at the eastern end of the pass called the Moravian Gate. Brzezinka and Oswiecim together formed part of that minutely organized factory of torture and death that the Nazis called Konzentrationslager Auschwitz.

By now, fourteen years after the last batch of prisoners was herded naked into the gas chambers by dogs and guards, the story of Auschwitz has been told a great many times. Some of the inmates have written of those memories of which sane men cannot conceive. Rudolf Franz Ferdinand Hoess, the superintendent of the camp, before he was executed wrote his detailed memoirs of mass exterminations and the experiments on living bodies. Four million people died here, the Poles say.

And so there is no news to report about Auschwitz. There is merely the compulsion to write something about it, a compulsion that grows out of a restless feeling that to have visited Auschwitz and then turned away without having said or written anything would somehow be a most grievous act of discourtesy to those who died here.

Brzezinka and Oswiecim are very quiet places now; the screams can no longer be heard. The tourist walks silently, quickly at first to get it over with and then, as his mind peoples the barracks and the chambers and the dungeons and flogging posts, he walks draggingly. The guide does not say much either, because there is nothing much for him to say after he has pointed.

For every visitor, there is one particular bit of horror that he knows he will never forget. For some it is seeing the rebuilt gas chamber at Oswiecim and being told that this is the "small one." For others it is the fact that at Brzezinka, in the ruins of the gas chambers and the crematoria the Germans blew up when they retreated, there are daisies growing.

There are visitors who gaze blankly at the gas chambers and the furnaces because their minds simply cannot encompass them, but stand shivering before the great mounds of human hair behind the plate-glass window or the piles of babies' shoes or the brick cells where men sentenced to death by suffocation were walled up.

One visitor opened his mouth in a silent scream simply at the sight of boxes—great stretches of three-tiered wooden boxes in the women's barracks. They were about six feet wide, about three feet high, and into them from five to ten prisoners were shoved for the night. The guide walks quickly through the barracks. Nothing more to see here.

A brick building where sterilization experiments were carried out on women prisoners. The guide tries the door—it's locked. The visitor is grateful that he does not have to go in, and then flushes with shame.

A long corridor where rows of faces stare from the walls. Thousands of pictures, the photographs of prisoners. They are all dead now, the men and women who stood before the cameras, and they all knew they were to die.

They all stare blank-faced, but one picture, in the middle of a row, seizes the eye and wrenches the mind. A girl, 22 years old, plumply pretty, blond. She is smiling gently, as at a sweet, treasured thought. What was the thought that passed through her young mind and is now her memorial on the wall of the dead at Auschwitz?

Into the suffocation dungeons the visitor is taken for a moment and feels himself strangling. Another visitor goes in, stumbles out and crosses herself. There is no place to pray at Auschwitz.

The visitors look pleadingly at each other and say to the guide, "Enough."

There is nothing new to report about Auschwitz. It was a sunny day and the trees were green and at the gates the children played.

† † †

Like many of the news stories and editorials in this section, the final one will be remembered by many from news pictures, from television, from the now-celebrated description of Premier Nikita Khrushchev at Roswell Garst's farm in Iowa, as Garst pelted newsmen with silage; from Mr. K's petulance on being denied a visit to Disneyland; from the premier's visit to a supermarket, where photographers stood ankle-deep in butter displays and climbed onto displays of cans to get better pictures. It was the most widely advertised—and celebrated—tour that took place up to the visit Richard Nixon made to China more than ten years later. And it summed up, too, how powerful and how ubiquitous the mass media had become in Douglass Cater's age of *The Fourth Branch of Government.*

† † †

MR. KHRUSHCHEV VISITS AN IOWA FARM

By the Associated Press, September 23, 1959.

Coon Rapids, Ia., Sept. 23. (AP)—Nikita Khrushchev plowed his way afoot and by car today through some of the world's richest farmland.

The Soviet premier, rugged and bouncy too, trampled through part of a mile-square corn field, looked at fat cattle and tried to get an idea how it is that it takes so few Americans to raise so much food and even have a surplus.

His host was a capitalist farmer, Roswell (Bob) Garst, who operates thousands of acres in this area of West Central Iowa. Garst had met the premier previously on two trips to Russia. He invited the premier to visit him when he visited America.

At one point, Garst threw his arm around his guest and remarked:

"You know, between us, we two farmers could soon settle problems faster than the diplomats."

Garst caught sight of Henry Cabot Lodge, U.S. ambassador to the United Nations, who is guiding the world's top Communist around the country.

"Oh, excuse me!" Garst exclaimed.

Khrushchev's last visit in this land of the tall corn was to the Iowa State university at Ames, a famed agricultural and engineering school.

There he won cheers from girl students of home economics when he told them he wished them success in finding good husbands.

At Ames, Khrushchev saw a lot of prize pigs, got a small plastic hog as a souvenir, and agreed with this comment by an escort:

"The more I see of some humans the better I like pigs."

During the visit to Ames, Khrushchev also twitted Lodge. He had this to say about the aristocratic New Englander:

"I am very glad that Mr. Lodge is with me. In all his life, he probably didn't take in as many smells as he did today."

The premier's visit to the Garst farm near Coon Rapids was full of excited confusion.

Khrushchev didn't arrange it at all, but his very presence created chaos in a cornfield.

Newsmen and photographers, hundreds of them, had to push and shove their way up so close that the premier and Garst scarcely could make their way along beside the rows of towering corn over a silage trench, on past modern farm machinery to a cattle feeding lot.

Garst was exploding all along the way. He called up a neighbor mounted on a horse to push them back. A reporter yelled: "The Cossacks are coming."

One newsman got kicked. Garst let go with a few kicks in the general direction of the hard-working press. One of those on the receiving end was the dignified Harrison Salisbury, veteran Moscow correspondent of the New York Times. The kicking occurred as the group was moving out of a cornfield to a silo.

Finally, national guardsmen and state troopers, State department security officers, and even Lodge locked arms and formed a ring around the premier. Garst no longer had to haul his guest along by the hand.

At one point a great one-row mechanical corn-chopper bore down on Premier Khrushchev and about 200 photographers, reporters, and security men. But this disaster was averted.

Garst, a bull-voiced not normally even-tempered man, at one point threatened to kick all the newsmen within range to get a space cleared around the premier so that he could see the corn.

At another point he picked up a handful of chopped silage and threw it at some photographers to disperse them.

A state trooper at one point was ordered by his superior to "shoot" if newsmen made any more efforts to crowd into the path of the Khrushchev party.

A man with a temper, himself, Khrushchev didn't flash it during all the bedlam. But he did wave his arms in a "get back" motion and joshingly remarked that "we'll turn the bulls loose against you.". . .

† † †

16

THE PRESS IN AN AGE
OF FUTURE SHOCK

History, unfortunately for the student who is laboring with the subject, does not neatly segment itself into decades. The 1920s really began with the armistice in 1918; they ended with the stock market crash in October, 1929. When the 1960s began they seemed little different from the 1950s, and that new decade, which *Newsweek* had heralded at its calendar beginning as "The Soaring Sixties," did not end, perhaps, until May, 1970, when four students died in a fusillade at Kent State University. So this last section of the anthology begins roughly in January, 1960, and comes up into the mid-1970s. Last week's big news stories are not here, for a cutoff point had to be decided upon, and that point was, again roughly, about the time when the affair called Watergate ended its stay on the front pages.

The American people are too close to much of this recent history to know how important it really is. We have become too addicted, with the help of television commentators and instant replay in sports, to the journalistic practice of immediate decision-making. A world that seemed in 1963 to have come to an end somehow continued (and 1975 revelations about the President who was killed in 1963 took much luster off his beloved presidency). Ten years later some people would be asking why the death of Kennedy had seemed so important at the time. The problem of choice that marked earlier sections of this anthology was even more a problem in an age of ubiquitous television, pop music, advertising, an age of chatter, noise, and trivia. Note these events, almost in kaleidoscope, that we are not able to treat at all:

The development of the Peace Corps, and its disillusioning aftermath; warfare in Algeria, carried to the streets of Paris; the entire map of Africa changing as new nations come into being; Greeks and Turks making war on the island of Cyprus; the arrest, trial, and execution of Adolph Eichmann; the coming of the

European Common Market; uprising in the Congo against the Belgians; Pope John, the changing face of Catholicism, and Pope Paul; the Berlin wall, where John Kennedy made a speech; dozens of celebrities, instant and otherwise, like William F. Buckley, Jr., Abbie Hoffman, Gloria Steinem, Johnnie Carson, Stokely Carmichael, Barbra Streisand, Tiny Tim, Mark Spitz, Alice Cooper, and Jimmy Connors; dozens of stories about the revolution in civil rights; the land of Plato and Aristotle taken over in a coup; Indians at Alcatraz, and at Wounded Knee; intervention in the Dominican Republic; a right wing phenomenon called the John Birch Society; a movement involving people called hippies that divided America along age lines; four boys from Liverpool known as the Beatles; professional football all over television; the assassination of Robert F. Kennedy; a temporary town in New York state called Woodstock; Ralph Nader, consumer concern, and drastic changes in automobiles; plane bombings, highjackings, earthquakes, tornadoes, hurricanes, and blizzards, the spot news stories that always seem so alike; a movement in the Middle East called Black September, and dead Israeli athletes at Munich. And a dance called the twist, the jet set, psychedelic art, panty hose, educational television, the pill, marijuana, Muhammad Ali, McDonald hamburgers, Green Berets, miniskirts, bikinis, X and R movies, new baseball franchises, Jesus freaks, canned beer, gay liberation, astrology, Bob Dylan, four-letter words in polite society, ZPG, Nehru jackets, God is dead, Biafra, Archie Bunker, foreign cars, Colonel Sanders fried chicken, Polack jokes, filter cigarettes, *Everything You Always Wanted to Know About Sex,* Amtrak, cloverleafs, busing, streaking, "make love, not war," and the age of Aquarius.

And whatever else happened after this manuscript went to the publisher.

For the press it was an amazing time. In some respects more important journalistic developments took place than had happened in the whole of history prior to that time. John Kennedy carried the presidential press conference beyond what it had been in the administration of Eisenhower, though it seemed to slip back under subsequent presidents. Governmental secrecy, and a new thing known as the "credibility gap," marked the period, with the invasion of the Bay of Pigs and the Cuban missile crisis and all the problems attendant upon the war in Vietnam, not to mention the complex of stories known as Watergate. Relations between press and government soured, reaching a low point in the Nixon days, as later documents will suggest.

Legal conflicts became commonplace, as the issue of "free press-fair trial" became dramatized even more after the Sam Sheppard case of the 1950s and the report of the Warren Commission. The CBS television program, "The Selling of the Pentagon," and the controversial affair of the Pentagon Papers exacerbated the situation. The questions of accessibility and confidentiality, both fraught with many complications, were incessantly debated. The publicity powers of government were increased in an age of televised hearings and touring dignitaries. Increasingly, Daniel Boorstin's assertions in *The Image,* which dealt with what he termed the "pseudo-event," seemed to sum up much of the journalism of the time.

Criticism of the press, which had been known in earlier times, as in the writings of Upton Sinclair, George Seldes, A. J. Liebling, and Elmer Davis, and in the Hutchins Report of 1947, continued. It came from all segments of the ideological spectrum, and at one time the critics ranged from Vice President Spiro T. Agnew on the right to the writers of the underground press on the left. When the Chicago convention of the Democratic party took place in 1968 new criticisms were voiced, and publications came into being designed to tell truths presumably not permitted in the establishment journals. There was militance from previously quiescent minorities. The black press became part of the "black power" movement, and American Indians surged forth with their own journalism. It seemed as though the ideas voiced by Alvin Toffler in *Future Shock,* especially those describing each of us as having his own little subculture, were coming true.

And there were the developments in technology that were changing the face, if not the nature, of journalism: offset printing, photoengraving, computer-printed newspapers, pictures on television by satellite, and that somehow fantastic trip to the moon taken in 1969, not only by three astronauts, but by the American people. It was little wonder that the old-time comic strip, Buck Rogers, disappeared from American newspapers.

So, it may be that the documents in this section, those that seem closest to us, will prove the hardest to grasp in a historical sense. The author confesses to an insecure feeling about understanding the recent past, and to a feeling of frustration. Choosing documents of the past fifteen years or so was more difficult than any other time period considered.

1960 began with much excitement in the press over the coming presidential election. The Democrats had fielded many aspirants—Lyndon B. Johnson, Hubert H. Humphrey, Stuart Symington, Adlai Stevenson again, and of course John F. Kennedy. The Republicans appeared ready to go with Richard M. Nixon, a vocal vice president, an obvious choice. One of the commentators treating the election was James Reston of the *New York Times,* "Scotty" to his intimates, a reporter and columnist who had succeeded Arthur Krock as head of the Washington bureau of the mighty newspaper. Reston was about as good a columnist as the period could offer and one known to permit humor to intrude itself into his ivory tower speculating. His computer invention named "Uniquack" showed up in the column from time to time, and it was there for a column in early 1960 on the coming campaign.

† † †

A UNIQUACK THAT TALKS
VIEWS THE CAMPAIGN

By James Reston, *New York Times,* January 16, 1960. Copyright 1960 by The New York Times Company. Reprinted by permission.

Good Morning, Machine. Please identify yourself.

ANSWER: I am the 1960 model of the electronic truth detector, Uniquack. The new feature this year is that I can talk.

QUESTION: What a pity. Please explain.

A—When plugged in near a fireplace and filled with alcohol, I can tell nothing but the truth.

Q—That must be very awkward. Republican or Democrat?

A— Independent: transistorized mugwump.

Q—Who's going to win the election?

A—Kennedy.

Q—How do you know?

A—Every President in this century has had a double letter in his name. William McKinley—two l's in William. Theodore Roosevelt—2 o's. Then there were William Howard Taft, Woodrow Wilson, Warren Harding, Calvin Coolidge, Herbert Hoover, Franklin Roosevelt, and of course Harry.

Q—What about Eisenhower? Wasn't he President?

A—We must await the judgment of history on that. And anyway, his initials are D.D.

Q—So you rule out Richard Milhous Nixon, Adlai Ewing Stevenson, Hubert Humphrey, Lyndon Johnson, Stuart Symington, and Chester Bowles?

A—I don't rule them out. I merely state the facts as reported by Huntington Cairns and the *Scientific American.* The Republicans might have won with Rockefeller, but they insisted on defying the teachings of history.

Q—Do you have any other brilliant observation?

A—The human race is nuts.

Q—That is not brilliant, and please don't use slang in the *Times.* What do you think of the candidates?

A—They all seem determined to prove that they are what they aren't and vice versa.

Q—Please go on.

A—Kennedy, who is young, has bobbed his hair in order to look old. Johnson, a Southerner, says he's a Westerner. Stevenson, a statesman, pretends he's a politician. Nixon, a politician, pretends he's a statesman. Symington, a conservative, votes like a radical. Rockefeller, a rich man, is the poor man's friend. It's all very unscientific.

Q—I take it you don't think much of human logic.

A—I haven't seen much of it lately. The President says everything's dandy, and takes another trip. Everybody knows everything's not dandy, but they say it's nice to see the President getting around like that. Dozens of committees study defense, education, and housing, and issue millions of words saying we'd better pull up our socks. The President says our socks are just where they ought to be. He adds that he knows more about socks than anybody else, having worn them all his life. And everybody says that's absolutely true.

Q—You have a wicked tongue, machine. Is there any little knob or screw I can turn to tone you down?

A—Please don't monkey with the machinery. Where is the logic? An election is a judgment on the future and everybody talks about the past. Rockefeller could have clobbered any Democrat in the race, so the Republicans bet everything on Nixon. You ask what Nixon believes, and they tell you he likes Ike.

Q—And the Democrats?

A—They are five times as illogical as the Republicans because they have five times as many candidates.

Q—You don't think much of their campaign?

A—It's not a campaign but a civil war. Johnson passes the first civil-rights bill in eighty years. He blocks the open war against the Supreme Court in the Senate. He maneuvers the censure of McCarthy. So the liberals scorn him as a conservative.

Q—What do you see ahead, machine?

A—I see a great ceremony on October 14, 1960, the President's seventieth birthday. I see the President with his arm on the Vice President's shoulder, I see the passing of the mantle and I hear the President's voice appealing for continuity, peace, and prosperity.

Q—Anything else?

A—I see the American people crowded around their television screens. I see the Vice President accepting the mantle and looking very young and appealing, and I can't help thinking what a pity it is he doesn't have a double letter in his name, like G. Mennen ("Soapy") Williams.

† † †

Early 1960 brought a shock that most Americans, and quite clearly the Eisenhower administration, were not prepared to cope with. A spy plane of the "U-2" variety, piloted by Francis Gary Powers, was forced down over the Soviet Union. The executive branch, at a time when President Eisenhower was preparing to meet with the premier of the Soviet Union, first denied any knowledge of the plane, its pilot, or its purposes. Then the administration was forced to admit that Eisenhower, the presidential untouchable of all untouchables, had lied, and that the government, by inference, also had lied. The summit conference was canceled, and the nation went for a time into another of its tizzies.

† † †

REDS SHOOT DOWN U.S. JET

By the Associated Press, May 5, 1960.

Moscow, May 5. (AP)—Premier Khrushchev told the Soviet Parliament in a bristling speech today that Soviet armed forces have shot down a plane he described as a U.S. military craft. He threatened to retaliate with rockets if American bombers appear over the Soviet Union.

Khrushchev's speech cast gloom over prospects for the summit conference which will open in 11 days. He issued an unveiled threat to United States allies, took a hefty slap at Vice-President Nixon, and charged that President Eisenhower's freedom of movement at the summit is being restricted by "certain U. S. circles."

Khrushchev referred angrily to President Eisenhower's suggestion that Nixon might sit in for him at the summit if the President's presence is required in Washington domestic matters.

He said he had met Nixon several times and it was difficult for him not to gain the impression Nixon was the last person to think of stopping the cold war or ending the arms race.

"I am afraid that if Nixon becomes entitled to carry on negotiations at the summit, it would be, as we say in Russia, like sending a goat to take care of the cabbage," the Premier said.

The Supreme Soviet (parliament) burst into a wave of applause as Khrushchev announced the downing of an American plane May 1.

[A single-engine jet U-2 research plane has been missing since May 1 after a takeoff in Turkey, Pentagon officials said. It is assumed to have come down near Lake Van, not far from the border of Soviet Armenia.

[In this general area a U.S. C-130 transport was downed by Soviet forces in 1958. By U.S. reckoning, the Soviets accounted for only 6 of 17 men lost then. The U-2, a ship assigned to NASA—National Aeronautics and Space Administration—is a flying laboratory assigned to make weather observations and check air for radioactivity].

Khrushchev called the plane incident an aggressive act, and asked rhetorically of the United States:

"If you think you can take such measures, why don't you think we can take similar measures when a plane appears over our territory and threatens the security of our country? We have the same rights as you, the same means as you.

"We have no bombers on duty, but we have rockets on duty. They are more accurate and trustworthy than your bombers."

Then came the threat to U.S. allies. Khrushchev said it is high time for those countries which have provided the United States with bases to realize they are playing with fire and that they, too, can suffer retaliatory blows.

The Soviet leader contended the American plane was sent on a mission to impress and frighten the Soviet Union on the eve of the summit. He said this was the act of "bandits," and added:

"One must conclude that the aggressive forces in the United States are taking action to interfere with the summit."

He speculated whether the plane was sent with the consent of the head of the U.S. armed forces—President Eisenhower—or by the U.S. military without the President's knowledge.

"If it was done without the President's knowledge, the people should know about it," Khrushchev said. . . .

† † †

The affair of the U-2 perhaps helped the presidential hopes of John Fitzgerald Kennedy, a U.S. senator since 1953, a congressman prior to that time, a young man of obvious ability, ambition, and appeal. So well oiled was the Kennedy machine that the July convention of the Democrats, it seemed in retrospect, had belonged to the senator all along. His opponent in the election was, of course, Richard Nixon, who made the mistake of agreeing to meet Kennedy in a series of television "debates"—though debates proved to be scarcely the best descriptive word. In the first of these appearances, Nixon seemed uncomfortable, Kennedy assured, Nixon looking tired and in need of a shave, Kennedy fresh and extremely photogenic. Viewers will long debate the debates, and their opinions about who "won" will depend in part upon their political persuasions. But it seemed quite likely in the fall of 1960 that the winner was Kennedy, who also was the winner in the election—one of the closest in our history. For sure television was a winner; there is little question that television increasingly played a major role in American politics.

† † †

DEBATE WINNER? VOTERS OF NATION

By Godfrey Sperling, Jr., *Christian Science Monitor*, September 27, 1960. Reprinted by permission from The *Christian Science Monitor*. Copyright 1960 The Christian Science Publishing Society. All rights reserved.

Chicago— The focal point of some 130,000,000 eyes, the presidential candidates squared off in the first of four unprecedented joint appearances before a vast TV audience.

The winner? The American public was the winner.

The silent Chicago streets, the cavernous tall park, the almost empty theaters. All this attested to the public's intense interest in the two candidates and a clash that centered on the farm, the aged, the schools, the economic growth rate, the lowering of the national debt, the relative maturity and experience of the two men. But the impact naturally spilled over into America's posture in the world today, and who was best qualified to provide leadership for the next four or eight years.

For reporters who have been following the candidates around the United States, there was little that was new in what the two men said. Senator John F. Kennedy, again, was saying that America's performance, vis-a-vis the Soviet Union, was not good enough. Vice-President Richard M. Nixon was saying it had, indeed, been good enough. And both were agreeing that there must be a step up for the future—militarily, scientifically, educationally, economically.

In the main, the verbal exchanges here showed that the objectives of the two candidates are quite similar. The difference lies in the means—and the cost of the means.

Mr. Nixon said, as he has said before, that he has tabulated the Democratic program and thinks it will cost $13,200,000,000 to perhaps $18,000,000,000 more, while, he said, his own program would cost some $2,000,000,000 to $4,000,000,000 more.

Senator Kennedy later countered by asserting that the revenue for his program would come readily from the expanded growth that would accompany this program.

Even this was not a narrowing or sharpening of issues. It had all been said before as the presidential campaign jets moved back and forth across the country.

But here, for the first time, all these little speeches on all these different issues were being wrapped up into one easily understood package. And the pulling together of all this information was of inestimable value to a public intent on learning more about the candidates and getting a better grasp of the issues.

The men as TV performers? Both were superb. But was this a display of outstanding mental capacity or was this, at least in part, the expression of countless little memorized speeches? The limitations of TV could not answer this with a certainty, although the viewers—and particularly those who had already chosen up sides—probably resolved this question to their own satisfaction.

Actually, the question-from-panel format is not one that brings about a true clash of the "debaters." There was really little opportunity for either of the candidates to probe the other's mind—or to pressure the other with an incisive query. . . .

† † †

John F. Kennedy, the new President. He was fresh, young, handsome; his inauguration was one of the notable ones in history. His speech enjoined Americans to selfless dedication ("Ask not what your country can do for you. . ."); his New Frontier spirit seemed likely to carry America to new heights. All of this might have been the story of Kennedy in history had it not been for one word—Cuba. In April, 1961, the Bay of Pigs invasion took place, an American-guided effort to assist displaced Cubans in seizing back their island country from Premier Fidel Castro. Secrecy marked the invasion, and the debate would begin over the extent to which the press had been denied knowledge of what the government was doing.

† † †

INVADERS STRIKE INLAND IN CUBA

By the Associated Press, April 17, 1961.

Invaders landed in Cuba by sea and air today, launching the long-awaited battle to topple Fidel Castro. Intense fighting was reported.

Cuba charged before the United Nations that the invaders came from Florida and Guatemala and the United States must bear the responsibility. The United States vigorously denied the charge.

Prime Minister Castro told his people by radio the onslaught was backed by planes and warships and was launched by mercenaries organized by the United States. His regime severed all communications to the United States.

"Already our troops are advancing against the enemy, sure of their victory," the bearded revolutionary asserted in an appeal for Cubans to maintain order and discipline.

Castro declared the invaders struck in Southern Las Villas province and fighting had broken out at all points where the invaders landed. Exile sources said invasion beachheads also were planted southeast of Havana and in extreme eastern and western Cuba.

Dr. Jose Miro Cardona, the rebel leader who broke with Castro over Communist influence in Cuba, issued a statement saying the battle had begun to rid Cuba of Castro's "despotic rule" and "communism's cruel oppression." One Cuban exile source in the United States said Miro Cardona had left for Cuba but his public relations chief in New York denied this.

Monitored radio broadcasts by the Fidel Castro regime indicated today that invaders may have penetrated about 25 miles inland from landings southeast of Havana.

The Columbia Broadcasting system said that Cuban government broadcasts, intercepted in Miami, voiced a Red Cross appeal for medical help at Jaguey Grande in Matanzas and at the Las Villas beachhead. . . .

Another official government broadcast ordered the U.S. naval base to halt all flights except those cleared with the Castro authorities.

The directive said that all air traffic into and out of the Navy base will be stopped by Cuban planes unless flight plans are filed four hours before the flights.

Raul Roa, Cuban foreign minister, told the United Nations the United States had permitted the rebels to train in Florida and had permitted planes to fly from U.S. soil. Claiming pledges of support from Mexico, Brazil and Ecuador, Roa declared Cuba will fight to the finish.

The U.S. delegate, Adlai E. Stevenson, replied: "These charges are totally false and I deny them categorically." He called Castro a tyrant who had tried to overthrow other governments in Latin America. . . .

† † †

The Bay of Pigs was a military and diplomatic disaster for the United States. Years later it was learned that the *New York Times* had known of the invasion beforehand but had determined that it would not be in the national interest to divulge the information. President Kennedy, it was said, was regretful that the *Times* had not told the story. The second role Kennedy played in respect to Cuba came in October, 1962, when the "missile crisis" took place, a crisis in which the government of the United States faced down the government of the Soviet Union and demanded removal of Soviet missile emplacements on the island in the Caribbean.

† † †

CUBAN BLOCKADE IS PROCLAIMED

By the Associated Press, October 23, 1962.

Washington (AP)—President Kennedy proclaimed a U.S. naval blockade against Cuba last night, saying the Soviets have started to turn Cuba into an offensive military base capable of raining nuclear destruction on all the Americas.

Speaking grimly to the nation in a suddenly called radio-TV broadcast, Kennedy said the United States would wreak "a full retaliatory response upon the Soviet Union" if any nuclear missile is fired on any nation in this hemisphere.

Kennedy reported that within the last week the United States has received "unmistakable evidence" that—contrary to Soviet assurances—nuclear-type, long-range missile sites and atomic-capable Soviet jet bombers are being established in Cuba.

Kennedy uttered what seemed an implied warning that the United States may have to bomb offensive sites in Cuba if the build-up continues. He put it this way:

"Should these offensive military preparations continue, thus increasing the threat to the hemisphere, further action will be justified. I have directed the armed forces to prepare for any eventualities; and I trust that, in the interest of both the Cuban people and the Soviet technicians at these sites, the hazards to all concerned of continuing this threat will be recognized."

And the President cautioned the Soviets that, if they react by aggression somewhere else in the world, they "will be met with determination."

"Any hostile move anywhere in the world against the safety and freedom of peoples to whom we are committed—including in particular the brave people of West Berlin—will be met by whatever action is needed," he said.

He emphasized, both in his prepared text and in his delivery, that the steps he was ordering now were only "initial" ones.

Even before the President finished speaking, U.S. Ambassador Adlai E. Stevenson requested an urgent meeting of the U.N. Security

Council to seek the withdrawal of offensive weapons from Cuba. Stevenson acted on a directive from Kennedy.

No immediate official Russian reaction to the President's speech was forthcoming. . . .

† † †

The Soviet Union removed the missiles. Americans, some of whom had been busily constructing atomic fallout shelters, wiped their brows. And many journalists expressed anger over the news blackout that had accompanied deliberations over the missile matter.

One clear triumph for the Kennedy administration came in what the press later termed the "space race." Though the United States initially had placed a great emphasis upon space exploration, it was the Soviet Union that put the first satellite into orbit—their "Sputnik," of late 1957. Though the United States followed Sputnik with other satellites, they seemed puny alongside those of the Russians, and space exploration by American astronauts lagged behind that of the Soviet Union, which called its explorers "cosmonauts." Though the first American astronaut in outer space, John Glenn, did not achieve anything truly comparable to the Soviet feats he still gave a needed boost in both morale and propaganda to the American people, and throughout the 1960s the space story became a major one for the press to cover.

† † †

THE U.S. PUTS A MAN INTO OUTER SPACE

By the Associated Press, February 20, 1962.

CAPE CANAVERAL, Fla.—(AP)—John H. Glenn Jr. flew twice around the world in his space ship today, then rejected the idea of coming down before completing his full three-orbit mission.

Despite minor trouble with his craft's automatic control system he sailed over Cape Canaveral for the second time at 11:56 p.m. (CST) and continued on into his third circuit.

Scientists prepared to bring him down after one more swing.

"I feel real good," Glenn told fellow astronaut Alan B. Shepard on the ground as he passed more than 100 miles above the cape the second time.

"I can see the whole state of Florida laid out like a map. I can see all the way back to the Mississippi Delta," he reported.

Just 30 minutes earlier, as his capsule sped over Hawaii, Glenn was asked by ground officials if he were ready to continue the full course.

"Affirmative," replied the calm, confident Glenn. "I'm ready to go."

The trouble, which developed during the first orbit, was in the attitude control system that determines the capsule's position in space. Streams of hydrogen peroxide gas spurt from 18 nozzles on the capsule surface, maintaining the proper attitude.

When the problem cropped up, Glenn switched to a new partially manual system, which is referred to as "flying by wire."

This involves operating the control stick to send an electronic signal to a black box, which in turn signals the jets to operate.

Glenn was reported in excellent condition and performing like the test pilot he is as he whirled around the world. He appeared to be right at home in the weightless world. . . .

The whole world watched and listened as Glenn's spacecraft traveled on at 17,530 miles an hour.

An Atlas rocket blasted him aloft at 8:47 a.m. He completed his first orbit in 88.29 minutes.

Glancing down at the earth at altitudes ranging from 100 to 160 miles, Glenn had a panoramic view stretching 1,800 miles from horizon to horizon. He described the view as "tremendous" and "a beautiful sight." . . .

† † †

Of all twentieth century presidents, John F. Kennedy had the most telling way with the press, surpassing even that master of the oral exchange, Franklin D. Roosevelt. Kennedy's sense of humor carried him through many travails, and so did his preparation and understanding of issues. It is difficult to believe that even the most ardent Kennedy-haters could not be charmed by some of the exchanges at the press conferences, which were fully aired on television. One exchange was remembered as much as anything the President said in those few conferences of his brief administration.

† † †

KENNEDY COMMENTS ON SENATOR GOLDWATER

From Harold W. Chase and Allen H. Lerman, eds., *Kennedy and the Press* (New York: Crowell, 1965), p. 508.

Q. Mr. President, Senator [Barry M.] Goldwater [R., Arizona] accused your administration today of falsification of the news in order to perpetuate itself in office. Do you care to comment on that?

THE PRESIDENT. What was he referring to?

Q. He was making a speech here at the Women's National Press Club, and his point was that you and your administration are mismanaging the news, and using it to perpetuate yourself in office.

THE PRESIDENT. Well, as I have said before, I think it would be unwise at this time to answer or reply to Senator Goldwater. I am confident that he will be making many charges even more serious than this one in the coming months. And, in addition, he himself has had a busy week selling TVA [Tennessee Valley Authority] and giving permission to or suggesting that military commanders overseas be permitted to use nuclear weapons, and attacking the President of Bolivia while he was here in the United States, and involving himself in the Greek election. So I thought it really would not be fair for me this week to reply to him.

† † †

Posterity—at least the foreseeable posterity—is not likely to require a definition of the time period later referred to as, simply, the "four days." John F. Kennedy had not had an especially remarkable presidency, and in November, 1963, he seemed in special trouble. Congress was recalcitrant, bills were moving slowly, he did not seem to be exerting the needed leadership. There was a minor party revolt in Texas, so he went there, speaking in Fort Worth the morning of November 22, and then proceeding through the streets of nearby Dallas in a pleasant motorcade, greeted by friendly crowds, accompanied by his wife, who was as charming and photogenic as he. Near the Texas School Book Depository shots rang out, and the President and Governor John Connally of Texas were both hit. The President's car sped to Parkland Hospital, and there the President died. The American people listened, stunned, from Friday afternoon through the following Monday: the arrest of the accused man, Lee Harvey Oswald; the plane landing in Washington; the solemn words of the new president; the parade of dignitaries coming to the White House; the procession of mourners at the bier; the funeral and the words of Ecclesiastes; the riderless horse; the slow march to Arlington National Cemetery—and the new set of horrors at the Dallas police station, where a cabaret owner named Jack Ruby shot and killed the accused assassin, Oswald. The press document that best seems to tell the story of the Kennedy assassination is that written by the United Press International representative who in those days closed presidential conferences with the traditional "Thank you, Mr. President."

† † †

AN EYEWITNESS ACCOUNT OF THE KENNEDY ASSASSINATION

By Merriman Smith, UPI White House Reporter, November 23, 1963.

Washington, Nov. 23 (UPI)—It was a balmy, sunny noon as we motored through downtown Dallas behind President Kennedy. The procession cleared the center of the business district and turned into a handsome highway that wound through what appeared to be a park.

I was riding in the so-called White House press "pool" car, a telephone company vehicle equipped with a mobile radio-telephone. I was in the front seat between a driver from the telephone company and Malcolm Kilduff, acting White House press secretary for the President's Texas tour. Three other pool reporters were wedged in the back seat.

Suddenly we heard three loud, almost painfully loud cracks. The first sounded as if it might have been a large firecracker. But the second and third blasts were unmistakable. Gunfire.

The President's car, possibly as much as 150 to 200 yards ahead, seemed to falter briefly. We saw a flurry of activity in the Secret Service follow-up car behind the Chief Executive's bubble-top limousine.

Next in line was the car bearing Vice President Lyndon B. Johnson. Behind that, another follow-up car bearing agents assigned to the Vice President's protection. We were behind that car.

Our car stood still for probably only a few seconds, but it seemed like a lifetime. One sees history explode before one's eyes and for even the most trained observer, there is a limit to what one can comprehend.

I looked ahead at the President's car but could not see him or his companion, Gov. John B. Connally of Texas. Both men had been riding on the right side of the bubble-top limousine from Washington. I thought I saw a flash of pink which would have been Mrs. Jacqueline Kennedy.

Everybody in our car began shouting at the driver to pull up closer to the President's car. But at this moment, we saw the big bubble-top and a motorcycle escort roar away at high speed.

We screamed at our driver, "Get going, get going." We careened around the Johnson car and its escort and set out down the highway, barely able to keep in sight of the President's car and the accompanying Secret Service follow-up car.

They vanished around a curve. When we cleared the same curve we could see where we were heading—Parkland Hospital, a large brick structure to the left of the arterial highway. We skidded around a sharp left turn and spilled out of the pool car as it entered the hospital driveway.

I ran to the side of the bubble-top.

The President was face down on the back seat. Mrs. Kennedy made a cradle of her arms around the President's head and bent over him as if she were whispering to him.

Gov. Connally was on his back on the floor of the car, his head and shoulders resting in the arms of his wife, Nellie, who kept shaking her head and shaking with dry sobs. Blood oozed from the front of the Governor's suit. I could not see the President's wound. But I could see blood spattered around the interior of the rear seat and a dark stain spreading down the right side of the President's dark gray suit.

From the telephone car, I had radioed the Dallas bureau of UPI that three shots had been fired at the Kennedy motorcade. Seeing the bloody scene in the rear of the car at the hospital entrance, I knew I had to get to a telephone immediately.

Clint Hill, the Secret Service agent in charge of the detail assigned to Mrs. Kennedy, was leaning over into the rear of the car.

"How badly was he hit, Clint?" I asked.

"He's dead," Hill replied curtly.

I have no further clear memory of the scene in the driveway. I recall a babble of anxious voices, tense voices—"Where in hell are the stretchers.... Get a doctor out here.... He's on the way.... Come on, easy there." And from somewhere, nervous sobbing.

I raced down a short stretch of sidewalk into a hospital corridor. The first thing I spotted was a small clerical office, more of a booth than an office. Inside, a bespectacled man stood shuffling what appeared to be hospital forms. At a wicket much like a bank teller's cage, I spotted a telephone on the shelf.

"How do you get outside?" I gasped. "The President has been hurt and this is an emergency call."

"Dial nine," he said, shoving the phone toward me.

It took two tries before I successfully dialed the Dallas UPI number. Quickly I dictated a bulletin saying the President had been seriously, perhaps fatally, injured by an assassin's bullets while driving through the streets of Dallas.

Litters bearing the President and the Governor rolled by me as I dictated, but my back was to the hallway and I didn't see them until they were at the entrance of the emergency room about 75 to 100 feet away.

I knew they had passed, however, from the horrified expression that suddenly spread over the face of the man behind the wicket.

As I stood in the drab buff hallway leading into the emergency ward trying to reconstruct the shooting for the UPI man on the other end of the telephone and still keep track of what was happening outside the door of the emergency room, I watched a swift and confused panorama sweep before me.

Kilduff of the White House press staff raced up and down the hall. Police captains barked at each other, "Clear this area." Two priests hurried in behind a Secret Service agent, their narrow purple stoles rolled up tightly in their hands. A police lieutenant ran down the hall with a large carton of blood for transfusions. A doctor came in and said he was responding to a call for "all neurosurgeons."

The priests came out and said the President had received the last sacrament of the Roman Catholic Church. They said he was still alive, but not conscious. Members of the Kennedy staff began arriving. They had been behind us in the motorcade, but hopelessly bogged for a time in confused traffic.

Telephones were at a premium in the hospital and I clung to mine for dear life. I was afraid to stray from the wicket lest I lose contact with the outside world.

My decision was made for me, however, when Kilduff and Wayne Hawks of the White House staff ran by me, shouting that Kilduff would make a statement shortly in the so-called nurses' room a floor above and at the far end of the hospital.

I threw down the phone and sped after them. We reached the door of the conference room and there were loud cries of "Quiet!" Fighting to keep his emotions under control, Kilduff said, "President John Fitzgerald Kennedy died at approximately one o'clock."

I raced into a nearby office. The telephone switchboard at the hospital was hopelessly jammed.

Frustrated by the inability to get through the hospital switchboard, I appealed to a nurse. She led me through a maze of corridors and back stairways to another floor and a line pay booth. I got the Dallas office.

[Afterward] I ran back through the hospital to the conference room. There Jiggs Fauver of the White House transportation staff grabbed me and said Kilduff wanted a pool of three men immediately to fly back to Washington on Air Force One, the presidential aircraft.

"He wants you downstairs, and he wants you right now," Fauver said.

Down the stairs I ran and into the driveway, only to discover Kilduff had just pulled out in our telephone car.

Charles Roberts of *Newsweek* magazine, Sid Davis of Westinghouse Broadcasting and I implored a police officer to take us to the airport in his squad car.

As we piled out of the car on the edge of the runway about 200 yards from the presidential aircraft, Kilduff spotted us and motioned for us to hurry. We trotted to him and he said the plane could take two pool men to Washington; that Johnson was soon to take the oath of office aboard the plane and would take off immediately thereafter.

I saw a bank of telephone booths beside the runway and asked if I had time to advise my news service. He said, "But for God's sake hurry."

Then began another telephone nightmare. The Dallas office rang busy. I tried calling Washington. All circuits were busy. Then I called the New York bureau of UPI and told them about the impending installation of a new President aboard the airplane.

Kilduff came out of the plane and motioned wildly toward my booth. I slammed down the phone and jogged across the runway. A detective stopped me and said, "You dropped your pocket comb."

Aboard Air Force One on which I had made so many trips as a press association reporter covering President Kennedy, all of the shades of the larger main cabin were drawn and the interior was hot and dimly lighted.

Kilduff propelled us to the President's suite two-thirds of the way back in the plane. The room is used normally as a combination conference and sitting room and could accommodate eight to ten people seated.

I wedged inside the door and began counting. There were 27 people in this compartment. Johnson stood in the center with his wife, Lady Bird. U.S. District Judge Sarah T. Hughes, 67, a kindly faced woman, stood with a small black Bible in her hands, waiting to give the oath.

The compartment became hotter and hotter. Johnson was worried that some of the Kennedy staff might not be able to get inside. He urged people to press forward, but a Signal Corps photographer, Capt. Cecil Stoughton, standing in the corner on a chair, said if Johnson moved any closer, it would be virtually impossible to make a truly historic photograph.

It developed that Johnson was waiting for Mrs. Kennedy, who was composing herself in a small bedroom in the rear of the plane. She appeared alone, dressed in the same pink wool suit she had worn in the morning when she appeared so happy shaking hands with airport crowds at the side of her husband.

She was white-faced but dry-eyed. Friendly hands stretched toward her as she stumbled slightly. Johnson took both of her hands in his and motioned her to his left side. Lady Bird stood on his right, a fixed half-smile showing the tension.

Johnson nodded to Judge Hughes, an old friend of his family and a Kennedy appointee.

"Hold up your right hand and repeat after me," the woman jurist said to Johnson.

Outside a jet could be heard droning into a landing.

Judge Hughes held out the Bible and Johnson covered it with his large left hand. His right arm went slowly into the air and the jurist began to intone the Constitutional oath, "I do solemnly swear I will faithfully execute the office of President of the United States. . ."

The brief ceremony ended when Johnson in a deep, firm voice, repeated after the judge, ". . . so help me God."

Johnson turned first to his wife, hugged her about the shoulders and kissed her on the cheek. Then he turned to Kennedy's widow, put his left arm around her and kissed her cheek.

As others in the group—some Texas Democratic House members, members of the Johnson and Kennedy staffs—moved toward the new President, he seemed to back away from any expression of felicitation.

The two-minute ceremony concluded at 3:38 p.m. EST and seconds later, the President said firmly, "Now, let's get airborne."

Col. James Swindal, pilot of the plane, a big gleaming silver and blue fan-jet, cut on the starboard engines immediately. Several persons, including Sid Davis of Westinghouse, left the plane at that time. The White House had room for only two pool reporters on the return flight and these posts were filled by Roberts and me, although at the moment we could find no empty seats.

At 3:47 p.m. EST, the wheels of Air Force One cleared the runway. Swindal roared the big ship up to an unusually high cruising altitude of 41,000 feet where at 625 miles an hour, ground speed, the jet hurtled toward Andrews Air Force Base.

When the President's plane reached operating altitude, Mrs. Kennedy left her bedchamber and walked to the rear compartment of the plane. This was the so-called family living room, a private area where she and Kennedy, family and friends had spent many happy airborne hours chatting and dining together.

Kennedy's casket had been placed in this compartment, carried aboard by a group of Secret Service agents.

Mrs. Kennedy went into the rear lounge and took a chair beside the coffin. There she remained throughout the flight. Her vigil was shared at times by four staff members close to the slain chief executive—David Powers, his buddy and personal assistant; Kenneth P. O'Donnell, appointments secretary and key political adviser; Lawrence O'Brien, chief Kennedy liaison man with Congress, and Brig. Gen. Godrey McHugh, Kennedy's Air Force aide.

Kennedy's military aide, Maj. Gen. Chester V. Clifton, was busy most of the trip in the forward areas of the plane, sending messages and making arrangements for arrival ceremonies and movement of the body to Bethesda Naval Hospital.

As the flight progressed, Johnson walked back into the main compartment. My portable typewriter was lost somewhere around the hospital and I was writing on an over-sized electric typewriter which Kennedy's personal secretary, Mrs. Evelyn Lincoln, had used to type his speech texts.

Johnson came up to the table where Roberts and I were trying to record the history we had just witnessed.

"I'm going to make a short statement in a few minutes and give you copies of it," he said. "Then when I get on the ground, I'll do it over again."

It was the first public utterance of the new Chief Executive, brief and moving.

When the plane was about 45 minutes from Washington, the new President got on a special radio-telephone and placed a call to Mrs. Rose Kennedy, the late President's mother.

"I wish to God there was something I could do," he told her, "I just wanted you to know that."

Then Mrs. Johnson wanted to talk to the elder Mrs. Kennedy.

"We feel like the heart has been cut out of us," Mrs. Johnson said. She broke down for a moment and began to sob. Recovering in a few seconds, she added, "Our love and our prayers are with you."

Thirty minutes out of Washington, Johnson put in a call for Nellie Connally, wife of the seriously wounded Texas Governor.

The new President said to the Governor's wife:

"We are praying for you, darling, and I know that everything is going to be all right, isn't it? Give him a hug and a kiss for me."

It was dark when Air Force One began to skim over the lights of the Washington area, lining up for a landing at Andrews Air Force Base. The plane touched down at 5:59 p.m. EST.

† † †

Ten years after the assassination it was difficult to remember the American mood of that weekend of the four days. And the war in Vietnam had obliterated the memory of the relief felt by so many Americans that a presidential transition had been made without causing a rupture within the land. One newspaper, the *St. Louis Post-Dispatch,* commented movingly, a week after the assassination, on the role now being played by Lyndon B. Johnson, who had *not* been that newspaper's favorite politician.

† † †

A NEW PRESIDENT'S STRONG HAND

St. Louis Post-Dispatch, November 29, 1963. Reprinted by permission of the publisher.

In a week of deeply moving events, the new President's address to Congress was an inspiring and strikingly impressive occasion.

Lyndon Baines Johnson stood before the nation as a man of strong character, warm humanity, and high professional competence. In less than half an hour he won the confidence of Congress and of the country. His eloquent words, and the profound sincerity that illumined them, made one feel, with a rush of gratitude, that once again the United States had emerged from crisis with a leadership worthy of its tradition.

* * *

Not only the President's appeal for unity and dedication, but the congressional response, gave cause for hope that legislative and executive arms alike will indeed reflect the national resolution to erect a memorial to John F. Kennedy in the form of a cleansed national spirit.

There was no mistaking the meaning of the ovation that greeted the President's call for "an end to the teaching and preaching of hate and evil and violence." Even more remarkable was the prolonged applause that followed his appeal for prompt passage of the civil rights bill.

Nobody can rightly expect, or wish, that President Johnson should make his administration a pale copy of his predecessor's. He must stamp his own character upon the course of policy, draw upon his own sources of judgment and counsel, decide for himself what order of priorities and emphasis to put upon the several goals he chooses for his administration. When he promised continuity with the Kennedy administration, he was not promising identity.

But it was heartening that the broad principles for which he asked continuity included every essential aspiration of President Kennedy. Action on civil rights, action on tax reduction, the exploration of space, the fundamental strengthening of our educational system, an economy of full employment, the fight against poverty abroad as well as at home, powerful leadership of the free world, an unflagging search for peace—these are the goals that deserve continuity, because they are the urgent tasks of a forward-moving society.

President Johnson pledged himself to them, and no one could doubt that he meant it.

He also meant it, we are sure, when he emphasized the obligation to match national strength with national restraint. The extraordinary gathering of foreign heads of state and political leaders at President Kennedy's funeral has just given us a sobering reminder of the enormous power this nation wields in the world. Mr. Johnson gives evidence of grasping the fact that our power is not so much a cause for shallow elation as for the most solemn determination to use it with wisdom and justice. It is gratifying that one of his first acts was to send messages to Premier Khrushchev offering honorable friendship and continued negotiations to reduce tensions; and he reinforced that position in his address to Congress.

*   *   *

Nothing in his address, however, surpassed in impressiveness his appeal for congressional action on the civil rights bill, the tax bill, the education bills, foreign aid, and the long postponed appropriation measures. Until he spoke, the idea had been gaining ground that Congress might well go home now, leaving its work unfinished, under the guise of helping President Johnson settle into the organization of his Administration. The President wants help, true enough, but he wants it in the form of legislation, not abdication.

The shock and the strain of the past week might well have justified the President in postponing the start of his struggle for a few weeks, and so it is heartening that he chose instead to fling his full and very considerable talents at once into the battle which Mr. Kennedy was waging when he fell.

Now the nation's attention falls on Congress. How will Congress respond, when the tears and emotions of recent days are past, when the impact of tragedy has been dulled, when workaday habits supplant the elevation of spirit? Will it go back to business as usual— the business of obstruction, filibuster and delay? Or will Senate and House together rise to the challenge which President Johnson posed, and which we are confident the nation indorses?

†   †   †

One aftermath of the Kennedy assassination that was especially relevant to the press was a considerable amount of soul-searching. The 1960s became a time of governmental commissions, several of which analyzed and commented on various aspects of media performance. The most famous, important, and ultimately controversial of all of these was the President's Commission on the Assassination of President John F. Kennedy, which was headed by Chief Justice Earl Warren and which made its report in 1964. It dealt with many issues of the assassination, of course, including the still debated issue of the identity of the assassin. So far as the press was concerned the major question was that of "trial by newspaper," the identification of Oswald as the assassin, the likelihood that Oswald thus could never have had a fair trial, the implications of the role played by the mass media in creating an atmosphere that made possible the shooting of Oswald by Ruby, the likelihood, as a result, that Ruby too could not have had an impartial trial. It was a report fraught with issues that are still debated. An excerpt follows.

† † †

A STATEMENT BY THE WARREN COMMISSION

From *Report of the President's Commission on the Assassination of President John F. Kennedy* (Washington, D.C.: Government Printing Office, 1964), pp. 240-241.

. . . While appreciating the heavy and unique pressures with which the Dallas Police Department was confronted by reason of the assassination of President Kennedy, primary responsibility for having failed to control the press and to check the flow of undigested evidence to the public must be borne by the police department. It was the only agency that could have established orderly and sound operating procedures to control the multitude of newsmen gathered in the police building after the assassination.

The Commission believes, however, that a part of the responsibility for the unfortunate circumstances following the President's death must be borne by the news media. The crowd of newsmen generally failed to respond properly to the demands of the police. Frequently without permission, news representatives used police offices on the third floor, tying up facilities and interfering with normal police operations. Police efforts to preserve order and to clear passageways in the corridor were usually unsuccessful. On Friday night the reporters completely ignored [Police Chief] Curry's injunction against asking Oswald questions in the assembly room and crowding in on him. On Sunday morning, the newsmen were instructed to direct no questions at Oswald; nevertheless, several reporters shouted questions at him when he appeared in the basement. . . .

Curry's subordinates had the impression that an unannounced transfer of Oswald to the county jail was unacceptable because Curry did not want to disappoint the newsmen; he had promised that they could witness the transfer. It seemed clear enough that any attempt to exclude the press from the building or to place limits on the information disclosed to them would have been resented and disputed by the newsmen, who were constantly and aggressively demanding all possible information about anything related to the assassination. . . .

The general disorder in the Police and Courts Building during November 22-24 reveals a regrettable lack of self-discipline by the newsmen. The Commission believes that the news media, as well as the police authorities, who failed to impose conditions more in keeping with the orderly process of justice, must share responsibility for the failure of law enforcement which occurred in connection with the death of Oswald. On previous occasions, public bodies have voiced the need for the exercise of self-restraint by the news media in periods when the demand for information must be tempered by other fundamental requirements of our society. . . .

† † †

Of the issues treated by the press in the 1960s and early 1970s none was more searing than that of the war in southeast Asia. The United States had historically been more concerned with Asia than with other parts of the world, and our involvement in that continent and its affairs dated at least to Commodore Perry and the opening of Japan to the western world. Such involvement continued through the war with Spain and up through World War II. As for involvement in that part of Southeast Asia once known as Indochina, it is simplistic to suggest that such involvement began only in the 1960s; it went back at least to the administrations of Truman and Eisenhower. But the United States had been giving military assistance to the government of Ngo Dinh Diem in an attempt to bolster it after the Geneva accords of 1954, which had divided Indochina. With the Gulf of Tonkin resolution of August, 1964, the American role in Vietnam became full-scale. It was a well-reported war, despite much censorship, and even though the press-government rapport that had marked coverage of World War II was missing. The press corps in South Vietnam, like the people at home, had divided into "hawks" and "doves," and the doves covering the war were creating the most attention in the early 1960s. David Halberstam of the *New York Times* and Malcolm Browne of the Associated Press won Pulitzer prizes, and the reputable Harrison Salisbury of the *Times* made a controversial trip to North Vietnam for his newspaper. One of the dispatches by Malcolm Browne described the aftermath of the death of the leader of South Vietnam.

† † †

AN ASSASSINATION IN SOUTHEAST ASIA

By Malcolm W. Browne, Associated Press, November 3, 1963.

Saigon (AP)—A Buddhist-led provisional regime controlled a nervous Saigon today after a bloody coup that brought downfall and death to President Ngo Dinh Diem and his borther, Ngo Dinh Nhu.

The new regime declared the Ngo Dinh brothers dead, but did not explain how they died.

Roy Essoyan, an Associated Press reporter, saw photographs of bodies identified as those of Diem and Nhu.

The picture of Diem showed him lying beside a personnel carrier with a soldier leaning over him. His body, dressed in a dark suit, was bullet riddled and there was evidence he had been shot in the head.

Nhu's body, bearing bruises as though he had been beaten, was lying on a stretcher. He met his death by stabbing, it was said.

Judging from the nature of the wounds, it seemed unlikely that the two men had committed suicide, although that was the official explanation.

It was not known where the two bodies were. . . .

Officially, coup leaders said they were looking for members of the Ngo Dinh family in order to hand over the bodies.

There were no family members known to be in Saigon. Mrs. Nhu's children were said to be safe at the family's villa at Dalat.

There was a rumor that the two Roman Catholic brothers were shot while resisting arrest, after they fled the presidential palace.

Jubilant crowds celebrated the fall of the Diem regime yesterday by exulting in the streets. But early today they had returned to their homes. The city was quiet.

The wave of celebration was heightened by the release of Buddhist monks from jails. They had been arrested earlier this year by the Diem government.

† † †

Much of the news of the 1960s was either about the war or closely related to it. Controversy over the war and the extent of U.S. participation in it lay behind the election of 1964. There had been little question that the Democrats would nominate President Lyndon B. Johnson, for he was proving a popular and successful chief executive. The Republicans already had nominated Senator Barry Goldwater of Arizona, a man of great integrity and extremely conservative persuasions. The Goldwater forces, like those of John Kennedy in 1960, had been in control for some time; they had the Republican convention sewed up much ahead of the opening date, and the moderate forces of George Romney and Nelson Rockefeller were doomed, their speeches shunted to television times that kept them from being heard by prime time listeners. They were heckled by the Goldwater followers, who were weary of a long succession of left-leaning Republican candidates. An especially terrifying glimpse of the anger and frustration of the far right was offered when former President Eisenhower made an attack upon "sensation-seeking columnists and commentators." It was a campaign in which the American press, so long identified with Republicanism on the editorial pages, made historic declarations in favor of the more moderate-sounding Lyndon Johnson, and it was especially shocking when the *New York Herald Tribune,* the leading Republican paper of the land, endorsed a Democratic president.

† † †

A REPUBLICAN PAPER BACKS PRESIDENT JOHNSON

New York Herald Tribune, October 4, 1964.

For the Presidency: Lyndon B. Johnson.

Travail and torment go into those simple words, breaching as they do the political traditions of a long newspaper lifetime. But we find ourselves, as Americans, even as Republicans, with no other acceptable course.

For many Republicans, this has been a season of soul-searching—whether out of loyalty to the party and the two-party system, to embrace Goldwater; whether to defect to Johnson; or whether, caught between two unpalatable alternatives, to abstain from choice.

For us, as we suspect may be true for others, these considerations were decisive:

Abstention is impossible. Office-holders and candidates for office, beholden to the party, are limited by their obligations in what they can say. A newspaper cannot take refuge in this; and no agony of indecision can make the choice go away, unless we maintain that the White House should be vacant for the next four years. One or the other has to be elected; the choice is only which, not whether.

* * * * * *

We opposed Barry Goldwater for the nomination. We felt that his simplistic views on world affairs, and his appeal—whether calculated or not—to ugly racial passions in this climactic year of the struggle for equal rights, were alone enough to rule him out as the Republican standard-bearer.

But he won.

We then hoped that he might prove our fears unfounded, rise to his responsibilities as nominee, show himself equal to the office he sought, and thus make it possible to close ranks behind him.

He didn't. At every step of the post-nomination way, two things became ever more evident: 1) that Senator Goldwater, for all his obvious sincerity, simply does not have the combination of personal talents necessary for the Presidency of the United States; and 2) that his course, if pursued as he has pursued it, would wreck not only the Republican party but the two-party system.

* * * * * *

The more he discusses foreign affairs, the clearer it becomes that his vision is limited; that he has no grasp of the infinite complexities of a dangerous, frustrating and volatile world. The constant confusions over what he really means suggest little talent for the nuances of diplomacy. He has shown himself, in sum, a poor risk for the most personal and most awesome of a President's responsibilities, the conduct of foreign relations in an age when survival may, in crisis, depend on his judgment—and his judgment alone.

His whole Southern strategy, his embrace of Senator Thurmond, his thinly veiled equations of Negro rights with violence in the streets—these have been a mockery of the fundamental Republican dedication to equal rights. However pure his own heart, his tactics dishonor the heritage of a century.

At San Francisco his first response to victory was one of unabashed arrogance. He rejected all moderate counsel; worse, much worse, he raised a banner for the extremists, the bigots, the implacable "antis," even while issuing, in effect, a manifesto for a new party, taking the Republican name but excluding the Republican soul.

His first great responsibility was choice of a Vice-Presidential candidate. He passed up every man of Presidential stature within the Republican ranks, to choose instead a party functionary of little distinction then, and distinguished since only for the vigor of his vituperation.

Goldwater's unity gesture at Hershey was utterly superficial and soon forgotten (he himself was quick to insist that he had made no concessions); his carefully selected lieutenants, taking over the party machinery, sought ruthlessly and at once to convert a great national party into a narrow ideological faction.

If Senator Goldwater were to succeed in transforming the Republican party into a narrow Goldwater party—which is clearly the intent of the men behind him, and in which the Senator at least acquiesces—he would reduce a great political organization to a permanent, ineffectual opposition. By destroying the inner balance of the party, he would destroy the balance of political power in the nation.

The mass defection now evident from the Goldwater ticket can't be laid simply to sour grapes, or disgruntlement by poor losers. It's a nationwide, grass-roots defection, a mass exodus based on lack of confidence and respect. Senator Goldwater could have made it possible for many, even most, of these people to support him; instead, he made it extraordinarily difficult, if not impossible.

We believe, strongly, in Republican principles; we feel that the Republican party is best fitted to govern a free nation. And we urgently want to see the Republican party, already dangerously diminished, grow stronger.

But this, in our judgment, does not justify making Barry Goldwater President of the United States.

* * * * * *

In supporting Lyndon Johnson, we do so with our eyes open and our fingers crossed. We hold no brief for the Democratic doctrine of ever-encroaching Federal authority; we fear a continued spending spree; we despise the traditional Democratic practice of buying votes by the bloc, with special-interest legislation wrapped in compassionate slogans.

But in Mr. Johnson we are offered a man of vast experience and manifest competence. In the Senate he proved himself one of the ablest legislative leaders of the age. As President, he has moved with sureness and responsibility through almost a year of crises—not least of these, the crisis of assassination and succession.

Moreover, Lyndon Johnson's greatest talent is the one needed now as seldom before in our history: that of reconciling the seemingly irreconcilable, and pulling opposites into a consensus. In a nation torn by racial and sectional strife, its divisions exacerbated by the ugly passions stirred up (on both sides) by the Goldwater candidacy, the nation needs a President who can bind up its wounds and let it find its soul again.

Senator Goldwater says he is offering the nation a choice. So far as these two candidates are concerned, our inescapable choice—as a newspaper that was Republican before there was a Republican party, has been Republican ever since and will remain Republican—is Lyndon B. Johnson.

† † †

In the 1960s many American cities went through what the press came to call "long hot summers." The ghettoes exploded as blacks, sometimes prodded by leaders frustrated by the continuing inferior position of the black race, protested and rioted: in Harlem, Chicago, Washington, Newark, Detroit, Rochester, and in Watts, a section of Los Angeles. The Watts story took place in 1965, and the situation there was made even worse by the agitation of a few persons working within the news media, some of whom went to the scenes of disturbances with the intent of making them "media events."

† † †

NEGROES RIOT IN LOS ANGELES

By Art Berman, *Los Angeles Times,* August 15, 1965.

The guerrilla war of South Los Angeles claimed its 25th victim Saturday night as bands of armed Negro looters took to the streets and snipers defied the efforts of 21,000 national guardsmen and law officers to bring peace to the area.

With no end in sight, Lt. Gov. Glenn M. Anderson signed a disaster proclamation and invoked an 8 p.m. curfew in the 50-square-mile riot area.

One of the new victims was a 5-year-old Negro boy, Bruce Moore. Police said he was killed by a sniper bullet while he was in the yard of his home at 8800 Mary St., in the Firestone area. He was pronounced dead at St. Francis Hospital.

The latest fatalities were a Negro shot and killed by National Guardsmen who said he ignored commands to halt at a blockade. Another Negro was shot, police said, while looting a liquor store.

Firemen trying to control a blaze in a store at 47th St. and Broadway were pinned down by snipers shortly before midnight. Forty guardsmen and police came to their rescue and used tear gas—the first employed during the rioting—to disperse the attackers. Five firemen were hospitalized after inhaling the tear gas.

The Firestone sheriff's substation at 7901 S. Compton Ave. fell under siege from armed men zipping past in cars taking potshots at the building.

Two more looters were killed before midnight and two deputies were wounded in a shoot-out with looters at Holmes St. and Florence Ave.

Numerous buildings were set afire from 40th to 49th St. along Broadway, but firemen, some reportedly wearing bullet-proof vests, were prevented from fighting the flames by sniper fire.

Violence also flared in Venice. At 7th St. and Broadway, there, a fire truck responding to a false alarm was set afire by a Molotov cocktail and 11 people were arrested for failing to disperse, as heavy crowds began to mass. . . .

† † †

Such was, in part, the racial story of the decade, perhaps the major continuing domestic story of the time. In 1968, another presidential study group, headed by Governor Otto Kerner of Illinois, issued a report, after the explosion in Watts and after similar urban destruction in Newark and Detroit. This commission was somewhat kinder to the mass media than the Warren Commission had been.

† † †

THE PRESS AND CIVIL RIGHTS

From the *Report of the National Advisory Commission on Civil Disorders* (New York: Dutton, 1968), pp. 362-363.

. . . the Commissioners read newspapers, listened to the radio, watched television, and thus formed their own impressions of media coverage. All of these data, impressions, and attitudes provide the foundation for our conclusions.

The Commission also determined, very early, that the answer to the President's question ["What effect do the mass media have on the riots?"] did not lie solely in the performance of the press and broadcasters in reporting the rights proper. Our analysis had to consider also the overall treatment by the media of the Negro ghettos, community relations, racial attitudes, urban and rural poverty—day by day and month by month, year in and year out.

On this basis, we have reached three conclusions:

First, that despite incidents of sensationalism, inaccuracies, and distortions, newspapers, radio and television, on the whole, made a real effort to give a balanced, factual account of the 1967 disorders.

Second, despite this effort, the portrayal of the violence that occurred last summer failed to reflect accurately its scale and character. The overall effect was, we believe, an exaggeration of both mood and event.

Third, and ultimately most important, we believe that the media have thus far failed to report adequately on the causes and consequences of civil disorders and the underlying problems of race relations. . . .

†   †   †

The year of the assassination of John F. Kennedy—1963—was also the year when 200,000 Americans jammed the Mall in Washington in a peaceful civil rights demonstration, the largest in the history of the nation. Television offered, and recordings of the event still offer, documentary memories of this gigantic event. They are memories that will long endure, for they include the voice of the black leader, the Reverend Martin Luther King, Jr. He had placed himself in the forefront of the civil rights movement beginning with the Supreme Court desegregation ruling of 1954, including the subsequent developments in Birmingham, Alabama, Greensboro, North Carolina, and all the other places where black people, often in association with whites, were trying to make the idea of freedom more than a dream. It was King who voiced his dream on the steps of the Lincoln Memorial. He later won a Nobel prize for peace and then died, victim of a sniper's bullet, on a Memphis motel balcony in April, 1968. The magazine *Ebony,* by the 1960s much more than an imitator of *Life* for the black race, editorialized on his death.

†   †   †

THE PRINCE OF PEACE IS DEAD

Ebony, XXIII, No. 7 (May, 1968), p. 172.

Of all black men who ever lived and of all men of modern times, either black or white, none has more honestly earned the designation of a true man of peace than the late Dr. Martin Luther King Jr. Without the slightest feeling of irreligiosity, any thinking man today can accept the Rev. Dr. Martin Luther King Jr. as a prince of peace in a world more sorely troubled than at any other time in history.

Now the prince of peace is dead.

A hidden assassin armed with a deadly weapon of war and the eye of a deerslayer slew the prince of peace with a single shot.

Martin Luther King died at 7:02 on the evening of a bright spring day, April 4, 1968.

No more will he link arms with those in the forefront of a phalanx of marchers for freedom.

No more will his oratory fill a church, a hall, a stadium in a fervent plea for peace and brotherhood throughout the world.

No more will he calmly suffer the cattle prods and clubs of arrogant police, the jeers and insults of racist whites, the jailings and beatings by country lawmen or the snide remarks of some fellow blacks who called him an Uncle Tom.

No more will he have a dream. No more will he go to the mountaintop.

Violent and final death came to this apostle of nonviolence in Memphis, Tenn., less than an hour's flight from his home in Atlanta, Ga. Dr. King had come to Memphis to help those who needed his help and who had asked him for it. They were "little people"—Negro garbage collectors who were striking for a living wage and improved working conditions. They wanted to march on City Hall in quest of their rights and nobody could lead a march as well as Dr. King. They did march in silent, nonviolent protest—but Dr. King was not there to lead them. They marched on Monday, April 8—the day before Dr. King's funeral in Atlanta.

It was quite fitting that Dr. King's death came during a mission among little people. A dozen years earlier he had begun his rise to fame during a Montgomery bus boycott among the little people who sprang to the aid of Rosa Parks, a seamstress, who started the whole thing when she refused to move from the white section of a city bus. She was just too tired to stand in the back after working for white folks all day.

During the short 12 years of his career, Dr. King became one of the best known civil rights leaders of all times. He rose to such eminence that he shook hands with kings, conferred with popes, counseled presidents and defied mayors. Celebrities in all fields flocked to his support and his Southern Christian Leadership Conference became one of the most militant, least violent civil rights organizations in U.S. history.

The world had its eyes on the Negro's struggle for equal rights in the U.S. and, in 1964, Dr. King was awarded the Nobel Prize for peace. Dr. King's $54,600 cash award went to help finance the civil rights movement. He kept . . . the trophy, the medal and the certificate.

As befits a leader, Dr. King consorted with kings but he never forgot his mission—to help the poor, the persecuted, the deprived. Factory workers, sharecroppers, laborers, the unemployed and the unemployables, the church sister and the backslider, all revered the man who had dedicated his life to helping the unfortunate.

And now that life is ended.

The violence, the hate, the looting and burning that spread across this nation after Dr. King's death is something Dr. King would have deplored just as he had deplored the violence that brought death to civil rights workers Medgar Evers, Viola Liuzzo, Michael Schwerner, James Chancy, Andrew Goodman, the Rev. James Reeb, Jimmie Lee Jackson and a host of others whose lives were snuffed out because they believed that all men are created equal.

If this violence on both sides continues, then the death of Dr. King will have been in vain. If white against black, nation against nation, class against class is to be the way of the world in the future, as it too often has been in the past, then Dr. King is the lucky one. He will have to see and suffer it no longer. We who are left will be the ones who live in tragedy.

The prince of peace is dead. It is up to the millions who still live to see that his dream is brought to pass.

† † †

Civil rights protests were one kind of protest that marked the 1960s. Another was the protest of youth, and of different groups associated with youth, and the late years of the decade would always be for some, the years of student protest. For some these years later held a significance comparable to the depression or World War II. As with most movements it is difficult to date the beginning, for there had been foreshadowings long before the fall of 1964, when the Free Speech Movement began at the University of California in Berkeley. The movement spread—compounded of hatred of the war, promotion of civil rights, identification with various ethnic groups, frustration with the impersonality of the thing called the "multiversity" by both friends and critics, an affiliation with the counterculture of hippies, drugs, and rock music, a need to participate more fully in decision-making in America. Out of the protest movements arose what was later known as the underground press, which had had its beginnings as early as the 1950s, with the *Village Voice,* and moved increasingly "aboveground" as the movement declined after the shootings at Kent State. One of the best known, most vigorous, most lasting of the underground newspapers was the one published in the city where the action began in 1964, the *Berkeley Barb.*

† † †

RISE UP ANGRY! NO MORE LYING DOWN!

By North Star, *Berkeley Barb,* May 8-14, 1970.

Dial May for Murder.

Thursday, May 15th, 1969, James Rector was blasted off a rooftop by Alameda County pigs. A few days later, black students were shot and killed in North Carolina.

Tuesday, May 4th, 1970, four students died in front of a National Guard firing squad, ripped off by those funky Sunday soldiers that bullshit radicals tell me are my friends. (I tested that theory once during the People's Park rebellion, and almost got my fucking head blown off.)

Nothing much came out of Rector's death. And hardly anyone even KNEW about the blacks who were offed in North Carolina. But maybe this time things will be different.

It wasn't Berkeley. It wasn't Columbia. No. It was KENT STATE, right out there in the heartland of America. . . .

† † †

Now, in the late sixties, there would be newspapers representing not only blacks and the young people of the counter-culture but newspapers for other minorities as well. Mexican-Americans had a new label—Chicanos. And an underground press came to identify with this protesting minority, too.

† † †

CULTURAL NATIONALISM: A FIGHT FOR SURVIVAL

Chicano Student Movement, August, 1969.

Chicanos throughout the southwest and across the country are beginning to unite behind La Causa. Aware of power through numbers and unity, the Chicano communities are demanding changes in the racist institutions of this country. Refusing to accept an imposed anglo value system, Chicanos are creating their own life style under the banner of cultural nationalism. A rich past of aztec and revolutionary heroes, destroys the "dirty Mexican" and "lazy Mexican" labels. In other words, a positive self-image replaces the negative stereotype.

Cultural nationalism is based on people power. The language, the food, the art, the legends constitute the image of a people. If that image is strong, then their cause can only be strong. In the face of oppression, culture can protect the people from destruction and assimilation. Especially important in any battle for survival is the preservation of the people's language because a language shapes and moulds a person's view of the world. It also creates a greater sense of brotherhood among those who share this common way of communication when confronted by outsiders who speak a different language. . . .

† † †

Another group discovering itself and calling for militant action in the late sixties was the American Indian. The movies, in such pictures as *Soldier Blue* and *Little Big Man,* were painting a picture of the Indians and the cavalry much different from that in *They Died with Their Boots On,* and books like *Cheyenne Autumn* and *Bury My Heart at Wounded Knee* were carrying the story of the Indian to other audiences. One of the publications that arose out of the American Indian call for action minced no words in stating its position.

† † †

AN AMERICAN INDIAN CRY FOR JUSTICE

Wounded Knee Newsletter, Council Bluffs, Iowa, January, 1975.

The 97 Tribes of the International Treaty Council have taken the stand that Native American people should now be dealing with International courts or the State Department. They are preparing cases and addresses to be heard before the United Nations.

In refusing to recognize the 1868 Treaty, [Judge Warren] Urbom said, "A single national policy for governmental action must be developed. It should not be made by a federal judge or the handful who may review this decision on appeal." Refusing to make a decision which recognizes the rights of Native Americans, he merely continues the injustices which have been forced upon Indian people for hundreds of years.

Many Native Americans are more than disappointed at this decision, and they feel that Urbom has signed a death warrant for them, dooming them to starvation for want of their basic human rights and forcing a continuing and prolonged struggle in the United States government courtrooms.

An Indian woman remarked, "We are only here on this earth for a short time. It has been too long already that the Indian people have suffered at the hands of the U.S. govt. We can only take the oppression for so long." . . .

† † †

Something closely associated with the press of protest was a journalistic phenomenon that came to be known as the "new journalism." It had many practitioners, notably Tom Wolfe, the writer who best articulated what the new journalism was all about. Wolfe was not, except superficially, what would appear to be a leader of journalistic reform. He spoke in a language, however, that was vastly appealing to youth, writing books with swinging titles like *The Electric Kool-Aid Acid Test, The Kandy-Kolored Tangerine-Flake Streamline Baby,* and *Radical Chic.* Wolfe contended, with both force and charm, that the novel was dead, that the new journalism was taking its place, that the new journalists were applying the techniques of the novel to their writing. As the new journalism moved into the 1970s it appeared to have gone somewhat beyond the Wolfe-stated bounds; to some of its backers it was not only fictional techniques applied to journalism but the journalist as participant, the journalist as protagonist, the journalist as possessor of truth (and not merely a reporter of "facts"), the journalist as active reformer (provided he/she was to the left in politics).

Another of the beloved members of the new cult was Norman Mailer, who wrote *The Armies of the Night* about the 1967 march on the Pentagon and won new recognition for himself. Mailer had burst into our literary consciousness when he published *The Naked and the Dead* in 1948, but through much of an almost twenty-year spread he had seemed an unrealized talent, though he always had stout defenders. Mailer, in his book about the 1967 protest, was not only a participant; he was an actor. For being an actor was another of the components, for some, of new journalism.

Rachel Carson would not have thought of herself as a journalist, for she was a scientist and a poet, author of *The Sea Around Us* and *Under the Sea-Wind.* But she belongs to journalistic history in the way that Lincoln Steffens and Ida M. Tarbell belong, for in 1962 she published her book, *Silent Spring,* a beautifully written and impassioned tract that dealt with pesticides and herbicides. Her book launched a movement roughly known as ecology, and though she is not often listed as being a new journalist, her writing is in that tradition.

† † †

A CRY AGAINST THE USE OF INSECTICIDES

By Rachel Carson, *Silent Spring* (Boston: Houghton Mifflin, 1962), p. 174.

. . . If a huge skull and crossbones were suspended above the insecticide department [of a store] the customer might at least enter it with the respect normally accorded death-dealing materials. But instead the display is homey and cheerful, and, with the pickles and olives across the aisle and the bath and laundry soaps adjoining, the rows upon rows of insecticides are displayed. Within easy reach of a child's exploring hand are chemicals in *glass* containers. If dropped to the floor by a child or careless adult everyone nearby could be splashed with the same chemical that has sent spraymen using it into convulsions. These hazards of course follow the purchaser right into his home. A can of a mothproofing material containing DDD, for example, carries in very fine print the warning that its contents are under pressure and that it may burst if exposed to heat or open flame. A common insecticide for household use, including assorted uses in the kitchen, is chlordane. Yet the Food and Drug Administration's chief pharmacologist has declared the hazard of living in a house sprayed with chlordane to be "very great." Other household preparations contain the even more toxic dieldrin. . . .

† † †

Part of the new journalism, and much of the student protest of the age, was embodied in the various incidents surrounding the 1968 presidential nominating convention of the Democratic party in Chicago. It was a convention that had thrown some parts of the population into great alarm for fear the Yippies—an anarchist and often entertaining faction of hippiedom—would put LSD into the Chicago water system or fornicate in the city parks. It was a convention marked by fear, and by police brutality, for the presence of all the long-haired youths, plus the tight machine run by Mayor Richard J. Daley, led to violence in the streets, including attacks upon members of the press. Out of the convention grew such nonestablishment journals as the *Chicago Journalism Review,* plus another presidential study. That well-known trade publication, *Editor & Publisher,* offered a commentary.

† † †

ABOUT THE ATTACKS ON REPORTERS

Editor & Publisher, September 7, 1968, p. 6. Reprinted by permission of the publisher.

Mayor Richard Daley's supporters and critics are rallying behind their respective banners to support his actions, and that of his police force, during the turmoil in Chicago last week or to pin the label of police brutality on him and the city without question.

It promises to be a ruckus every bit as noisy and brutal as the battles in Grant and Lincoln Parks and outside of the Conrad Hilton Hotel on Michigan Ave. The mayor is trying to take his own case for the defense to the American people via the television networks at whose hands he believes he suffered originally.

Much has been written and said on both sides of this controversy already and it appears that the debate will never be concluded to the satisfaction of either side. But, one thing has been missing so far:

There has not been any statement from Chicago authorities, or any attempt at an explanation by them, as to why more than two dozen newsmen—reporters and cameramen for all media—were set upon by the police during the demonstrations.

Many of these newsmen were identifiable by inscriptions on their helmets and armbands or by the nature of their photographic equipment. They were present, obviously, to cover the course of events whatever they might be. Not only were they prevented from doing that job but some of them were badly beaten in the attempt.

One or two cases of mistaken identity on the first night of rioting might have been understandable. But repeated instances night after night indicate lack of orders from superiors, or complete lack of control by them, or a deliberate attempt by the police to prevent coverage of the events, as some newsmen have charged.

Either one of them represented a colossal blunder in judgment and we trust Mayor Daley's explanations will be to the point.

The leaders of the Chicago demonstrations have stated clearly that they will try to re-create these incidents in other places throughout the political campaign this fall. We hope that civilian and police officials in these other cities don't get it into their heads that they can brush these things under the rugs by preventing full news coverage on the air or in print.

†   †   †

A new presidential commission, headed by Daniel Walker of Chicago, issued its report after the incidents in Chicago, and dealt, of course, with all of the violence and not merely that directed at members of the press. It asked these questions: 1) Was any news staged and manufactured by demonstrators and newsmen? 2) Were newsmen calculated targets of violence by police? 3) Were any police attacks on newsmen unwarranted and unprovoked? Here is an excerpt from the report.

†   †   †

THE PRESS AND THE POLICE IN CHICAGO

From *Rights in Conflict,* the *Report to the National Commission on the Causes and Prevention of Violence* (New York: Bantam ed., 1968), p. 330.

. . . A total of 49 newsmen are described . . . as having been hit, maced, or arrested, apparently without reason, by the police. Forty-three were hit, three were maced and three were arrested. Of the newsmen involved, 22 were reporters, 23 were photographers and 4 were members of the TV crews.

In ten of these incidents, photographic or recording equipment was deliberately broken; in one, the police intentionally knocked a reporter's notebook out of his hand.

In over 40 instances, the newsman involved was clearly identifiable as such; that is, even aside from photographers carrying the identifying apparatus of their trade, newsmen wore helmets, carried visible press badges or press passes hanging around their necks. In only four situations do the facts indicate that the newsmen were so mixed in with the crowd that the police could have hit them under the mistaken apprehension that they were demonstrators.

Forty-five of the incidents occurred at night, four during the daytime. Fourteen of the newsmen were from Chicago and the balance were from out of town. The average age was about 31 years; 28 were in the 20 to 30 year age bracket; ten were from 31 to 35; seven were over 35. We do not know the ages of the other four. . . .

† † †

In such incidents as the Chicago convention there came a focusing of national attention upon the media; certainly, throughout the 1960s, all of the media were under scrutiny, and sometimes under attack—not without reason, on occasion, such as when the chairman of the Federal Communications Commission addressed the National Association of Broadcasters in 1961. The chairman was Newton N. Minow, and he spoke after that time some sentimentalists viewed as "the golden age" of television, the year of Sid Caesar, Edward R. Murrow, Paddy Chayefsky, *Marty, Requiem for a Heavyweight,* and *Your Show of Shows.* In his speech Minow offered a metaphor that later became a symbolic term for television in the soaring sixties.

† † †

THE VAST WASTELAND OF THE TUBE

By Newton N. Minow, *New York Times,* May 10, 1961. Reprinted by permission of Mr. Minow.

. . . When television is good, nothing—not the theatre, not the magazine or newspapers—nothing is better. But when television is bad, nothing is worse. I invite you to sit down in front of your television set when your station goes on the air and stay there without a book, magazine, newspaper, profit-and-loss sheet or rating book to distract you and keep your eyes glued to that set until the station signs off. I can assure you that you will observe a vast wasteland.

You will see a procession of game shows, violence, audience participation shows, formula comedies about totally unbelievable families, blood and thunder, mayhem, violence, sadism, murder, Western badmen, Western goodmen, private eyes, gangsters, more violence, and cartoons. And endlessly, commercials—many screaming, cajoling and offending. And most of all, boredom. True, you will see a few things you will enjoy. But they will be very, very few. And if you think I exaggerate, try it.

Is there one person in this room who claims that broadcasting can't do better?

Well, a glance at next season's proposed programming can give us little heart. Of seventy-three and one-half hours of prime evening time, the networks have tentatively scheduled fifty-nine hours to categories of "action adventure," situation comedy, variety, quiz and movies.

Gentlemen, your trust accounting with your beneficiaries is overdue. Never have so few owed so much to so many. . . .

If parents, teachers and ministers conducted their responsibilities by following the ratings, children would have a steady diet of ice cream, school holidays and no Sunday school. What about your responsibilities? Is there no room on television to teach, to inform, to uplift, to stretch, to enlarge the capacities of our children? Is there no room for programs deepening their understanding of children in other lands? Is there no room for a children's news show explaining something about the world for them at their level of understanding? Is there no room for reading the great literature of the past, teaching them great traditions of freedom? There are some fine children's shows but they are drowned out in the massive doses of cartoons, violence and more violence. Must these be your trademarks? Search your conscience and see if you cannot offer more to your young beneficiaries whose future you guard so many hours each and every day. . . .

† † †

Much later in the decade there came two other famous statements on the role of the mass media, especially the role of television. The year was 1969, the first year of the Nixon presidency, and the first of the commentaries was by Walter Cronkite, the evening newscaster of the Columbia Broadcasting System, who by that time was becoming the chief father figure in America and, with little doubt, the leading personal journalist of his time. Cronkite had come out of a print news background; in his authoritative way he seemed to inspire confidence in the listener, and he never suggested that the medium of television could possibly do as adequate a job in treating certain news events as the more traditional print media. But he was weary of what he saw as mindless attacks upon his profession and his medium.

† † †

BROADCAST NEWS AND HALF-FREE SPEECH

By Walter Cronkite, William Allen White Memorial Lecture, University of Kansas, March 24, 1969.

. . . I do not doubt that, freed from the governmental requirement for public service, some broadcasters would drop all news from their schedules and become nothing but electronic movie exhibitors.

It would be better if broadcasters with that inclination got out of the news business anyway. The way would then be clear for the broadcaster who had a genuine desire for community service (and there are, and would be, many), his desire buttressed by the certainty that good, thorough, trustworthy, independent news programming also can be profitable.

I trust that the generation of newsmen already is here that dreams of having a good country television station just as we used to dream of a good country newspaper. Economically it is going to be possible.

Whether we in broadcast journalism succeed immediately in striking off all the government restrictions that shackle us, it is important that we prevent any more from being clamped on.

It is important that we establish once and for all that the First Amendment guarantee of freedom is as applicable to broadcasting as it is to the press.

It is important that all branches of government—Congress and commissions—know that they have no more right to call us to account for our news judgment than they have to call to account the newspaperman; that *ex post facto* examination of our judgment is a serious harassment that makes a mockery of press freedom.

And it is important that the press join us in recognizing that a threat against the freedom of one newsman, whatever his medium, is a threat against all.

And it is important that all of us journalists join in the most important phase of our mutual battle—to convince the people that our fight for freedom of the press and speech is not a self-serving struggle but is in defense of their right to know.

We are their eyes and their ears. To blind and to mute us is to blind and deafen them, and a democracy cannot survive with a people so handicapped.

I said at the beginning of this talk, and I say again at the end: This business of ours of broadcasting the news is not perfect. It is no more perfect than newspapering. It is never going to be perfect.

But we who are in it are going to continue our efforts to make it as nearly perfect as we can.

There are and there will be moments when the problems seem insurmountable, the challenges unmeetable; when we are beset by self-doubts.

In those moments we shall cling to one certainty which shall sustain us. And that is that we are all *professional* journalists dedicated to truth, honesty, to telling it as it is without fear or favor— and that there is no politician or bureaucrat who can make that claim.

† † †

A much different tack was taken in November of 1969 when Vice President Spiro T. Agnew spoke before the Midwest Regional Republican Committee in Des Moines, Iowa. Agnew had made himself one of the most vocal vice presidents in history in little more than a year. When Richard Nixon had tapped him for the position in 1968 he was so unknown that a familiar response was "Spiro who?" Agnew recognized that he was not, as he phrased it, a "household word." He soon became one, attacking "effete snobs," and "nattering nabobs of negativism," splattering alliterations clear across the landscape. He and his superior officer had become weary by late 1969 of the instant analyses of the news provided by television commentators, especially when the analyses were unfriendly to President Nixon, when they criticized the increasingly unpopular war in Vietnam. Agnew's speech was the strongest piece of criticism thrown at the press in the entire period.

† † †

SOME COMMENTS ON TELEVISION NEWS COVERAGE

By Spiro T. Agnew, Midwest Regional Republican Committee, Des Moines, Iowa, November 13, 1969, from *Vital Speeches,* XXXVI (December 1, 1969), p. 99.

. . . how is this network news determined? A small group of men, numbering perhaps no more than a dozen anchormen, commentators and executive producers, settle upon the 20 minutes or so of film and commentary that's to reach the public. This selection is made from the 90 to 180 minutes that may be available. Their powers of choice are broad.

They decide what 40 to 50 million Americans will learn of the day's events in the nation and in the world.

We cannot measure this power and influence by the traditional democratic standards, for these men can create national issues overnight.

They can make or break by their coverage and commentary a moratorium on the war.

They can elevate men from obscurity to national prominence within a week. They can reward some politicians with national exposure and ignore others.

For millions of Americans the network reporter who covers a continuing issue—like the ABM or civil rights—becomes, in effect, the presiding judge in a national trial by jury.

It must be recognized that the networks have made important contributions to the national knowledge—for news, documentaries and specials. They have often used their power constructively and creatively to awaken the public conscience to critical problems. The networks made hunger and black lung disease national issues overnight. The TV networks have done what no other medium could have done in terms of dramatizing the horrors of war. The networks have tackled our most difficult social problems with a directness and an immediacy that's the gift of their medium. They focus the nation's attention on its environmental abuses—on pollution in the Great Lakes and the threatened ecology of the Everglades.

But it also was the networks that elevated Stokely Carmichael and George Lincoln Rockwell from obscurity to national prominence.

Nor is their power confined to the substantive. A raised eyebrow, an inflection of the voice, a caustic remark dropped in the middle of a broadcast can raise doubts in a million minds about the veracity of a public official or the wisdom of a Government policy. . . .

† † †

One thing that the networks did, in a news sense, and in the very year of the Agnew speech, was to take American viewers to the moon. For man reached the moon in the summer of 1969, an event that provided a respite from the long procession of grim, ugly episodes that the press, of necessity, had been reporting. The moon landing had been forecast as an event of the 1960s by President John F. Kennedy; in the White House to praise the incredible accomplishment was Kennedy's adversary of 1960, Richard Nixon. Newspapers got out type face that had not been used since the end of World War II; even cautious papers like the *New York Times* gave almost sensational treatment to the event. This is the story many readers read on that July day.

† † †

ONE GIANT LEAP FOR MANKIND

By United Press International, July 22, 1969.

SPACE CENTER, Houston (UPI)—Man reached the moon Sunday at 4:17:45 p.m. EDT.

The landing by Neil A. Armstrong and Edwin E. "Buzz" Aldrin Jr. in a spaceship named Eagle culminated a millenium of dreams and a $24-billion American project that opened the world of the universe to mankind.

So technically smooth was the landing and so confident were Armstrong and Aldrin that they decided to go ahead with their moonwalk Sunday night rather than waiting until Monday morning.

For several long minutes the world seemingly stood still while their final altitude figures in the cool space fliers called out their final altitude figures in their drop toward the lunar surface.

Capsule Communicator Charles M. Duke—Eagle you're looking great. Coming up 9 minutes.

Mission Control—We're now in the approach phase. Everything looking good. Altitude 5,200 feet.

Astronaut Edwin E. Aldrin Jr.—Manual altitude. Control is good.

Duke—Roger. Copy.

Mission Control—Altitude, 4,200 feet.

Duke—Houston, you're go for landing. Over.

Aldrin—Roger. Understand go for landing.

Duke—We're go. Think tight. We're go.

Aldrin—2,000 feet. Into the AGS abort guidance system. 47 degrees.

Duke—Roger.

Aldrin—37 degrees.

Duke—Eagle, looking great. You're go.

Mission Control—Altitude, 1,600.

Duke—1,400 feet. Still looking good.

Aldrin—35 degrees.

Duke—35 degrees.

Aldrin—750 coming down to 23. 700 feet-21 down, 33 degrees . . . feet down to 19. 540 down to 30 . . . 15. 400 feet down at 9. A forward. 350 feet down at 4 static.

The figures given for foward and down by Eagle are reports of their speed—velocity in feet per second—both across the face of the moon and down toward its surface.

Aldrin—300 feet. Down 3½, 47 forward. One minute, 1½ down, 70. Altitude velocity light. 15 forward. Coming down nicely. 200 foot. 4½ down, 5½ down, 9 forward. 100 feet, 3½ down, 9 forward, 75 feet. Looking good. Down ½. 6 forward, 60 second lights on. Down 2½. Forward. Picking up some dust. Big shadow. For 4 forward. 4 forward drifting to the right a little. Down ½. 30 seconds.

Astronaut Neil A. Armstrong—contact light. Okay, engine stopped. ACA at a descent. Mode control both auto. Descent engine command override off. Engine arm off 413 is in.

When Armstrong reported "contact light," probes on the lunar module's landing pads had touched the moon.

Armstrong—Houston. We uh . . . Tranquillity Base here. The Eagle had landed.

Duke—Roger, Tranquillity. We copy. You are on the ground. You got a bunch of guys about to turn blue. We're breathing again. Thanks a lot.

At the time of landing the moon was about 238,548 miles from earth. Michael Collins, the third astronaut of the Apollo 11 team, kept the command ship Columbia in a 69-mile-high lunar orbit while Armstrong and Aldrin eased their way down.

Collins would have been able to swoop in and rescue his colleagues, had anything gone wrong on the descent, but now that they were on the lunar surface, they were beyond his reach.

One of the few problems during the descent occurred when Armstrong observed the Eagle's automatic guidance system was heading the ship into a rough landing site.

He told ground control:

"Houston, that seemed like a very long final phase. The auto target was taking us right into a football field size crater with a lot of boulders . . . it required us flying manually over the rockfield to find a real good area."

Armstrong skimmed the spaceship about 200 feet above the crater and landed four miles downrange from the proposed landing bullseye on the lunar Sea of Tranquillity.

NASA said the landing site appeared to be at .799 degrees north latitude and 23.46 degrees east longitude.

They had 55 seconds of fuel left for the descent engine when they landed.

"Very smooth touchdown," confirmed Aldrin.

Ground controller Charles M. Duke then told Collins in the command ship:

"He has landed, Tranquillity Base. Eagle is in Tranquillity."

Almost all the world bore witness Sunday to mankind's greatest achievement.

But in Communist China—home for one-fifth of mankind—there was no report, no announcement, no word that two humans had reached the moon.

Communist China apparently took very extensive steps to make sure that its citizens were not able to hear broadcasts of America's moon landing.

The Voice of America (VOA) said Monday the Red Chinese began "very extensive" jamming of VOA broadcasts from Taiwan, Nationalist China, when it started to give the report of Apollo 11 landing operation on Sunday.

Collins, like Armstrong, is 38 years old, and is a lieutenant colonel in the Air Force. Aldrin, 39, a full Air Force colonel, has been called one of the best scientific minds America has ever sent into space, and it did not take long for him to put that mind to work:

"We'll get to the details of what's around here, but it looks like a collection of just about every variety of shape, angularity, granularity and every variety of rock you could find. The color, well, it varies pretty much depending on how you're looking . . . there doesn't appear to be too much of a general color at all. However, it looks as though some of the rocks and boulders—of which there are quite a few in the near area—it looks as though they're going to have some interesting colors to them."

Duke replied:

"Sounds good to us, Tranquillity. We'll let you press on through the simulated countdown in preparation for lunar blastoff Monday. And we'll talk to you later."

Then Duke added:

"Tranquillity. Be advised there are lots of smiling faces in this control room . . . and all over the world."

Armstrong responded:

"There are two of them up here."

Duke: "Roger. It was a beautiful job, you guys."

Collins: "And don't forget the one in the command module."

Duke: "Roger."

After Eagle had been on the moon for about 3 hours, Aldrin radioed back:

"This is the LEM pilot. I'd like to take this opportunity to ask every person listening in, whoever and wherever they may be, to pause for a moment and contemplate the events of the past few hours, and to give thanks in his or her own way."

"Now comes the gymnastics," said Armstrong, as he started to depressurize the spacecraft at 10:27 p.m. EDT to begin the moonwalk.

At 10:28 p.m. EDT, Armstrong began breathing oxygen from his back pack moon walk breathing unit.

Armstrong and Aldrin then opened the hatch of their Eagle lunar lander and prepared for a walk on the moon.

Armstrong slid carefully through the hatch of his Eagle moon lander feet first and started down the nine steps of its ladder toward the lunar surface.

He stepped from the footpad of his Eagle moon lander to the lunar surface at 10:56:31 p.m. EDT Sunday.

"That's one small step for man. One giant leap for mankind," he said.

He said the surface was powdery.

"I only go in an eighth of an inch, but I can see my foot prints . . . in the fine particles."

"There seems to be no difficulty in moving around," he said as he tested man's equilibrium on the surface of the other world for the first time.

The television camera that televised the historic moment to earth was mounted inside an equipment bay that Armstrong opened as he climbed down the latter.

Armstrong and Aldrin launched off the moon at 1:54 p.m. EDT Monday in the Eagle, ending a lunar surface stay of 21 hours 36 minutes.

They first blasted off from the Sea of Tranquillity into an egg-shaped orbit and then performed three smooth course corrections to catch up with Michael Collins in the command ship Columbia.

The rendezvous occurred about 5:15 p.m. EDT and the two spacecraft linked about 5:35 p.m. The exact time of the rendezvous was not immediately determined because the pilots didn't report to earth. First indication that the docking maneuver was achieved came when ground controllers overheard a discussion between the two spacecraft.

After 60 epic hours on and around the moon, they fired their rocket engine and headed toward a Thursday splashdown in the Pacific and 18 days in isolation that will be their initial heroes' reward.

"You'll have to open up the LRL doors," Collins radioed as the engine fired at 12:56 a.m. EDT. He referred to the lunar receiving laboratory, an $11 million building here where the three pilots will be quarantined on their return to guarantee that no moon germs peril the earth.

A little over 7 hours earlier, Armstrong and Aldrin, flying "right down U.S. 1," piloted their Eagle lunar module to a rendezvous and docking with Collins' command ship Columbia.

"How does it feel to have some company?" ground controller Charles M. Duke asked Collins after Armstrong and Aldrin crawled back aboard.

"Damned good, I'll tell ya," said Collins, who flew the Columbia in a lonely, 70-mile orbit for 28 hours while Armstrong and Aldrin took Eagle to a moon landing and Armstrong's first human step there.

Monday night Armstrong and Aldrin, first men on the moon, linked up with Columbia, crawled into the command ship with their 80 pounds of rocks and dirt from the moon, and jettisoned the Eagle.

"There she goes," Collins radioed. That was at 7:40 p.m. EDT, just about three hours after Armstrong and Aldrin completed a space chase through 1200 miles and rendezvous and docking with Columbia.

Part of the time between the rendezvous and the jettisoning of Eagle was spent by the astronauts vacuuming the insides of both spaceships and all their moonsuits as part of their anti-contamination program.

Although scientists concede there is only a remote possibility that the astronauts might bring back some unknown organism from the moon, they ordered a 21-day quarantine on them, their rock samples and their equipment.

The 21 days began when Eagle landed on the lunar surface Sunday in a swirl of moondust, so if everything goes according to plan Armstrong, Aldrin, and Collins won't be out of quarantine until Sunday, Aug. 10, 18 days from their splashdown.

When the Apollo 11 pilots do get out, they're sure to be accorded wild welcomes back to earth almost anywhere in the world they go.

The astronauts were told that *The New York Times* had used the largest headline type in history on the story of the lunar landing and moon walk. "I'm glad it was fit to print," one of them said.

Armstrong, 7 minutes, 17 seconds after launch from the moon, told anxious ground controllers, "Eagle is in safe orbit, having left Tranquillity Base and leaving behind a replica of our Apollo 11 badge and olive branch."

The astronauts also left the U.S. flag, two scientific experiments and more than $1 million worth of equipment they no longer needed, including a $250,000 camera.

† † †

In some respects the moon landing was a diversion, a way to get the minds of the American people off the continuing war in Vietnam, a war that had become the most divisive military engagement in our history. Into the 1970s the war continued to be the major international as well as domestic story, especially when, in 1970, the invasion of Cambodia set off the campus disturbances that led to the shootings at Kent State and possibly brought an end not only to the counter-culture, which seemed to die in May, 1970, but finally to the war itself. In November of 1969 a story was published in the *New York Times* that bore little suggestion of its horrific implications, or of its future; the story was even displayed at the bottom of the page. Briefly stated, it was about "My Lai," the story of how a lieutenant shot Vietnamese civilians in 1968.

The story of My Lai developed into one of such scope that it undoubtedly played a major role in causing stronger public opinion opposing further American involvement in the war. And then, in the summer of 1971, came the Pentagon Papers. This was a story that began with the decision by Secretary of Defense Robert S. McNamara to produce a history of the United States involvement in Indochina. The result of his decision was about 3,000 pages of history and more than 4,000 pages of documents—the story of America in Vietnam from World War II to May, 1968. These documents then were photographed and turned over to the *New York Times* by Daniel Ellsberg, who himself had been involved in the project and who decided the story should be told to the world. On June 13, 1971, the *Times,* which had assigned Neil Sheehan, a former reporter of the war in Vietnam, to compile the papers, began to publish the story and the documents. After the first three installments appeared, the Justice Department obtained from the Federal District Court in New York a temporary restraining order against further publication. The government contended in its suit that publication of the documents would constitute great harm to the national security. On June 30, 1971, the Supreme Court, by a vote of 6 to 3, freed the *Times,* and by inference other newspapers as well, to print the articles, contending that the First Amendment to the Constitution had not been placed in jeopardy.

The war in Vietnam, the My Lai story, the Pentagon Papers— these had done little harm to the presidency of Richard M. Nixon. He had astutely seized upon such matters as the moon landing. He was "winding down the war," his backers believed. And he had gone to China. All of this helped him in defeating, overwhelmingly, the Democratic candidate, George McGovern, in November, 1972. Nixon's announcement that he would go to China was startling to his old foes, who remembered the red-chasing days of the young representative from California, and to some friends, too, who were shocked that the President could make common cause with Mao Tse-tung and Chou En-lai. But everyone conceded that the trip to China was a history-making event.

† † †

PRESIDENT NIXON GOES TO CHINA

Kansas City Star (From the *Star's* Press Services), February 21, 1972.

Peking (Monday)—Richard M. Nixon, a symbol of the capitalist world, arrived in Communist-ruled China today with the expressed hope that his discussions here will help bring a new day to the world.

President Nixon's plane touched down in Peking at 11:28 a.m. (9:29 Kansas City time). The weather was sunny but the temperature was 34.

On hand to greet the President and Mrs. Nixon were a handful of Chinese officials in blue, quilted coats and an honor guard comprising army, navy and air force units.

Premier Chou En-lai waited at the ramp to greet his guest. Mrs. Nixon gave a slight wave and the President applauded briefly when the band began playing.

The President and Chou shook hands at the foot of the ramp, then Chou shook hands with Mrs. Nixon and William P. Rogers, secretary of state.

Then came Dr. Henry Kissinger, assistant to the President for national security affairs who arranged advance details of the trip.

The red and gold flag of the Chinese People's Republic and the Stars and Stripes were fluttering in a slight breeze. Anti-imperialist slogans were visible around the airport.

Yeh Ching-ying, vice-chairman of the military commission of the Central Committee of the Communist party of China, was at Chou's side.

The Nixons went down the receiving line of officials, shaking hands. When the reception was finished a Chinese army band played the Star Spangled Banner while Nixon stood with Chou. That was followed by the Chinese anthem, "March of the Volunteers."

There were no more than 100 officials and aides at the airport. No diplomats from other countries were present.

The President received a studiously correct but minimal official welcome—the tribute due a chief of state, but without any acclaim for a government that still does not officially recognize the People's Republic of China. . . .

Mao Tse-tung, chairman of the Chinese Communist party, had not been expected to be at the airport, and he was not. . . .

† † †

The key story of the mid-1970s all began, so far as the press was concerned, with a story published June 18, 1972, in the *Washington Post*—an italicized note at the end observing that two reporters named Bob Woodward and Carl Bernstein had assisted with the story. It turned into a complex of events now roughly known as "Watergate," the name of the building where the headquarters of the Democratic National Committee were burglarized by five men. Throughout the summer and fall, to the discredit of both press and government, little was done about the break-in, which was termed by some a routine burglary. In the spring of 1973 the story began to break big, even though the *Post* itself had been zealously investigating it since that day in June—the story Woodward and Bernstein later told in a book, *All the President's Men,* that became a best-seller, a movie, and made them national celebrities. The story of Watergate has been detailed in a score of books and led to the collapse of the Nixon presidency and the accession of Gerald Ford to the leadership of the American people in August, 1974.

† † †

FIVE ARRESTED IN WATERGATE BURGLARY

By Alfred E. Lewis, *Washington Post,* June 18, 1972.

Five men, one of whom said he is a former employee of the Central Intelligence Agency, were arrested at 2:30 a.m. yesterday in what authorities described as an elaborate plot to bug the offices of the Democratic National Committee here.

Three of the men were native-born Cubans and another was said to have trained Cuban exiles for guerrilla activity after the 1961 Bay of Pigs invasion.

They were surprised at gunpoint by three plain-clothes officers of the metropolitan police department in a sixth-floor office at the plush Watergate, 2600 Virginia Ave., NW, where the Democratic National Committee occupies the entire floor.

There was no immediate explanation as to why the five suspects would want to bug the Democratic National Committee offices or whether or not they were working for any other individuals or organizations.

A spokesman for the Democratic National Committee said records kept in those offices are "not of a sensitive variety" although there are "financial records and other such information."

Police said two ceiling panels in the office of Dorothy V. Bush, secretary of the Democratic Party, had been removed.

Her office is adjacent to the office of Democratic National Chairman Lawrence F. O'Brien. Presumably, it would have been possible to slide a bugging device through the panels in that office to a place above the ceiling panels in O'Brien's office.

All wearing rubber surgical gloves, the five suspects were captured inside a small office within the committee's headquarters suite. . . .

† † †

Various commentators helped the American people keep their sanity during the frenzied age of Watergate. One of these was Russell Baker of the *New York Times;* another was Art Buchwald, who had been with the *Herald Tribune* in Paris for many years and then returned to the United States to write from Washington. Whether describing the woes of a woman named "Mrs. Robinson," when a song of that name by Simon and Garfunkel appeared, or the professional football scene and the household conflicts resulting from the husband glued to the television set for almost six months of the year, Buchwald was a delightful observer of American life. Many of his columns in 1973 were about Watergate. In this one he also helped to portray in print a television detective who was one of the most popular characters of that frenzied, confused time.

† † †

COLUMBO TRIES TO LEARN THE TRUTH OF WATERGATE

By Art Buchwald, April 10, 1973. Reprinted by permission of Mr. Buchwald.

WASHINGTON—Peter Falk playing his famous role of Columbo walked into the East Room of the White House in his dirty raincoat and flashed his police card. "Inspector Columbo," he said, showing it to President Nixon. "Say, this sure is a nice house you got here. How much does a place like this cost?"

"I'm having a private party for my staff," the President said indignantly. "What do you want?"

"Oh, I really apologize," Columbo said. "I didn't mean to come busting in on a party. Say, is that a real oil painting of George Washington? It's a fantastic work of art—don't get me wrong. I don't know anything about painting."

"Will you state your business, Inspector?"

"I'm just making some routine inquiries about the Watergate bugging case. You see, I'm on loan to the Senate investigating committee from the Los Angeles Police Department. It will only take a few minutes."

"We have nothing to hide here," the President said. "This is my assistant, H. R. Haldeman, my legal aide, John Dean III, my former assistant, Charles Colson, the former secretary of commerce, Maurice Stans, and the former attorney general, John Mitchell, and his wife Martha."

"This is really a great honor," Columbo said. "I never thought I would get to meet so many important people. Wait till I tell my wife. She's really going to be bowled over."

"What exactly is it you want to know?" the President asked.

"Oh, yes," Columbo said, taking out his pad and pencil. "Now let me see."

Martha Mitchell said, "Inspector, I'd like to tell you a few things about the Watergate . . ."

"Martha, will you shut up?" John Mitchell interrupted.

"They're not going to hang this on my John," Martha said.

"Martha!"

"Can I offer you a drink, Inspector?" the President said.

"Just some orange juice if you've got it, Mr. President. I have a bad stomach. You know in this job you never eat properly. Last night I had a tuna fish sandwich on a roll and . . ."

"Will you get on with it, Inspector?" H. R. Haldeman said.

"I'm sorry, where was I? Oh, yes, now about the Watergate. This is just routine, you understand, but where were each of you the night of the break-in?"

"I was watching 'Patton,'" the President said.

"I was in Mexico City at a bank," Maurice Stans said.

"I was reading FBI files," John Dean III said.

"I was cutting the budget," H. R. Haldeman replied.

"I'll tell you where John was," Martha Mitchell said.

"Martha, clam up," John Mitchell said.

"Well, if I don't tell him, I'll tell United Press," Martha said.

"You see," Columbo said, shutting his notebook, "I knew this would be a waste of time. I told them no one in the White House knows anything about Watergate. Say, that is some rug. Do you mind if I take a picture of it to show the folks in Los Angeles?"

Just then the butler came in with Columbo's glass of orange juice.

"Thank you very much," Columbo said to the butler. "I didn't get your name.

"Alfonse, sir."

"Where were you on the night of the break-in, Alfonse?"

"I was polishing the silver."

"You're lying, Alfonse. You were at the Watergate."

"See here, Columbo," the President said. "You're relying on hearsay evidence."

"No, I'm not, Mr. President. This coaster that the orange juice was served on says 'Property of the Watergate Bar and Grill.'"

"My God," said H. R. Haldeman, "the butler did it."

"Why didn't we think of that?" John Dean III said.

"Thank heavens, Columbo, you discovered the culprit," John Mitchell said. "Now we can all sleep tonight."

Martha Mitchell piped, "Wait a minute, Mr. Columbo, there's a lot more to this than you think."

"Dammit, Martha!" yelled John Mitchell, "will you keep your big trap shut?"

† † †

In August, 1974, the shattering story came—the resignation of a president, the accession of another. It had seemed inevitable that Congress would institute impeachment proceedings against Richard Nixon. Hearings in July—shown on nationwide television—were convincing even the President's strongest supporters that the President had known that a Watergate "cover-up" was taking place. Nixon's resignation became the major news event of the year.

† † †

RICHARD NIXON RESIGNS

By the Associated Press, August 8, 1974.

WASHINGTON (AP)—President Nixon announced his resignation tonight, ending his long fight to preserve a presidency shattered by the Watergate scandals.

Vice President Gerald R. Ford was to take the oath of office as Nixon's successor at noon Friday.

Nixon announced his resignation effective at noon Friday. He said to quit was "abhorrent to every instinct in my body," but that his resignation was in the national interest.

"America needs a full time president and a full time Congress," Nixon said.

He said the Watergate scandals prevent him from fulfilling that role, and divert Congress from other vital business.

The announcement came after Nixon informed Ford at midday of the decision.

A spokesman for Ford said Chief Justice Warren Burger was flying back from Europe to administer the presidential oath.

A White House spokesman said the 61-year-old outgoing president and his family would leave the executive mansion on Friday and fly to their San Clemente, Calif., home.

The spokesman said the family would use a plane from the government's VIP fleet at Andrews Air Force Base, rather than Air Force One, the presidential jet Nixon used for the past six years.

Nixon, in his final address from the Oval Office of the White House, said he leaves without bitterness toward his foes, with thanks for those who have supported him through the months of Watergate disclosures and crises.

"The leadership of America will be in good hands," Nixon said.

Nixon, his face grim but his voice steady, said he was stepping aside in the national interest. His base of support in Congress, he said, had eroded to the point at which he would not have backing for the crucial decisions that confront the president.

In that situation, he said, the constitutional process that would have been served by impeachment has been fulfilled, and there is no longer a need to prolong the struggle.

Nixon said he would have preferred to fight to the end for the job he won in an historic landslide nearly two years ago.

"But the interests of the nation must always come before any personal consideration," Nixon said.

"I have never been a quitter," Nixon declared.

"To leave office before my term is completed is abhorrent to every instinct in my body. But as President I must put the interests of America first."

Nixon said he did so in resigning the job he had sought through nearly two decades of setbacks and comebacks. It was six years to the day after his triumphant Republican nomination for a second try at the White House, a 1968 campaign he won narrowly over Sen.

Hubert H. Humphrey. In 1972, the campaign scarred by Watergate, Nixon trounced Sen. George McGovern, sweeping 49 of the 50 states.

Nixon vowed that he will continue to work for the "great causes" to which he has been devoted throughout his political life.

Nixon said he began his presidency 5½ years ago by dedicating his service to the furtherance of peace. "I've done my very best . . . to be true to that pledge," he said.

The President said he believes that because of his quest, the world today is a safer place. "This more than anything is what I hope will be my legacy to you, to our country, as I leave the presidency," he said.

The President's momentous address lasted but 17 minutes.

† † †

And, so, we come to the last document in this anthology, offered in full recognition of the fact that stories, editorials, and controversies related to the history of American journalism have been breaking regularly since then. The mood of the American people, in the months and years after Watergate, became, for some, one of cynicism, of despair. Yet, for some, the disillusionment of the Watergate affair gave way to a feeling of hope, of optimism, for the nation had gone through the experience without the eruption that had crippled so many nations of the world in past decades. A note of hope and optimism seems the way to end this collection of writings from the journalistic past of America, a collection that began with the ballads of old England and continued to the dark days of Watergate. The final commentator is a Virginia conservative named James J. Kilpatrick, whose conservativism often seems nineteenth century liberalism or traditionalism more than a defense of any notion springing up on the right of the political spectrum. Kilpatrick knows that one can look to the past, to history, to experience, for guidance, and he looked to the past in a Thanksgiving-time column of 1974.

† † †

THE VOICES OF AMERICAN HISTORY

By James J. Kilpatrick, November 28, 1974. Copyright 1974 Washington Star Syndicate, Inc. Reprinted by permission of Mr. Kilpatrick. Scrabble, Va.

I write on a bitter afternoon here in the Blue Ridge Mountains. The frozen hills lie huddled in dark shawls; the threadbare oaks, lifting gaunt arms in ragged sleeves, are shivering in the cold. All day we have had quick flurries of snow; and when I open the door of my office to let the two collies come in, the keen air smells of snow on its way.

It is a sullen afternoon, having nothing to recommend it. Except for a few chattering sparrows, nothing can be heard but a north wind howling in the eaves. Even the deer hunters must have given up. My theme is Thanksgiving; and there is not much inspiration in bleak fields and stolid cattle.

This is the day that is specially set aside for Americans to give thanks. In many homes a sardonic question will arise this year: Which blessings? Thanks for what? One hundred thousand miners are on strike: Not much cheer in their homes. Other thousands of auto workers are idle. It is a paralyzing thing to be out of a job. The ritual voicing of thanks will stick like a bone in the throat.

How long has it been since we read any good news? Too long, it will be said, too long. I shuffle the day's papers on my desk. The market is down and homebuilding is down and automobile dealers are close to panic. Crime is up; divorce is up; the government's deficit grows with every passing day. Most of the economists see no relief for months to come.

Over the past year or so, one reflects, we have seen the highest office in our land scarred by corruption and stained by lies. We have seen reputations toppled and confidence destroyed. Fewer than 40 percent of the people bothered to vote this month. Face it, we are told: Our country is sick! For this we give thanks?

If we look only at the passing hour, Thanksgiving does come hard this year. We ought to look at much more.

I turn on the lamps, pushing the darkness away, and the passing hour recedes. My office walls are lined with books. Here are the law books, row on row, red and khaki; they stand as straight as riflemen on review. Here are the Annals of America, eagle-crested, bound in blue and gold. Here are the shelves on history and government; here are books on the press; here the biographies of famous men.

The wind pierces the storm windows, rustling the curtains, and suddenly the room is filled with voices. These are the voices of Jamestown in the bitter winter of 1607; voices of Yorktown and of Valley Forge; voices that ring like bronze bells. One has only to listen to hear Tom Jefferson and Ben Franklin, John Marshall laughing and John Randolph scolding, Abe Lincoln lifting his voice above a crowd in Illinois: "Our reliance is in the love of liberty which God has planted in us ..."

The books are clamoring to be heard. Here is a worn copy of the Constitution, here the Declaration of Independence, here the letter of a young soldier in the Revolution: "We seem always hungry, and most always wet, and by night chilled to the bone." They speak across the generations—soft voices from the South, hard voices from the West, Lee and Douglass side by side, soldier and slave alike freed of the past. "I am as strong as a bull moose," cries Teddy Roosevelt. He is on a top shelf next to old Mark Hanna. "You can use me to the limit."

The voices speak of war, of depression, of the human struggle that won the West. They speak of slavery, dust bowls, soup lines, sweatshops, floods and earthquakes. Look, they cry! America has known all this! And America has survived!

Do we hear them? Or do we hear only the ticking of a clock, the wind in the eaves, the creaking of a rafter? Is the American dream no more than that: a dream? We know better. It has all happened; it is all there to build on—the successes, the failures, the trials and errors, the good men and bad, the blood and tears and laughter.

I open the door to walk over to our home. The collies rush past my legs, delighting in the cold. In the east, I see, the clouds are breaking. Tomorrow will not be so bad after all. Maybe it is hard to give thanks for today; but we fortunate Americans can give thanks for what has been, and knowing that, for what will be.

† † †

BIBLIOGRAPHICAL ESSAY

My students know me as a maker of lists. I propose to offer such a list as a conclusion to this anthology, but I also offer it because there is a chance that the appetites of some readers have been whetted enough to make them want to sample a bit more from that vast banquet table of American journalism. So, here are some suggestions, offered with the apologetic statement that they are only suggestions and a pretty selective listing.

First, there are two good places to go anytime for bibliographical help: for books through 1958 see Warren C. Price, *The Literature of Journalism: An Annotated Bibliography* (Minneapolis: University of Minnesota Press, 1959), and for the ten-year period that follows, see Warren C. Price and Calder M. Pickett, *An Annotated Journalism Bibliography: 1959-1968* (Minneapolis: University of Minnesota Press, 1970). These books will point you to thousands of titles, and the volumes are organized so that you may find specific kinds of readings with little difficulty (if, for example, you want to read more about World War II it should be easy to make a list of books dealing with the journalism of that period). For books published since 1968 see book reviews in *Journalism Quarterly;* you will find that most of the important volumes are reviewed there.

Two huge books are valuable in that they let you see what the great newspaper pages looked like: Edwin Emery, ed., *The Story of America as Reported by Its Newspapers from 1690 to 1965* (New York: Simon and Schuster, 1965), and Michael C. Emery, R. Smith Schuneman and Edwin Emery, eds., *America's Front Page News: 1690-1970* (Minneapolis: Vis-Com, 1970). Another similar volume is Michael Wynn Jones' *A Newspaper History of the World* (New York: Morrow, 1974). But don't be misled by that word "world"; the book has front pages from only Britain and the United States, and some of these are on the esoteric side.

449

An excellent book of readings, now a standard, is Frank Luther Mott and Ralph D. Casey's edited volume, *Interpretations of Journalism* (New York: Crofts, 1937). A book long out of print and somewhat out of date is Allan Nevins' *American Press Opinion: Washington to Coolidge* (New York: Heath, 1928). But it is a marvelous collection—for editorials that reach into the 1920s. I have found two that take us through legal history—Leonard W. Levy, ed., *Freedom of the Press from Zenger to Jefferson* (Indianapolis: Bobbs-Merrill, 1966) and Harold Nelson, *Freedom of the Press from Hamilton to the Warren Court* (Indianapolis: Bobbs-Merrill, 1966) especially valuable, and there are of course many collections that offer basic documents in legal aspects of the press.

Few will question my affection for Louis L. Snyder and Richard B. Morris, eds., *A Treasury of Great Reporting* (New York: Simon and Schuster, 1962, rev. ed.), though some observers feel that it is rather on the sensational side. Sensational, but great fun, and quite inclusive. Snyder's *Masterpieces of War Reporting: The Great Moments of World War II* (New York: Messner, 1962) is the best thing I have seen that deals exclusively with World War II—and not just from the American viewpoint. Other collections of reporting go 'way back but don't reach far into the recent past. Laurence Greene's *America Goes to Press: The News of Yesterday* (Indianapolis: Bobbs-Merrill, 1936) has some excellent examples, as does Ward Greene's *Star Reporters and 34 of Their Stories* (New York: Random House, 1948). And there are a number of recent collections that deal with reporting. These include Bryce W. Rucker, ed., *Twentieth Century Reporting at Its Best* (Ames: Iowa State University Press, 1964), Curtis D. MacDougall, *Reporters Report Reporters* (Ames: Iowa State University Press, 1968), and John Hohenberg, ed., *The Pulitzer Prize Story* (New York: Columbia University Press, 1959).

Recent years have brought so many titles in mass media, mass culture, mass communication, public opinion, propaganda and censorship—mass everything—that a listing of these would be a big subject in itself. But I have found especially valuable a collection by Reo M. Christenson and Robert O. McWilliams, *Voice of the People* (New York: McGraw-Hill, 1967). A special kind of anthology was compiled by Edward W. Barrett, *Journalists in Action* (Manhasset, N.Y.: Channel Press, 1963); it is entirely by people who went to the Columbia School of Journalism. A similar volume was edited by Ruth Adler, *The Working Press: Special to the New York Times* (New York: Putnam, 1966) and consists of contributions to "Times Talk." There also are the volumes compiled by the Overseas Press Club, which are largely accounts by reporters of their own experiences: *Eye Witness* (New York: Alliance, 1940); *The Inside Story* (New York: Prentice-Hall, 1940); *Deadline Delayed* (New York: Dutton, 1947); plus two interesting books edited by David Brown and W. Richard Bruner about the Overseas Press Club and its reporters, *How I Got That Story* (New York: Dutton, 1964) and *I Can Tell It Now* (New York: Dutton, 1964).

As I write in this bicentennial year I am struck by the dozens of books about the American Revolution that I have just in my own library. Let me confine myself here to documents, and not all those biographies of Franklin, Jefferson, the Adamses and Paine. First, there is Bernard Bailyn's edited work, *Pamphlets of the American Revolution, 1750-1776* (Cambridge: Harvard University Press, 1965). A similar volume of great value is Merrill Jensen, ed., *Tracts of the American Revolution, 1763-1776* (Indianapolis: Bobbs-Merrill, 1967). And the eminent historian, Samuel Eliot Morison, edited a volume called *Sources and Documents Illustrating the American Revolution, 1764-1788, and the Formation of the Federal Constitution* (Oxford, England: Oxford University Press, 1948). For a specialized look at a long-neglected historical matter—the Tory press—there is a collection by Catherine S. Crary, *The Price of Loyalty* (New York: McGraw-Hill, 1973).

Many books have been written, too, about the press and the Civil War; again I refer you to the Price and the Price-Pickett volumes. A handy volume on the pre-war press is Louis Ruchames, *The Abolitionists* (New York: Putnam, 1963). Another, one of several in this field published in recent years, is Martin Dann, ed., *The Black Press* (New York: Putnam, 1971); the time span involved here is 1827-1890. And, although it is not devoted exclusively to journalism, you should find Joanne Grant, ed., *Black Protest* (New York: Fawcett, 1968), valuable.

Now for a few rather celebrated individuals in our journalistic history. Let us begin with the writings of Mark Twain, noting that of course a book such as *The Innocents Abroad* is—well, sort of—journalism all by itself. Charles Neider compiled some of the travel writings in *The Travels of Mark Twain* (New York: Coward-McCann, 1961). The Nevada days are found in Samuel L. Clemens, *Mark Twain of the Enterprise* (Berkeley: University of California Press, 1957). One that reveals the great man as somewhat of a rebel was edited by Maxwell Geismar, *Mark Twain and the Three R's: Race, Religion, Revolution and Related Matters* (Indianapolis: Bobbs-Merrill, 1973). It is especially commended to those of you who hope to find in Mr. Twain a founding father of the new left. The San Francisco days are the subject of Edgar M. Branch, ed., *Clemens of the Call* (Berkeley: University of California Press, 1969).

The journalism of another famous figure, Walt Whitman, has been collected in Henry M. Christman, ed., *Walt Whitman's New York* (New York: Macmillan, 1963). Some interesting writings of Horace Greeley, apart from those in his newspapers, can be found in *An Overland Journey from New York to San Francisco in the Summer of 1859* (New York: C. M. Saxton, Barker & Co., 1860). And here are a few more, too, from the great age of personal journalism: Edwin L. Godkin, *Reflections and Comments* (New York: Scribner, 1895; Henry Watterson, *The Editorials of Henry Watterson* (New York: Doran, 1923); William Allen White, *The Editor and His People* (New York: Macmillan, 1924); Oliver Knight, ed., *I Protest: Selected*

Disquisitions of E. W. Scripps (Madison: University of Wisconsin Press, 1966); Arthur Brisbane, ed., *Editorials from the Hearst Newspapers* (New York: Albertson, 1906); Frank I. Cobb, *Cobb of the World* (New York: Dutton, 1924); and *Casual Essays of the [New York] Sun* (New York: Cooke, 1905).

There has been a big vogue for Stephen Crane of late, so you will find that his writings—and remember, the man had a pretty short life—can be found in *The New York City Sketches of Stephen Crane and Related Pieces* (New York: New York University Press, 1966) and *The War Dispatches of Stephen Crane* (New York: New York University Press, 1964), both volumes edited by R. W. Stallman and E. R. Hageman. Crane's contemporary, James Creelman, put his reminiscences into a volume called *On the Great Highway* (Boston: Lothrop, Lee, Shepard, 1901). Still another, Richard Harding Davis, the grand soldier of fortune, published *The Notes of a War Correspondent* (New York: Harper, 1910), and near the end of his life published *With the Allies* (New York: Scribner, 1915) and *With the French in France and Salonika* (New York: Scribner, 1916). Another reporter of the war of 1914-1918, Will Irwin, wrote *A Reporter at Armageddon* (New York: Appleton, 1918).

It is not necessary to go far to find the writings of the muckrakers, but an especially valuable collection is Arthur M. and Lila Weinberg, eds., *The Muckrakers* (New York: Simon and Schuster, 1961). Why not take a look at Lincoln Steffens' *The Shame of the Cities* (New York: McClure, Phillips, 1907) itself? Ella Winter, who was the wife of Steffens, and Herbert Shapiro compiled a volume called *The World of Lincoln Steffens* (New York: Hill & Wang, 1962). And while we're on the subject of reformers and rebels, a delightful book that offers the work of the Wobblies is Joyce Kornbluh, ed., *Rebel Voices: An I. W. W. Anthology* (Ann Arbor: University of Michigan Press, 1964).

Humor, wit, social commentary: there are many collections, and I commend you immediately to *anything* by James Thurber. If you want to read more by Finley Peter Dunne, the "Mr. Dooley" man, there are Dunne, *Mr. Dooley in Peace and War* (Boston: Small, Maynard, 1898-1899) and *The World of Mr. Dooley* (New York: Collier, 1962). H. L. Mencken is all over the place, but especially interesting is *The American Scene: A Reader* (New York: Knopf, 1965). Though Donald Day's edited volume is called *The Autobiography of Will Rogers* (Boston: Houghton Mifflin, 1949) it is in great part the columns of the famous entertainer and occasional journalist. The man who offered us the piece you read on archy and mehitabel, Don Marquis, is available in *The Best of Don Marquis* (Garden City, N.Y.: Doubleday, 1946). A sample work by the *New Yorker* (and elsewhere) writer, Robert Benchley, is *My Ten Years in a Quandary and How They Grew* (New York: Harper, 1936). I offer here two titles by Heywood Broun, *Sitting on the World* (New York: Putnam, 1924), and *It Seems to Me* (New York: Harcourt, Brace, 1935), noting that he did a great deal of writing. I offer only one title by Ernest Hemingway, a collection compiled by William White, *By-Line: Ernest Hemingway* (New York: Scribner, 1967). It is interesting, by the way, to see that this great stylist was often the hackiest of hacks.

The 1930s and 1940s offered so many collections that it seemed as though every journalist in the land had found a publisher; and the pattern has continued into the present time. These seem some of the better collections, some of these by people represented earlier in the anthology: Raymond Clapper, *Watching the World* (New York: Whittlesey House, 1944); Meyer Berger, *Meyer Berger's New York* (New York: Random House, 1960); Arthur Krock, *The Consent of the Governed and Other Deceits* (Boston: Little, Brown, 1971), and *In the Nation: 1932-1966* (New York: McGraw-Hill, 1966); Walter Lippmann, *The Essential Lippmann: A Political Philosophy for Liberal Democracy* (New York: Random House, 1963); A. J. Liebling, *The Press* (New York: Ballantine, 1961); Elmer Davis, *By Elmer Davis* (Indianapolis: Bobbs-Merrill, 1964); Robert J. Casey, *Bob Casey's Grand Slam* (Indianapolis: Bobbs-Merrill, 1962); Ralph McGill, *The Fleas Come with the Dog* (New York: Abingdon Press, 1954); I. F. Stone, *In a Time of Torment* (New York: Random House, 1967); Max Lerner, *The Unfinished Country* (New York: Simon and Schuster, 1959); Vermont C. Royster, *A Pride of Prejudices* (New York: Knopf, 1967); Richard Rovere, *The American Establishment* (New York: Harcourt, Brace, 1962); James Reston, *Sketches in the Sand* (New York: Knopf, 1967); John Lardner, *The World of John Lardner* (New York: Simon and Schuster, 1961); Harry Golden, *The Best of Harry Golden* (Cleveland: World, 1967); William F. Buckley, Jr., *The Jeweler's Eye* (New York: Putnam, 1968); Art Buchwald, *Son of the Great Society* (New York: Putnam, 1966); Jimmy Breslin, *The World of Jimmy Breslin* (New York: Viking, 1967); Russell Baker, *All Things Considered* (Philadelphia: Lippincott, 1965); Mike Royko, *I May Be Wrong, but I Doubt It* (Chicago: Regnery, 1968); Bill Vaughan, *Bird Thou Never Wert* (New York: Simon and Schuster, 1962); Sydney J. Harris, *Last Things First* (Boston: Houghton Mifflin, 1961); and Nicholas von Hoffman, *Left at the Post* (Chicago: Quadrangle, 1970). What occurs to me, sadly, is that several of these people were, to steal from the von Hoffman title, "left at the post" themselves. There just wasn't enough room in this book.

I wish that there were more published collections of great broadcast journalism. But you can find Edward R. Murrow in *In Search of Light* (New York: Knopf, 1967); Eric Sevareid in *In One Ear* (New York: Knopf, 1952); Lowell Thomas in *History as You Heard It* (Garden City, N.Y.: Doubleday, 1959); H. V. Kaltenborn in *I Broadcast the Crisis* (New York: Random House, 1938), and Alistair Cooke in *Letters from America* (London: R. Hart-Davis, 1951). Many collections of magazine journalism exist; here are some samples: Max Ascoli, ed., *Our Times: The Best from The Reporter* (New York: Farrar, Straus, 1960); Henry M. Christman, ed., *One Hundred Years of The Nation* (New York: Macmillan, 1965); Horace Knowles, ed.,

Gentlemen, Scholars and Scoundrels (New York: Harper, 1959), a collection from Harper's, and Saturday Review, *The Saturday Review Reader* (New York: Bantam, 1951), one of a series.

A special note: it seems to me that the 1930s exist for us in journalistic collections better than any other decade. There are the "inside" books of John Gunther. There are the volumes called *Headlining America* (Boston: Houghton Mifflin); Frank Luther Mott was the editor, and I wish this series had been continued. *New York Times* writers described the dismal decade in *We Saw It Happen* (New York: Simon and Schuster, 1939). A vital piece of journalism of the time, something intended originally for publication in *Fortune,* was James Agee and Walker Evans, *Let Us Now Praise Famous Men* (Boston: Houghton Mifflin, 1960). A book of recent years stands as a special document: the tape-recorded interviews of Studs Terkel's *Hard Times* (New York: Pantheon, 1970). This is journalism of the present, and of the future, as well as history. World War II also offered some fine memoirs. See, especially, Hugh Baillie, *Two Battlefronts* (New York: United Press, 1943); Margaret Bourke-White, *They Called It Purple Heart Valley* (New York: Simon and Schuster, 1944); Robert J. Casey, *I Can't Forget* (Indianapolis: Bobbs-Merrill, 1941); Curt Riess, ed., *They Were There* (New York: Putnam, 1944); Leland Stowe, *No Other Road to Freedom* (New York: Knopf, 1941); W. L. White, *They Were Expendable* (New York: Harcourt, Brace, 1943); and of course three by Ernie Pyle, all published by Henry Holt—*Here Is Your War* (1943); *Brave Men* (1944), and *Last Chapter* (1946). Dozens of other titles should be here, but they can be located elsewhere.

At the moment I am unable to say that the postwar era has been quite as fruitful; it has been such a fast-moving time. I wish that I could have included an excerpt from John Hersey's *Hiroshima* (New York: Knopf, 1946), but Mr. Hersey will permit the book to be published only in its entirety. A good volume on that ugly little war of the early fifties is Marguerite Higgins' *War in Korea* (Garden City, N.Y.: Doubleday, 1951). A good memoir of the cold war years is C. L. Sulzberger's *The Big Thaw* (New York: Harper, 1956), and there have been dozens of books about the war in Vietnam and the election campaigns of recent years. Using the technique of Studs Terkel, a historian named Peter Joseph did a good book about recent years called *Good Times: An Oral History of America in the Nineteen Sixties* (New York: Charterhouse, 1973).

And collections of the new journalism are so numerous that I feel almost no embarrassment at having included so little of this controversial genre. For a sampling of Tom Wolfe, chief guru of this group, try *The Kandy-Kolored Tangerine-Flake Streamline Baby* (New York: Farrar, Straus, 1965). Wolfe himself provided a history of the new journalism and then, working with E. W. Johnson, did an anthology called *The New Journalism* (New York: Harper & Row, 1973). And three others about this recent trend are Ronald Weber, ed., *The Reporter as Artist* (New York: Hastings House, 1974); Charles D. Flippen, ed., *Liberating the Media* (Washington:

Acropolis, 1974), and Thomas King Forcade, ed., *Underground Press Anthology* (New York: Ace, 1972). These books, and some of the foregoing, and the many magazines and newspapers in which most of this appeared, should keep you busy for some time.

INDEX

466

Voices of The Past *was copyedited by Jane C. Foss; interior style and cover design by Marcie Clark. The text was set in ten point Schoolbook, eleven point leading. Typesetting by S M Data Center, Ashland, Ohio. Production manager, Elaine Clatterbuck.*